THE
OVERSTREET
COMIC BOOK
COMPANION

THE
OVERSTREET
COMIC BOOK
COMPANION

IDENTIFICATION AND PRICE GUIDE

7TH
EDITION

ROBERT M. OVERSTREET

The CONFIDENT COLLECTOR™

AVON BOOKS ◆ NEW YORK

Important Notice: All of the information, including valuations, in this book has been compiled from the most reliable sources, and every effort has been made to eliminate errors and questionable data. Nevertheless, the possibility of error always exists in a work of such immense scope. The publisher and the author will not be held responsible for losses which may occur in the purchase, sale, or other transaction of property because of information contained herein. Readers who feel they have discovered errors are invited to *write* and inform us so they may be corrected in subsequent editions.

Cover artwork: Batman, by Kelley Jones,™ and © 1995 by DC Comics, Inc. All rights reserved.

THE CONFIDENT COLLECTOR: THE OVERSTREET COMIC BOOK COMPANION INDENTIFICATION AND PRICE GUIDE (7th edition) is an original publication of Avon Books. This work has never before appeared in book form.

AVON BOOKS
A division of
The Hearst Corporation
1350 Avenue of the Americas
New York, New York 10019

Acknowledgments

My appreciation is given to David Alexander, Dave Anderson, Jon Berk, Gary Colabuono, Larry Curcio, Gary Dolgoff, Richard Evans, Steve Fishler, Michael Goldman, Jamie Graham, Daniel Greenhalgh, Bruce Hamilton, John Hauser, Bill Hughes, Rob Hughes, Joseph Koch, Joe Mannarino, Harry Matetsky, Peter Morolo, Michael Naiman, Matt Nelson, Richard Olson, Jim Payette, Chris Pedrin, Bill Ponseti, Ron Pussell, Todd Reznik, Robert Rogovin, Rory Root, Robert Roter, Chuck Rozanski, John Snyder, Craig Soifer, Tony Starks, Terry Stroud, Joe Verenault, Jerry Weist and Harley Yee for their constant input concerning pricing, data and general information about market fluctuations.

Special thanks is also given to Kelley Jones for his beautiful cover art as well as his interview for this edition; to Benn Ray for the Kelley Jones interview; to James Bullock for his toy market report; to Steve Fritz for his gaming card report; to the entire Gemstone staff for their work in layout and design and to Avon Books for their support.

Our managing editor Todd Hoffer is due special consideration for his hard work in overseeing this project from inception to finish. Thanks Todd for a job well done.

Finally, thanks is also given to our Overstreet's Fan Magazine network of advisors for their up-to-date pricing information reflected in the pages of this book.

Table of Contents

THE
OVERSTREET
COMIC BOOK
COMPANION

An Overview to Comic Book Collecting

INTRODUCTION

Welcome to the world of comic books—
one of the most entertaining and self
rewarding hobbies ever. Comic books
have been appreciated and collected for decades
by fans young and old. Events like the death and
return of Superman have projected our hobby
through the news media to the largest audience
ever. With the addition of premiums offered with
the comic books (such as trading cards, posters,
etc.), more and more young collectors are becom-
ing established as regulars at the local newsstands
and comic specialty shops everywhere.

© MEG

About the listings—This book includes current
<u>popular</u> comic books in alphabetical order by title.
Not all comic books are listed, only the most collectible from the past three decades. The listings
are up-to-date and include the latest hot titles. All important contents and
artists are also pointed out.

Comic books not listed—Comic books not listed in this book can be found
in the annual **Overstreet Comic Book Price Guide** available at your local
bookstores and comic shops.

About pricing—With the experience of over two decades, Overstreet has
developed a unique, accurate system of pricing unmatched by any other pricing guide on the market. We are always in touch with pricing experts all over
the country. This means that you can depend on our prices being the most
current and dependable anywhere. Remember, the prices in this book are
retail prices that collectors would probably pay. Dealers pay less when buying for stock.

Many people become attracted to this hobby as a means to invest dollars
and make money. While this is well and good, we at Overstreet have always
tried to encourage newcomers to collect comic books simply for fun and plea-
sure. Investing in new comics can be very risky, and requires special knowledge. Buy what you like to read. If it becomes valuable in the future, consider
it a bonus.

COLLECTING
IN THE 1990s

C omic book collecting has become more fun and exciting than ever before. The stands are filled with a broad selection of every type of comic book imaginable; but look closely. There is something new about today's comic book. The inside pages are printed on slick paper that makes the colors jump. The covers are beautiful, exciting and dazzling. Most comic book companies, especially Marvel, DC, Image, Valiant and Dark Horse, are placing these eye-catching specialty covers on their comic books.

Yes, the face of today's newsstand has really changed with more pizzazz and glitter for the collector. Gimmicks to encourage point of purchase sales abound. Take your pick. Holograms, prism, foil, embossed, die-cut, talking covers, scratch and sniff, you name it. Check out that die-cut Sabretooth cover by Marvel, or that X-Factor #92 with the Havok hologram on the cover, or that foil embossed plastic coated cover of X-O Manowar #0, or that multi-color foil WildC.A.T.S Trilogy cover by Image.

Collecting on a budget—Collectors check out their local newsstand or comic specialty store for the latest arrivals. Hundreds of brand new comic books are displayed each week for the collector—much more than anyone can afford to purchase. Due to this, today's reader must be careful and budget his money wisely in choosing what to buy.

Trading Cards—Very popular today are the trading cards which are being offered by most publishers. Much like the baseball card market, comic cards are now offered by more and more outlets. In fact, many baseball card collectors and dealers are moving over into the comic market. Because of this, today's comic book market is growing and changing faster than ever before. The card sets and rare issues are a very popular and interesting alternative to comic book collecting.

Pogs—More varied types of special giveaways are now being included in comic books, magazines, food products, etc. to boost sales. One of the most unique is the milk cap or pog phenomenon. Pogs (<u>P</u>assion <u>O</u>range <u>G</u>uava)

4

originated in Hawaii, and is connected to a popular game. Pogs are now popular in California, Japan and Canada, and are spreading eastward. DC, SkyBox, Marvel, Image, Eclipse and others are currently getting into this market.

Collecting artists—Many collectors enjoy favorite artists and follow their work from issue to issue, title to title. In recent years, some artists have achieved stardom status. Autograph signings occur at all major comic conventions as well as special promotions with local stores. Fans line up by the hundreds at such events to meet these super stars. Some of the current top artists of new comics are: Todd McFarlane, Rob Liefeld, Alex Ross, Jim Lee, Joe Quesada, Billy Tucci, Steven Hughes, Frank Miller, Jeff Smith, Geof Darrow, Mike Allred, J. Scott Campbell, Joseph Linsner, Dave McKean, Sam Kieth, Marc Silvestri, Dale Keown and Kelley Jones.

Collecting by companies—Some collectors become loyal to a particular company, and only collect its titles. It is another way to specialize and collect in a market that expands faster than your pocket book.

Collecting number ones—For decades, comic enthusiasts have always collected number ones. It is yet another way to control spending and build a very interesting collection for the future. Number ones have everything going for them. Some introduce new characters. Other issues are sometimes underprinted, creating a rarity factor. A number one collection crosses many subjects, as well as companies, and makes an intriguing display.

Pricing on computer discs—Overstreet prices and general listings are now available on computer discs. These discs are updated every month with the latest listings and prices. Check your local computer stores and comic shops for copies. Also, check ads in all the trade publications.

© DC

Grading Comic Books

LET'S GRADE COMICS—Comic books have to be graded before a value can be determined. Grading can be difficult at first, but becomes easier with practice. Be honest and objective, and learn what defects affect grade. First, grade the cover, then grade the insides. Beginners should get assistance from an experienced collector or dealer to learn the correct procedure. Consult the **Overstreet Comic Book Grading Guide** for further, more detailed information on grading.

THE EIGHT BASIC COMIC BOOK GRADES

MINT (MT) Near perfect in every way. Flat, clean and new as it appeared on the newsstand.

NEAR MINT (NM) Nearly perfect, with the slightest minute defects visible with very close examination.

VERY FINE (VF) An excellent copy with outstanding eye appeal. Sharp, bright and clean with supple pages.

FINE (FN) A nice, above average copy that shows minor wear but is still fairly flat, clean and glossy, collectible and desirable.

VERY GOOD (VG) The average used comic book most commonly found. A fairly desirable book that shows moderate wear.

GOOD (GD) All pages and covers are intact, although there may be small pieces missing. Commonly creased and soiled, but complete.

FAIR (FR) Very heavily read and soiled, but still complete.

POOR (PR) Usually too low a grade for most collectors.

How to Store Comic Books

If comic books are not stored properly, the paper can turn yellow. This is caused by pollutants in the air.

When looking at comic books that have been stored for long periods of time, you will begin to understand how important proper storage methods are.

In some cases where a collection was stored improperly, the books have brown or yellowed pages approaching brittleness. Collections of this type were probably stored in too much heat or moisture, or exposed to atmospheric pollution (sulfur dioxide), or light. On the other hand, other collections of considerable age (30 to 50 years) have emerged with snow white pages, and little signs of aging. Thus, we learn that proper storage is important to guarantee the long life of our comic book collections.

Store books in a dark, cool place with an ideal relative humidity of 50 percent and a temperature of 40 to 50 degrees or less. Air conditioning is recommended. Do not use regular cardboard boxes, since most contain harmful acids. Use acid-free boxes instead. Seal books in Mylar (Mylar is a registered trademark of the DuPont Company) or other suitable wrappings, bags or containers. Store them in the proper containers or cabinets, to protect them from heat, excessive dampness, ultraviolet light (use tungsten lights), polluted air, and dust.

If comic books are sealed in plastic bags, place them in boxes, and store in a cool dark room in cabinets or on shelving. Plastic bags should be changed every two to three years since most contain harmful acids. Cedar chest storage is recommended, but the ideal method of storage is to stack your comics in Mylar sleeves vertically in acid-free boxes. The boxes can be arranged on shelving for easy access. Storage boxes, plastic bags, backing boards, Mylar bags, archival supplies, etc., are available from many dealers and comic shops.

How to Get Started

Most collectors usually hear about comics from a friend. In this case, the friend educates the new collector on where to buy and sell, and what the market is all about. New comic books are available in many different kinds of stores: Grocery stores, Wal-Mart, K-Mart, book stores, comic book stores, and card and comics specialty shops are a few examples.

The beginner begins buying new issues in mint condition directly off the newsstand from their local source (subscription copies are available from several mail-order services). Each week new comics appear on the stands that are destined to become true collectors items. The trick is to locate a store that carries a complete line of comics. You may have to go to more than one store to find the books you need. Missed issues may have to be ordered from mail order dealers (see ads in the **Overstreet Comic Book Price Guide**).

Before you buy any comic to add to your collection, you should carefully inspect its condition. Unlike stamps and coins, defective comics are generally not highly prized. The cover should be properly cut and printed. Remember that every blemish or sign of wear depreciates the beauty and value of your comics. If the comic is bagged, check to be sure all the contents are there.

Before long, you may need to create a list of your collection for reference. This list should show each issue you have along with its condition. Later this list will be important when you try to fill in missing issues.

Advanced collectors usually buy multiple copies of popular titles for trade or sale later. Buying the right investment titles is tricky business that requires special knowledge. With experience, the beginner will improve his buying skills. Remember, if you play the new comics market, be prepared to buy and sell fast as values rise and fall rapidly.

Collecting
Back Issues

A back issue is any comic currently not available on the stands. Collectors who get hooked on a current title often want to find the earlier issues in order to complete the run.

Comic books have been published and collected for over 90 years. However, the earliest known comic book dealers didn't appear until the late 1930s.

Locating back issues—The first place to begin, of course, is with your friends and collectors who may have unwanted back issues or duplicates for sale. Look in the yellow pages to see if you have a comic book store available. If you do, they would know of other collectors in your area. Advertising in local papers could get good results. Go to regional markets and look for comic book dealers. There are many trade publications in the hobby that would put you in touch with out-of-town dealers. The **Overstreet Comic Book Price Guide** and **Overstreet FAN** have ads buying and selling old comic books. Some dealers publish regular price lists of old comic books for sale. Get on their mailing list.

Putting a quality collection of old comics together takes a lot of time, effort, and money. Many old comics are not easy to find. Persistence and luck play a big part in acquiring needed issues. Most quality collections are put together over a long period of time by placing mail orders with dealers and other collectors.

Comics of early vintage are extremely expensive if they are purchased through a regular dealer or collector. Unless you have unlimited funds to invest in your hobby, you will find it necessary to restrict your collecting in certain ways. However you define your collection, you should be careful to set your goals well within affordable limits.

Proper Handling of Comic Books

Comic books are very fragile and easy to damage. Because of this, most dealers and collectors hesitate to let anyone personally handle their rare comics. It is common courtesy to ask permission before handling another person's comic book. Usually they prefer to handle the book themselves. In this way, if the book is damaged, it would be their responsibility, not yours. Remember, the slightest crease or chip could render an otherwise Mint book to Near Mint or less.

Be very careful when handling an old comic book. Consult the **Overstreet Comic Book Grading Guide** and learn the proper way to hold a comic book. Treat them very gently.

The following steps are provided to aid the beginner in the proper handling of comic books: 1. Remove the comic from its protective sleeve or bag very carefully. 2. Gently lay the comic (unopened) in the palm of your hand so that it will stay relatively flat and secure. 3. You can now leaf through the book by carefully rolling or flipping the pages with the thumb and forefinger of your other hand. Caution: Be sure the book always remains somewhat flat or slightly rolled. Avoid creating stress points on the covers with your fingers, and be particularly cautious in bending covers back too far on Mint books. 4. After examining the book, carefully insert it back into the bag or protective sleeve. Watch corners and edges for folds or tears as you replace the book.

Polybagged comics—It is the official policy of Overstreet to grade comics regardless of whether they are still sealed in their polybag or not. The polybag and its entire contents may be preserved so that all components of the original manufactured product remain together.

Terminology

Many of the following terms and abbreviations are used in the comic book market and are explained here. For a more complete list of terms, consult **The Overstreet Comic Book Grading Guide:**

a–Story art; **a(i)**–Story art inks; **a(p)**–Story art pencils; **a(r)**–Story art reprint.

Adult material-Contains story and/or art for mature readers. Re: sex, violence, strong language.

Adzine–A magazine primarily devoted to the advertising of comic books and collectibles as its first publishing priority as opposed to written articles.

Annual–A book that is published yearly.

Arrival date–The date written or stamped on the cover of comics by either the local wholesaler or the retailer. The date precedes the cover date by approximately 15 to 75 days and may vary considerably from one locale to another, or from one year to another.

B&W–Black and white art.

Baxter paper–A high quality, white, heavy paper used in the printing of some comics.

Bi-monthly–Published every two months.

Bronze Age–(1.) Non-specific term not in general acceptance by collectors which denotes comics published from approximately 1970 through 1980. (2.) Term which describes the "Age" of comic books after the Silver Age.

c–Cover art; **c(i)**–Cover inks; **c(p)**–Cover pencils; **c(r)**–Cover reprint.

Cameo–When a character appears briefly in one or two panels.

CCG– Collectible Card Games

Centerfold–The two folded pages in the center of a comic book at the terminal end of the staples.

Chromium cover-A special chromium foil used on covers.

Terminology

Colorist–Artist that applies color to the pen and ink art.

Comic book dealer–(1.) A seller of comic books. (2.) One who makes a living buying and selling comic books.

Con–A Convention or public gathering of fans.

Condition–The state of preservation of a comic book.

Debut–The first time that a character appears anywhere.

Die-cut cover-When areas of a cover are cut away for special effect.

Embossed cover-When a pattern is pressed into the cover creating a raised area.

Fanzine–An amateur fan publication.

File Copy–A high grade comic originating from the publisher's file.

First app.–Same as debut.

Flashback–When a previous story is being recalled.

Foil cover-A thin metallic foil that is hot stamped on comic covers.

Gatefold cover-A double cover folded in itself.

G. A.–Golden Age (The period between 1938 and 1945).

i–Art inks.

Hologram cover-True 3-D holograms are prepared and affixed to comic book covers for special effect.

Hot stamping-The process of pressing foil, prism paper and inks on cover stock.

Indicia–Publishing and title information usually located at the bottom of the first page or the bottom of the inside front cover or inside back cover.

Infinity cover–Shows a scene that repeats itself to infinity.

Inker–Artist that does the inking.

Intro–Same as debut.

JLA–Justice League of America.

JLI–Justice League International.

JSA–Justice Society of America

The King– Jack Kirby.

Linticular covers-(aka flicker covers)-Images that move when viewed at different angles specially prepared and affixed to cover.

Logo–The title of a strip or comic book as it appears on the cover or title page.

LSH–Legion of Super-Heroes.

Terminology

Mylar™–An inert, very hard, space age plastic used to make high quality protective bags and sleeves used for comic book storage. Mylar™ is a trademark of the DuPont Co.

nd–No date.

nn–No number.

One shot–When only one issue is published of a title, or when a series is published where each issue is a different title (e.g. Four Color Comics).

Origin–When the story of the character's creation is given.

p–Art pencils.

Painted cover–Cover taken from an actual painting instead of a line drawing.

Paper cover–Comic book cover made from the same newsprint as interior pages. These books are extremely rare in high grade.

Penciller–Artist that does the pencils.

Photo cover–Made from a photograph instead of a line drawing or painting.

Pog-(passion orange guava)-A game that originated in Hawaii which uses small paper milk caps or discs.

Prism cover–Special reflective foil material with 3-dimensional repeated designs. Used for special effect.

R or r–Reprint.

Rare–10 to 20 copies estimated to exist.

Reprint comics—Comic books that contain newspaper strip reprints.

S. A.–Silver Age (period from Showcase #4 in 1956 to 1969).

Scarce–20 to 100 copies estimated to exist.

Silver proof–A black & white actual size print on thick glossy paper given to the colorist to indicate colors to the engraver.

S&K–Simon and Kirby (artists).

Splash page/ panel–A large panel that usually appears at the front of a comic story.

Super-hero–A costumed hero crime fighter with powers beyond those of mortal man.

Super-villain–A costumed criminal with powers beyond those of mortal man.

Swipe–A panel, sequence, or story obviously borrowed from previously published material.

X-over–When one character crosses over into another's strip.

Zine–See Fanzine.

How to Sell
Your Comics

If you have a collection of comics for sale, large or small, the following steps should be taken. (1) Make a detailed list of the books for sale, being careful to grade them accurately, showing any noticeable defects; i.e., torn or missing pages, centerfolds, etc. (2) Decide whether to sell or trade wholesale to a dealer all in one lump sum or to go through the long process of advertising and selling piece by piece to collectors. Both have their advantages and disadvantages.

In selling to dealers, you will get the best price by letting everything go at once–the good with the bad–all for one price. Decide on what dealer you would like to contact by looking in our ads found in the Overstreet annual, or monthly magazine. Send them your list and ask for bids. The bids received will vary depending on the demand, rarity and condition of the books you have. The more in demand and the better the condition, the higher the bids will be.

On the other hand, you could become a "dealer" and sell the books yourself. Type up your copy, carefully pricing each book (using the **Overstreet Price Guide** as a reference). Price books according to how fast you want them to sell. Send finished ad copy with payment to the editor of the place you are running the ad. Repeat this process until most books are gone.

Remember, if you decide to be your own dealer, you will have overhead expenses in postage, mailing supplies and advertising cost. Some books might even be returned for refund due to misgrading, etc.

If you sell all your books at one time to a dealer, you will get instant cash, immediate profit, and eliminate the long process of running several ads to dispose of the books. But if you have patience, and a small amount of business sense, you could realize more profit selling them directly to collectors yourself.

Where to Buy and Sell

Comic Book Specialty Shops—Most cities have comic book specialty shops that buy and sell old comic books. You may find these in the Yellow Pages or possibly via ads in the newspapers. There is a directory of these shops in this price guide.

Comic Book Conventions—Comic book conventions are now being held the year round in most of the larger cities. These conventions are an excellent source for buying and selling comic books. If you are an inexperienced collector, be sure to compare prices before you buy. Many of these conventions are listed in this price guide.

Flea Markets—Flea markets include all types of dealers selling everything imaginable. These markets are held all over the country 12 months a year. Many comic book dealers who buy and sell comic books set up at flea markets.

Antiques and Collectibles Shows—Although most of these shows are displaying different collectibles than comic books, they do sometimes have dealers who sell comics.

Card Shows—More and more card shows are beginning to include comic cards and comic books.

Computer Nets—Several good computer networks are now operating on a 24 hour a day basis buying and selling comic books and cards.

Collections can also be sold by simply running an ad in one of the many magazines now published in the comic book market.

Mail Order Dealers

There are many comic book mail order dealers across the country and Canada. The vast majority of all mail order comic book dealers are honest and fair. They commonly keep in stock literally thousands of comics, all of which must be graded before they are advertised for sale. A job this complex is no simple task. On occasion, a comic gets through that may have been accidently overgraded or undergraded. If you by chance receive a book through the mail that you feel does not meet its advertised grade, don't panic. Simply call or write the dealer and discuss calmly the reasons for your opinion. The vast majority of dealers will gladly refund your money if you return the book in the original condition sent within a reasonable amount of time, even if they don't agree with your grading evaluation.

Many seasoned collectors successfully acquire comics by mail by following a few other simple steps. Before ordering, you may want to consider the following suggestions:

(a.) Call and ask the dealers to supply a few references. Reputable dealers will be happy to do it. They hope you will eventually become a reference as well.

(b.) Order a few things to see if you like their pricing and grading system. These tests are safely done with lower value orders. After you are satisfied with your initial "test" orders you may feel more comfortable spending larger amounts of money.

(c.) Continue to talk with the dealers by telephone occasionally. This is a great way to get to know them and for them to get to know you. Telephone calls are an excellent investment and can eliminate many unnecessary misunderstandings.

(d.) Write your orders clearly and legibly! Include all the information needed to successfully fill your order. Follow the ordering instructions listed by the dealer. Always write out your complete name and address on your order, as sometimes checks and envelopes may become separated from letters.

(e.) Always include a telephone number with your correspondence so that the dealer may contact you if questions arise or if there is a problem with your order.

(f.) Understand that checks are slower to process than money orders or cashier's checks. Knowing this, the best approach seems to be to make a few orders using checks, since they provide an excellent record of the transaction, even though your order will take a little longer. After you become comfortable with the mail order dealer and feel you have a good business relationship, your order can be expedited with the use of either cashier's check or money orders.

(g.) Be as courteous and reasonable with the dealers as you would like them to be courteous and reasonable with you. Many a good mail order relationship has been spoiled because individuals did not practice even the most basic human relations skills.

(h.) If you return books, be able to prove it. This is accomplished via postal receipts and insurance slips. Dealers and customers are not responsible for items until they sign for them. Never chance it! Always make sure there is some sort of official record proving the comics were returned, even for an inexpensive order. Retain all related documentation for at least one full year after the transaction. Good customers keep good records!

(i.) If nothing seems to work to solve this problem, contact the publication, periodical, or newspaper that carried the dealer's advertisement. Sometimes they can step in and contact the dealer on your behalf. It is important to do this in writing! List the **FACTS** about the transaction in question without being dramatic or sensational. Call afterwards to make sure your letter was received. Inform the dealer about your letter or, better yet, send him/her a copy of the letter. Make the goal of your letter and your efforts resolving the problem, not hurting reputations or feelings. Telephone calls won't work all by themselves. Put your concern or complaint in writing.

The author has been successfully ordering by mail since the 1950s, with a high level of satisfaction. Along with comic book conventions and shops, mail order continues to be a key source for scarce material as well as an expedient, efficient, and cost effective method for collectors from all over the world to buy, sell and trade comic books.

TOY COLLECTING IN 1995 THE YEAR IN REVIEW

by James Bullock

In 1989, the world of comic book related collectibles was a confused place. It was a time in which comics like **X-Men** #94, **Hulk** #181, **Amazing Spider-Man** #129 and **Batman** issues with Joker appearances were the hot items. It was also the time in which the toy industry gave super-hero based action figure lines their first shot in three years. This consisted of Toy Biz's, a newcomer at that time, D.C. Heroes line and, later that year, Kenner's  Dark Knight collection which accompanied the release of the

first Batman movie. Slowly figures began creeping their way onto the convention floors, but they were scarcely noticed. Today, however, action figures are taking the collectibles world by storm. Nearly half of all tables at comic shows deal figures and conventions exclusively devoted to toys are growing across the country. Furthermore, considering the rate at which the hobby is growing, there is no sign of a collapse on the horizon. What  then is responsible for the sudden powerful resurgence of toy collecting? The majority of the credit can be attributed to a concept which is at the foundation of American economics: competition. After Mattel's **He-Man** line went under, Hasbro and Kenner were the two major action figure producers of the 80's. It was not until

Collecting Toys In 1995

late that decade that Toy Biz and Playmates appeared on the scene and began stealing glances in the toy aisles. At that historic point, a battle ensued to claim a dominant share of the market. You are most likely wondering, "What does any of this have to do with 'Toy Collecting in 1995'?" Well, it was this battle that is essentially responsible for the industry transformation which dictates toy production today.

The most typical tactic, employed generally by the big boys who had the capital to do it, has been to win with sheer quantity. Kenner, for example, puts out several assortments a year of **Batman** in numerous costume variations while Toy Biz, of which incidentally Marvel is now a large stockholder, has released part of its intended assortments of over one hundred new figures for this year alone. The hope is, apparently, that the more figures one has, the more space in the toy aisle one takes up, the less choice for the customer in terms of companies and, consequently, the greater the relative market share one holds. Such

a response was not adopted by all, thankfully. Specifically, Todd Toys, founded by comic artist extraordinaire Todd McFarlane, entered the action figure world in the Fall of 1994 with one simple yet overlooked philosophy: quality over quantity! Mr. McFarlane dedicated himself personally to every stage of figure development from sculpting to coloration to insure that the figures were of the

highest quality. The result of Todd Toys' astronomical success has been the setting of new industry standards of figure
articulation. The first series of Todd Toys' debut **Spawn** line
was comprised of six figures which redefined toy excellence,
only to be outdone this year by none other than a second
assortment of **Spawn** toys. Within the span of one short year,
Todd Toys has obtained a firm foothold among the top dogs

of the toy industry, not
by beating them at
their own game but,
rather, by re-examin-
ing the rules.

In addition to Todd Toys' appearance on the scene, the
toy world has seen many other changes since Fall of 1994.
Toy Biz, whose **X-Men** line has brought them tremendous
success for the past few years, ended its Marvel Super Heroes

line
which
consist-
ed of,
basical-
ly, the most popular non-mutant Marvel characters. Instead, it
launched several independent lines which each supplemented
their own animated series: **Spider-Man**, the **Fantastic Four**
and **Iron Man**, the latter of the two of which comprised the
Sunday morning "Marvel Action Hour." These lines, when

combined with the already huge
X-Men and **X-Force** lines, has
given Toy Biz a pretty large
slice of the market pie. Hasbro's
3 3/4 inch **G.I. Joe** line saw its
final days this year. The series,
which has suffered from declin-
ing interest for a while, conclud-
ed with a spin-off assortment, **Sgt. Savage**. The year was not
a total flop for the "Real American Hero," though, as the 30th
anniversary commemorative figures did incredibly well.

Another dying line, **Teenage Mutant Ninja Turtles**, has

Collecting Toys In 1995

been receiving far less attention from its producer. Instead Playmates has wisely chosen to put their eggs in two better baskets: **Star Trek** and the **WildC.A.T.S**. **Star Trek** enjoyed

an increase in consumer interest due, in large part, to the release of the hit movie *Star Trek: Generations* last year. In fact, a separate line of figures was created based on characters from the film. **WildC.A.T.S**, being the second Image based toy line after **Spawn**, can attribute most of its success to its comic book following as well as Playmates' high standard of figure quality. Bandai, previously best known for their beautifully crafted Robotech mecha of the 80's, cashed in with its **Power Ranger** license. Also noteworthy is Bandai's new **Tick** line based on the comic book and subsequent Saturday morning cartoon which, I must add, is hilarious.

All of these and many other occurrences over the past year are indicative of the critical point of transition in which we now find ourselves. 1995 has hosted what appears to be the climax of the "toy war" which has shaped the industry as well as simultaneously bringing the hobby of toy collecting out of the basement and into the mainstream. The future, from this pivotal vantage point, appears very exciting.

It would be an understatement to say that quite a few X-Men and X-Force figures have been released this year. For months now toy stores have been wholesaling their left over figures at prices as low as 2 for $3.99! ! ! Whoa! Toys 'R' Us exclusives that were intended to be giveaways were and are being dumped at $1.98 each. No one can say where these figures will go. Although they are "a dime a dozen," need I remind anyone that first series Storms were blown out by the boxload in 1992 for $2.98? At this price, you might as well stow one

away, just in case. Also, watch for
Phoenix to be good. Early reports indicate that her production is around
50,000 units. **Spawn** Second series figures are even harder to get a hold of than
the first. **Malebolgias** are showing up
one per case and are typically pulled and
sold for $ 50-$70 by
dealers. The
"**Speckled-Gun**"

Commando Spawn is also in great demand
as are **Badrock** and **Angela**. Another difficult figure to find is **"Hamburger Head"**
Spawn.

The Batman lines by
Kenner have been produc-
ing some major collectibles.
From the last few assort-
ments came **Killer Croc**, **Phantasm** and
Poison Ivy .The **Riddler** and **Bane** have
become the figures to watch for. Early estimates have **Bane**'s production number to
also be in the 50,000 range so expect his value to rise.

The full size action figures are on the way, but, in the
mean time, the Justoys bendables and Kenner's Action
Masters are causing quite a stir.
Many variations of the bendable
figures and cards exist which are
causing completionists a great
deal of stress and driving up
prices. Remember, these are
among the first Star Wars toys in
almost a decade. When the new movies come out they'll be
sought after. Also, the **Action Masters** are rumored to be canceled, which has left the rarest item of the set, the **Star Wars**
four-pack, in monstrous demand. Also, the single carded

Collecting Toys In 1995

Chewbacca is nearly impossible to find. Watch for both sets and all other pre-movie **Star Wars** stuff to be in great demand down the road.

The market for original **Star Wars** toys has never been stronger. High-end market prices are growing steadily, but the low-end shows the swiftest movement. Carded **Return of the Jedi** figures which used to be stacked in $5 boxes are being bought up by the collector/ investor with less capital. High-end items like **Power of the Force** and "**12 Back**" **Star Wars** figures are being invested in by zealous collectors with more to spend. Loose figures have also been on the move and show no signs of slowing down.These toys are being stashed away for at least the next several years by newcomers and long time collectors alike. Therefore, a drop in supply and consequent continuation of the price trend should be anticipated since constant demand is almost insured.

Unless a toy is key and of high value or is relatively inexpensive, it tends to draw less attention. Mid-range toys ($30-$100) are invested in significantly less.

Secret Wars has seen its first resurgence in interest in quite a long while. Although the low to mid-range figures still tend to collect dust, key figures are on the move. The three European exclusives have experienced increases in demand

and price. Values for the lower priced figures have had no significant changes but demand and sales are showing a trend toward growth.

Recent reports reveal that **Super Powers** figures are in their highest demand yet and prices are heading for the Moon. All other third series and some second series figures are HOT but first series sales tend to be generally sluggish unless priced below guide.

A few years ago **Transformer** toys came out of the woodwork having collectibility potential and now, with a huge fan following and few boxed specimens available, these toys are hot. The most sought after **Transformers** are the gift sets like the **Devastator** gift set which consists of six **Constructicons** in one box.

The **Marvel Super Heroes** line was essentially canceled by Toy Biz to be replaced by **Spider-Man**, **Iron Man**, **FF** and any other assortments. As a result, collectors are clamoring to complete their sets before shortages become more evident and drive up prices. Yesterday's most elusive figures, **Invisible Woman** I and **Daredevil** I, have slowed down a bit while virtually all of the rest climb. Currently, the best figures, with the previous exceptions, are **Spider-Man** series I, the entire second series especially **Venom**. The fourth series rereleases are a bomb on the secondary market and the fifth and final series enjoys only moderate attention with most figures in the $6-$8 range.

Collectible Card Games

A new collectible has hit the hobby industry like a Juggernaut. Introduced in 1993, collectible card games (CCG's) have become the 800 lb. Kird Ape of the hobby world, although a cooling off period is expected. Collectible card games are much like trading cards in that they are bought in packs. The originator of the CCG was the company Wizards of the Coast (WotC), who released the first widely accepted card game, **Magic: The Gathering**.

Not only had WotC introduced the concept of games to collectible cards, but it also introduced another concept, deliberate rarity. A pack of **Magic** cards contains a set number of COMMON cards, a lesser number of UNCOMMON cards, and finally, one RARE card in each pack.

The rare card actually has two values to it. The first obviously, is due to its scarcity. The second is due to whether it makes or breaks a card game. The end result is both serious gamers and hardcore collectors pay premiums for certain rare cards. Thus PLAYABILITY is a factor in establishing value with these new cards.

That kind of success breeds imitation. Most card game aficionados estimate by the end of 1995 there will be upwards to 75 different card games in the open market. Don't be surprised if some are total busts. Other current hot games include **Star Trek**, **Illuminati**, **Sim City**, **Wyvern**, **On The Edge**, and **Doom Trooper**. Comic-based card games such as **Marvel**

Collectible Card Games

OverPower, **WildStorms** and **Powercardz** are just entering the market.

It is estimated that there are over 35,000 tournament players in the U.S. alone. By tournament, we mean those who reg-

ularly go to shows like Encounters, Origins, Total Confusion in Boston and Dreamation in New Jersey just to play **Magic** and other card games on a regular basis. It is also estimated that there are at least double that amount who aren't regular tournament players. That puts the total population of game card players at 70,000 or more. At least 90% of them

play **Magic: The Gathering**, the most popular of the card games.

So, when **Magic's** creator, Wizards of the Coast, announces that they have a new expansion to their game, even the guys who don't play the game are going to sit up and take notice. That's just what happened when the release of WotC's **Ice Age** was announced.

According to WotC, **Ice Age** consists of over 350 cards, with a pretty good mix of rare cards, uncommons and commons for every starter box or booster pack.

One of the best card games out there is Atlas Games' **On The Edge**. It is a hard, fast game with a lot of surprises. It's just the kind of game that will keep you going back for more. The set itself consists of 117 cards. It is made up of commons and uncommons, and only sold in booster packs.

Collectible Card Games

After production problems and a lot of promise, Mayfair Games' **Sim City** is finally on the market. This unique game doesn't involve players beating the bejeezus out of each other. Instead, like the computer game it's based on, you and other players act as rival contractors trying to build a city, all the while trying to be the first to accumulate 250 simoleons.

The initial **Sim City** card set features 517 cards. Starter decks have 5 rare, 19 uncommons and 36 commons. Boosters have 1 ultra rare long card (which is twice the length of a standard cards), 1 rare, 5 uncommon and 8 common cards.

The first set of cards from **Caliber Game Systems** (CGS) is **Powercardz**. It was revealed that one surprising addition to the game is a 180-card **Spawn** set. This set features characters

that have appeared in the first 30 issues of **Spawn**. Of course, this will also include the **Vioator** and **Angela** series as well.

The **Spawn Powercardz** is a totally self-contained game. However, it is also completely compatible with the 300-card set of **Powercardz**. If **Power** turns out to be a success, you had better get ready for a lot of other interesting projects from CGS.

Cardz entered the game card hobby this June with its first set, **Hyborian Gates**. The 450-card set has one particularly distinguishing feature that is sure to have fantasy art collectors very curious about it. All the artwork was done by Boris

Collectible Card Games

Vallejo and Julie Bell. As most fantasy art card dealers can tell you, Vallejo and Bell are two of the biggest names in the business.

The cards come in common, uncommon, rare and ultra rare distribution. There is also 50 special Gate cards that allow players to travel from one dimension to another. All the cards are printed on playing card stock. The cards will be sold in 110-card starter decks and 15-card booster packs.

Sick of Marvel plots these days? Fleer's new **Marvel OverPower** game card set should make up for it. After all, you can now have the Thing whomp on Gambit's head with a lamppost, just as it should be.

As most people in the industry have known for quite some time, this game has been in the works for a long time.

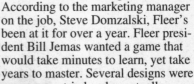

According to the marketing manager on the job, Steve Domzalski, Fleer's been at it for over a year. Fleer president Bill Jemas wanted a game that would take minutes to learn, yet take years to master. Several designs were tried and eventually rejected. Finally, they took the best of several ideas and threw out the rest.

OverPower is a mission-oriented game. There are special cards that give certain missions to complete. You and your opponent have a team of five Marvel heroes/villains each, and while one player tries to get his heroes to complete one of these missions, the other player is having his characters do their darndest to stop it.

Fleer has designed six pre-sorted starter decks. Each deck is themed. Two are based on the X-Men, two on classic Marvel heroes, and two are based on Marvel villains. The deck also comes in with a wide selection of compatible mission, character enhancement and interrupt cards. The reason

for the presorting of the cards is so you can open up a deck
and start playing immediately.

From there, you can add more heroes, villains, mission
and other cards from booster packs. According to Domzalski,
the cards in the boosters are not in the starter decks. This way
you can then start building your own Marvel hero teams to
your own specifications. For the premier edition there are 45
of them alone.

We're not done with comic-related games. WildStorm
Productions announced a game set of its own, called
WildStorms: The Expandable Super-Hero Card Game. It
features all of the WildStorm characters including Gen 13,
Wild C.A.T.S., StormWatch, Team 7 and all the others. This

one is more a direct combat game
with the objective being to try to control three different battlefields.

Set composition is
made of over 120
characters, with the
actual full set being
about 315 cards. A
starter deck is com-
posed of 60 cards, of
which 45 are common
and the rest range
from uncommon to
super-rare. Booster
packs contain 15
cards, of which the mix is 11 common, 3 uncommon and 1
rare.

The long-rumored *Star Trek CCG Warp Packs* finally hit
the market. The best thing of all is the packs are free. For
those who don't know, the *Warp Pack* consists of 12 different
cards from the game. Better still is 5 of the cards in the pack
are new. Best of all, 1 of these new cards is of Montgomery
Scott. For those who have just come from the other side of a
wormhole, Scotty actually made two appearances with the
Star Trek TNG crew, which are the core of the game, one on
the TV show and the other on the last movie. Anyone can get

Collectible Card Games

a *Warp Pack* by writing directly to
Decipher c/o Free Warp Pack Offer, 253
Granby Street, Norfolk, VA 23510-1813.
Include an SASE.

The **Star Trek Two Player** game
contains 24 new cards. The first quarter
million of these pre-sorted sets contain
another preview card that should keep
Trekkers going ballistic: Spock. As
Decipher has been promising since last
year, the 60-card decks are made to be
opened and played immediately. They are being produced in
conjunction with Parker Bros., who are marketing them to
major toy and other general retail outlets. These cards will
have white borders and an unlimited production run (with the
exception of the Spock card).

The name of the collectible card game **Rage** (based on the
storytelling game **Werewolf: The Apocalypse** by White
Wolf Inc.) sums up what it's like to play the game. You control a pack of werewolves (called Garou), and when you're
not banding to fight the evil force known as Wyrm, you're

battling other packs (controlled by
your opponents) for the position of
pack dominance. In your deck (which
of course you customize) you have
various combatants, items and special
powers. You achieve victory by con-
quering the Wyrm, by overpowering
rival Garou or by performing heroic
tasks. Enjoy. This game will have you
howling at the moon.

KELLEY JONES
INTERVIEW

An Interview with Batman Artist Kelley Jones

by Benn Ray

With the release of Batman Forever, the whole country is goin' Bat-nuts. If you haven't picked up an issue of **Batman** *lately, what's wrong with ya? Batman's got a funky new look in the comic and the guy behind the hand behind the pencils is Kelley Jones.*

The way you draw Batman tends to be very dark, even cryptic. Do you see this as a departure from previous Batmans or is it a natural progression of them?

© DC

It's a circle. That's the way I have done him since **Red Rain** and Elseworlds. Part of his repertoire of tricks is to intimidate people long before he ever gets there. He is in a city where something like him is necessary. Why should he be so straight when you have as bizarre a villain gallery as he's got? Secondly, so many people have done him generically for a long time, I thought that he needed [it]. Denny O'Neil said he felt it was as big of a boost artistically, when I came on, as when Neal Adams came on back in the late 60's early 70's. Those are two polar opposites on how to do him, but I think they both work.

What is your key to getting inside the world of Batman?

Basically he's the cape and cowl to me. I try to make it as close to the atmosphere that everything has to reek of Batman whether he is there or not. The cape and cowl, sometimes it's normal and other times it's going to stretch, but that's part of the expressionism. I balance it with the realism. If I was handling something like **Iron Man**, I would be very straight about it, but here it doesn't work as well.

Do you see him as a darker or more edgy force than his character is being written?

No. He's a good person who had a lot of bad things happen to him and this is how he deals with it. I don't think he is crazy, he's just very obsessed. When I draw him, I think of him when he's on the job. He is completely focused on whatever he is after. His body language changes, like if you pull a string across the floor and you watch a cat. They don't care what else is going on. He's just completely tensed and focused until the job is done. He is a mixture of super hero and horror, and you have to bring in both. I would prefer more of the horror element and that's even if he's just dealing with thugs. He has to scare. It's a lot more threatening than a gun, the police or somebody who can lift cars. He can't do any of those things, but he can put the fear of God in them. That and he has to use his brain. One of the things that I really wanted to do was more detective work, more of the actual leg work, more of the finding out all the clues, not just how something was done, but if someone was really guilty.

I've noticed a lot more of that detective element since your work on the Batman series.

Kelley Jones

I even put that signal on the cover of [**Batman** #] 516. In one hand there is a candle and in the other a magnifying glass. There is the horror and then there is the dark side of that whole thing, but he goes about it using his brain.

Do you see Gotham as dark and horrifying as the Batman?
The city isn't just a dark place, it's like a character.

It's almost mythical. Did you ever see the Woody Allen film *Shadows and Fog*? **It reminds me of that.**
Yeah. It's as if you took an old European city and stuck it in America. There are lots of places in Gotham where the buildings are so crowded cars really don't fit, you just walk from place to place. It goes from almost Italian (those hill towns in Italy) to London to New York, all stuck together. Gotham [is] this great ideal, but it festers. That's why this crime exists; that's why you get these bizarre criminals. As opposed to other cities, this is where weird things are going to happen.

What is your favorite Bat-character to draw?
Oh man! Aside from the Bat, it's a toss up between Gordon and Alfred. I really like Alfred. He's a great charac-ter. He's very underrated until he's not there. Part of Alfred's job is to make Bruce Wayne assume his station in society properly so he can be Batman better.

I think it's entirely credible to see this guy that's wholly effectual as Batman, but in everyday life, without Alfred, he's completely clueless.
He is totally clueless. There is a great scene Doug [Moench] wrote: he [Bruce Wayne] does not have Alfred there. He doesn't know that somebody that went to his party shouldn't be there. It turns out to be a criminal. He

can't remember anyone who's there. He's not prepped,
but he can remember a guy's voice that he heard five
years earlier and then zone in on him. That was one of
those great little telling moments of characterization. He
doesn't even recognize people who he does business
with, but he hears this guy's voice and he instantly knows
that guy is Johnny LaMonica — criminal! What's he doing
here???

Alfred would've been there to keep him informed.
Right! Right!

What is it about Gordon that you like?
The dynamic between Batman and Gordon. Batman is
doing what Gordon would love to do, not as a fun thing,
but as "Yes!! He can go out there and take care of this
crime." That's why he'll feed him information. What's
always happened is that secondary characters just get
played as plot devices to get the story finished. Bruce has
to mend these relationships. The biggest one he's got to
mend after Alfred is Gordon. Gordon's going to have to
figure out some things for himself too.

© DC

**Robin doesn't seem to
show up too much in
Batman anymore. Is it
just the way the story
happens to be running
right now or is there
some other reason?**
I'm not big on Robin in
Batman. He has his own
book, and I would prefer to
read that on it's own.
Batman's a loner. It doesn't

Kelley Jones

matter how good of a character Robin would be, it's not necessary for Batman, and I don't think he functions as well. He's someone who's revenging the death of his parents, why would he put anyone else in a position to suffer or die to achieve that revenge? He's got to keep the responsibility just down to himself.

So, fundamentally, you can't accommodate Robin?
I just couldn't see how he could put a fourteen year old kid in the line of fire.

What direction do you see Batman going in now? What is up-coming for him? Anything earth shattering or back breaking?
I want to deal with his ethics. After all the things that have happened in the last few years, has Bruce Wayne been effected positively or negatively? What is the difference between him and Azreal? Gordon always allowed him to operate because he operated with some kind of ethics. When Gordon perceived those ethics gone, he saw Batman as no different as the Joker or anyone else. So he has to re-earn not only Gordon's trust, but his own. Can

© DC

he go out there and do this without going too far? Can he use his judgment better than he did in choosing Jean Paul Valley?

Do you have any other plans to go back to Deadman in his own book?
Right now I'm pretty devoted to what I'm doing on **Batman**. I would love to do a monthly **Deadman**. He is clearly not a

super hero, he's more of a tragic horror character.
Deadman was about loss. He was flawed and therefore
denied. Even though he thought he was doing the right
thing, he went about it the wrong way.

He's like a classic tragic figure.
Yeah, absolutely. I borrowed heavily on that attitude with
Batman. He's always on the edge, not of going insane or
anything, but of just skipping some of the rules.

What was it like working on Sandman?
It was very, very easy. I had my views of Sandman and that
world, and Neil [Gaiman] just let me go. The books we
did really stand out because we got very close to agreeing
on what this character was all about. I never wanted
Sandman to appear too similar from page to page because
in dreams things always change. He had told me once that
he had felt that those were some really stand out
moments, and I agree. Sometimes a great idea is even
greater if you don't beat it to death.

There are a lot of beaten dead horses out there.
You have to always keep in balance an ability to do your
job professionally and an ignorance about what it is you're
doing, so that you don't shut out any possibilities of great-
ness. A great moment to me isn't Batman kicking in a door
and beating the hell out of someone, a great moment to
me is how Batman's listening in on something, or how he
can recognize someone's voice across a crowded masked
ball, and know that's the guy he met only one time five
years earlier. That's creepy to me.

**The "kicking in the door as a great moment" mental-
ity in comics is quite rampant. I think everybody is
too accustomed to it.**
When I think back on great moments, that's not it for me.

39

Kelley Jones

I can only do what was great for me. For example, in the
X-Men years ago, Wolverine was outside hunting a deer.
All he did was see if he could touch it without it knowing
he was there. I don't remember anything else about that
issue. That stuck with me, not some nihilistic alienation
type stuff, but those little moments that I can relate to.
When I'm doing **Batman** with Doug, we're always think-
ing along those lines. There is a one page thing I had

© DC

thrown at Doug about, "Boy it
would be really nice to see
him threaten someone without physically touching him,
hitting him, kicking him, or
anything like that, just threatening him." Doug wrote this
beautiful thing where
[Batman] basically tells [a
Mafia boss to] stay out of this,
he gets the information and
then just flushes the toilet on
him. He rips open the curtain
and there he is standing naked and Batman's just staring
right in his face going "Don't screw with me." Then he
leaves. It's right on the edge of being sadistic, but it's not
violent.

There's also a lot of humor to that.
It's very funny. That's what is so sorely lacking in comics.
A lot of times you'll see a scene where it's just guys shoot-
ing guns, or it's an armor plated villain, and that has it's
place, but I can't relate to that. Everyone can relate to just
taking a shower. The both of us have to reintroduce people to those kind of thoughtful moments in mainstream
comics.

40

Your re-introductions function very well in the Batman series.

We'll get better. I want people to go "Hey, that was worth it." People are attracted when each one of the components gives it a 100%. You just need to have everyone taking it very seriously. I remember someone asked Peter Cushing or Christopher Lee, I forget which one, how come their film stood out over everyone else's. They both said, almost in unison, that they took it as seriously as if it was **Hamlet**. That's what you have to do with these things, you have to take it very seriously. If everyone's doing that, 9 times out 10 you'll get a good book.

The rare kind. The ones you actually get excited to read.

Comics now have become speculation, who's hot, who's not, all that stuff. Every once and awhile people will back-handly pat someone on the head for some obscure book just so they can say we're literary, then they'll turn right around and bolster something you know will be gone in a year. If you only read a book for the drawing, or if you read a book just for the writing, it's a failed comic.

How about comics today? What do you like? What do you see that's going on that you find exciting and interesting?

I like guys who draw from the gut and pull things from God knows what sources. I like what Matt Wagner does. Matt has a way of doing things, he'll take the purity of a character that will be doing good things and put him in a world of perversity, and somehow that character elevates his world, and it never comes off stereotyped. I like Sam Keith a lot. You never know what you're going to get with Sam, and that's my biggest criteria for an artist. I'm sure I'm missing a few. The saddest thing in comics is that it got homogenized. Jack Kirby was a great influence

Kelley Jones

and for awhile they were trying to make people be Kirby-esque. That was years ago, but they stopped that because only Kirby could be Kirby. You can't imitate it, and now the homogenization has happened again. I don't even know when a guy quits and comes back. You become replaceable because there's thirty five guys doing the same thing. You have to go in saying "I want to do something that's going to make people forget for just those few moments and just really enjoy it and think about it and want to be a fan of that." After that, if they attach my name to it, which they should, then that's the benefit of it.

Who would you most like to work with right now?
I would like to work with James Robinson. I'd love to work with Matt Wagner. We've talked about it. To be honest with you, right now I'm in one of those very lucky periods working with Doug, John Beatty [inker], and now Greg Wright [colorist]. I feel like one of the lost things of comics was the idea of teams, where there was penciler, inker, and writer all working together, and that's what we're doing. Essentially I'm in a good position right now. If you're happy at home you don't stray.

And you're happy at home?
Yeah! Right now I'm really happy. I am floored continually that I'm actually drawing Batman in **Batman** comics. This is not a job to me, it's like a real honor. This is an American cultural icon, and I'm very flattered that I've been asked to do this.

Is there a dream book that you'd like to work on?
I'm doing it.

© DC

How to Use
This Book

The author of this book has included a selection of key titles covering a variety of subjects that are mostly collected from 1956 to the present day. The comic book titles are listed alphabetically for easy reference. All key issues and important contents are pointed out and priced in three grades-good, fine and near mint.

Most comic books listed are priced in groups: 11-20, 21-30, 31-50, etc. The prices listed in the right hand columns are for each single comic book in that grouping.

The pricings shown represent the current range, but since prices do change constantly, the values in the book should be used as a guide only.

A general selection of titles is represented here, so for more detailed information please consult **The Overstreet Comic Book Price Guide** master guide.

Comic
Book
Listings

Absolute Vertigo (Winter 1995) © DC

Action Comics #586 © DC

ABSOLUTE VERTIGO
1995 (.99, color, Mature readers)
DC Comics

	Good	Fine	N-Mint
Winter '95-Previews of upcoming titles including Jonah Hex, Invisibles, The Eaters & Ghostdancing	0.10	0.40	1.00

ACTION COMICS (Action Comics Weekly #601-642)
No. 202, Mar, 1955-Present
National Periodical Publ./DC Comics

	Good	Fine	N-Mint
1-Reprint (1988, 50¢-c)			0.50
202-220: 202-1st code approved issue	26.00	77.00	180.00
221-240: 224-1st Golden Gorilla story	21.00	62.00	145.00
241, 243-251: Last Tommy Tomorrow	16.00	47.00	110.00
242-Origin/1st app. Brainiac (7/58)1	20.00	350.00	825.00
252-Origin & 1st app. Supergirl; intro of new Metallo			
	140.00	407.00	950.00
253-2nd app Supergirl	29.00	88.00	205.00
254-1st meeting Of Bizarro & Superman	27.00	81.00	190.00
255-1st Bizarro Lois Lane	19.00	56.00	130.00
256-261: 261-Origin/1st app. Streaky the Super Cat			
	10.00	30.00	78.00
262, 264-266, 268-270	9.30	28.00	65.00
263-Origin Bizarro World	14.00	38.00	90.00
267-3rd Legion app. (8/60)	40.00	130.00	305.00
271-275, 277-282: 282-Last 10¢ issue	7.90	24.00	55.00
276-6th Legion app.	19.00	58.00	135.00
283-Legion Of Super-Villains app.	8.30	25.00	58.00
284-Mon-El app.	8.30	25.00	58.00
285-12th Legion app. (2/62)	8.30	25.00	58.00

	Good	Fine	N-Mint
286-289: 287-14th Legion app.	4.30	13.00	30.00
290(7/62)-17th Legion app; Phantom Girl app	4.30	13.00	30.00
291, 292, 294-299	3.20	8.00	24.00
293-Origin Comet (Superhorse)	8.90	27.00	62.00
300-(5/63)	4.30	13.00	30.00
301-303, 305-308, 310-320	2.00	6.00	14.00
304-Origin/1st app. of Black Flame (9/63)	2.70	8.00	19.00
309-Legion app.; Batman & Robin-c & cameo	2.60	7.70	18.00
321-333, 335-340	1.80	5.00	11.00
334-Giant (G-20); r/origin Supergirl, Legion	3.60	11.00	25.00
341-346, 348-359: 344-Batman x-over	1.30	3.00	8.00
347, 360: (Giants G-33 & G-45)	2.30	7.00	16.00
361-372, 374-380: 377-Legion begins	1.10	3.00	6.50
373-Giant Supergirl (G-57); Legion-r	2.50	6.00	15.00
381-424: 411-Eclipso origin-r	1.10	2.20	5.50
425-Adams art; The Atom begins	1.80	5.00	11.00
426-436, 438, 439: 432-1st SA Toyman	1.00	2.00	5.00
437, 443-(100 pg. giants)	1.50	4.00	9.00
440-1st Grell-a on Green Arrow	1.00	3.00	6.00
441-Grell-a on Green Arrow continues	0.80	2.10	5.00
442, 444-499: 484-40th anniversary issue	0.70	1.40	3.50
500-Superman life story (1.00, 68pgs)	1.00	2.00	5.00
501-551, 554-582: 521-1st app. Vixen	0.40	0.80	2.00
552, 553-Animal Man-c/stories (2 & 3/84)	0.80	2.10	5.00
583-Alan Moore scripts	1.70	4.00	10.00
584-Byrne-a begins; New Teen Titans app.	0.40	0.80	2.00
585-599: 598-1st app. Checkmate	0.30	0.60	1.50
600-(2.50, 84 pgs.)	1.00	1.90	4.75
601-642 (1.50, 52 pgs.): 611-614: Catwoman	0.40	0.70	1.75
643-Monthly issues, Perez-c/a, scripts begin	0.40	0.70	1.75
644-649, 651-661, 663-666, 668-679: 660-Death of Lex Luthor.			
674-Re-intro Supergirl. 679-Last 1.00-c	0.20	0.40	1.00
650-(1.50, 52 pgs.)-Lobo cameo	0.30	0.60	1.50
662-Superman reveals id to Lois Lane	0.80	1.50	3.75
667-(1.75, 52 pgs.)	0.40	0.70	1.75
680-682	0.30	0.50	1.25
683-Doomsday cameo	0.80	2.00	5.00
683-2nd & 3rd printings	0.30	0.50	1.25
684-Doomsday battle issue	0.80	2.10	5.00
685, 686-Funeral For A Friend issues; Supergirl app.			
	0.40	0.80	2.00
685-2nd & 3rd printings	0.30	0.50	1.25
687-(1.95)-Collector's Ed. w/die-cut-c	0.40	0.80	2.00

687-(1.50)-Newsstand Ed. w/mini-poster	0.30	0.60	1.50
688-699,701-703-(1.50): 688-Guy Gardner-c/sty. 697-Bizarro-c/sty.			
703-(9/94)-Zero Hour	0.30	0.60	1.50
695-(2.50)-Variant foil embossed-c	0.50	1.00	2.50
700-(2.95, 68 pgs.)-Fall of Metropolis pt.1	0.60	1.20	3.00
700-Platinum	2.00	4.00	10.00
0,704-710: 0-(10/94). 704-(11/94)	0.30	0.60	1.50
711-begin 1.95-c; 712–	0.40	0.80	2.00
Annual 1 ('87)-Arthur Adams-a; Batman app.	1.00	2.50	6.00
Annual 2 ('89, 1.75)-Perez-c/a	0.40	0.80	2.00
Annual 3 ('91, 2.00, 68 pgs.)	0.40	0.80	2.00
Annual 4, 5 ('92-'93, 2.50, 68 pgs.)	0.50	1.00	2.50
Annual 6 ('94, 2.95)-Elseworlds story	0.60	1.20	3.00

ADDAMS FAMILY (TV cartoon)
Oct, 1974-No. 3, Apr, 1975 (Hanna-Barbera)
Gold Key

1	7.10	21.00	50.00
2, 3	3.20	8.00	30.00

ADVENTURE COMICS
No. 200, May,1954-No. 503, Sept, 1983
National Periodical Publications/DC Comics

200	50.00	150.00	340.00
201-208	32.00	96.00	225.00
209-Last pre-code; origin Speedy	33.00	99.00	230.00
210-1st app. Krypto (Superdog)-c/sty (3/55)	192.00	575.00	2300.00
211-213, 215-220: 220-Krypto app.	26.00	77.00	180.00
214-2nd app. Krypto	43.00	129.00	300.00
221-246	21.00	64.00	150.00
247-1st app. Legion Of Super Heroes (4/58)	320.00	960.00	3200.00
248-252, 254, 255: Green Arrow in all	16.00	49.00	114.00
253-Superboy/Robin first meet	23.00	69.00	160.00
256-Origin Green Arrow by Kirby	64.30	190.00	450.00
257-259	15.00	45.00	105.00
260-1st Silver Age origin of Aquaman (5/59)	70.00	210.00	490.00
261-266, 268, 270: 266-(11/59)-Aquagirl tryout (origin/1st app.);			
not same as later character	10.60	32.00	74.00
267-2nd Legion Of SuperHeroes (12/59)	89.30	270.00	625.00
269-Intro Aqualad (2/60)	22.00	66.00	155.00
271-Origin Luthor retold	24.00	71.00	165.00
272-274, 276-280: 276-3rd Metallo	8.30	25.00	58.00
275-Origin Superman/Batman team retold	20.00	59.00	138.00

	Good	Fine	N-Mint
281, 284, 287-289: 288-Bizarro cover	8.30	25.00	58.00
282-5th Legion app.; intro/origin Starboy	17.00	51.00	120.00
283-Intro Phantom Zone	19.00	56.00	130.00
285-1st Tales of Bizarro World story in Adv.	14.00	41.00	95.00
286-1st Bizarro Mxyzptlk; Bizarro-c	12.00	36.00	85.00
290-8th Legion app., last 10¢ issue	17.00	51.00	120.00
291, 292, 295-298: 295-Bizarro-c	5.40	16.00	38.00
293-13th Legion app.; 1st Bizarro Luthor	10.40	31.00	73.00
294-1st Bizarro M. Monroe, Pres. Kennedy	10.40	31.00	73.00
299-1st Gold Kryptonite (8/62)	6.90	21.00	48.00
300-Legion series begins (9/62)	50.00	140.00	315.00
301-Origin Bouncing Boy	13.00	40.00	93.00
302-305: 303-1st app. Matter Eater Lad	8.90	27.00	62.00
306-310: 1st Legion of Substitute Heroes	6.60	20.00	46.00
311-320: 316-Origins & powers of Legion	4.70	14.00	33.00
321-Intro Time Trapper	4.30	13.00	30.00
322-330: 327-Intro Lone Wolf in Legion	3.40	10.30	24.00
331-340: 340-Intro Computo in Legion	3.00	7.50	18.00
341-Triplicate Girl becomes Duo Damsel	2.30	5.80	14.00
342-345, 347, 350, 351	1.80	4.40	10.50
346, 348, 349: 346-Intro Karate Kid	1.80	4.60	11.00
352, 354-360	1.40	3.50	8.50
353-Death of Ferro Lad in Legion	3.00	6.00	15.00
361-364, 366, 368-370	1.40	2.80	7.00
365, 367, 371, 372: 371-Intro Chemical King	1.60	3.20	8.00
373, 374, 376-380: 380-Last Legion in Adv.	1.40	2.80	7.00
375-Intro Quantum Queen & Wanderers	1.50	3.00	7.50
381-Supergirl begins (1st full length story, 6/69	0.80	1.60	4.00
382-389, 391-400	0.60	1.10	2.75
390, 403-(80 pg. giants G-69 & G-81)	1.80	4.00	9.00
401, 402, 404-410: 409,410-(52 pgs.)	0.70	1.30	3.25
403-Giant G-81 (68 pgs.); Legion-r	1.40	2.80	7.00
411, 413, 418, 419: 411-415,417-420-(52 pgs.)	0.30	0.60	1.50
412-r/origin/1st Animal Man/Str. Adv. #180	1.00	2.00	5.00
414-r/2nd Animal Man/Str. Adv. #184	0.70	1.30	3.25
415, 420-Animal Man-r/Str. Adv. #190, 195	0.30	0.70	1.70
416-Giant DC-100 Pg. Super Spect. #10; G.A.-r	0.50	1.00	2.50
417-Vigilante; Frazetta Shining Knight-r	0.30	0.60	1.50
421-424: 424-Last Supergirl in Adv.	0.30	0.50	1.25
425-New look begins (change to adventure)	0.40	0.80	2.00
426-427, 432-458; 432-440-Spectre stories	0.40	0.80	2.00
428-1st app. Black Orchid (6-7/73)	1.60	3.00	8.00
429,430-Black Orchid-c/stories	0.80	1.60	4.00

Adventure Comics # 429 © DC

Adventures into the Unknown #150 © ACG

431-Spectre stories	1.00	2.00	5.00
459, 460-New Gods/Darkseid story concludes from New Gods #19 (#459			
is dated 9-10/78) w/o missing a month	0.80	1.60	4.00
461, 462: (68 gps.)-Death of Earth II Batman	1.00	2.00	5.00
463-466: (1.00, 68 pgs.)	0.30	0.60	1.50
467-Starman by Ditko, Plastic Man begin	0.60	1.20	3.00
468-490: Last comic-size iss.	0.30	0.50	1.25
491-499: 491-100 pg. digests begin	0.30	0.50	1.25
500-All Legion reprints	0.40	0.80	2.00
501-503: Golden Age reprints	0.30	0.60	1.50

ADVENTURES INTO THE UNKNOWN
No. 51, Jan,1954-No. 174, Aug, 1967
American Comics Group

51(3-D effect-c/story)-Only white-c	22.00	65.00	152.00
52-58 (3-D effect-c/stories)-Black-c	20.00	59.00	138.00
59-3-D effect story only	14.00	42.00	98.00
60-Woodesque-a by Landau	8.00	24.00	56.00
61-Last pre-code issue (1-2/55)	7.70	23.00	54.00
62-70	5.00	15.00	35.00
71-90	3.60	11.00	25.00
91,96(#95 on inside),107,116-All contain Williamson-a			
	4.60	14.00	32.00
92-95,97-99,101-106,108-115,117-127	3.10	9.40	22.00
100	3.60	10.70	25.00
128-Williamson/Krenkel/Torres-r; last 10¢	3.10	9.40	22.00
129-150	2.60	7.70	18.00
151-153: 153-Magic Agent app.	2.10	6.40	15.00
154-Nemesis begins (origin), ends #170	2.90	9.00	20.00

	Good	Fine	N-Mint
155-167, 169-174: 157-Magic Agent app.	2.00	6.00	14.00
168-Ditko-a(p)	2.70	8.10	19.00

ADVENTURES OF BOB HOPE, THE
No. 32, Apr-May, 1955-No. 109, Feb-Mar, 1968
National Periodical Publications

	Good	Fine	N-Mint
32-40: 32-1st code approved issue	8.90	27.00	62.00
41-50	7.40	22.00	52.00
51-70	5.00	15.00	35.00
71-93, 95-105: 95-1st monster issue (11/65)	2.60	7.70	18.00
94-Aquaman cameo	2.90	8.60	20.00
106-109-Monster-c/stories by N. Adams-c/a	4.30	13.00	30.00

ADVENTURES OF CYCLOPS AND PHOENIX
May, 1994-No. 4, Aug, 1994 (2.95, color, mini-series)
Marvel Comics

	Good	Fine	N-Mint
1-Characters from X-Men	0.80	1.60	4.00
2–4	0.60	1.20	3.00

ADVENTURES OF JERRY LEWIS, THE (Advs. of Dean Martin
& Jerry Lewis No. 1-40) (See Super DC Giant)
No. 41, Nov, 1957-No. 124, May-June, 1971
National Periodical Publications

	Good	Fine	N-Mint
41-60	4.90	15.00	34.00
61-80: 68, 74-Photo-c	3.60	11.00	25.00
81-91,93-96,98-100: 89-Bob Hope app	2.30	6.90	16.00
92-Superman cameo	2.90	8.60	20.00
97-Batman/Robin x-over; Joker-c/story	4.00	12.00	28.00
101, 103, 104-Neal Adams-c/a	3.00	10.30	24.00
102-Beatles app.; N. Adams-c/a	4.00	12.00	28.00
105-Superman x-over	2.60	8.00	18.00
106-111,113-116	1.20	2.90	7.00
112-Flash x-over	2.60	7.70	18.00
117-Wonder Woman x-over	1.80	4.60	11.00
118-124	1.00	2.00	5.00

ADVENTURES OF SUPERMAN (Formerly Superman)
Jan, 1987-Present
DC Comics

	Good	Fine	N-Mint
424	0.40	0.80	2.00
425-449: 449-Invasion	0.40	0.70	1.75
450-462	0.30	0.60	1.50
463-Superman/Flash race	0.60	1.20	3.00
464-Lobo-c/app. pre-dates Lobo #1	0.80	1.60	4.00

465-479, 481-491: 491-Last $1.00-c	0.20	0.40	1.00
480-(1.75, 52 pgs.)	0.40	0.70	1.75
492-495	0.30	0.50	1.25
496-Doomsday cameo	0.80	2.10	5.00
496, 497-2nd printings	0.30	0.50	1.25
497-Doomsday battle issue	0.80	2.10	5.00
498, 499-Funeral for a Friend; Supergirl app.	0.60	1.20	3.00
498-2nd & 3rd printings	0.30	0.50	1.25
500-(2.95, 68 pgs.)-Collector's Ed. w/card	0.60	1.20	3.00
500-(2.50, 68 pgs.)-Reg. Ed. w/different-c	0.50	1.00	2.50
500-Platinum Edition	9.00	26.00	60.00
501-(1.95)-Collector's Ed. w/die-cut-c	0.40	0.80	2.00
501-(1.50)-Regular Ed. w/mini-poster, diff.-c	0.30	0.60	1.50
502-517: 502-Supergirl-c/story. 508-Challengers of the Unknown app.			
510-Bizarro-c/story. 517-(9/94)-Zero Hour	0.30	0.60	1.50
505-(2.50)-Holo-grapfx foil-c ed.	0.50	1.00	2.50
0,518-524: 0-(10/94). 518-(11/94)	0.30	0.60	1.50
525-526: 525-begin 1.95-c	0.40	0.80	2.00
Annual 1 ('87)-Starlin-c & scripts	0.30	0.60	1.40
Annual 2 ('90)-Lobo app.	0.40	0.80	2.00
Annual 3 ('91, 2.00)-Armageddon 2001	0.40	0.80	2.00
Annual 4 ('92, 2.50)-Guy Gardner/Lobo c/story	0.50	1.00	2.50
Annual 5 ('93, 2.50)-Bloodlines Earthplague	0.50	1.00	2.50
Annual 6 ('94, 2.95, 68 pgs.)-Elseworlds story	0.60	1.20	3.00

ADVENTURES OF THE FLY (The Fly #1-6; Fly Man #32-39)
Aug, 1959-No. 30, Oct, 1964; No. 31, May, 1965
Archie Publications, Radio Comics

1-Shield app.; origin The Fly; S&K c/a	60.00	170.00	385.00
2-Williamson, S&K	32.00	96.00	225.00
3-Origin retold	26.00	77.00	180.00
4-S&K-c; Powell-a, Shield x-over	13.00	39.00	90.00
5-10: 7-1st S.A. app. Black Hood. 8-1st S.A. app. Shield (also in #9)			
	9.00	26.00	60.00
11-13, 15-20: 20-Origin Flygirl retold	5.00	15.00	35.00
14-Intro & origin Flygirl	7.10	21.00	50.00
21-30: 30-1st S.A. app. Comet	3.40	10.30	24.00
31-Black Hood, Shield, Comet app.	4.00	12.00	28.00

ADVENTURES OF THE JAGUAR, THE
Sept, 1961-No. 15, Nov, 1963
Archie Publications (Radio Comics)

1-Origin & 1st app. The Jaguar	18.00	54.00	125.00

	Good	Fine	N-Mint
2, 3: 3-Last 10¢ issue	8.90	27.00	62.00
4-6: Catgirl app.	6.30	19.00	44.00
7-10	4.30	13.00	30.00
11-15: 13, 14-Catgirl, Black Hood app.	3.40	10.30	24.00

AGENT THREE-ZERO
Sept, 1993 (3.95, color, 52 pgs.)
Galixinovels,Inc

1-Polybagged w/card & mini-poster; Platt-c/a (1st work)			
	1.60	3.20	8.00

AGENT THREE-ZERO: THE BLUE SULTANS QUEST/
BLUE SULTAN-GALAXI FACT FILES
1994 (2.95, color w/text-no comics, limited series:4)
Galaxi Novels

1-(2.95)-Flip book w/Blue Sultan	0.60	1.20	3.00
1-(3.95)-Polybagged w/trading card; flip book w/Blue Sultan			
	0.80	1.60	4.00
1-(5.95)-Platinum embossed edition; flip book w/Blue Sultan			
	1.00	2.50	6.00

AGENTS OF LAW
Mar, 1995 - Present (2.50, color)
Dark Horse Comics

1-4	0.50	1.00	2.50

AGE OF APOCALYPSE:THE CHOSEN
Apr 1995-Present (2.50, color)
Marvel Comics

1-Wraparound-c	0.60	1.20	3.00

AKIRA
Sept, 1988-No. 33, 1992 (3.50, color, deluxe)
Epic Comics

1	3.10	9.40	22.00
1, 2-2nd printings	0.70	1.40	3.50
2	1.50	3.80	9.00
3-5	1.20	2.90	7.00
6-15	0.90	2.30	5.50
16-33: 17-Begin 3.95-c	0.70	1.40	3.50

ALIENS, THE (Captain Johner and...)(Also see Magnus Robot Fighter)
Sept-Dec, 1967; No. 2, May, 1982

Gold Key
1-Reprints from Magnus #1,3,4,6-10, all by Russ Manning

	2.10	6.40	15.00
2-Same contents as #1 ... 0.80 | 1.60 | 4.00

ALIENS (Also see Dark Horse Presents #24)
May 1988-No. 6, July, 1989 (1.95, B&W, mini-series)
Dark Horse Comics

1-1st appearance Aliens in comics	3.60	11.00	25.00
1-Second printing	1.20	2.90	7.00
1-Third - Sixth printings	0.40	0.80	2.00
2	2.60	8.00	18.00
2-Second printing	0.60	1.20	3.00
2-Third printing	0.40	0.80	2.00
3	1.40	4.30	10.00
4	1.20	2.90	7.00
5, 6	0.80	2.10	5.00
3-6: 2nd printings	0.40	0.80	2.00
Aliens Mini Comic 1 (2/89, 4x6")-Included in Aliens Portfolio			
	1.30	3.00	8.00
Aliens Platinum Edition (See Dark Horse Presents...)			
	1.70	4.00	10.00

ALIENS
V2 #1, Aug, 1989-No. 4, 1990 (2.25, color, mini-series)
Dark Horse Comics

V2 #1	1.40	4.00	10.00
V2 #1-2nd printing ('90, 2.25)	0.50	0.90	2.25
2-4	1.00	2.50	6.00

ALIENS:BERSERKERS
Jan 1995 - Present (2.50, color, limited series:4)
Dark Horse Comics

1-4	0.50	1.00	2.50

ALIENS: COLONIAL MARINES
Jan,1993-No. 10, July, 1994 (2.50, color, limited series)
Dark Horse Comics

1–10	0.50	1.00	2.50

ALIENS: EARTH ANGEL
Aug, 1994 (2.95, color, one-shot)
Dark Horse Comics

	Good	Fine	N-Mint
nn-Byrne-a/story; wraparound-c	0.60	1.20	3.00

ALIENS: EARTH WAR
June, 1990-No. 4, Oct, 1990 (2.50, color, limited series)
Dark Horse Comics

	Good	Fine	N-Mint
1-Sam Kieth-a(p) in all	1.70	4.00	10.00
1-2nd print	0.50	1.00	2.50
2	1.30	3.30	8.00
3, 4	1.10	2.70	6.50

ALIENS: GENOCIDE
Nov, 1991-No. 4, Feb, 1992 (2.50, color, mini-series)
Dark Horse Comics
1-4-Suydam painted-c: 4-Wraparound-c; pull-out poster

	Good	Fine	N-Mint
	0.50	1.00	2.50

ALIENS: HIVE
Feb, 1992-No. 4, May, 1992 (2.50, color, mini-series)
Dark Horse Comics

	Good	Fine	N-Mint
1-4: Kelley Jones-c/a in all	0.50	1.00	2.50

ALIENS: LABYRINTH
Sept, 1993-No. 4, Jan, 1994 (2.50, color, mini-series)
Dark Horse Comics

	Good	Fine	N-Mint
1-4: 1-Painted-c	0.50	1.00	2.50

ALIENS: MONDO PEST
Apr, 1995 (2.95, color, one-shot, 44 pgs.)
Dark Horse Comics

	Good	Fine	N-Mint
nn-reprints Dark Horse Comics #22-24	0.60	1.20	3.00

ALIENS: MUSIC OF THE SPEARS
Jan, 1994-No. 4, Apr, 1994 (2.50, color, limited series)
Dark Horse Comics

	Good	Fine	N-Mint
1–4	0.50	1.00	2.50

ALIENS/PREDATOR: THE DEADLIEST OF THE SPECIES
July, 1993-Present (2.50, color, limited series:12)
Dark Horse Comics

	Good	Fine	N-Mint
1	0.80	1.60	4.00
2-11-Bolton painted-c: 1-3-Guice-p	0.50	1.00	2.50
1-Embossed foil platinum ed. no price/no ads	4.30	13.00	30.00

ALIENS: ROGUE
Apr, 1993-No. 4, July, 1993 (2.50, color, mini-series)
Dark Horse Comics

1–4	0.50	1.00	2.50

ALIENS: SACRIFICE
May, 1993 (4.95, color, one-shot, 52 pgs.)
Dark Horse Comics

nn-Peter Milligan scripts; painted-c/a	1.00	2.00	5.00

ALIENS: SALVATION
Nov, 1993 (4.95, color, one-shot)
Dark Horse Comics

nn-D. Gibbons script	1.00	2.00	5.00

ALIENS: STRONGHOLD
May 1994-No. 4, Sep, 1994 (2.50, color, mini-series)
Dark Horse Comics

1–4	0.50	1.00	2.50

ALIENS VS. PREDATOR (See Dark Horse Presents #36)
June, 1990-No. 4, Dec, 1990 (2.50, mini-series, color)
Dark Horse Comics

1	1.70	5.00	12.00
1-2nd printing	0.50	1.00	2.50
0-(7/90, 1.95, B&W)-r/DHP 34-36	2.10	6.40	15.00
2, 3	1.50	3.80	9.00
4-Dorman painted-c	1.00	2.00	5.00

ALIENS VS. PREDATOR: DUEL
Mar, 1995-Present (2.50, color, limited series)
Dark Horse Comics

1,2	0.50	1.00	2.50

ALIENS vs. PREDATOR: WAR
May 1995-Present (2.50, color, limited series)
Dark Horse Comics

0–2	0.50	1.00	2.50

ALIEN 3
June, 1992-No. 3, Aug, 1992 (2.50, color, mini series)
Dark Horse Comics

1-3-Suydam painted-c	0.50	1.00	2.50

	Good	Fine	N-Mint

ALIEN WORLDS
Dec, 1982-No. 9, Jan, 1985
Pacific Comics/Eclipse

	Good	Fine	N-Mint
1	0.30	0.60	1.50
2-9: 2, 4-Dave Stevens-c/a	0.20	0.40	1.00
3-D No. 1-Art Adams 1st pub. art	0.60	1.20	3.00

ALL AMERICAN MEN OF WAR
No. 127, Aug-Sept, 1952-No. 117, Sept-Oct, 1966
National Periodical Publications

	Good	Fine	N-Mint
127 (1952)	80.00	231.00	540.00
128 (1952)	54.00	161.00	375.00
2 (12-1/52-53) - 5	44.00	133.00	310.00
6–10	31.00	92.00	215.00
11-18: Last pre-code issue	26.00	77.00	180.00
19-28	19.00	56.00	130.00
29, 30, 32-Wood-a	20.00	60.00	140.00
31, 33-40	16.00	49.00	115.00
41-50	11.40	34.00	80.00
51-66	8.60	26.00	60.00
67-1st app. Gunner & Sarge	18.00	54.00	125.00
68-70	8.00	25.00	58.00
71-80	6.00	18.00	42.00
81, 83-88: 88-Last 10¢ issue	5.00	15.00	35.00
82-Johnny Cloud begins	7.10	21.00	50.00
89-100:	4.00	10.70	25.00
101-117: Johnny Cloud app. 111,115 & 117	2.40	7.30	17.00

All American Men of War #128 © DC

Alpha Flight #130 © MEG

ALL-STAR SQUADRON
Sept, 1981-No. 67, Mar, 1987
DC Comics

1-46, 48-67	0.20	0.40	1.00
47-McFarlane-a (1st full story)	0.80	1.60	4.00
Annual 1-3 (11/82-9/84)	0.20	0.40	1.00

ALL-STAR WESTERN (Weird Western Tales #12 on)
Aug-Sept, 1970-No. 11, Apr-May, 1972
National Periodical Publications

1	1.80	5.00	11.00
2-El Diablo by Morrow begins	0.80	1.60	4.00
3-8: 3-Origin El Diablo	0.80	1.60	4.00
9-Frazetta-r (3 pgs.)	1.10	2.20	5.50
10-1st app. Jonah Hex (2-3/72)	10.00	30.00	70.00
11-2nd app. Jonah Hex	5.00	15.00	35.00

ALPHA FLIGHT (See X-Men #120, 121)
Aug, 1983-No. 130, Mar, 1994 (#52 on are direct sale)
Marvel Comics Group

1-(52 pgs.)-Byrne-a begins; Wolverine cameo	0.50	1.00	2.50
2-12: 12-Double size	0.40	0.70	1.75
13-Wolverine app.	0.70	1.70	4.00
14-16: 16-Wolverine cameo	0.30	0.50	1.25
17-X-Men x-over; Wolverine cameo	0.40	0.80	2.00
18-28: Last Byrne issues	0.30	0.50	1.25
29-32, 35-49: 39-Portacio-i begins	0.20	0.40	1.00
33, 34-Wolverine app. 34-Origin retold	0.70	1.70	4.00
50-Double size	0.30	0.50	1.25
51-Jim Lee's 1st work at Marvel	1.00	2.00	5.00
52, 53: Wolverine; 53-Lee/Portacio-a	0.60	1.20	3.00
54, 63, 64-No Jim Lee art	0.20	0.40	1.00
55-62: Jim Lee art(p)	0.50	1.00	2.50
65-74, 76-86: 74-Wolverine, Spider-Man	0.30	0.50	1.25
75-(1.95, 52 pgs.)	0.40	0.80	2.00
87-90: Wolverine app.; Jim Lee-c	0.60	1.20	3.00
91-99, 101-105, 107-119,121-129	0.30	0.60	1.50
100-(2.00, 52 pgs.) Avengers app.	0.40	0.70	1.75
106-Northstar revelation issue	0.60	1.10	2.75
106-2nd printing	0.30	0.50	1.25
120-(2.25)-Polybagged w/poster	0.40	0.70	1.75
130-(2.25, 52 pgs.)	0.50	0.90	2.25
Annual 1 (9/86, 1.25)	0.30	0.50	1.25

	Good	Fine	N-Mint
Annual 2-(12/87, 1.25)	0.20	0.40	1.00
Special V2#1 (6/92, 2.50)-Wolverine-c/story	0.50	1.00	2.50

AMAZING ADULT FANTASY (Amazing Adventures No. 1-6; Amazing Fantasy No. 15)
No. 7, Dec, 1961-No. 14, July, 1962
Marvel Comics Group (AMI)

7-Ditko-c/a in all	36.00	109.00	435.00
8-Last 10¢ issue	30.00	90.00	355.00
9–13	26.00	80.00	315.00
14-Prof. X prototype	30.00	89.00	355.00

AMAZING ADVENTURES (Amazing Adult Fantasy #7 on)
June, 1961-No. 6, Nov, 1961
Marvel Comics Group (AMI)

1-Origin Dr. Droom (1st Marvel Super-Hero) Ditko & Kirby art in all; Kirby monster c-1-6	100.00	300.00	900.00
2	42.00	125.00	375.00
3-6: 6-Last Dr. Droom	38.00	113.00	340.00

AMAZING ADVENTURES
Aug, 1970-No. 39, Nov, 1976
Marvel Comics Group

1-Inhumans (by Kirby in 1-4, ends #10) & Black Widow (ends #8) double feature begins	2.40	7.30	17.00
2–4	1.60	3.20	8.00
5-8: N. Adams-a	1.70	4.00	10.00
9, 10: 9, 10-Magneto app.	1.10	2.20	5.50
11-New Beast begins (1st app.), ends #17	2.50	6.00	15.00
12-17: 13-Brotherhood of Evil Mutants app.	1.00	3.00	6.00
18-1st app. Killraven, N. Adams-a	1.40	4.00	10.00
19-39	0.60	1.20	3.00

AMAZING FANTASY (Formerly Amazing Adult Fantasy)
No. 15, Aug, 1962 (Sept, 1962 in indicia)
Marvel Comics Group (AMI)

15-Origin & 1st app. Spider-Man by Ditko (11 pgs.); 1st app. Aunt May & Uncle Ben; Kirby/Ditko-a (5 pgs.)	1470.00	4410.00	23000.00

AMAZING SPIDER-MAN, THE (See Giant-Size Spider-Man)
March, 1963-Present
Marvel Comics Group
1-Origin retold; Ditko-c/a #1-38; Kirby/Ditko-c; 1st Fantastic Four x-over

(ties w/F.F. #12 as 1st Marvel x-over)	970.00	2910.00	15500.00
1 (Golden Records Reprint)	11.00	34.00	80.00
(with Golden Records (1966)	29.00	86.00	200.00
2-1st app. The Vulture	240.00	720.00	2400.00
3-1st app. Doc Octopus	151.00	453.00	1360.00
4-Origin & 1st app. The Sandman	131.00	393.00	1180.00
5-Dr. Doom app.	123.00	368.00	980.00
6-1st app. Lizard	109.00	328.00	875.00
7, 8, 10: 8-Early FF backup story	86.00	257.00	600.00
9-Origin & 1st app. Electro	96.00	289.00	675.00
11, 12: 12-Doc Octopus unmasks Spidey-c/story			
	50.00	150.00	350.00
13-1st app. Mysterio	63.00	189.00	440.00
14-1st app. the Green Goblin (Norman Osborn); Hulk x-over			
	124.00	372.00	1240.00
15-1st app. Kraven The Hunter; 1st mention of Mary Jane Watson (not			
shown)	52.00	156.00	365.00
16-1st Daredevil x-over (yellow costume)	39.00	118.00	275.00
17-2nd app. Green Goblin (c/story)	64.00	191.00	445.00
18-1st app. Ned Leeds (later Hobgoblin)	40.00	120.00	280.00
19-Sandman app.	32.00	96.00	225.00
20-1st app. & origin The Scorpion	39.00	118.00	275.00
21-2nd app. The Beetle (see Str. Tales#123)	26.00	77.00	180.00
22-1st app. Princess Python	23.00	69.00	160.00
23-3rd app. Green Goblin (c/story)	39.00	117.00	272.00
24	22.00	66.00	155.00
25-1st app. Mary Jane Watson (cameo) (face not shown, but			
introduced as Mary Jane)	27.00	81.00	190.00
26-4th app. Green Goblin; 1st Crime Master	29.00	88.00	205.00
27-5th app. Green Goblin	27.00	81.00	190.00
28-Origin/1st app. Molten Man	39.00	118.00	275.00
29, 30	19.00	56.00	130.00
31-38: 31-Intro Harry Osborn (later becomes 2nd Gr. Goblin), Gwen Stacy,			
& Prof. Warren. 38-Last Ditko issue; 2nd app. Mary Jane Watson (cameo,			
face not shown, 7/66)	17.00	51.00	120.00
39-Green Goblin-c/story; id revealed	24.00	71.00	165.00
40-Origin Green Goblin (1st time told)	36.00	107.00	250.00
41-1st app. Rhino	17.00	50.00	120.00
42-3rd app. Mary Jane Watson (cameo, last 2 panels) (1st time her face is			
shown) (11/66)	16.00	47.00	110.00
43-49	11.00	32.00	75.00
50-Intro Kingpin (7/67)	45.00	135.00	315.00
51-2nd app. of Kingpin	16.00	49.00	115.00

	Good	Fine	N-Mint
52-60: 56-Intro Capt. George Stacy	9.00	26.00	60.00
61-74: 69, 70-Kingpin app. 69-Kingpin-c. 74-Last 12¢ issue			
	6.40	19.00	45.00
75-89, 91-93, 95, 99: 84, 85-Kingpin-c/stories	5.30	16.00	37.00
90-Death of Capt. Stacy	6.00	18.00	42.00
94-Origin retold	8.30	25.00	58.00
96-98: Drug books not approved by CCA; Green Goblin storyline.			
97, 98-Green Goblin-c	11.00	32.00	75.00
100-Anniversary issue (9/71)	22.00	66.00	155.00
101-1st app. Morbius; last 15¢ issue (10/71)	23.00	69.00	160.00
101-2nd printing (9/92, silver ink)	0.50	1.00	2.50
102-Origin/2nd app. Morbius (25¢, 52 pgs.)	16.00	47.00	110.00
103-118: 109-Dr. Strange-c/story (6/72)	3.00	9.00	21.00
119, 120-Spider-Man vs. Hulk	4.90	15.00	34.00
121-Green Goblin kills Gwen Stacy	14.00	43.00	100.00
122-Death of Green Goblin	17.00	51.00	120.00
123-128: 123-Cage app. 124-1st app. Man-Wolf (9/73), origin #125			
	3.10	9.40	22.00
129-1st app. Jackal & The Punisher (2/74)	39.00	118.00	275.00
130-133, 138-141,152-160: 131-Last 20¢ iss.			
	1.90	6.00	13.00
134-Punisher cameo app. (7/74)	3.10	9.40	22.00
135-2nd full Punisher app. (8/74)	9.00	28.00	65.00
136-Re-intro Green Goblin (Harry Osborn)	5.00	15.00	35.00
137-Green Goblin c/story (Harry Osborn)	5.70	17.10	40.00
142,143-Gwen Stacy clone cameos	3.40	10.00	24.00
144-Full app. of Gwen Stacy clone	2.60	8.00	18.00
145,146-Gwen Stacy clone storyline continues	2.60	8.00	18.00
147-Spider-Man learns Gwen Stacy is clone	2.60	8.00	18.00
148-Jackal revealed	3.60	11.00	25.00
149-Spider-Man clone-s begins, origin of Jackal	10.70	32.10	75.00
150-Spider-Man decides he is not the clone	7.10	21.40	50.00
151-Spider-Man disposes of clone body	4.30	13.00	30.00
161-Punisher cameo; Nightcrawler app.	1.70	5.00	12.00
162-Punisher, Nightcrawler app.	2.70	8.10	19.00
163-173, 181-190: 169-Clone story recapped. 181-Origin retold			
	1.30	3.30	8.00
174, 175-Punisher app.	2.60	7.70	18.00
176-180: Green Goblin app.	2.40	7.00	17.00
191-193, 195-199, 203-208, 210-219	1.30	3.00	8.00
194-1st app. Black Cat	2.10	6.00	15.00
200-Giant origin issue (1/80)	4.30	13.00	30.00
201, 202-Punisher app.	3.10	9.40	22.00

Amazing Spider-Man #196 © MEG

Amazing Spider-Man #393 © MEG

209-Origin & 1st app. Calypso (10/80)	1.70	4.20	10.00
220-237: 225-Foolkiller-c/story (2/82)	1.30	3.00	8.00
238-1st app. Hobgoblin (Ned Leeds) (3/83) (w/Tattooz card intact)			
	11.00	34.00	80.00
238-Without Tattooz	3.60	11.00	25.00
239-1st Hobgoblin/Spidey battle (2nd app.)	6.00	18.00	42.00
240-243, 246-248: 241-Origin Vulture	1.30	3.00	8.00
244-Hobgoblin cameo (3rd app.)	1.80	5.00	11.00
245-Lefty Donovan w/Hobgoblin powers battles Spider-Man (10/83);			
Hobgoblin cameo (4th app.)	2.30	6.90	16.00
249-251-Hobgoblin/Spidey battle storyline	2.00	6.00	14.00
252-1st app. black costume for Spidey (5/84)	4.60	13.70	32.00
253-1st app. The Rose	1.50	3.80	9.00
254-Jack O'Lantern app.	1.20	2.90	7.00
255, 263, 264, 266-273, 277-280, 282, 283: 279-Jack O'Lantern-c/story.			
282-X-Factor x-over	1.00	2.00	5.00
256-1st app. Puma	1.10	2.20	5.50
257-2nd app. Puma; Hobgoblin cameo	1.80	5.00	11.00
258-Hobgoblin app. (minor)	1.90	6.00	13.00
259-Full Hobgoblin app.; origin M. J. Watson	3.10	9.40	22.00
260-Hobgoblin story	1.80	5.00	11.00
261-Hobgoblin-c/story	1.90	6.00	13.00
262-Spider-Man unmasked	1.50	4.00	9.00
265-1st app. Silver Sable (6/85)	1.60	5.00	11.00
265-Silver ink 2nd printing	0.60	1.20	3.00
274-Zarathos (Spirit Of Vengeance) app.(3/86)	1.00	2.00	5.00
275-(52 pgs.)-r/origin by Ditko ; Hobgoblin-c/s	2.00	6.00	14.00
276-Hobgoblin story	2.00	5.00	12.00
281-Hobgoblin battles Jack O'Lantern	1.90	6.00	13.00

	Good	Fine	N-Mint
284-Punisher cameo app., Gang War begins, ends #288; Hobgoblin-c/sty			
	1.70	4.00	10.00
285-Punisher app.; minor Hobgoblin app.	2.10	6.00	15.00
286-Hobgoblin-c/app. (minor)	1.00	2.50	6.00
287-Hobgoblin app. (minor)	1.00	2.50	6.00
288-Hobgoblin full app.	1.50	3.80	9.00
289-(1.25, 52 pgs.)-Death of Ned Leeds (1st Hobgoblin); Macendale (Jack			
O'Lantern) becomes new Hobgoblin	3.40	10.00	24.00
290-292	1.00	2.00	5.00
293, 294-Parts 2 & 5 of Kraven story	1.50	3.80	9.00
295-297	1.00	2.50	6.00
298-Todd McFarlane-c/a begins (3/88); 1st app. (cameo) Eddie Brock who			
becomes Venom (not in costume)	5.70	17.00	40.00
299-1st app. (cameo) Venom in costume	3.60	11.00	25.00
300-(52 pgs.)-Last black costume; 1st full Venom story			
	10.00	30.00	70.00
301-305	2.30	6.90	16.00
306-311, 313, 314	1.80	4.60	11.00
312-Hobgoblin battles Green Goblin	3.30	9.90	23.00
315-317: Venom app.	3.00	8.60	20.00
318-323, 325: 319-Biweekly begins	1.30	3.30	8.00
324-Sabretooth app.; McFarlane-c (no art)	1.90	5.60	13.00
326, 327, 329-No McFarlane	0.80	1.60	4.00
328-Hulk app.; last McFarlane-a	1.80	4.60	11.00
330, 331: Punisher app.	0.80	1.60	4.00
332, 333-Venom-c/story	1.70	4.20	10.00
334-336, 338-343	0.60	1.20	3.00
337-Hobgoblin app.	0.80	1.60	4.00
344-1st app. Cletus Kasady (Carnage)	1.70	4.00	10.00
345-1st full app. Cletus Kasady	1.70	5.00	12.00
346, 347-Venom app.	1.70	4.00	10.00
348, 349, 351-359:359-(1.25-c)	0.50	1.00	2.50
350-(1.50, 52 pgs.)-Origin retold	0.60	1.20	3.00
360-Carnage cameo	1.40	3.50	8.50
361-Intro Carnage	2.60	8.00	18.00
361-2nd printing; silver-c	0.40	0.80	2.00
362, 363-Carnage & Venom-c/story	1.50	4.00	9.00
362-2nd printing	0.30	0.60	1.50
364, 366-374, 376-387: 373-Venom back-up. 374-Venom-c/story.			
376-Cardiac app. 378-Maximum Carnage, part 3. 381, 382-Hulk app.			
383-The Jury app. 384-Venom/Carnage app.	0.40	0.70	1.75
365-(3.95)-Silver hologram on-c, pull-out poster; 1st app S-Man 2099			
	1.00	2.50	6.00

365-2nd printing; gold hologram on-c	0.80	1.60	4.00
375-(3.95)-Holo-grafx-c; Vs. Venom-c/story	1.00	2.40	5.75
388-(2.25, 68 pgs.)-Newsstand Edition; 2 back-up stories: Venom; Cardiac			
& Chance	0.50	0.90	2.25
388-(2.95)-Collectors Edition w/foil-c	0.60	1.20	3.00
389-396,398-399, 401-404: 389-Begin 1.50-c; Green Goblin app.; bound-in			
card sheet. 394-Power & Responsibility Pt. 2. 396-Daredevil-c & app.			
403-Carnage app.	0.30	0.60	1.50
390-(2.95) Collectors Edition; polybagged w/16 pg. insert & animation			
print	0.60	1.20	3.00
394-(2.95, 48 pgs.)-Deluxe edition; flip book w/Birth of a Spider-Man Pt. 2;			
Silver foil both-c	1.00	2.00	5.00
397-(2.25-c)-Flip book w/Ultimate Spider-Man			
	0.50	0.90	2.25
400-(2.95)-Death of Aunt May	1.00	2.00	5.00
400-(3.95)-Death of Aunt May-Double -c-embossed			
	1.20	2.40	6.00
Annual 1-('64)-1st Sinister Six; new 41 pg sty	47.80	143.00	430.00
Annual 2-('65)-New Doctor Strange sty (early)	20.00	60.00	200.00
Special 3-(11/66)-Avengers vs Hulk x-over	9.30	28.00	65.00
Special 4-(11/67)-Spidey battles Human Torch (new 41 pg. story)			
	9.30	28.00	65.00
Special 5-(11/68)-Peter Parker's parents; New 40 pg. Red Skull story			
	10.00	30.00	70.00
Special 6-(11/69)-r/41 pg. Sinister Six story from Annual #1			
	4.20	10.00	25.00
Special 7-(12/70)-All reprints	4.20	10.00	25.00
Special 8-(12/71)-All reprints	4.20	10.00	25.00
King Size 9-(1973)-r/Spec. Spider-Man magazine (Green Goblin c/story,			
40 pgs re-edited from orig. 58 pgs)	4.20	10.00	25.00
Annual 10-12 (1976-78)-All new-a	1.30	3.00	8.00
Annual 13 ('79)-John Byrne-a	1.30	3.30	8.00
Annual 14 ('80)-Miller-c/a	1.50	3.80	9.00
Annual 15 ('81)-Punisher app., Miller-c/a	2.90	8.60	20.00
Annual 16-20 (1982-86)	1.20	2.90	7.00
Annual 21 ('87)-Wedding issue; direct sale	1.50	3.80	9.00
Annual 21 ('87)-Wedding issue; newsstand	1.50	3.80	9.00
Annual 22 ('88)-Evolutionary War	1.30	3.30	8.00
Annual 23 ('89)-Atlantis Attacks; Liefeld-p	1.20	2.90	7.00
Annual 24 ('90, 2.00)	0.80	1.60	4.00
Annual 25 ('91, 2.00)-1st solo Venom story	2.00	5.00	12.00
Annual 26 ('92, 2.25)-New Warriors-c/story; Venom solo story, cont'd			
in Spect. S-M Annual #12	1.20	2.90	7.00

	Good	Fine	N-Mint
Annual 27-('93, 2.95)-Polybagged w/card; 1st app. Annex			
	0.60	1.20	3.00
Annual 28-('94, 2.95, 68 pgs.)-New Carnage-c/story			
	0.60	1.20	3.00
...: Skating on Thin Ice 1-('90, 1.25, Canadian)	1.00	2.00	5.00
...: Skating on Thin Ice 1-(2/93, 1.50, Amer.)	0.40	0.80	2.00
...: Double Trouble 2-('90, 1.25, Canadian)	0.60	1.20	3.00
...: Double Trouble 2-(2/93, 1.50, American)	0.40	0.80	2.00
...: Hit and Run 3-('90, 1.25, Canadian)-Ghost Rider-c/story			
	0.60	1.20	3.00
...: Hit and Run 3-(2/93, 1.50, American)	0.40	0.80	2.00
...: Carnage (6/93, 6.95) r/ASM #344,345,359-363			
	1.20	2.90	7.00
...: Chaos in Calgary 4-(2/93, 1.50, American)	0.40	0.80	2.00
...: Deadball 5-('93, 1.60, Canadian)-Green Goblin-c/story;			
features Montreal Expos	0.30	0.60	1.50
...: Soul of the Hunter nn (8/92, 5.95)	1.00	2.50	6.00
Giveaways: See Overstreet Price Guide listings			

AMAZING SPIDER-MAN SUPER SPECIAL
Apr, 1995-Present (3.95, color, limited series)
Marvel Comics

	Good	Fine	N-Mint
1-Flip book	0.70	1.70	4.00

AMAZING X-MEN
Mar 1995 - Present (1.95, color, limited series)
Marvel Comics

	Good	Fine	N-Mint
1-Age of Apocalypse	0.70	1.70	4.00
2–4	0.40	0.80	2.00

AMERICAN, THE
July, 1987-No. 8, 1989 (1.75, B&W)
Dark Horse Comics

	Good	Fine	N-Mint
1-(1.50)	0.60	1.20	3.00
2	0.40	0.80	2.00
3–5	0.40	0.80	2.00
6–8	0.40	0.70	1.75
American Collection (B&W, 5.95)	1.00	2.50	6.00
Special 1 ('90, 2.25)	0.50	0.90	2.25

AMERICAN FREAK: A TALE OF THE UN-MEN
Feb, 1994-No. 5, June, 1994 (1.95, color, limited series)

American Freak #5 © DC

Angela #2 © Todd McFarlane

DC Comics			
1–5	0.40	0.80	2.00

AMERICAN: LOST IN AMERICA, THE
July, 1992-No. 4, Oct, 1992 (2.50, color, mini-series)
Dark Horse Comics

1-4: 1-Dorman painted-c. 2-Joe Phillips painted-c. 3-Mignola-c.			
4-Jim Lee-c	0.50	1.00	2.50

AMERICAN SPLENDOR SPECIAL: A STEP OUT OF THE NEST
Aug, 1994 (2.95, B&W, one-shot)
Dark Horse Comics

1-H. Pekar-story	0.60	1.20	3.00

AMERICA'S BEST TV COMICS
1967 (Giant Size, 68 pgs., 25¢, one-shot)
American Broadcasting Company

1-Fantastic Four, Casper, Amazing Spider-Man	7.10	21.00	50.00

ANGELA
Dec 1994 - Present (2.95, color)
Image Comics

1-Spawn app.	0.80	2.00	5.50
2-3:-N. Gaiman/s, G.Capullo/a	0.80	1.60	4.00
Special Edition	4.00	8.00	20.00

ANGEL AND THE APE (Becomes Meet Angel)(See Showcase #77)
Nov-Dec, 1968-No. 6, Sept-Oct, 1969
National Periodical Publications

1	3.00	9.00	21.00

	Good	Fine	N-Mint
2–6	1.90	6.00	13.00

ANIMA
Mar, 1994-Present (1.75/1.95, color)
DC Comics

	Good	Fine	N-Mint
1–6	0.40	0.70	1.75
7-(9/94)-Begin 1.95-c; Zero Hour	0.40	0.80	2.00
0, 8-14: 0-(10/94). 8-(11/94)	0.40	0.80	2.00
15-begin 2.25-c	0.50	0.90	2.25

ANIMAL MAN (See Strange Adventures #180 for 1st app.)
Sept, 1988-Present (Color, mature)
DC Comics

	Good	Fine	N-Mint
1-Bolland-c #1-63	1.40	4.30	10.00
2	1.30	3.30	8.00
3, 4	0.80	2.10	5.00
5-10: 6-Invasion tie-in	0.80	1.60	4.00
11-20: 11-Begin $1.50-c	0.60	1.20	3.00
21-26: 26-Last Grant Morrison scripts	0.60	1.20	3.00
27-49, 51-55, 57-59	0.40	0.80	2.00
50-(2.95, 52 pgs.)-Last issue by Tom Veitch	0.60	1.20	3.00
56-(3.50, 68 pgs.)	0.70	1.40	3.50
60-82: 60-Begin 1.95-c	0.40	0.80	2.00
83-begin 2.25-c; 84-86	0.50	0.90	2.25
Annual 1 (3.95,'93)- Children's Crusade Pt. 3	0.80	1.60	4.00

ANIMANIACS
May, 1995-Present (1.50, color)
DC Comics

	Good	Fine	N-Mint
1-4	0.30	0.60	1.50

ANIMANIACS: A CHRISTMAS SPECIAL
Dec, 1994 (1.50, color, one-shot)
DC Comics

	Good	Fine	N-Mint
nn ("1" on cover)	0.30	0.60	1.50

ANNEX
Aug, 1994-No. 4, Nov, 1994 (1.75, color, limited series)
Marvel Comics

	Good	Fine	N-Mint
1-4: 1-Spider-Man app.	0.40	0.70	1.75

ANTHRO (See Showcase #74)
July-Aug, 1968-No. 6, July-Aug, 1969

National Periodical Publications

1	4.70	14.00	33.00
2–6	2.60	7.70	18.00

ANYTHING GOES
Oct, 1986-No. 6, 1987 (Mini-series)
Fantagraphics Books

1-Flaming Carrot app.	0.60	1.20	3.00
2-4, 6	0.40	0.80	2.00
5-TMNT app., 2nd time in color	0.60	1.20	3.00

APPARITION
1995-, (3.95, B&W, 52 pgs.)
Caliber Comics

1	0.80	1.60	4.00

APPLESEED
Sept, 1988-Book IV #4, Aug, 1991 (B&W)
Eclipse International

1	1.70	4.00	10.00
2-5(1/89)	0.60	1.20	3.00
Book II, 1(2/89)-5(7/89)-A. Adams-c	0.60	1.20	3.00
Book III Vol. 1(8/89)-4 (2.75)	0.60	1.20	3.00
Book III Vol. 5 (3.50-c)	0.60	1.20	3.00
Book IV #1-4 (1/91- 8/91, 3.50-c)	0.60	1.20	3.00

AQUAMAN (See Adventure #260, Detective #293, Showcase #30-33, & World's Finest Comics #125)
Jan-Feb, 1962-No. 63, Aug-Sept, 1978
National Periodical Publications/DC Comics

1-Intro Quisp	40.00	110.00	375.00
2	25.00	75.00	175.00
3–5	14.00	41.00	95.00
6-10: 9-Sea Devils app.	9.30	28.00	65.00
11–20	7.40	22.00	52.00
21-32, 34-40	5.40	16.00	38.00
33-Intro Aqua-Girl (see Adv. 266)	7.40	22.00	52.00
41-47, 49	2.10	6.00	15.00
48-Origin reprinted	2.90	8.60	20.00
50-52: Deadman by N. Adams	3.90	11.60	27.00
53-56: 56-(3-4/71)	1.40	4.00	8.50
57-63: 57-(8-9/77). 58-Origin retold	1.00	2.00	5.00

	Good	Fine	N-Mint

AQUAMAN
Feb, 1986-No. 4, May, 1986 (Mini series)
DC Comics

	Good	Fine	N-Mint
1	0.80	1.60	4.00
2–4	0.50	1.00	2.50
Special 1 ('88, 1.50)	0.40	0.80	2.00

AQUAMAN
Dec, 1991-No. 13, Dec, 1992 (1.00/1.25, color)
DC Comics

	Good	Fine	N-Mint
1-5-(1.00)	0.20	0.40	1.00
6-13-(1.25)	0.30	0.50	1.25

AQUAMAN
Aug, 1994-Present (1.50, color)
DC Comics

	Good	Fine	N-Mint
1,2-Peter David scripts begin: 2-(9/94)	0.40	0.80	2.00
0,3-8: 0-(10/94). 3-(11/94)-Superboy-c & app. 4-Lobo app.	0.30	0.60	1.50
9-begin 1.75-c; 10-Green Lantern app., 11	0.40	0.70	1.75
Annual 1 ('95, 3.50)-Year One Story	0.70	1.40	3.50

AQUAMAN: TIME & TIDE
Dec, 1993-No. 4, Mar, 1994 (1.50, color, mini-series)
DC Comics

	Good	Fine	N-Mint
1-4-Peter David scripts. 1-Origin begins	0.30	0.60	1.50

ARCANA ANNUAL
1994 (3.95, color, 68 pgs.)
DC Comics (Vertigo)
Annual 1-Children's Crusade story, Tim Hunter app.

	Good	Fine	N-Mint
	1.00	2.00	5.00

ARCHER & ARMSTRONG
July (June inside), 1992-Present (2.50, color)
Valiant Comics

	Good	Fine	N-Mint
0-(7/92)-Barry Smith-c/a	1.00	3.00	6.00
0-(Gold Logo)	3.00	9.00	20.00
1-(8/92)-Miller-c; Smith/Layton-a; origin/1st app. Archer	0.80	1.60	4.00
2-2nd app. Turok (c/sty); Smith-a(p)	0.80	1.50	3.75
3, 4-Smith-c/a/script	0.70	1.40	3.50
5–7	0.70	1.30	3.25

Arcana Annual #1 © DC

Astonishing X-Men #2 © MEG

8-(4.50, 52 pgs)-Combined w/Eternal Warrior #8; Barry Smith-c/a/scripts;
1st app. Ivar the Time Walker   0.80   1.60   4.00
9-25: 10-2nd app. Ivar. 10,11-Smith-c. 21,22-Shadowman app. 22-w/bound-
in trading card. 25-Eternal Warrior app.   0.50   1.00   2.50

ARCHIE AS PUREHEART THE POWERFUL (Capt. Pureheart #4-6)
(See Jughead as Captain Hero & Life With Archie)
Sept, 1966-No. 6, Nov, 1967 (All 12¢ issues)
Archie Publications (Radio Comics)
1-Super-hero parody; Pureheart & Evilheart (Reggie) app.
                                                 7.40   22.00   52.00
2   5.00   14.00   32.00
3-6   3.00   9.00   22.00

ARCHIE MEETS THE PUNISHER
Aug, 1994 (2.95, color, one-shot, 52 pgs.)
Marvel Comics and Archie Comics Publications
1-B.Lash-s, J.Buscema-a on Punisher; S.Goldberg-a on Archie; same
contents as The Punisher Meets Archie   0.60   1.20   3.00

ARGUS
Apr 1995-Present (1.50, color, limited series:6))
DC Comics
1-3   0.30   0.60   1.50
4-begin 1.75-c   0.40   0.70   1.75

ARMEGEDDON 2001
May, 1991-No. 2, Oct, 1991 (2.00, 68 pgs.)
DC Comics

	Good	Fine	N-Mint
1-Intro Waverider	0.60	1.20	3.00
1-2nd & 3rd printings	0.40	0.70	1.75
2	0.50	1.00	2.50

ARMORINES (See X-O Manowar #25)
June, 1994-Present (2.25, color)
Valiant Comics

1–12: 7-Wraparound-c	0.50	0.90	2.25

ARRGH!
Dec, 1974-No. 5, Sept, 1975 (25¢)
Marvel Comics Group

1-Satire	0.60	1.20	3.00
2–5	0.40	0.70	1.75

ART OF ZEN INTERGALACTIC NINJA, THE
1994 (2.95, color)
Entity Comics

1,2	0.60	1.20	3.00

ASH
Nov, 1994-Present (2.50, color)
Event Comics

1-Quesada-p/story; Palmioti-i/story; Barry Smith pinup			
	0.80	1.60	4.00
2-M. Mignola Hellboy pinup, 3–	0.50	1.00	2.50

ASSASSINETTE
1994 - Present (2.50, B&W)
Pocket Change Comics

1-3:1-Silver foil-c	0.50	1.00	2.50

ASTER
Oct, 1994-Present (2.95, color)
Entity Comics

0-4:1,3,4-Foil logo, 2-Foil-c, 3-variant	0.60	1.20	3.00

ASTONISHING TALES
Aug, 1970-No. 36, July, 1976
Marvel Comics Group

1-Dr. Doom begins; Ka-Zar (by Kirby in #1,2)	3.00	9.40	22.00
2-Kraven the Hunter-c/story	1.70	4.00	10.00
3-6: B. Smith-a. 5-Red Skull app.	2.10	6.40	15.00

7, 8: 8-Last Dr. Doom (52 pgs.)	1.70	4.00	10.00
9-Lorna-r	0.60	1.20	3.00
10-Smith/Sal Buscema-a	1.00	2.50	6.00
11-Origin Ka-Zar	1.00	2.50	6.00
12-Man Thing by Adams	1.00	2.50	6.00
13-24: 19-Starlin-a(p)	0.40	0.80	2.00
25-1st app. Deathlok; series begins (8/74)	5.00	15.00	35.00
26-28, 30: Deathlok-c/stories in all	1.90	6.00	13.00
29-No Deathlok story; Guardians-c/sty. r/origin & 1st app. Guardians of			
the Galaxy from Marvel Super-Heroes #18	2.10	6.40	15.00
31-36: 36-Deathlok-c/stories end	1.40	4.30	10.00

ASTONISHING X-MEN
Mar 1995 - Present (1.95/ color)
Marvel Comics

1-Age of Apocalypse	0.70	2.10	5.00
2-4	0.50	1.00	2.50

ASTRO BOY
Aug, 1965 (One-shot, TV, 12¢)
Gold Key

1 (10151-508)-Scarce; 1st app. in comics	39.00	118.00	275.00

ASYLUM
1993-Present (2.50, color)
Millennium Publications

1-4: 1-Bolton-c/a; Russell 2 pg. illos	0.50	1.00	2.50

ATLAS
Feb 1994-No. 4, Aug, 1994 (2.50, color, limited series)
Dark Horse Comics

1-4	0.50	1.00	2.50

ATOM, THE (Atom & Hawkman #39 on)(See Showcase #34-36)
June-July, 1962-No. 38, Aug-Sept, 1968
National Periodical Publications

1	97.00	291.00	680.00
2	38.00	114.00	265.00
3-1st Time Pool story; 1st Chronos (origin)	25.00	75.00	175.00
4, 5	17.00	51.00	120.00
6, 8-10: 8-JLA x-over	14.00	41.00	95.00
7-1st Atom & Hawkman team-up (pre Hawkman #1)			
	31.00	92.00	215.00

	Good	Fine	N-Mint
11–15	9.00	26.00	60.00
16-20	6.40	19.00	45.00
21-28, 30	4.70	14.00	33.00
29-1st solo G.A. Atom app. in S.A.	15.00	45.00	105.00
31-35, 37, 38	4.30	13.00	30.00
36-G.A. Atom x-over	6.00	18.00	42.00

ATOM AND THE HAWKMAN (Formerly The Atom)
No. 39, Oct-Nov, 1968-No. 45, Oct-Nov, 1969
National Periodical Publications

	Good	Fine	N-Mint
39-45: 43-Last 12¢ issue	4.00	12.00	28.00

ATOM ANT (TV)
Jan, 1966 (Hanna-Barbera, 12¢)
Gold Key

	Good	Fine	N-Mint
1 (10170-601)	19.00	56.00	185.00

ATOM SPECIAL
1993 (2.50, color, 68 pgs.)
DC Comics

	Good	Fine	N-Mint
1	0.50	1.00	2.50
2-(2.95-c, 1995)	0.60	1.20	3.00

AUGIE DOGGIE (TV)
Oct, 1963 (Hanna-Barbera, 12¢)
Gold Key

	Good	Fine	N-Mint
1	12.90	39.00	90.00

AVENGELYNE
May 1995-Present (2.50/3.50, color)
Maximum Press

	Good	Fine	N-Mint
1-Newstand (2.50)-Photo-c, poster insert	0.40	1.00	2.50
1-Direct Market (3.50)-Chromium-c, poster insert			
	0.50	2.00	3.50
1-"Glossy Edition"	3.60	11.00	25.00
2-polybagged w/card	0.40	1.00	2.50

AVENGERS, THE (Also see Giant-Size... & West Coast Avengers)
Sept, 1963-Present
Marvel Comics Group

	Good	Fine	N-Mint
1-Origin & 1st app. The Avengers	188.00	564.00	1880.00
2-Hulk leaves Avengers	71.00	214.00	500.00
3-Sub-Mariner & Hulk battle Avengers; Spider-Man cameo (4 panels)			

(1/64)	50.00	140.00	320.00
4-1st S.A. Capt. America & Bucky (3/64)	110.00	330.00	1100.00
4 (1966 Golden Records reprint)	9.00	26.00	60.00
with Golden Records (1966)	16.00	49.00	115.00
5-Hulk app.	28.00	84.00	195.00
6-8: 6-Intro Zemo & Masters of Evil	21.00	62.00	145.00
9-Intro Wonder Man who dies in same story	22.00	66.00	155.00
10-Early Hercules app.	19.00	58.00	135.00
11-Spider-Man-c & x-over (12/64)	23.00	69.00	160.00
12-15: 15-Death of Zemo	13.00	39.00	90.00
16-New Avengers line-up	14.00	43.00	100.00
17-19: 19-Origin Hawkeye	10.00	29.00	68.00
20-22: Wood inks	6.40	19.00	45.00
23-30: 25-Dr. Doom-c/story. 28-Giant Man becomes Goliath			
	4.60	14.00	32.00
31-40	3.20	8.00	23.00
41-52, 54-56: 46-Re-intro Ant-Man. 47-Magneto-c/story.			
	2.40	7.30	17.00
48-1st app. new Black Knight	2.70	8.10	19.00
53-X-Men app.	4.00	12.00	28.00
57-Intro S.A. Vision (10/68)	8.60	26.00	60.00
58-Origin The Vision	5.70	17.00	40.00
59-65: 65-Last 12¢ issue	2.70	8.10	19.00
66, 67-Smith-a	2.40	7.30	17.00
68-70	2.00	5.00	12.00
71-1st Invaders (12/69); Black Knight joins	2.70	8.10	19.00
72-82, 84-86, 88-91: 80-Intro Red Wolf	1.80	5.00	11.00
83-Intro The Liberators	1.80	5.00	11.00
87-Origin Black Panther	3.20	8.00	25.00
92-Adams-c; last 15¢-c	1.90	6.00	13.00

Avengelyne #2 © Rob Liefeld

Avengers #376 © MEG

	Good	Fine	N-Mint
93-Adams c/a (52 pgs.)	6.30	19.00	44.00
94-96: Adams-c/a	4.30	12.90	30.00
97-G.A. Marvel heroes x-over	2.10	6.00	15.00
98-Smith c/a; Goliath becomes Hawkeye	3.60	11.00	25.00
99-Smith-c/a	3.60	11.00	25.00
100-Smith-c/a; featuring all Avengers	10.00	30.00	70.00
101-106, 108, 109	1.50	3.80	9.00
107-Starlin-a	1.70	5.10	12.00
110, 111-X-Men app.	2.70	8.10	19.00
112-1st app. The Mantis	1.70	5.10	12.00
113-124, 126-130: 116-118: Silver Surfer app.	1.20	2.90	7.00
125-Thanos-c & brief app. (7/74)	2.30	6.90	16.00
131-140: 134, 135-True origin Vision	1.20	2.40	6.00
141-163: 150-Kirby art; new line up begins	1.00	2.00	5.00
164-166: Byrne-a	1.20	2.40	6.00
167-191: 168-Guardians of the Galaxy app. 174-Thanos cameo.			
181-191-Byrne-a	0.80	1.60	4.00
192-213, 215-262: 200, 250-Double size	0.50	0.90	2.25
214-Ghost Rider-c/story	1.00	2.00	5.00
263-1st app. X-Factor; cont. in F. F. #286	1.20	2.40	6.00
264-299: 272-Alpha Flight app.	0.60	1.20	3.00
300-(2/89, 1.75, 68 pgs.)-Thor joins	0.80	1.60	4.00
301-304: 302-Re-intro Quasar	0.40	0.80	2.00
305-Byrne scripts begin	0.60	1.20	3.00
306-325, 327, 329-343: 314-318-Spidey x-over. 327-2nd app. Rage			
	0.40	0.80	2.00
326-1st app. Rage (11/90)	1.20	2.90	7.00
328-Origin Rage	1.00	3.00	6.00
344-346, 348, 349, 351-359, 361, 362, 364, 365, 367, 368, 370-373: 368-Bloodties Pt. 1; Avengers/X-Men x-over. 373-Last 1.25-c			
	0.30	0.60	1.50
347-(1.75, 56 pgs.)	0.40	0.80	2.00
350-(2.50)-Double gatefold-c; flip-book	0.50	1.00	2.50
360-(2.95)-Embossed foil-c; 30th anniversary	1.00	2.00	5.00
363-(2.95, 52 pgs.)-All silver foil-c	0.60	1.20	3.00
366-(3.95, 68 pgs.)-Embossed gold foil-c	0.80	1.60	4.00
369-(2.95)-Pt. 5 Bloodties-Foil embossed-c	0.60	1.20	3.00
374,376-389: 374-Begin 1.50-c; bound-in trading card sheet. 380-Deodato-a			
	0.30	0.60	1.50
375-(2.00, 48 pgs)	0.40	0.80	2.00
375-(2.50, 48 pgs) Silver ink logo w/poster	0.50	1.00	2.50

Marvel Double Feature…Avengers/Giant-Man #379-382 (2.50, 52 pgs.)-
    Same as Avengers #379-382 w/Giant-Man flip book-part of 4 piece Giant-

Man portrait puzzle	0.50	1.00	2.50
Special 1 (9/67)-New art	6.00	19.00	45.00
Special 2 (9/68)-New art	2.90	9.00	20.00
Special 3 (9/69)-r/#4 plus 3 new Kirby stories	3.30	9.90	23.00
Special 4 (1/71)-Kirby-r/#5, 6	1.20	2.90	7.00
Special 5 (1/72)-Spidey x-over	1.20	2.90	7.00
Annual 6 (11/76)	1.20	2.40	6.00
Annual 7 (11/77)-Thanos app.; Starlin c/a; Warlock dies. (see Incredible			
Hulk #178)	3.90	12.00	27.00
Annual 8 ('78)	0.90	1.80	4.50
Annual 9 ('79)	0.70	1.40	3.50
Annual 10 ('81)-1st app. Rogue; X-Men cameo	3.00	7.50	18.00
Annual 11-16 (1982-87)	0.70	1.40	3.50
Annual 17 ('88)-Evolutionary War	0.80	1.60	4.00
Annual 18 ('89, 2.00)	0.60	1.20	3.00
Annual 19, 20 ('90 & '91, 2.00)	0.50	1.00	2.50
Annual 21 ('92, 2.25, 68 pgs.)	0.50	0.90	2.25
Annual 22 ('93, 2.95)-Polybagged w/card	0.60	1.20	3.00
Annual 23 ('94, 2.95, 68 pgs.)	0.60	1.20	3.00
...:The Yesterday Quest-(10/94, 6.95)-r/181,182,185-187			
	1.20	3.00	7.00

AVENGERS, THE (TV)
Nov, 1968 ("John Steed & Emma Peel" cover title)(15¢)
Gold Key

1-Photo-c	27.00	81.00	190.00

AVENGERS COLLECTOR'S EDITION, THE
1993 (Ordered through mail w/candy wrapper, 20 pgs.)
Marvel Comics

1-Contains 4 bound-in trading cards	0.40	0.80	2.00

AVENGERS LOG, THE
Feb, 1994 (1.95, color)
Marvel Comics

1-Gives history of all members; Perez-c	0.40	0.80	2.00

AVENGERS STRIKEFILE
Jan, 1994 (1.75, color)
Marvel Comics

1	0.40	0.70	1.75

	Good	Fine	N-Mint

AVENGERS: THE TERMINATRIX OBJECTIVE
Sept, 1993-No. 4, Dec, 1993 (1.25, color, mini-series)
Marvel Comics

	Good	Fine	N-Mint
1-(2.50)-Holo-grafx foil-c	0.50	1.00	2.50
2-4-Old vs. new Avengers	0.30	0.50	1.25

AZRAEL
Feb 1995-Present (1.95, color)
DC Comics

	Good	Fine	N-Mint
1-D. O'Neill/s	0.60	1.20	3.00
2-7-D. O'Neill/s: 5,6-Ras Al Ghul app.	0.40	0.80	2.00

Babe #1 © John Byrne

Backlash #4 © Aegis Ent.

BABE
July, 1994-Oct, 1994 (2.50, color, limited series)
Dark Horse Comics
1-4-John Byrne-story/a: 3,4-Proto Tykes backup story

0.50	1.00	2.50

BABE 2
Mar 1995 - May 1995 (2.50, color, limited series:2)
Dark Horse Comics
1, 2-J.Byrne s/a

0.50	1.00	2.50

BABYLON 5
Jan 1995-Present (1.95, color)
DC Comics

1, 2-Based on the television series	0.60	1.20	3.00
3–6	0.40	0.80	2.00
7–begin 2.50-c	0.50	1.00	2.50

BACKLASH
Nov, 1994-Present (1.95/2.50, color)
Image Comics

1-Double-c	0.60	1.20	3.00
2-6; 5-Intro Mindscape, w/2 pinups	0.40	0.80	2.00
7-begin 2.50-c	0.50	1.00	2.50
8-(1.95) WildStorm Rising Pt. 8, Newstand Ed.	0.40	0.80	2.00
8-(2.50) WildStorm Rising Pt. 8, Direct Market	0.50	1.00	2.50

BADGER, THE
Dec, 1983-No. 70, Apr, 1991

	Good	Fine	N-Mint
Capital Comics/First Comics			
1–4	0.30	0.60	1.50
5-First Comics begins publishing	0.30	0.60	1.50
6–49	0.20	0.40	1.00
50-(3.95, 52 pgs.)	0.70	1.40	3.50
51-70: 52-54: Tim Vigil-c/a	0.40	0.80	2.00
V2#1 (Spr, '91, 4.95)	0.80	1.60	4.00

BADGER: SHATTERED MIRROR
July, 1994-Oct, 1994 (2.50, color, limited series)
Dark Horse Comics

	Good	Fine	N-Mint
1–4	0.50	1.00	2.50

BADGER: ZEN POP FUNNY-ANIMAL VERSION
July, 1994-No. 2, Aug, 1994 (2.50, color, limited series)
Dark Horse Comics

	Good	Fine	N-Mint
1,2	0.50	1.00	2.50

BADROCK
Mar 1995-Present (1.75, color)
Image Comics

	Good	Fine	N-Mint
1-variant-c (3?)	0.40	0.70	1.75

BADROCK AND COMPANY
Sept, 1994 -Feb 1995 (2.50, color, limited series)
Image

	Good	Fine	N-Mint
1–6: Indicia on issue #6 reads "October 1994"	0.50	1.00	2.50

BAMM BAMM & PEBBLES FLINTSTONE (TV)
Oct, 1964 (Hanna-Barbera)
Gold Key

	Good	Fine	N-Mint
1	5.40	16.00	38.00

BANANA SPLITS, THE (TV)
June, 1969-No. 8, Oct, 1971 (Hanna-Barbera)
Gold Key

	Good	Fine	N-Mint
1-Photo-c	2.60	7.70	18.00
2–8	1.50	3.80	9.00

BARBIE
Jan, 1991-Present (1.00/1.25/1.50, color)
Marvel Comics

	Good	Fine	N-Mint
1-Polybagged w/Barbie pink card	0.80	1.60	4.00

2–44: 14-33-(1.25)	0.30	0.50	1.25
45-56: 45-Begin 1.50-c	0.30	0.60	1.50

BARBIE & KEN
May-July, 1962-No. 5, Nov-Jan, 1963-64
Dell Publishing Co.

01-053-207(#1)-Based on toy dolls	38.00	114.00	265.00
2–4	26.00	79.00	185.00
5 (Rare)	30.00	80.00	210.00

BARBIE FASHION
Jan, 1991-Present (1.00/1.25/1.50, color)
Marvel Comics

1-Polybagged w/doorknob hanger	0.40	0.80	2.00
2–44: 14-33-(1.25)	0.30	0.50	1.25
45-48: 45-Begin 1.50-c	0.30	0.60	1.50

BARB WIRE(See Comics' Greatest World)
Apr, 1994-Present (2.00/2.50, color)
Dark Horse Comics

1-Foil logo	0.60	1.20	3.00
2–4	0.40	0.80	2.00
5-9-(2.50)	0.50	1.00	2.50

BARNEY AND BETTY RUBBLE (TV)
Jan, 1973-No. 23, Dec, 1976 (Hanna-Barbera)
Charlton Comics

1	3.40	10.30	24.00
2–10	1.70	4.00	10.00
11-23: 11(2/75)-1st Mike Zeck-a (illos)	1.20	2.40	6.00

BAR SINISTER
Jun 1995 - Present (2.50, color)
Windjammer

1-3 Mike Grell/s	0.50	1.00	2.50

BARTMAN
1993-Present (1.95, color)
Bongo Comics Group

1-(2.95)-Foil enhanced-c w/poster	0.70	1.30	3.25
2	0.40	0.80	2.00
3-(2.25)-w/trading card; 4–5	0.50	0.90	2.25

	Good	Fine	N-Mint

Batman #126 © DC

Batman #251 © DC

BASIL WOLVERTON'S FANTASTIC FABLES
Oct, 1993-No. 2, Dec, 1993 (2.50, B&W, limited series)
Dark Horse Comics

	Good	Fine	N-Mint
1, 2-Wolverton-c/a(r)	0.50	1.00	2.50

BATGIRL SPECIAL
1988 (1.50, color, one-shot)
DC Comics

1	0.50	1.00	2.50

BAT LASH (See Showcase 76)
Oct-Nov, 1968-No. 7, Oct-Nov, 1969 (All 12¢ issues)
National Periodical Publications

1-2nd app. Bat Lash	2.00	6.00	14.00
2–7	1.40	3.50	8.50

BATMAN (Also see Detective Comics)
No. 90, Mar, 1955-Present
National Periodical Publ./Detective Comics/DC Comics

90, 91, 93-99: 90-1st code approved issue. 97-2nd Bat-Hound-c/story; Joker app.	42.00	130.00	275.00
92-1st app. Bat-Hound-c/story	52.00	157.00	345.00
100	113.00	338.00	1450.00
101-104, 106-109	41.00	122.00	285.00
105-1st Batwoman in Batman Comics	51.00	154.00	360.00
110-Joker story	40.00	120.00	280.00
111-120	29.00	86.00	200.00
121, 122, 124-125, 128, 130	21.00	62.00	145.00
123, 127: Joker stories	24.00	71.00	165.00
126-Batwoman-c/story	21.00	62.00	145.00

129-Origin Robin retold	25.00	75.00	175.00
131-135,137-139,141-143: 131-Intro 2nd Batman & Robin series. 139-Intro 1st Bat-Girl. 143-last 10¢ issue	15.00	45.00	105.00
136-Joker-c/story	21.00	62.00	145.00
140, 144-Joker story. 140-Superman cameo	14.00	43.00	100.00
145, 148-Joker-c/story	17.00	51.00	120.00
146, 147, 149, 150	11.00	34.00	80.00
151, 153, 154, 156-158, 160-162, 164-168, 170: 164-New Batmobile (6/64)	8.60	26.00	60.00
152-Joker story	8.60	26.00	60.00
155-1st S.A. Penguin (4/63)	37.00	111.00	260.00
159, 163-Joker-c/story	10.00	30.00	70.00
169-2nd SA Penguin app.	14.00	41.00	95.00
171-1st Riddler app. (5/65) since 12/48	50.00	148.00	345.00
172-175, 177, 178, 180, 183, 184	5.00	16.00	37.00
176-Giant G-17; Joker-c/story; Catwoman-r	7.00	22.00	52.00
179-2nd app. Silver Age Riddler	13.00	39.00	90.00
181-1st Poison Ivy	6.00	17.00	40.00
182 (Giant G-24) Joker-c/story	6.60	20.00	46.00
185 (Giant G-27)	6.00	18.00	41.00
186-Joker-c/story	3.90	11.60	27.00
187 (Giant G-30)-Joker-c/story	6.60	20.00	46.00
188, 189, 191, 192, 194-196, 199;	2.40	7.30	17.00
189-1st S.A. app. Scarecrow	7.10	21.40	50.00
190-Penguin app.	4.00	10.70	25.00
193 (Giant G-37)	5.00	14.10	33.00
197-4th SA Catwoman app. cont./Det.#369	7.10	21.00	50.00
198 (Giant G-43)-All villain issue; Joker/Penguin/Catwoman-r; Catwoman-r from Det. #211	9.00	28.00	65.00
200-Retells origin Batman & Robin	19.00	58.00	135.00
201-Joker story	3.00	9.40	22.00
202, 204-207, 209, 210	1.70	5.10	12.00
203, 218 (Giants G-49 & G-67)	3.70	11.10	26.00
208 (G-55): New origin Batman by Gil Kane	3.70	11.00	26.00
211, 212, 214-217: 212-Last 12¢ issue	2.20	5.40	13.00
213 (G-61)-New origin Robin; r/origin Alfred, Joker (Det. 168)	5.70	17.00	40.00
218-(80-Pg. Giant G-67)	3.70	11.10	26.00
219-N. Adams-a	3.30	10.00	23.00
220, 221, 224-227, 229-231	1.60	5.00	11.00
222-Beatles issue	3.60	11.00	25.00
223, 228, 233 (Giants G-73, G-79, G-85)	2.30	7.00	16.00
237-N. Adams-a	4.30	13.00	30.00

	Good	Fine	N-Mint
232-1st app. Ras Al Ghul	5.70	17.00	40.00
234-1st S.A. app. Two Face, Adams-a	12.00	36.00	85.00
235, 236, 239-242	1.70	4.20	10.00
238-100 pg. DC-8; Neal Adams-c	1.80	4.60	11.00
243-245: N. Adams-a	2.60	7.70	18.00
246-250, 252, 253	1.70	4.20	10.00
251-Adams-c/a; Joker-c/story	5.40	16.00	38.00
254, 256-259, 261: All 100 pg. issues	2.20	5.40	13.00
255-(100 pgs.)-Adams-c/a	2.90	8.60	20.00
260-(100 pgs.)-Joker c/story	4.30	12.90	30.00
262-285, 287-290, 292, 293, 295-299: 266-Catwoman back to old			
costume	1.10	2.70	6.50
286, 291, 294-Joker-c/story	1.50	3.80	9.00
300-Double size	1.50	3.80	9.00
301-320, 322-352: 316-Robin returns. 332-1st solo Catwoman story			
	1.50	4.00	9.00
321, 353, 359: Joker-c/stories	1.70	4.20	10.00
354-356, 358, 360-365, 367, 369, 370	1.10	2.70	6.50
357-1st app. Jason Todd (3/83); see Det. 524	1.30	3.30	8.00
366-1st J. Todd in Robin costume; Joker-c/sty	2.60	8.00	18.00
368-Jason Todd becomes Robin	1.70	5.10	12.00
371-399, 401-403: 371-Cat-Man-c/story	0.60	1.20	3.00
400-(1.50, 68 pgs.)-Dark Knight Special; Stephen King intro; tribute by			
various artists	2.40	7.30	17.00
404-Miller scripts begin, Year 1; 1st Modern Catwoman appearance			
	2.00	6.00	14.00
405-407: Year 1, Miller scripts	1.00	2.50	6.00
408-410: New origin Jason Todd	1.00	2.00	5.00
411-416, 421-425: 423-McFarlane-c	0.50	1.00	2.50
417-420: Ten Nights Of The Beast	1.70	4.00	10.00
426-A Death in The Family begins	1.20	3.00	7.25
427-A Death in The Family Part 2	1.00	2.60	6.25
428-Death Of Robin (Jason Todd)	1.10	2.80	6.75
429-A Death In The Family ends; Joker-c/story	1.00	2.00	5.00
430-432	0.40	0.80	2.00
433-435: Many Deaths Of The Batman	0.50	1.00	2.50
436-Year 3 begins; 1st app. Timothy Drake	1.00	2.00	5.00
436-2nd printing	0.20	0.40	1.00
437-439: 439-Year 3 ends	0.50	1.00	2.50
440, 441	0.20	0.40	1.00
442-1st app. Timothy Drake in Robin costume	1.00	2.00	5.00
443-456, 458, 459, 462-464	0.30	0.60	1.50
457-1st new Robin in costume	1.40	3.50	8.50

457-Direct sale has #000 in indicia	1.00	2.00	5.00
460, 461-2 part Catwoman story	0.40	0.80	2.00
465-Robin rejoins Batman	0.30	0.60	1.50
466-487: 476-Last 1.00-c	0.30	0.50	1.25
488-Cont'd. from Sword of Azrael #41	.70	5.00	12.00
489-Bane-c/story; 1st Azrael in Bat costume	1.50	3.80	9.00
490-Riddler-c/story; Azrael & Bane app.	1.30	3.00	7.50
491-Knightfall lead-in: Joker-c/story; Azrael & Bane app.; Kelley Jones-c			
begin, end #510	1.00	2.00	5.00
492-Knightfall Pt 1; Bane app.	1.50	4.00	9.00
492-Platinum edition	2.90	9.00	20.00
493-Knightfall Pt. 3	1.10	3.00	6.50
494-Knightfall Pt. 5; Joker-c & app.	0.90	1.80	4.50
495,496-Knightfall Pts. 7 & 9: 495-Bane & Joker brief apps.			
496-Joker-c/story; Bane cameo	0.80	1.60	4.00
497-Knightfall Pt 11; has B&W outer-c; Batman vs. Bane-c/story			
	1.70	4.00	10.00
497-2nd printing	0.30	0.50	1.25
497-Newsstand ed. without outer-c	0.40	0.80	2.00
498,499-Knightfall Pts. 15 &17 (see Showcase 93 #'s 7 & 8): 498-Bane &			
Catwoman-c & app. 499-Bane app.	0.50	1.00	2.50
500-(2.50, 68 pgs.)-Knightfall Pt. 19; new costume; Bane-c/story			
	0.50	1.00	2.50
500-(3.95)-Collector's ed. w/die-cut double-c w/foil by Quesada &			
2 bound-in postcards; Bane app.	0.90	1.80	4.50
501-508,510,511: 501-508-Knightquest. 503, 504-Catwoman app. 507-Jim			
Balent-a(p). 510-KnightsEnd Pt. 7. 511-(9/94)-Zero Hour; Batgirl-c			
	0.30	0.60	1.50
509-(2.50, 52 pgs)-KnightsEnd Pt.1	0.50	1.00	2.50
0,512-519: 0-(10/94)-Origin retold. 512-(11/94)-Dick Grayson becomes			
Batman. 515- Troika-Pt. 1	0.30	0.60	1.50
515-(2.50)All black embossed-c. Troika-Pt.1	0.50	1.00	2.50
520-begin 1.95-c; 521-return of Alfred	0.40	0.80	2.00
Annual 1 (8-10/61)	50.00	140.00	455.00
Annual 2	20.00	59.00	195.00
Annual 3 (Sum/62)-Joker-c/story	21.00	62.00	205.00
Annual 4, 5 ('63)	9.50	29.00	95.00
Annual 6, 7 (7/64)	7.50	23.00	75.00
Annual 8 ('82)	0.90	1.80	4.50
Annual 9, 10, 12 ('88, 1.50)	0.60	1.20	3.00
Annual 11 ('87, 1.25)-Alan Moore scripts	1.00	2.00	5.00
Annual 13 ('89, 1.75)	0.50	0.90	2.25
Annual 14 ('90)-Origin Two Face	0.60	1.20	3.00

	Good	Fine	N-Mint
Annual 15 ('91, 2.00)-Joker app.	0.40	0.80	2.00
Annual 15-2nd printing	0.40	0.80	2.00
Annual 16 ('92, 2.50)-Joker c/story	0.50	1.00	2.50
Annual 17 ('93, 2.50)-Azrael in Bat-costume; intro Ballistic			
	0.50	1.00	2.50
Annual 18 ('94, 2.95)	0.60	1.20	3.00
Special 1 (4/84)	1.00	2.00	5.00

BATMAN(Books & Trade Paperbooks)

	Good	Fine	N-Mint
…: A Lonely Place Of Dying TPB ('90, 3.95)	0.80	1.60	4.00
…& Dracula: Red Rain Hardcover ('91, 24.95)	6.30	19.00	44.00
…& Dracula: Red Rain Soft-c ('92, 9.95)	1.70	4.00	10.00
Arkham Asylum Hard-c ('89, 24.95)	3.60	10.70	25.00
Arkham Asylum trade pb (14.95)	2.10	6.40	15.00
Birth of the Demon Hard-c (1992, 24.95)	3.60	10.70	25.00
Birth of the Demon Soft-c (1993, 12.95)	1.90	5.60	13.00
Blind Justice nn ('92, $7.50)-r/Det. #598-600	1.30	3.00	7.50
Bride of the Demon hardcover (1990, 19.95)	3.00	8.60	20.00
Bride of the Demon Soft-c (12.95)	1.90	5.60	13.00
…: Castle of the Bat (5.95) Elseworlds story	1.00	3.00	6.00
…: Collected Legends of the Dark Knight nn (1994, 12.95)-r/Legends of the			
Dark Knight #32-34, 38, 42, 43	1.90	5.60	13.00
…: Dark Joker-The Wild ('93, 9.95, TPB)-Elseworlds story			
	1.70	4.00	10.00
…: Dark Joker-The Wild ('93, 24.95, HB)	3.60	10.70	25.00
Death In The Family TPB ('88, 3.95)	1.00	2.00	5.00
2nd, 3rd prints	0.80	1.60	4.00
Digital Justice Hard-c ('90, 24.95)	3.60	10.70	25.00
…:Faces TPB ('95, 9.95)	1.70	4.00	10.00

Batman #516 © DC

Batman: Dark Joker The Wild © DC

Gothic nn ('92, $12.95)-r/Legends/DK #6-10	1.90	5.60	13.00
Greatest Batman Stories Hard-c (24.95)	7.00	21.00	50.00
Greatest Batman Stories Soft-c (15.95)	2.60	7.70	18.00
Greatest Batman Stories Vol. 2 ('92, 16.95)	2.40	7.30	17.00
Greatest Joker Stories Hard-c (19.95)	5.70	17.00	40.00
Greatest Joker Stories Soft-c (14.95)	2.30	6.90	16.00
Greatest Joker Stories (Stacked Deck …Expanded Edition)			
(1992, 29.95) Longmeadow Press Publ.	4.30	13.00	30.00
…Many Deaths of the Batman TPB (3.95)	0.80	1.60	4.00
…: Prey nn ('92, 12.95)-Gulacy/Austin-a	1.90	5.60	13.00
…: Shaman nn ('93, 12.95)-r/Legends DK 1-5	1.90	5.60	13.00
…Son Of The Demon Hardcover ('87)	7.00	21.00	50.00
…Son Of The Demon Hardcover ('87, signed & numbered)			
	11.00	32.00	75.00
…Son Of The Demon Soft-c ('87, 8.95)	1.30	3.90	9.00
…Son Of The Demon Soft-c 2nd-4th printings ('89, 9.95)			
	1.70	4.00	10.00
…Tales of the Demon (1991, 17.95)	2.60	8.00	18.00
…Ten Nights of the Beast ('94, 5.95)-r/Batman #'s 417-420			
	1.00	2.50	6.00
…:The Last Angel ('94, 12.95, TPB)	2.00	5.60	13.00
…: Venom Trade Paperback (1993, 9.95)-r/Legends of the Dark			
Knight #16-20; embossed-c	1.70	4.00	10.00
Year One Trade Paperback (1988, 9.95)	1.70	4.00	10.00
2nd, 3rd prints	1.70	4.00	10.00
Year One Hardcover (12.95)	1.90	5.60	13.00
Year Two Soft-c ('90, 9.95)	1.70	4.00	10.00
BATMAN (One shots)			
…And Other DC Classics ('89 Giveaway, Diamond Comic Distr.)			
	0.20	0.40	1.00
…Catwoman Defiant ('92, 4.95, one shot)	1.00	2.00	5.00
…Full Circle ('91, 5.95, deluxe)`	1.00	2.50	6.00
…Gallery, The 1 ('92, 2.95)-Reprints	0.60	1.20	3.00
…Gotham By Gaslight ('89, 3.95)	0.80	1.60	4.00
…/Green Arrow: The Poison Arrow ('92, 5.95)	1.00	2.50	6.00
…Holy Terror nn ('91, 4.95)	1.00	2.00	5.00
…/Houdini: The Devil's Workshop ('93, 5.95)	1.00	2.50	6.00
…: In Darkest Knight nn ('94, 4.95)-Elseworlds	1.00	2.00	5.00
…Judge Dredd: Judgement On Gotham ('91, 5.95, 68 pgs.)			
	1.00	2.50	6.00
…Judge Dredd: Judgement On Gotham 2nd printing (5.95)			
	1.00	2.50	6.00

	Good	Fine	N-Mint
...Judge Dredd: Vendetta in Gotham ('93, 5.95)	1.00	2.50	6.00
...: Mask of the Phantasm (2.95)-Movie adapt.	0.60	1.20	3.00
...: Mask of the Phantasm (4.95)-Movie adapt.	1.00	2.00	5.00
...Master Of The Future ('91, 5.95)	1.00	2.50	6.00
...Mitefall ('95, 4.95)	1.00	2.00	5.00
...Movie Special ('89, 2.50, regular)	0.50	1.00	2.50
...Movie Special ('89, 4.95, deluxe)	1.00	2.00	5.00
...Penguin Triumphant ('92, 4.95, one-shot)	1.00	2.00	5.00
.../Punisher: Lake of Fire ('94, 4.95, DC/Marvel)	1.00	2.00	5.00
...Bloodstorm ('94, 24.95, Hardcover)K.Jones/p	4.00	10.70	25.00
...Returns Movie Special ('92, 3.95)	0.80	1.60	4.00
...Returns Movie Prestige ('92, 5.95. squarebound)-Dorman painted-c			
	1.00	2.50	6.00
...: Seduction of the Gun nn (2/93, 2.50)	0.50	1.00	2.50
.../Spawn: War Devil nn (1994, 4.95, 52 pgs.)	1.00	2.00	5.00
...: The Blue, the Grey, and the Bat ('92, 5.95)	1.00	2.50	6.00
...: Vengeance of Bane Special nn (1/93, 2.50, 68 pgs.)-Origin/1st app. Bane			
	3.00	8.60	20.00
...: Vengeance of Bane Special nn-2nd printing	0.50	1.00	2.50

BATMAN ADVENTURES, THE(TV; Fox animated series 33-begin 1.75-c)
Oct, 1992-Present (1.25/1.50, color)
DC Comics

	Good	Fine	N-Mint
1	1.20	2.90	7.00
1-Silver Edition 2nd printing (1.95)	0.40	0.80	2.00
2-19: 2, 12-Catwoman-c/story. 3, 16-Joker-c/story. 11-Man-Bat-c/story.			
16-Begin $1.50-c	0.50	0.90	2.25
7-Spec. Ed. bagged w/Man-Bat trading card	1.30	3.00	8.00
20-24,26-31	0.30	0.60	1.50
25-(2.50, 52pgs)-Superman app.	0.50	1.00	2.50
33-begin 1.75-c; 34–	0.40	0.70	1.75
...: Mad Love (2/94, 3.95, 68 pgs.)-Joker-c/sty	1.20	2.40	6.00
....:The Collected Adventures Vol. 1 ('93, 5.95)	1.20	2.40	6.00
....:The Collected Adventures Vol. 2 ('94, 5.95)	1.20	2.40	6.00
Annual 1 ('94, 2.95)	0.60	1.20	3.00
Annual 2 (3.50)-Demon app.	0.70	1.40	3.50
...Holiday Special 1 ('95, 2.95)	0.60	1.20	3.00

BATMAN AND THE OUTSIDERS
Aug, 1983-No. 32, April, 1986
DC Comics

	Good	Fine	N-Mint
1-32: 32-Team disbands	0.20	0.40	1.00
Annual 1,2 (9/84 & 9/85)	0.20	0.40	1.00

BATMAN CHRONICLES
1995 (2.95, color, Quarterly)
DC Comics

1-Dixon/Grant/Moench-s	0.60	1.20	3.00

BATMAN FAMILY, THE (Combined with Detective Comics w/#481)
Sept-Oct, 1975-No. 20, Oct-Nov, 1978
National Periodical Publ./DC Comics

1-Origin Batgirl-Robin teamup retold	0.80	1.60	4.00
2-5, 7, 8, 10, 14-16: 10-1st revival Batwoman	0.60	1.10	2.75
6, 9-Joker's daughter on cover	0.60	1.20	3.00
11-13: Rogers art. 11-Man-Bat begins	0.80	1.60	4.00
17 (1.00 size)-Starlin art	0.60	1.10	2.75
18-20: Huntress by Staton	0.30	0.60	1.50

BATMAN FOREVER
1995 (3.95/5.95, Color)
DC Comics

nn-Newsstand, Movie adaptation	0.80	1.60	4.00
nn-Direct Market, Movie adaptation	1.20	2.40	6.00

BATMAN: GOTHAM NIGHTS II
Mar 1995 - Present (1.95, color,limited series:4)
DC Comics

1-4	0.40	0.80	2.00

BATMAN/GRENDEL
1993-No. 2, 1993 (4.95, color, mini-series, 52 pgs.)
DC Comics/Comico

1-Devil's Riddle; by Matt Wagner	1.10	2.20	5.50
2-Devil's Masque; by Matt Wagner	1.10	2.20	5.50

BATMAN: LEGENDS OF THE DARK KNIGHT
Nov, 1989-Present (1.50/1.75/1.95, color)
DC Comics

1-Blue, yellow, orange, pink outer cover variations; all worth the same			
	1.00	2.00	5.00
2	0.60	1.20	3.00
3–5	0.40	0.80	2.00
6-10: Grant Morrison scripts	0.60	1.20	3.00
11-15, 17, 18: 17-20-"Venom". 18-Last 1.50-c	0.40	0.80	2.00
16-Intro drug Bane uses; begin Venom story	1.00	2.00	5.00

	Good	Fine	N-Mint
19-49, 51-59: 46-49-Catwoman story. 59, 60-Knightquest x-over			
	0.40	0.80	2.00
50-(3.95, 68 pgs.)-Foil-c w/pin-ups; Joker	1.00	2.00	5.00
60-63: 62,63-KnightsEnd Pt. 4 & 10	0.40	0.70	1.75
64 -(9/94)-Begin 1.95-c	0.40	0.80	2.00
0,65-72: 0-(10/94)-Quesada/Palmiotti-c; 16 artists on story.			
65-(11/94); 71-73-Robinson-s	0.40	0.80	2.00
Annual 1 ('91, 3.95, 68 pgs.)	0.80	1.60	4.00
Annual 2 ('92, 3.50, 68 pgs.)	0.70	1.40	3.50
Annual 3 ('93, 3.50)	0.70	1.40	3.50
Annual 4 ('94,3.50, 68 pgs.)-Elseworlds-story	0.70	1.40	3.50
Annual 5 ('95, 3.95, 68 pgs.)	0.80	1.60	4.00
Halloween Special 1 ('93, 6.95)	1.20	3.00	7.00
Batman: Madness - …Halloween Special ('94, 4.95)			
	0.80	2.00	5.00

BATMAN: LEGENDS OF THE DARK KNIGHT : JAZZ
Apr 1995 - June 1995 (2.50, color, limited series:3)
DC Comics

	Good	Fine	N-Mint
1-3	0.40	1.00	2.50

BATMAN: MITEFALL
1995 (4.95, color, one-shot)
DC Comics

	Good	Fine	N-Mint
nn-Alan Grant scripts/Kevin O'Neill-a	0.80	2.00	5.00

BATMAN: RIDDLER-THE RIDDLE FACTORY
1995 (4.95, color, one-shot)
DC Comics

	Good	Fine	N-Mint
nn-Matt Wagner-s	0.80	2.00	5.00

BATMAN: RUN RIDDLER RUN
1992-No. 3, 1992 (4.95, color, mini-series)
DC Comics

	Good	Fine	N-Mint
1-3	1.00	2.00	5.00

BATMAN: SHADOW OF THE BAT
June, 1992-Present (1.50/1.75, color)
DC Comics

	Good	Fine	N-Mint
1-Alan Grant scripts in all	0.60	1.20	3.00
1-(2.50)-Deluxe edition; polybagged	1.00	2.00	5.00
2-7: 7-last 1.50-c	0.30	0.60	1.50
8-28: 16-18-Knightfall tie-ins. 19-28-Knightquest tie-ins with new			

Batman (Azrael). 25-Silver ink-c	0.40	0.70	1.75
29-(2.95, 52 pgs.)-KnightsEnd Pt. 2	0.60	1.20	3.00
30,31: 30-KnightsEnd Pt. 8. 31-(9/94)-Begin 1.95-c; Zero Hour			
	0.40	0.80	2.00
0,32-41-Grant-stories: 0-(10/94). 32-(11/94). 33-Robin-c			
35-Troika-Pt.2	0.40	0.80	2.00
35-(2.95) Embossed -c.	0.60	1.20	3.00
Annual 1 (1993, 3.50, 68 pgs.)	0.70	1.40	3.50
Annual 2 (1994, 3.95, 68 pgs.)	0.80	1.60	4.00

BATMAN: SWORD OF AZRAEL
Oct, 1992-No. 4, Jan, 1993 (1.75, color, mini-series)
DC Comics

1-Gatefold-c; Quesada c/a(p) in all; 1st app. Azrael			
	3.00	6.00	15.00
2-4: 4-Cont'd in Batman #488	1.40	4.00	10.00
Silver Edition 1, 2 (1993, 1.95)-Reprints	0.40	0.80	2.00
Trade Paperback nn ('93, 9.95)-r/1-4	1.70	4.00	10.00
Trade Paperback Gold Edition	2.10	6.40	15.00

BATMAN: THE CULT
1988-No. 4, Nov, 1988 (3.50, color, deluxe format)
DC Comics

1-Wrightson-c/a in all	1.00	2.00	5.00
2–4	0.80	1.60	4.00

BATMAN: THE DARK KNIGHT
March, 1986-No. 4, 1986 (2.95, color, squarebound)
DC Comics

Batman:Sword of Azrael #4 © DC

Batman: Shadow of the Bat #4 © DC

	Good	Fine	N-Mint
1-Miller story & pencils	2.10	6.40	15.00
1-2nd & 3rd prints	0.60	1.20	3.00
2-Carrie Kelly becomes Robin (female)	1.30	3.00	7.50
2-2nd & 3rd prints	0.60	1.20	3.00
3-Death Of Joker	1.00	2.00	5.00
3-2nd print	0.60	1.20	3.00
4-Death of Alfred	0.70	1.40	3.50
Hardcover, signed & numbered edition	25.00	75.00	175.00
Hardcover, trade edition	4.30	13.00	30.00
Softcover, trade edition (1st print only)	1.40	4.00	10.00
Softcover, trade edition (2nd thru 8th prints)	1.10	3.00	7.50

(Note: #2 second prints can be identified by matching the grey background colors on the inside front cover & facing page. The inside front cover of the second print has a dark grey background which does not match the lighter grey of the facing page.

BATMAN: THE KILLING JOKE
1988 (3.50, color, deluxe format, adult)
DC Comics

1-1st print; Alan Moore scripts	1.00	3.00	7.00
1-Later prints (2nd-8th)	0.70	1.40	3.50

BATMAN: TWO-FACE -CRIME AND PUNISHMENT
1995 (4.95, color, one-shot)
DC Comics

nn-Scott McDaniel-a	1.00	2.00	5.00

BATMAN: TWO-FACE STRIKES TWICE
1993-No. 2, 1993 (4.95, color, 52 pgs.)
DC Comics

1, 2-Flip book format w/Staton-a (G.A. side)	1.00	2.00	5.00

BATMAN VS. PREDATOR
1991-No. 3, 1992 (1.95, 4.95, color)
DC Comics

1-(1.95)-Newsstand version	0.50	1.00	2.50
1-(4.95)-Prestige version, w/8 trading cards	1.00	2.50	5.50
2-(1.95)-Newsstand version	0.50	1.00	2.50
2-(4.95)-Prestige version, w/pin-ups	1.00	2.00	5.00
3-(1.95)-Newsstand version	0.50	1.00	2.50
3-(4.95)-Prestige version; w/trading cards	1.00	2.00	5.00
Trade paperback ('93, 5.95)-r/1-4; new-c	1.00	2.50	6.00

BATMAN VS. PREDATOR II: BLOODMATCH
Late 1994- 1995 (2.50, color, limited series:4)
DC Comics & Dark Horse Comics
1-4-Huntress app.   0.50   1.00   2.50

BATTLESTONE
Nov, 1994 - Present (2.50, color)
Image Comics
1-2-Liefeld-plots   0.50   1.00   2.50

BATTLETECH
Feb 1995 (2.95, color)
Malibu Comics
#0   0.60   1.20   3.00

BATTLETECH: FALLOUT
Dec 1994-Present (2.95, color)
Malibu Comics
1: Two editions- Gold version with foil logo stamped "Gold Limited Edition"
                                       0.60   1.20   3.00
1-Full cover Holographic Limited edition   2.90   8.60   20.00
2-3   0.60   1.20   3.00

BEANY AND CECIL (TV)(Bob Clampett's…)
July-Sept, 1962-No. 5, July-Sept, 1963
Gold Key
01-057-209 (#1)   17.00   48.00   120.00
2–5   11.00   34.00   80.00

BEATLES, THE (Life Story)
Sept-Nov, 1964 (35¢)
Dell Publishing Co.
1-(Scarce)-Stories w/color photo pin-ups   45.00   135.00   450.00

BEAVIS AND BUTTHEAD (TV)
Mar, 1994-Present (1.95, color)
Marvel Comics
1-Silver ink-c; Punisher, Devil Dinosaur app.   1.00   2.00   5.00
1-2nd printing   0.40   0.80   2.00
2, 3: 2-Wolverine app. 3-Man-Thing; Spider-Man, Venom, Carnage & Mary
   Jane; Stan Lee cameo; N. Hansen-a; J. Romita Sr.-a (2 pg.)
                                       0.70   1.40   3.50
4-17: 5-War Machine, Thor, Loki, Hulk, Captain America & Rhino cameo

	Good	Fine	N-Mint

...6-Psylocke, Polaris, Daredevil and Bullseye app. 7-Ghost Rider &
...Sub-Mariner app. 8-Quasar & Eon app. 9-Prowler & Nightwatch app.
...11-Black Widow app. 12-Thunderstrike & Bloodaxe app.
...13- NightThrasher app. 14-Spider-Man 2099 app.

| ...15-Warlock app. 16-X-Factor app. | 0.40 | 0.80 | 2.00 |

BECK & CAUL INVESTIGATIONS
Jan, 1994-Present (2.95, B&W)
Gauntlet Comics (Caliber)

| 1–5 | 0.60 | 1.20 | 3.00 |
| ...Special 1 (8/94, 4.95) | 1.00 | 2.00 | 5.00 |

BEVERLY HILLBILLIES (TV)
Apr-June, 1963-No. 18, Aug, 1967; No. 19, Oct, 1969;
No. 20, Oct, 1970; No. 21, Oct, 1971
Dell Publishing

1-Photo cover	16.00	49.00	115.00
2-Photo cover	8.60	26.00	60.00
3-9: Photo covers	5.70	17.00	40.00
10-No photo cover	3.10	9.40	22.00
11-21: Photo covers. 18-Last 12¢ cover	4.30	12.90	30.00

BEWARE (Tomb of Darkness #9 on)
Mar, 1973-No. 8, May, 1974 (All Reprints)
Marvel Comics Group

| 1-Everett-c; Sinnott-r ('54) | 0.60 | 1.20 | 3.00 |
| 2-8: All horror reprints | 0.30 | 0.60 | 1.50 |

BEWARE THE CREEPER (See Showcase 73)
May-June, 1968-No. 6, March-April, 1969 (All 12¢ issues)

Beck & Caul #1 © Reginald Chaney & Paul Kowalski

Black and White #1 © Rob Liefeld

National Periodical Publications
1-Ditko-c/a	6.70	20.00	50.00
2-6: Ditko-a; c-2-5	5.00	14.00	32.00

BEWITCHED (TV)
Apr-June, 1965-No. 11, Oct, 1967; No. 12, Oct, 1968-No. 13, Jan, 1969;
No. 14, Oct, 1969
Dell Publishing
1-Photo cover	14.00	43.00	100.00
2-No photo cover	7.00	21.00	50.00
3-13: Photo covers	5.70	17.00	40.00
14-No photo cover	4.00	10.70	25.00

BIG BANG COMICS
Spring, 1994-Present (1.95, color)
Big Bang Comics
0–3; 0-Alex Ross-c	0.40	0.80	2.00

BIG BOOK OF URBAN LEGENDS, THE
1994 (12.95, B&W)
DC Comics
nn	2.00	5.60	13.00

BIONEERS
Aug, 1994-Present (2.75, color)
Mirage Publishing
1-W/bound-in trading card	0.60	1.10	2.75

BISHOP
Dec, 1994- Mar 1995 (2.95, color, limited series)
Marvel Comics
1-4-Foil-c	0.60	1.20	3.00

BLACK & WHITE
Oct, 1994 - Present ($1.95, color)
Image Comics, Inc.
1-3-Thibert-c/story	0.40	0.80	2.00

BLACKBALL COMICS
Mar, 1994-Present (3.00, color)
Blackball Comics
1-Trencher by Giffen, John Pain by O'Neill	0.60	1.20	3.00

	Good	Fine	N-Mint

BLACK FLAG
Jan 1995 - Present (2.50, color)
Maximum Press

	Good	Fine	N-Mint
1-Gatefold wraparound-c D.Fraga s/a	0.50	1.00	2.50

BLACK FLAG, PREVIEW EDITION
June, 1994-Present (1.95, B&W)
Image Comics

	Good	Fine	N-Mint
1-Fraga/McFarlane-c	0.40	0.80	2.00

BLACK GOLIATH
Feb, 1976-No. 5, Nov, 1976
Marvel Comics Group

	Good	Fine	N-Mint
1-Tuska-a in 1-3	0.90	1.70	4.25
2–5	0.50	0.90	2.25

BLACKHAWK
No. 108, Jan, 1957-No. 243, Oct-Nov, 1968; No. 244, Jan-Feb, 1976-
No. 250, Jan-Feb, 1977; No. 251, Oct, 1982- No. 273, Nov, 1984
National Periodical Publications

	Good	Fine	N-Mint
108-1st DC Blackhawk	48.00	144.00	335.00
109-117	15.00	44.00	103.00
118-Frazetta-r/Jimmy Wakely #4	15.00	46.00	108.00
119-130	10.00	31.00	72.00
131-140	7.00	22.00	52.00
141-163, 165, 166: 166-Last 10¢ issue	5.70	17.00	40.00
164-Origin retold	5.00	16.00	37.00
167-180	2.10	6.40	15.00
181-190	1.80	4.60	11.00
191-197, 199-202, 204-210: 197-New look	1.70	4.00	10.00
198-Origin retold	1.80	4.60	11.00
203-Origin Chop Chop (12/64)	1.50	3.80	9.00
211-243 (1968)	1.20	2.40	6.00
244-250 (1976)	0.40	0.80	2.00
251-273 (1982): 251-Origin retold	0.30	0.60	1.50

BLACK LIGHTNING
Feb 1995- Present (1.95, color)
DC Comics

	Good	Fine	N-Mint
1-5-T. Isabella/s	0.40	0.80	2.00
6-begin 2.25-c; 7–	0.50	0.90	2.25

BLACK MAGIC
Oct-Nov, 1973-No. 9, Apr-May, 1975
National Periodical Publications
1-Simon & Kirby reprints	0.30	0.60	1.50
2-9: Simon & Kirby reprints	0.20	0.40	1.00

BLACK ORCHID (See Adventure Comics #428)
Holiday, '88-'89-No. 3, 1989 (3.50, mini-series)
DC Comics
1,3: Neil Gaiman scripts/McKean-c/a in all. 1-1st app. new Black Orchid
	1.20	2.40	6.00
2-Arkham Asylum story; Batman app.	1.30	3.00	8.00

BLACK ORCHID
Sept, 1993-Present (1.95, color)
DC Comics (Vertigo)
1-10: Dave McKean-c start	0.50	0.90	2.25
1-Platinum edition	3.00	8.60	20.00
11–20	0.40	0.80	2.00
21-(begin 2.25 cover price) 22-	0.50	0.90	2.25
Annual 1-('93, 3.95)-Childrens Crusade tie-in	0.80	1.60	4.00

BLACK PANTHER, THE (See Avengers #52, 57, FF #52 & Jungle Action)
Jan, 1977-No. 15, May, 1979
Marvel Comics Group
1-Kirby-c/a & scripts in 1-12	1.20	2.90	7.00
2	0.60	1.20	3.00
3–10	0.50	1.00	2.50
11-15: 14, 15-Avengers x-over	0.40	0.80	2.00

BLACKWULF
June, 1994- Mar 1995 (1.50, color)
Marvel Comics
1-(2.50)-Embossed-c; Angel Medina-a	0.50	1.00	2.50
2–10	0.30	0.60	1.50

BLADE: THE VAMPIRE-HUNTER
July, 1994-Present (1.95, color)
Marvel Comics
1-(2.95)-Foil cover	0.60	1.20	3.00
2–10	0.40	0.80	2.00

	Good	Fine	N-Mint
BLAST-OFF (Three Rocketeers)			
Oct, 1965 (12¢)			
Harvey Publications			
1-Kirby-a	3.60	11.00	25.00
BLAZE			
Aug 1994-July 1995 (1.95, color)			
Marvel Comics			
1-(2.95)-Foil embossed-c	0.60	1.20	3.00
2-12: 2-Man-Thing-c/story, 12-Final issue	0.40	0.80	2.00
BLAZE: LEGACY OF BLOOD(See Ghost Rider)			
Dec, 1993-No. 4, Mar, 1994 (1.75, color, mini-series)			
Marvel Comics (Midnight Sons imprint)			
1–4	0.40	0.70	1.75
BLAZING COMBAT			
Oct, 1965-No. 4, July, 1966 (35¢, B&W, magazine)			
Warren Publishing Co.			
1-Frazetta painted-c on all	10.00	30.00	70.00
2	4.00	10.00	20.00
3, 4	3.00	8.00	15.00

BLAZING COMBAT: WORLD WAR I AND WORLD WAR II
Mar, 1994 (3.75, B&W)
Apple Press

| 1,2: 1-r/Colan, Toth, Goodwin, Severin, Wood-a. 2-r/Crandall, Evans, | | | |
| Severin, Torres, Williamson-a | 0.80 | 1.60 | 4.00 |

BLITZKRIEG
Jan-Feb, 1976-No. 5, Sept-Oct, 1976
National Periodical Publications

| 1-Kubert-c on all | 0.30 | 0.50 | 1.25 |
| 2–5 | 0.20 | 0.30 | 0.75 |

BLOOD AND GLORY (Punisher & Captain America)
Oct, 1992-No. 3, Dec, 1992 (5.95, color)
Marvel Comics

| Book 1-3: 1-Embossed-c | 1.00 | 2.50 | 6.00 |

BLOODBATH
Early Dec, 1993-No. 2, Late Dec, 1993 (3.50, color, limited series)
DC Comics

Blaze #2 © MEG

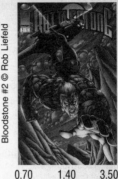

Bloodstone #2 © Rob Liefeld

1,2-New Superman app.; neon ink-c	0.70	1.40	3.50

BLOODFIRE
June, 1993-Present (2.95, color)
Lightning Comics

1-(3.50)-Foil cover; 1st app. Bloodfire	0.80	1.60	4.00
2-12: 2-Origin; contracts HIV virus via transfusion. 3-1st app. Dreadwolf, Judgment Day, Perg. 5-Polybagged w/card & collectors warning on bag. 12-(5/94)	0.60	1.20	3.00
0-(MAY on-c, June 1994 inside, 3.50)	0.70	1.40	3.50

BLOOD PACK
Mar 1995 - Jun 1995 (1.50, color, mini-series)
DC Comics

1–4	0.30	0.60	1.50

BLOODSHOT (See Eternal Warrior #4 & Rai #0)
Nov, 1992-Present (2.25, color)
Valiant Comics

1-(3.50)-Chromium embossed-c; Barry Smith-c & poster			
	0.80	1.60	4.00
2-(2.50-c)	0.50	1.00	2.50
3,4: 4-Eternal Warrior-c/story	0.50	0.90	2.25
5, 8-14: 5-Rai & Eternal Warrior app. 14-(3/94)	0.50	0.90	2.25
6-1st app. Ninjak (out of costume)	0.70	1.40	3.50
7-1st app. Ninjak in costume	0.80	2.00	5.00
0-(3/94, 3.50)-Chromium wraparound-c by Quesada(p)			
	0.70	2.00	4.00
0-Gold variant-c	3.60	7.20	18.00
15-37:15-(4/94) 16-W/bound-in trading card	0.50	0.90	2.25

	Good	Fine	N-Mint
...Yearbook 1 ('94, 3.95)	0.80	1.60	4.00

BLOODSTRIKE (See Supreme V2#3)
1993-Present (1.95, color)
Image Comics

1-10: Liefeld layouts early issues. 1-Blood Brothers prelude. 2-1st app. Lethal. 5-1st app. Noble. 6-1st app. Chapel as team leader. 7, 8-Jae Lee-c. 9-Liefeld pin-up. 9-Black and White part 6 by Thibert. 9,10-Has coupon #3 & 7 for Extreme Prejudice #0. 10-(4/94)	0.40	0.80	2.00
25-(5/94)-Liefeld/Fraga-c	0.40	0.80	2.00
11,12, 15, 17: 11-(7/94)	0.40	0.80	2.00
13,14, 16,17-22 (2.50) 16-Platt-c. Prophet app. 17-Polybagged w/trading card	0.50	1.00	2.50

BLOOD SYNDICATE
Apr, 1993-Present (1.50/1.75, color)
DC Comics (Milestone)

1-(2.95)-Collector's Ed.; polybagged w/poster, trading card, & acid-free backing board (direct sale only)	0.60	1.20	3.00
1-9, 11-17: 8-Intro Kwai. 15-Byrne-c. 16-Worlds Collide Pt. 6; Superman-c & app. 17-Worlds Collide pt. 13	0.30	0.60	1.50
10-(2.50, 52 pgs.)-Simonson-c	0.50	1.00	2.50
18-27: 18-Begin 1.75-c	0.40	0.70	1.75
25-(2.95, 52 pgs)	0.60	1.20	3.00
28-(2.50, 36 pgs.)	0.50	1.00	2.50
29-(0.99)	0.20	0.40	1.00

BLOODWULF
Feb 1995-Present (2.50, color, Limited series:4)
Image Comics

1-Liefeld-c w/4 dif. captions & alternate -c, 2–3	0.50	1.00	2.50

BLUE BEETLE
V2#1, 6/64-V2#5, 3-4/65; V3#50, 7/65-V3#54, 2-3/66;
#1, 6/67-#5, 11/68
Charlton Comics

V2#1-Origin Dan Garrett - Blue Beetle	6.00	18.00	42.00
2-5, V3 #50-54	4.40	13.00	31.00
1 (1967)-Question series by Ditko begins	9.70	29.00	68.00
2-Origin Ted Kord - Blue Beetle	4.00	11.00	26.00
3-5 (#1-5-Ditko c/a)	3.00	9.00	21.00

BOB MARLEY, TALE OF THE TUFF GONG
Aug, 1994-Present (5.95, color, limited series:3)
Marvel Comics

1-Book One: Iron	1.00	3.00	6.00

BOB , THE GALACTIC BUM
Feb 1995 - Jun 1995 (1.95, color, limited series:4)
DC Comics

1-4:1-Lobo app.	0.40	0.80	2.00

BOMBAST
1993 (2.95, color)
Topps Comics

1-Bagged w/Kirbychrome card; Savage Dragon x-over; Kirby-c; has coupon for Amberchrome Secret City Saga #0	0.60	1.20	3.00

BOMBA, THE JUNGLE BOY
Sept-Oct, 1967-No. 7, Sept-Oct, 1968 (TV tie-in)
National Periodical Publications

1-All are 12¢ cover	2.10	6.40	15.00
2–7	1.30	3.00	7.50

BONE
July, 1991-Present (2.95, B&W)
Cartoon Books

1-1st printing; Jeff Smith-c/a in all	17.10	51.00	120.00
1-2nd printing	2.10	6.40	15.00
1-3rd-5th printings	1.00	2.00	5.00
2-1st printing	7.10	21.40	50.00
2-2nd-3rd printings	1.00	2.00	5.00
3-1st printing	5.00	13.00	30.00
3-2nd -4th printings	1.00	2.00	5.00
4–7	1.40	2.80	7.00
8–19	0.60	1.20	3.00
Holiday Special ('93, no price, giveaway)	Free		
...Complete Bone Adventures (Vol. 1, 1993,12.95, r/ #1-#6)			
	1.90	5.60	13.00
...Complete Bone Adventures (Vol. 2, 1994,12.95, r/ #7-#12)			
	1.90	5.60	13.00

Note: Printings not listed sell for cover price

BOOF
July, 1994-Present (1.95, color)

	Good	Fine	N-Mint
Image Comics			
1–6	0.40	0.80	2.00

BOOF AND THE BRUISE CREW
July, 1994-Present (1.95, color)
Image Comics
1,2,5,3,4-6: 2-(8/94). 5-(8/94). 3-(9/94). 4-(10/94). 5-(11/94)

	0.40	0.80	2.00

BOOK OF THE DEAD
Dec, 1993-No. 4, Mar, 1994 (1.75, color, mini-series, 52 pgs.)
Marvel Comics
1-4: r/Ploog Frankenstein & Morrow Man-Thing. 1-Wrightson-r.
   2-Krigstein-r. 3-Starlin Man-Thing

	0.40	0.70	1.75

BOOKS OF MAGIC
1990-No. 4, 1991 (3.95, color, mini-series, mature)
DC Comics

1-Neil Gaiman scripts in all	1.70	5.00	12.00
2, 3: 2-John Constantine app. 3-Sandman app. (minor)			
	1.30	3.00	8.00
4-Death-c & app.	1.70	4.20	10.00
...Bindings ('95, 12.95, r #1-4)	1.90	6.00	13.00

BOOKS OF MAGIC,THE
May, 1994-Present (1.95, color, mature)
DC Comics (Vertigo)

1-Charles Vess-c	1.00	2.00	5.00

Boof #2 © Rob Liefeld

Books of Magic #15 © DC

1-Platinum	3.00	6.00	15.00
2,3: 5-14; Carles Vess-c	0.40	0.80	2.00
4-Death app.	1.00	2.00	5.00
15-begin 2.50-c	0.50	1.00	2.50

BORDERLINE
June 1992 (2.25, B&W)
Friction Press

0-ashcan ed. 1st app. Cliff Broadway	0.40	0.80	2.00
1-painted-c	0.60	1.20	3.00
1-Special Editon-bagged w/photo, S&N	2.00	4.00	10.00

BRAIN BOY
April-June, 1962-No. 6, Sept-Nov, 1963 (5, 6: painted-c)
Dell Publishing Co.

4 Color 1330 (#1)-Origin; Gil Kane-a	15.00	45.00	90.00
2(7-9/62), 3-6: 4-Origin retold	8.30	25.00	50.00

BRAM STOKER'S BURIAL OF THE RATS
Apr 1995-Present 2.50, color)
Roger Corman's Cosmic Comics

1,2-Movie Adaptation	0.40	1.00	2.50

BRAM STOKER'S DRACULA (See Dracula)
Oct, 1992-No. 4, Jan, 1993 (2.95, color, mini-series)
Topps Comics

1-Polybagged w/poster & 4 trading cards	0.60	1.20	3.00
1-2nd printing	0.60	1.20	3.00
1-Crimson Foil Edition (Limited to 500)	3.60	11.00	25.00
2-Polybagged w/poster & cards	0.60	1.20	3.00
3,4: Polybagged w/4 trading cards. 3-Contains coupon to win Crimson foil ed. of #1. 4-Contains coupon to win 1 of 500 uncut sheets of trading cards			
	0.70	1.30	3.25
3,4-With coupon missing	0.60	1.20	3.00

BRAVE AND THE BOLD, THE
Aug-Sept, 1955-No. 200, July, 1983
National Periodical Publications/DC Comics
1-Kubert Viking Prince, Silent Knight, Golden Gladiator begin

	180.00	540.00	1800.00
2	81.00	242.00	805.00
3, 4	48.00	144.00	480.00
5-Robin Hood begins	50.00	149.00	495.00

	Good	Fine	N-Mint
6-10: Robin Hood by Kubert	39.00	118.00	315.00
11-22,24: Silent Knight, Viking Price. 18,21-23-Grey tone-c. 24-Last Kubert Viking Prince	29.00	86.00	230.00
23-Viking Prince origin by Kubert	38.00	114.00	305.00
25-1st app. Suicide Squad (8-9/'59)	36.00	109.00	255.00
26, 27: Suicide Squad	32.00	96.00	225.00
28-Justice League intro (2-3/60)	300.00	900.00	3600.00
29-Justice League (4-5/60)-2nd app.	191.00	572.00	1905.00
30-Justice League (6-7/60)-3rd app.	156.00	467.00	1555.00
31-Cave Carson (scarce in high grade)(1st tryout series)	31.00	92.00	215.00
32, 33-Cave Carson	22.00	66.00	155.00
34-(2-3/61)-Brief origin & 1st app. S.A. Hawkman & Byth by Kubert (1st tryout series, all pre-date Hawkman #1)	125.00	375.00	1500.00
35-(4-5/61)-Hawkman; 2nd app.	40.00	110.00	455.00
36-Hawkman (6-7/61)-3rd app.	38.00	113.00	375.00
37-Suicide Squad (2nd tryout series)	22.00	67.00	200.00
38, 39: Suicide Squad, 38-Last 10¢ issue	25.00	75.00	175.00
40, 41-Cave Carson (2nd tryout series)	16.00	47.00	110.00
42-Hawkman (2nd tryout series)	25.00	75.00	250.00
43-Hawkman by Kubert; gives more detailed origin Hawkman	30.00	90.00	300.00
44-Hawkman; grey tone-c	20.00	60.00	200.00
45-49: Strange Sports Stories	6.40	19.00	45.00
50-Green Arrow & Jonn J'onnz, 1st team-up; 1st Manhunter x-over outside of Detective - predates H.O.M. #143	16.00	49.00	115.00
51-Aquaman & Hawkman (12-1/63-64)	17.50	52.50	175.00
52-3 Battle Stars; Sgt. Rock, Haunted Tank, Johnny Cloud & Mlle. Marie team-up for 1st time; Kubert-c/a	12.10	36.00	85.00
53-Atom & The Flash by Toth	6.40	19.00	45.00
54-Origin/1st app. Teen Titans (6-7/64)	29.00	86.00	200.00
55-Metal Men & The Atom (8-9/64)	3.20	8.00	28.00
56-Flash & Manhunter From Mars	3.20	8.00	28.00
57-Intro/origin Metamorpho (12-1/64-65)	16.00	49.00	115.00
58-2nd app. Metamorpho	7.00	21.00	48.00
59-Batman & Green Lantern, 1st Batman team-up in Brave & Bold	11.00	32.00	75.00
60-2nd app. Teen Titans	9.70	29.00	68.00
61, 62: Origin Starman & Black Canary by Anderson. 62-1st app. S.A. Wildcat (10-11/65); 1st S.A. app. of G.A. Huntress app.	11.00	32.00	75.00
63-Supergirl & Wonder Woman	2.70	8.10	19.00
64-Batman vs. Eclipso (2-3/66)	6.90	21.00	48.00

65, 66: 65-Flash & Doom Patrol. 66-Metamorpho & Metal Men			
	2.00	5.00	12.00
67-Batman & The Flash by Infantino; Batman team-ups begin, end #200			
	4.60	14.00	32.00
68-Batman/Joker/Penguin-c/story; Batman as Bat-Hulk (Hulk parody)			
	7.40	22.00	52.00
69-71: Batman team-ups	3.00	9.00	21.00
72-Spectre & Flash (6-7/67); 4th app. S.A. Spectre (pre-dates Spectre #1)			
(see Showcase #60)	3.10	9.40	22.00
73-Aquaman & Atom	2.60	7.70	18.00
74, 76-78: Batman team-ups	2.60	7.70	18.00
75-Batman & Spectre (12-1/67-68); 6th app. Spectre; came out between			
Spectre #1 & 2	3.10	9.40	22.00
79-Batman & Deadman by N. Adams-a	5.00	15.00	35.00
80-82: N. Adams-a	4.30	13.00	30.00
83-Teen Titans; N. Adams-a; last 12¢ issue	5.40	16.00	38.00
84-86: N. Adams-a. 85-1st new costume for Green Arrow. 86-Deadman			
storyline cont'd from Strange Advs. #216	4.00	12.00	28.00
87-92: Batman team-ups	2.70	8.10	19.00
93-Batman/House Of Mystery by N. Adams	3.70	11.00	26.00
94-Batman/Teen Titans	1.80	5.00	11.00
95-99: 97-Origin Deadman-r. 97-(52 pgs.)	1.70	4.20	10.00
100-(2-3/72, 25¢, 52 pgs.)-Deadman-r/by N. Adams-a; Green Arrow			
app.	3.60	10.70	25.00
101-Batman/Metamorpho	1.10	2.20	5.50
102-Teen Titans; N. Adams-a	1.40	3.50	8.50
103-110: Batman team-ups	1.10	2.20	5.50
111-Batman/Joker-c/story	1.80	5.00	11.00
112-117: 100 pg. issues. 113-r/B&B 34	1.10	2.70	6.50
118-Batman/Wildcat/Joker-c/story	1.80	5.00	11.00
119-128, 132-140: 120-(68 pgs.). 122-Swamp Thing (10/75)			
	0.60	1.20	3.00
129, 130-Joker-c/story	1.80	4.60	11.00
131-Batman/W. Woman vs. Catwoman-c/sty	1.00	2.50	6.00
141-Batman vs. Joker-c/story	1.80	5.00	11.00
142-190,192-199: 143, 144-(44 pgs.). 182, 197-1st & 2nd SA app.			
GA Batwoman. 183-Riddler. 197-Earth II Batman & Catwoman marry			
	0.60	1.20	3.00
191-Batman/Joker-c/story	1.20	3.00	7.00
200-Double size; 1st app. The Outsiders	1.30	3.30	8.00

Note: See Overstreet Annual Guide for more detailed listing of all issues.

	Good	Fine	N-Mint

BREAK-THRU
Dec, 1993-No. 2, Jan, 1994 (2.50, color, 44 pgs.)
Malibu Comics (Ultraverse)

	Good	Fine	N-Mint
1,2-Perez-c/a(p)	0.50	1.00	2.50

'BREED
Jan, 1994-No. 6, June, 1994 (2.50, color, limited series)
Malibu Comics (Bravura imprint)

	Good	Fine	N-Mint
1-(48 pgs.)-Origin & 1st app. of 'Breed by Starlin; contains Bravura stamps; spot varnish-c	0.70	1.40	3.50
2-6: 2-5-Contain Bravura stamps; Starlin-c/a/scripts. 6-Death of Rachel	0.50	1.00	2.50
...: Book of Genesis ('94, 12.95)-r/1-6	1.90	6.00	13.00

BREED II
Nov 1994 -Apr 1995(2.95, color, limted series:6)
Malibu Comics

	Good	Fine	N-Mint
1-6: J. Starlin s/p/i	0.60	1.20	3.00

BRIGADE
Aug, 1992-No. 4, 1993 (1.95, color, limited series)
V2#1, May, 1993-Present (1.95, color)
Image Comics

	Good	Fine	N-Mint
1-Liefeld-c; includes 2 Brigade trading cards; 1st app. Genocide	0.50	1.30	3.00
1-Gold foil embossed logo ed.	3.10	9.00	22.00
2-Has coupon for Image Comics #0 & cards	0.80	1.60	4.00
2-With coupon missing	0.40	0.80	2.00
3, 4: 3-Contains bound-in trading cards; 1st app. Birds of Prey. 4-Flip book format featuring Youngblood #5	0.40	0.80	2.00
V2#1-Gatefold-c; Liefeld co-plots; Bloodstrike app. cont'd in Bloodstrike #2; Blood Brothers part 1; 1st app. Boone & Hacker	0.40	0.80	2.00
V2#2-(6/93)-(V2#1 on inside in error)-Foil Merricote-c	0.40	0.80	2.00
V2#2-Newsstand ed. w/o foil-c	0.40	0.80	2.00
0-(9/93)-Liefeld story; Thibert-c(i); 1st app. Warcry; Wildcats & Youngblood app.	0.60	1.20	3.00
V2#3-9: 3-(9/93)-Liefeld story; Perez-c(i); 1st app. Roman. 6-8-Thibert-c(i); 1st app. Coral. 8-Liefeld story; Black and White part 5 by Thibert. 8,9-w/ coupon #2 & 6 for Extreme Prejudice #0. 9-(4/94)	0.40	0.80	2.00
25-(5/94)	0.40	0.80	2.00

10, 13-14: 10-(6/94)	0.40	0.80	2.00

11,12,15,16-(8/94, 9/94, 12/94 2.50, 36 pgs.)-WildC.A.T.s app.
16-Polybagged w/trading card; 17-19, 19-Glory app.

	0.50	1.00	2.50
Source Book 1 (8/94, 2.95)	0.60	1.20	3.00

BRINKE OF ETERNITY
Apr 1994 (2.75, color, one-shot)
Chaos! Comics

1	0.60	1.10	2.75
1–Signed ed.	1.00	2.00	5.00

BROOKLYN DREAMS
1994 (4.95, B&W, Mature readers, limited series:4)
Paradox Press

1–4	1.00	2.00	5.00

BROTHER POWER THE GEEK (See Vertigo Visions)
Sept-Oct, 1968-No. 2, Nov-Dec, 1968
National Periodical Publications

1-Origin	3.00	9.00	20.00
2	2.00	6.00	15.00

BROTHERS OF THE SPEAR
June, 1972-No. 17, Feb, 1976; No. 18, May, 1982
Gold Key/Whitman #18

1	2.10	6.00	15.00
2-Painted-c begin, end #17	1.30	3.30	8.00
3–10	0.90	1.80	4.50
11-17: 12-Line drawn-c. 13-17-Spiegle-a	0.40	0.80	2.00
18-r/#2; Leopard Girl-r	0.20	0.40	1.00

Breed #6 © Jim Starlin

Brinke of Eternity #1
© Brinke Stevens

	Good	Fine	N-Mint

BRUCE LEE
July, 1994-Present (2.95, color)
Malibu Comics Entertainment, Inc.

	Good	Fine	N-Mint
1-(44 pgs.)-Mortal Kombat preview, 1st app. in comics			
	0.60	1.20	3.00
2-6-(36 pgs.)	0.60	1.20	3.00

BRUTE & BABE
July, 1994-Present (Color)
Ominous Press

	Good	Fine	N-Mint
1-(3.95, 8 tablets plus-c)-"…It Begins…"; tablet format			
	0.80	1.60	4.00
2-(2.50, 36 pgs.)-"Mael's Rage"	0.50	1.00	2.50
2-(40 pgs.)-Stiff additional variant-c	0.50	1.00	2.50

BUBBLEGUM CRISIS: GRAND MAL
Mar, 1994-No. 4, June, 1994 (2.50, color, mini-series)
Dark Horse Comics

	Good	Fine	N-Mint
1-4-Japanese manga	0.50	1.00	2.50

BUCK ROGERS (…In the 25th Century #5 on)(TV)
Oct, 1964; No. 2, July, 1979-No. 16, May, 1982 (No #10)
Gold Key/Whitman #7 on

	Good	Fine	N-Mint
1-(10128-410)-1st S.A. app.; painted-c; 12¢	5.80	18.00	35.00
2-(1979)-Movie adaptation; painted-c	0.60	1.20	3.00
3-9, 11-16: 3, 4-Movie adapt. 5-New stories	0.30	0.60	1.50

BUGS BUNNY & PORKY PIG
Sept, 1965 (100 pgs., paper-c)
Gold Key

	Good	Fine	N-Mint
30025-509 (#1)	10.00	30.00	60.00

BULLWINKLE (TV)(…and Rocky #20 on)
Mar-May, 1962-No. 25, Feb, 1980 (Jay Ward)
Dell/Gold Key

	Good	Fine	N-Mint
Four Color 1270 (3-5/62)	22.00	66.00	155.00
01-090-209-(Dell, 7-9/62)	19.00	56.00	130.00
1 (Gold Key, 11/62)	15.00	45.00	105.00
2 (2/63)	11.00	32.00	75.00
3 (4/62) -11 (4/74)	6.40	19.00	45.00
12 (6/76)-Reprints	2.00	5.00	12.00
13 (9/76), 14-New stories	2.10	6.00	15.00

15-25	1.70	4.20	10.00
Mother Moose Nursery Pomes 01-530-207 (Dell, 5-7/62)			
	19.00	56.00	130.00

BULLWINKLE (TV)(...& Rocky #2 on)
July, 1970-No. 7, July, 1971
Charlton Comics

1	4.30	12.90	30.00
2–7	2.60	7.70	18.00

BUMMER
June, 1995-Present(3.50, B&W, mature)
Fantagraphics Books

1-	0.70	1.40	3.50

BY BIZARRE HANDS
Apr, 1994-No. 3, June, 1994 (2.50, B&W, limited series, mature)
Dark Horse Comics

1–3-Lansdale stories	0.50	1.00	2.50

Cable #2 © MEG

Cads & Dinosaurs #1 © Mark Shultz

	Good	Fine	N-Mint
CABLE (See New Mutants #87)			
May, 1993-Present (2.00, color)			
Marvel Comics			
1-(3.50, 52 pgs.)-Goil foil-c; Thibert-c/a	0.90	1.80	4.50
2-15: 4-Liefeld-a assist; last Thibert-a(p). 6-8-Storyline reveals that Baby			
Nathan did become Cable. 9-Omega Red-c/sty. 11-Bound-in card sheet			
	0.40	0.80	2.00
16-Newsstand edition	0.50	1.00	2.50
16-Enhanced edition	1.20	2.40	6.00
17-20-(1.95)-Deluxe edition, 20-w/bound in '95 Fleer Ultra cards			
	0.40	0.80	2.00
17-20-(1.50)-Standard edition	0.30	0.60	1.50
21-Return from Age of Apocalypse; 22–	0.40	0.80	2.00

	Good	Fine	N-Mint
CABLE - BLOOD AND METAL			
Oct, 1992-No. 2, Nov, 1992 (2.50, color)			
Marvel Comics			
1-Cable vs. Stryfe; John Romita, Jr.-c/a	0.70	1.40	3.50
2-Prelude to X-Cutioner's Song	0.50	1.00	2.50

	Good	Fine	N-Mint
CADILLACS AND DINOSAURS (TV)			
Feb, 1994-Present (2.50, color)			
Topps Comics			
V2#1-(2.95)-Collector's edition w/foil stamped logo; Stout-c; Giordano-a			
in all; Buckler-a	0.60	1.20	3.00
V2#1-Regular edition w/Giordano-c	0.50	1.00	2.50
V2#2, 3-Collector's ed. w/Stout-c & posters	0.50	1.00	2.50
V2#2, 3-Regular ed. w/o poster, Giordano-c	0.50	1.00	2.50
V2#4-9-Regular edition: 7-9-Wild Ones storyline			

	0.50	1.00	2.50
V2#4-6-Collector's edition; Kieth-c	0.50	1.00	2.50

CAGE (Also see Hero for Hire)
Apr, 1992-No. 20, Nov, 1993 (1.25, color)
Marvel Comics

1-(1.50)-Extra color on-c	0.40	0.80	2.00
2-11, 13-20: 3-Punisher-c & minor app. 19-Thing cameo. 20-Thing &			
Human Torch	0.30	0.50	1.25
12-(1.75, 52 pgs.)-Iron Fist app.	0.40	0.70	1.75

CAGES
1991-No. 10, 1992? (3.50, color)
Tundra

1-Dave McKean-c/a in all	1.70	5.00	12.00
2-Misprint exists	1.30	3.00	8.00
3, 4	0.80	1.60	4.00
5-10: 5-Begin 3.95-c	0.80	1.60	4.00

CAIN/VAMPIRELLA FLIP BOOK
Oct, 1994 (6.95, color, one-shot, squarebound)
Harris Comics

nn-Contains Cain #3 & #4; flip is r/Vampirella story from Creepy			
Fearbook (1993)	1.30	3.00	7.50

CALIBER PRESENTS
Jan, 1989-No. 24, 1991 (1.95, B&W)
Caliber Press

1-1st app. The Crow; Tim Vigil-c/a	11.00	32.00	75.00
2-Deadworld story; Tim Vigil-a	1.00	2.00	5.00
3-14: 9-Begin 2.50-c issues	0.60	1.20	3.00
15-24-(3.50)	0.70	1.40	3.50

CALIBER SPOTLIGHT
May 1995 (2.95, B&W)
Caliber Press

1–Kabuki app.	0.60	1.20	3.00

CAPTAIN ACTION
Oct-Nov, 1968-No. 5, June-July, 1969
National Periodical Publications

1-Origin; Wood art	9.00	28.00	65.00
2, 3, 5-Kane/Wood art	6.40	19.30	45.00

	Good	Fine	N-Mint
4	5.00	15.00	35.00
...& Action Boy ('67)-Ideal Toy giveaway; 1st app. Capt. Action			
	7.90	24.00	55.00

CAPTAIN AMERICA (Tales of Suspense #1-99; also see Giant-Size...)
No. 100, April, 1968 - Present
Marvel Comics Group

	Good	Fine	N-Mint
100-Story cont'd from Tales of Suspense #99; Flashback on Cap's			
revival with Avengers; Kirby-c/a begins	37.00	111.00	295.00
101-The Sleeper-c/story; Red Skull app.	9.00	28.00	74.00
102-108: 103, 104-Red Skull-c/story	4.90	15.00	39.00
109-Origin Capt. America retold	8.00	24.00	64.00
110, 111, 113-Classic Steranko-c/a. 110-Hulk-c/story			
	7.30	22.00	58.00
112-Origin retold; Last Kirby-c/a	3.40	10.00	27.00
114-116, 118-120: 115-Last 12¢ issue	2.50	8.00	20.00
117-1st app. Falcon (9/69)	3.80	11.00	30.00
121-140: 137, 138-Spider-Man x-over	1.70	4.20	10.00
141-153, 155-171, 176-179: 144-New costume Falcon. 153-1st app. (cameo)			
Jack Monroe. 155-Origin J. Monroe	1.20	3.00	7.00
154-1st full app. Jack Monroe (Nomad)	1.30	3.30	8.00
172-175: X-Men app.	1.90	5.60	13.00
180-Origin/1st app. Nomad (Steve Rogers)	1.30	3.00	8.00
181-Intro/origin new Cap.	1.00	2.50	6.00
182, 184-200	0.80	1.60	4.00
183-Death of new Cap.; Nomad becomes Cap			
	1.00	2.50	6.00
201-240, 242-246: 215-Retell origin. 230-Battles Hulk-c/story; cont'd in			
Incredible Hulk #232	0.60	1.20	3.00
241-Punisher app.; Miller-c	5.70	17.00	40.00

Captain America #278 © MEG

Captain America #431© MEG

247-255: Byrne art. 255-Origin; Miller-c	0.70	1.40	3.50
256-281, 284, 285, 289-322, 324-326, 329-331			
	0.40	0.80	2.00
282-1st app. new Nomad (Jack Monroe)	1.70	4.00	10.00
282-Silver ink 2nd printing (1.75)	0.40	0.70	1.75
283-2nd app. Nomad	0.80	1.60	4.00
286-288: Deathlok app.	0.50	1.00	2.50
323-1st app. new Super Patriot (11/86)	0.80	1.60	4.00
327-Capt. America battles Super Patriot	0.60	1.20	3.00
328-Origin/1st app. D-Man	0.60	1.20	3.00
332-Old Cap resigns	1.40	4.00	10.00
333-Super Patriot becomes new Cap.	1.30	3.00	8.00
334	0.80	2.10	5.00
335-340: 339-Fall Of The Mutants	1.00	2.00	5.00
341-343, 345-349	0.30	0.60	1.50
344-(1.50, 52 pgs.)	0.40	0.80	1.90
350-(1.75, 68 pgs.)-Return of Steve Rogers	0.80	1.60	4.00
351-354: 354-1st app. U.S. Agent	0.30	0.60	1.50
355-382, 384-396: 373-Return of Bullseye. 396-Last 1.00-c.			
396 & 397-1st app new Jack O'Lantern	0.30	0.60	1.40
383-(2.00, triple size)-Jim Lee-c	0.90	1.80	4.50
397-399, 401-424, 426: 405-410-New Jack O'Lantern app. in back-up story;			
407-Capwolf vs. Cable. 423-Vs. Namor	0.20	0.40	1.10
400-(2.25, 84 pgs.)-Double gatefold-c	0.60	1.20	3.00
425-(2.95, 52 pgs.)-Collectors Edition w/embossed foil-c; Fighting			
Chance part 1	0.60	1.20	3.00
425-(1.75, 52 pgs.)-Newsstand Ed.	0.40	0.70	1.80
427-442: 427-Bound-in trading card sheet; begin 1.50-c			
	0.30	0.60	1.50
Special 1 (1/71)-Origin retold	2.10	6.40	15.00
Special 2 (1/72)-All reprints	1.70	5.00	12.00
Annual 3, 5-7	0.50	1.00	2.50
Annual 4 (1977)-Magneto-c/story by Kirby (34 pgs.)			
	0.60	1.20	3.00
Annual 8 (9/86)-Wolverine-c/story	4.30	13.00	30.00
Annual 9 ('90, 2.00)-Nomad story	1.00	2.00	5.00
Annual 10 ('91, 2.00)-Origin retold	0.40	0.80	2.00
Annual 11 ('92, 2.25)	0.50	0.90	2.25
Annual 12 ('93, 2.95)-Polybagged w/card	0.60	1.20	3.00
Annual 13 ('94, 2.95)-Red Skull-c/story	0.60	1.20	3.00
...:Ashcan Edition ('95, .75)	0.20	0.30	0.75
...: Deathlok Lives! nn-(10/93, 4.95)-r/286-288			
	1.00	2.00	5.00

	Good	Fine	N-Mint
...Medusa Effect 1 ('94, 2.95, 68 pgs.)-Origin Baron Zemo			
	0.60	1.20	3.00
...Drug War 1 ('94, 2.00, 52 pgs.)	0.40	0.80	2.00
...: Streets of Poison-(7/94, 15.95)-r/#372-378			
	2.30	6.90	16.00

CAPTAIN AMERICA COMICS
No. 76, May, 1954-No. 78, Sept, 1954
Atlas Comics (Marvel)

76-78-Human Torch & Toro stories	82.00	246.00	575.00

CAPTAIN AMERICA/NICK FURY: BLOOD TRUCE
Feb 1995 (5.95, color, one-shot)
Marvel Comics

nn-Chaykin-s	1.00	3.00	6.00

CAPTAIN ATOM (Formerly Strange Suspense Stories)
No. 78, Dec, 1965-No. 89, Dec, 1967
Charlton Comics

78-Origin retold; Ditko-c/a in all	9.00	26.00	60.00
79-82: 82-Intro Nightshade	5.70	17.00	40.00
83-89: 83-86: Blue Beetle app. 83-1st Ted Kord Blue Beetle (11/66)			
	5.00	15.00	35.00
83-85 (Modern Comics-1977) - Reprints	0.20	0.40	1.00

CAPTAIN ATOM
Mar, 1987-No. 57, Sept, 1991
DC Comics

1-(44 pgs.)-Origin	0.40	0.80	2.00
2-49: 24, 25-Invasion tie-in	0.20	0.40	1.00
42-Death app.	0.60	1.20	3.00
50-(2.00, 52 pgs.)	0.40	0.80	2.00
51-57	0.20	0.40	1.00
Annual 1,2: 1-(1988, 1.25). 2-(1988, 1.50)	0.30	0.60	1.50

CAPTAIN GLORY
April, 1993 (2.95, color) (Created by Jack Kirby)
Topps Comics

1-Polybagged w/Kirbychrome trading card; Ditko-a & Kirby-c; has coupon for Amberchrome Secret City Saga #0	0.60	1.20	3.00

CAPTAIN JOHNER & THE ALIENS
May 1995 (2.95, color)

Valiant
1-r/backup stories from Gold Key Magnus #1-7

	0.60	1.20	3.00
2-r/backup stories from Gold Key Magnus #8-14			
	0.60	1.20	3.00

CAPTAIN MARVEL
April, 1966-No. 4, Nov, 1966 (25¢ Giants)
M. F. Enterprises
nn-(#1 on pg. 5)-Origin; created by Carl Burgos

	2.10	6.40	15.00
2-4: 3-(#3 on pg. 4)	1.30	3.30	8.00

CAPTAIN MARVEL (See Life of... & Marvel Super Heroes #12, 13)
May, 1968-No. 62, May, 1979
Marvel Comics Group

1	11.00	34.00	90.00
2-Super Skrull-c/story	4.30	11.00	30.00
3-5: 4-Battles Sub-Mariner	2.20	7.00	20.00
6-11: 11-B. Smith-c(p)	2.00	6.00	14.00
12-24: 14-Vs. Iron Man; last 12¢ issue; 16, 17-New costume. 21-Vs. Hulk; last 15¢ issue	1.00	3.00	9.00
25-Starlin-c/a begins; ends #34; Thanos cameo; begins 1st Thanos saga	3.60	11.00	25.00
26-Minor Thanos app.;1st Thanos-c	4.00	13.00	30.00
27-1st full Thanos story	3.00	9.00	25.00
28-2nd full Thanos story; Thanos-c/story	3.00	9.00	23.00
29, 30-Thanos (cameos only)	1.00	4.00	10.00
31, 32: Thanos-s. 31-Last 20¢ issue	2.00	6.00	15.00
33-1st origin Thanos; C. M. battles Thanos	4.00	11.00	30.00
34-Starlin-c/a ends	1.00	2.00	5.00
35, 37-56, 58-62: 58-Thanos cameo	0.30	0.60	1.50
36-Reprints origin/1st app. Capt. Marvel	1.00	2.00	5.00
57-Thanos app. (flashback)	1.00	3.00	7.00

(Also see Giant-size listing)

CAPTAIN MARVEL PRESENTS THE TERRIBLE FIVE
Aug, 1966; V2#5, Sept, 1967 (25¢)
M. F. Enterprises

1	1.70	5.00	12.00
V2#5 (Formerly Capt. Marvel)	1.00	2.50	6.00

	Good	Fine	N-Mint

CAPTAIN NICE
(TV)Gold Key

1-(10211-711)-Photo-c	6.40	19.00	45.00

CAPTAIN SAVAGE AND HIS LEATHERNECK RAIDERS
(Captain Savage and His Battlefield Raiders #9 on)
Jan, 1968-No. 19, Mar, 1970 (See Sgt. Fury 10)
Marvel Comics

1-Sgt. Fury cameo	1.70	4.00	10.00
2-10: 2-Origin Hydra	1.00	2.50	6.00
11–19	1.00	2.00	5.00

CAPTAIN STERNN: RUNNING OUT OF TIME
Sept, 1993-No. 5, Sept, 1994 (4.95, color, 52 pgs.)
Kitchen Sink Press

1-5: B. Wrightson-c/a/scripts	1.00	2.00	5.00
1-Gold Ink variant	2.90	9.00	20.00

CAPTAIN STORM
May-June, 1964-No. 18, Mar-Apr, 1967
National Periodical Publications

1-Origin	3.10	9.40	22.00
2-18: 3, 6, 13-Kubert art. 8-Grey tone-c	2.20	5.00	13.00

CAR 54, WHERE ARE YOU? (TV)
3-5/62-No. 7, 9-11/63; 7-9/64-No. 4, 1-3/65 (All photo-c)
Dell Publishing

4-Color 1257(#1, 3-5/62)	9.20	28.00	55.00
2(6-8/62)- 7	4.60	13.70	32.00
2, 3(10-12/64), 4('65)-r/2-4 of 1st series	3.60	10.70	25.00

CASEY JONES & RAPHAEL
Oct 1994 -Present (2.75, color, limited series:5)
Mirage

1-S. Bisley-c, K.Eastman s/p	0.60	1.10	2.75

CAT, THE
Nov, 1972-No. 4, June, 1973
Marvel Comics Group

1-Origin/1st app. The Cat; Wally Wood inks	2.10	6.00	15.00
2-Marie Severin/Mooney art	1.30	3.30	8.00
3, 4: 3-Everett-i. 4-Starlin/Weiss-a	1.30	3.30	8.00

CATALYST: AGENTS OF CHANGE (See Comics' Greatest World)
Feb, 1994-No. 7, Nov, 1994 (2.00, color)
Dark Horse Comics

1-7: 1-Foil stamped logo	0.40	0.80	2.00

CATFIGHT: DREAM WARRIOR
June, 1995-Present (2.75, B&W)
Insomnia Press

1-Hellina cameo	0.60	1.10	2.75

CATWOMAN (See Showcase 93 & Superman's Girlfriend... #70)
Feb, 1989-No. 4, May, 1989 (1.50, mini-series)
DC Comics

1	1.00	2.50	6.00
2	0.70	1.40	3.50
3,4: 4-Batman app.	0.50	1.00	2.50

CATWOMAN
Aug, 1993-Present (1.50, color)
DC Comics

1-(1.95)-Embossed-c;Bane app;Balent-c/a	0.80	1.60	4.00
2-3	0.60	1.20	3.00
4-14: 4-Brief Bane app. 6, 7-Knightquest x-over; Batman app. 8-1st app. Zephyr. 12-KnightsEnd Pt. 6. 13-KnightsEnd Aftermath.			
14-(9/94)-Zero Hour	0.40	0.80	2.00
0,15-20: 0-(10/94)-Origin retold. 15-(11/94)	0.40	0.80	2.00
21-(begin 1.95 cover price); 22-23			2.00
Annual 1 ('94, 2.95)-Elseworlds story; Batman app.			
	0.60	1.20	3.00
Annual 2 ('95, 3.95)-Year One story	0.80	1.60	4.00

CAVE KIDS (TV)
Feb, 1963-No. 16, Mar, 1967 (Hanna-Barbera)
Gold Key

1	5.00	15.00	35.00
2-5	1.70	5.00	12.00
6-16: 7, 12-Pebbles & Bamm Bamm app.	1.50	3.80	9.00

CEREBUS JAM
Apr, 1985
Aardvark-Vanaheim

1-Eisner, Austin, Sim-a; Cerebus vs. Spirit	1.00	2.00	5.00

	Good	Fine	N-Mint

Catwoman #12 © DC

Cerebus #179 © Dave Sim

CEREBUS THE AARDVARK (Also see Nucleus)
Dec, 1977-Present (1.70/2.00/2.25, B&W)
Aardvark-Vanaheim

	Good	Fine	N-Mint
0- (2.25)-'93-reprints	0.60	1.10	2.75
0-Gold	6.00	12.00	30.00
1-1st app. Cerebus	26.00	77.00	180.00
1-Counterfeit		no value	
2	7.00	21.00	50.00
3- 1st app. Red Sophia	5.70	17.00	40.00
4- 1st app. Elrod The Albino	3.60	10.70	25.00
5, 6	3.00	8.60	20.00
7–10	2.10	6.40	15.00
11, 12: 11- 1st app. of The Cockroach	2.40	7.30	17.00
13-15	1.30	3.30	8.00
16-20	1.00	2.00	5.00
21- Barry Smith letter	4.30	13.00	30.00
22- no cover price	1.60	4.70	11.00
23-30; 26-High Society begins	1.00	2.00	5.00
31-Origin Moonroach	1.20	3.00	7.00
32-40	0.80	1.60	4.00
41-50, 52; 50-High Society ends; 52-Church & State begins			
	0.60	1.20	3.00
51	1.70	5.00	12.00
53-Intro Wolveroach (cameo)	1.00	2.00	5.00
54-Wolveroach 1st full story	1.20	3.00	7.00
55, 56: Wolveroach app.; Normalman back-up stories by Valentino in each			
	1.00	2.00	5.00
57-79: 61, 62-Flaming Carrot App.; 65-Gerhard begins			
	0.50	1.00	2.50

80-195: 137-Begin 2.25-c. 175-(44 pgs.); 111-Chrch & State ends; 114-

Jaka's Story begins: 136-Jaka's Story ends; 139-Melmoth begins; 150-
Melmoth ends; 200-Mothers & Daughters ends;

	0.50	0.90	2.25
151-153: 2nd printings	0.50	0.90	2.25

CHAINS OF CHAOS
Nov 1994 - Jan 1995(2.95, color, limited series)
Harris Comics

1-3: 1-Intro The Rook, w/ Vampirella	0.70	1.40	3.50

CHALLENGERS OF THE UNKNOWN (See Showcase #6, 7, 11, 12)
Apr-May, 1958 - No. 77, Dec, 1970-71; No. 78, Feb, 1973-No. 80,
June, 1973; No. 81, June, 1977-No. 87, June-July, 1978
National Periodical Publications/DC Comics

1-Kirby art 1-8	153.00	459.00	1530.00
2	65.00	195.00	585.00
3	53.00	160.00	480.00
4-8: Kirby/Wood art	46.00	137.00	410.00
9, 10	22.00	67.00	200.00
11-15: 11-Grey tone-c. 14-1st Multi-Man app.			
	15.00	45.00	135.00
16-22: 22-Last 10¢ issue	13.00	38.00	115.00
23-30	8.00	24.00	55.00
31-Origin retold	9.00	26.00	60.00
32-40	4.00	12.00	28.00
41-60: 48-Doom Patrol app.	1.70	5.10	12.00
61-73, 75-77 (1971): 68-Last 12¢ issue	1.20	2.40	6.00
74-Deadman by Adams	2.00	6.00	14.00
78-87: 82-Swamp Thing begins	0.80	1.60	4.00

Challengers of the Unknown #63
© DC

Chaos Effect: Omega © Voyager

	Good	Fine	N-Mint
CHALLENGERS OF THE UNKNOWN			
Mar,1991-No. 8, Oct, 1991 (1.75, limited series)			
DC Comics			
1-Bolland-c	0.40	0.80	2.00
2-8: 7-Art Adams-c (swipe from Steranko)	0.40	0.70	1.75
CHAMBER OF CHILLS			
Nov, 1972-No. 25, Nov, 1976			
Marvel Comics			
1-Harlan Ellison adaption	1.00	2.00	5.00
2–25	0.40	0.80	2.00
CHAMBER OF DARKNESS (Monsters on the Prowl #9 on)			
Oct, 1969-No. 8, Dec, 1970			
Marvel Comics			
1-Buscema art (p)	4.60	14.00	32.00
2-Neal Adams script	1.70	5.00	12.00
3-B. Smith, Buscema art	1.70	5.00	12.00
4-Conanesque tryout by Smith (4/70)	5.00	15.00	35.00
5, 6, 8: 5-H.P. Lovecraft adaptation	1.00	2.00	5.00
7-Wrightson-c/a, his 1st at Marvel	1.70	4.00	10.00
1 (1/72, 25¢ Special)	1.00	2.50	6.00
CHAMPIONS, THE			
Oct, 1975-No. 17, Jan, 1978			
Marvel Comics			
1-Origin/1st app. Champions; Ghost Rider, Angel, Black Widow, Hercules,			
Ice Man in all	2.10	6.40	15.00
2-10,16	1.30	3.00	8.00
11-15,17: Byrne-a	1.10	3.40	8.00
Note: Ghost Rider-c: 1-4, 7, 8, 10, 14, 16, 17.			
CHAOS EFFECT, THE			
1994			
Valiant			
Alpha-w/trading card checklist		Free	
Omega-(11/94, 2.25)	0.50	0.90	2.25
Epilogue Pt. 1,2 (12/94, 1/95; 2.95)	0.60	1.20	3.00
CHAPEL			
Feb 1995-Present (2.50, color)			
Image Comics			
1–2	0.50	1.00	2.50

CHARLTON BULLSEYE
1975-No. 5, 1976 (Bi-monthly, B&W magazine format)
CPL/Gang Publications

1-Captain Atom by Ditko/Byrne intended for never published Capt. Atom #90; Jeff Jones-a	1.80	4.60	11.00
2-Part 2 Capt. Atom by Ditko/Byrne	1.70	4.20	10.00
3-Wrong Country by Sanho Kim	1.20	2.90	7.00
4-Doomsday + 1 by John Byrne	1.60	4.00	9.50
5-Doomsday + 1 by John Byrne, Neal Adams back-c; The Question by Toth; Toth-c	1.80	5.00	11.00

CHILDRENS CRUSADE, THE
Dec, 1993-No. 2, Jan, 1994 (3.95, color, limited series, mature)
DC Comics

1,2-Neil Gaiman scripts in both	1.00	2.00	5.00

CHIAROSCURO (THE PRIVATE LIVES OF LEONARDO DA VINCI)
July 1995-Present (2.50, color, mature readers)
DC Comics

16/28/952	0.50	1.00	2.50

CHROMA-TICK, THE (...Special Edition, #1,2)
Feb, 1992-No. 8, Nov, 1993 (3.95/3.50, color)
New England Comics

1,2-(3.95, 44 pgs)-Includes serially numbered trading cards	0.80	1.60	4.00
3-8-(3.50, 36 pgs): 6-Bound-in card	0.70	1.40	3.50

CLANDESTINE
Oct, 1994-Present (2.50, color)
Marvel Comics

1-(2.95)-Gold foil-c	0.60	1.20	3.00
2-10: 2-Wraparound-c	0.50	1.00	2.50
...Preview, The (1.50, 10/94)	0.30	0.60	1.50

CLASSIC PUNISHER
Dec, 1989 (4.95, B&W, deluxe format)
Marvel Comics

1-Reprints Marvel Preview #2	1.00	2.00	5.00

CLASSIC STAR WARS
Aug, 1992-No. 20, June, 1994 (2.50, color)
Dark Horse Comics

	Good	Fine	N-Mint
1-19: Star Wars-r. 8-Bagged w/card	0.50	1.00	2.50
20-(3.50, 52 pgs.)-Star Wars-r; bagged w/card			
	0.70	1.40	3.50

CLASSIC STAR WARS: A NEW HOPE
June, 1994 (3.95, color)
Dark Horse Comics

| 1-r/Star Wars 1-3, July-Sept '77 series | 0.80 | 1.60 | 4.00 |
| 2-r/Star Wars 4-6, Oct-Dec '77 series | 0.80 | 1.60 | 4.00 |

CLASSIC STAR WARS: RETURN OF THE JEDI
Oct 1994-Present (3.50, color, limited series)
Dark Horse Comics

| 1-2: 1-r/Star Wars:Return of the Jedi '83-84 series; polybagged w/trading | | | |
| card | 0.70 | 1.40 | 3.50 |

CLASSIC STAR WARS: THE EARLY ADVENTURES
Aug, 1994-Present (2.50, color)
Dark Horse Comics

| 1-9: 3-Polybagged w/trading card- R.Manning s/a | | | |
| | 0.50 | 1.00 | 2.50 |

CLASSIC STAR WARS: THE EMPIRE STRIKES BACK
Aug, 1994-No. 2, Sept, 1994 (3.95, color)
Dark Horse Comics

| 1,2-r/Star Wars #39-44 | 0.80 | 1.60 | 4.00 |

CLASSIC X-MEN (Becomes X-Men Classic #46 on)
Sept, 1986-No. 45, Mar, 1990
Marvel Comics

1-Begins reprints of New X-Men	1.00	2.00	5.00
2–4	0.80	1.60	4.00
5–9	0.60	1.20	3.00
10-Sabretooth app.	0.80	1.60	4.00
11-15: 11-1st origin Magneto (backup-s)	0.50	1.00	2.50
16, 18-20	0.40	0.80	2.00
17-Wolverine-c	0.80	1.60	4.00
21-25, 27-30: 27-Begin 1.25-c	0.40	0.70	1.75
26-Wolverine-c/story (r-X-Men 120)	0.80	1.60	4.00
31-38, 40-42, 44, 45	0.30	0.60	1.50
39-New Jim Lee backup-s (2nd on X-Men)	1.00	2.00	5.00
43-(1.75, 52 pgs.)	0.40	0.80	2.00

CLAW THE UNCONQUERED
5-6/75-No. 9, 9-10/76; No. 10, 4-5/78-No. 12, 8-9/78
National Periodical Publications

1-1st app. Claw	0.40	0.80	2.00
2, 3	0.30	0.60	1.50
4-12: 9-Origin	0.20	0.50	1.20

CLIVE BARKER'S BOOK OF THE DAMNED
Oct, 1991-No. 3, Nov, 1992 (4.95, color, semi-annual)
Epic Comics (Marvel)

Vol. 1-3: 3-McKean-a (1 pg.)	1.00	2.00	5.00

CLIVE BARKER'S HELLRAISER
1989-No. 20, 1993 (4.95, color, squarebound)
Epic Comics

Book 1	1.00	2.00	5.00
Book 2-4	1.00	2.00	5.00
5-9 (5.95-c)	1.00	2.50	6.00
10, 11, 13 (4.50): 10-Foil-c	0.90	1.80	4.50
12-Sam Kieth-a	1.00	2.00	5.00
14-20 (4.95-c): 20-By Gaiman/McKean	1.00	2.00	5.00
...Dark Holiday Special ('92, 4.95)-Conrad-a	1.00	2.00	5.00
...Spring Slaughter 1 ('94, 6.95, 52 pgs.)	1.20	2.90	7.00
...Summer Special 1 ('92, 5.95, 68 pgs.)	1.00	2.50	6.00

CLIVE BARKER'S NIGHTBREED
Apr, 1990-No. 24, Feb, 1993
Epic Comics (Marvel)

1	0.60	1.20	3.00
2-6: 5-Begin 2.25-c	0.50	0.90	2.25

Codename: Firearm #0 © Malibu

Codename: Strikeforce #4 © Image

	Good	Fine	N-Mint
7-19: 19-Last 2.25-c	0.50	0.90	2.25
20-24 (2.50-c)	0.50	1.00	2.50

CLIVE BARKER'S THE HARROWERS
Dec, 1993-Present (2.50, color)
Marvel Comics

	Good	Fine	N-Mint
1-(2.95)-Glow-in-the-dark-c; Colan-c/a in all	0.60	1.20	3.00
2-6: 2, 4, 5-Williamson-a(i)	0.50	1.00	2.50

CODENAME: FIREARM
June 1995-Present (2.95, color, limited series)
Malibu Comics

	Good	Fine	N-Mint
1-Robinson backup-s	0.60	1.20	3.00

CODENAME: STRYKE FORCE (See Cyberforce V1#4)
Jan, 1994-Present (1.95, color)
Image Comics

	Good	Fine	N-Mint
1-12-Silvestri-stories, Peterson-a: 4-StormWatch app.; 8-w/3 variant posters,			
	0.40	0.80	2.00
0-(2.50)	0.50	1.00	2.50
1-Gold embossed	3.00	6.00	15.00
1-Blue embossed	2.00	4.00	10.00
13-begin 2.25-C	0.50	0.90	2.25

COLLECTORS DRACULA, THE
1994-No. 2, 1994 (3.95, color/B&W, limited series, 52 pgs.)
Millennium Publications

	Good	Fine	N-Mint
1-Bolton-a (7 pgs.)	0.80	1.60	4.00

COLORS IN BLACK
Mar 1995-Jun 1995 (2.95, color, limited series:4)
Dark Horse Comics

	Good	Fine	N-Mint
1–4	0.60	1.20	3.00

COMBAT KELLY (...and the Deadly Dozen)
June, 1972-No. 9, Oct, 1973
Marvel Comics Group

	Good	Fine	N-Mint
1-Origin/1st app. Combat Kelly	1.00	2.00	5.00
2–9	0.30	0.60	1.50

COMICS' GREATEST WORLD (Also see Catalyst and X)
June, 1993-V4#4, Sept, 1993 (1.00, color)
Dark Horse Comics

Arcadia #1-4: 1-X; Frank Miller-c. 2-Pit Bulls. 4-Monster			
	0.60	1.20	3.00
3-Ghost;Dorman-c/Hughes-a	1.00	2.00	5.00
1-B&W press proof ed. (1,500 copies)	2.90	9.00	20.00
1-Silver-c; Distributor's retailer bonus w/print & cards			
	1.40	4.00	10.00
Retailers Premium Embossed Silver Foil Logo (r/1-4)			
	2.90	9.00	20.00
Golden City #1-4: 1-Rebel; Jerry Ordway-c. 2-Mecha; Dave Johnson-c.			
3-Titan; Simonson-c. 4-Catalyst; Perez-c	0.20	0.40	1.00
1-Gold -c; Distributor's retailer bonus w/print & cards			
	1.40	4.00	10.00
Retailer's Premium Embossed Gold Foil Logo (r/1-4)			
	2.90	9.00	20.00
Steel Harbor #2-4: 2-The Machine; Mignola-c. 3-Wolf Gang; Warner-c.			
4-Motorhead	0.20	0.40	1.00
1-Barb Wire; Dorman-c; Gulacy-p.	0.80	1.60	4.00
1-Silver-c; Distributor's retailer bonus w/print & cards			
	1.40	4.00	10.00
Retailer's Premium Red Foil Logo (r/1-4)	2.90	9.00	20.00
Vortex #1-4: 1-Division 13; Dorman-c. 2-Hero Zero; A. Adams-c.			
3-King Tiger; Chadwick-p; Darrow-c. 4-Vortex; F.Miller-c			
	0.20	0.40	1.00
1-Gold-c; Distributor's retailer bonus w/print & cards			
	1.40	4.00	10.00
Retailer's Premium Blue Foil Logo (r/1-4)	2.90	9.00	20.00

COMICS' GREATEST WORLD: OUT OF THE VORTEX (See Out Of The Vortex)

CONAN
Aug 1995-Present (2.95, color)
Marvel Comics

1—Hama-s	0.40	1.30	3.00

CONAN CLASSIC
June, 1994-Present (1.50, color)
Marvel Comics

1-r/Conan #1 by Barry Smith; r/original-c by Smith w/changes			
	0.30	0.60	1.50
2-11-r/Conan #2-11; B. Smith-a	0.30	0.60	1.50
2-Bound w/cover to Conan The Adventurer #2 by mistake			
	0.30	0.60	1.50

	Good	Fine	N-Mint
CONAN THE ADVENTURER			
June 1994-July 1995 (1.50, color)			
Marvel Comics			
1-(2.50)-Embossed foil-c; Kayaran-a	0.50	1.00	2.50
2–14; 14-final issue	0.30	0.60	1.50
2-Contents are Conan Classics #2 by mistake			
	0.30	0.60	1.50
CONAN THE BARBARIAN (See Savage Sword of Conan)			
Oct, 1970-No. 275, Dec, 1993 (See Giant-Size listing)			
Marvel Comics Group			
1-Origin/1st app. Conan by Barry Smith	25.00	75.00	225.00
2	9.00	28.00	85.00
3-Low distribution in some areas	18.00	55.00	165.00
4, 5	8.00	25.00	58.00
6–9	5.40	16.00	38.00
10, 11-(25¢ giants)	6.90	21.00	48.00
12, 13	3.90	11.60	27.00
14, 15-Elric app.	6.00	18.00	42.00
16, 19, 20	3.40	10.30	24.00
17, 18-No Smith art	1.80	5.00	11.00
21, 22: 22-Reprints story from #1	3.30	10.00	23.00
23-1st app. Red Sonja (2/73)	4.70	14.10	33.00
24-1st full Sonja story; last Smith art	3.90	11.60	27.00
25-Buscema-c/a begins	1.70	4.20	10.00
26-30	1.00	2.00	5.00
31-36, 38-40	0.60	1.20	3.00
37-Neal Adams-c/a; Last 20¢ issue	1.00	2.50	6.00
41-57, 59, 60: 44, 45-Adams inks. 48-Origin retold. 59-Origin Belit			
	0.40	0.80	2.00
58-2nd app. Belit (see Giant Size... #1)	0.60	1.20	3.00
61-99, 101-114, 116-199, 201-249, 251, 252: 242-Jim Lee-c.			
248-Art Adams-c. 252-Last 1.00-c	0.20	0.40	1.00
100-(52 pg. giant)-Death of Belit	0.60	1.20	3.00
115-Double size	0.20	0.50	1.20
200, 250-(1.50, 52 pgs.)	0.30	0.60	1.50
253-274	0.30	0.50	1.25
275-(2.50, 68 pgs.)-Last issue	0.50	1.00	2.50
King Size 1 (9/73)-Smith-r/#2, 4 plus-c	1.30	3.30	8.00
Annual 2 ('76)-New story	0.70	1.40	3.50
Annual 3 ('78)-Reprints	0.40	0.80	2.00
Annual 4-6 ('78, '79, '81)-New-a	0.30	0.60	1.50
Annual 7-12 ('82-'87)	0.30	0.50	1.25

Special Edition 1 (Red Nails)	0.70	1.40	3.50

CONAN THE KING
(Formerly King Conan)No. 20, Jan, 1984-No. 55, Nov, 1989
Marvel Comics

20-55: 48-55-(1.50)	0.30	0.60	1.50

CONCRETE (See Dark Horse Presents)
Mar, 1987-No. 10, Nov, 1988 (1.50, B&W)
Dark Horse Comics

1	2.00	5.00	12.00
1-2nd print	0.60	1.20	3.00
2	1.20	2.40	6.00
3-Origin	0.80	1.60	4.00
4–10	0.60	1.20	3.00
…: A New Life ('89, 2.95)-r/3, 4	0.60	1.20	3.00
…Celebrates Earth Day 1990 (3.50)	0.70	1.40	3.50
Color Special 1 (2/89, 2.95)	0.60	1.20	3.00
…: Eclectica 1, 2 (4/93-5/93, 2.95)	0.60	1.20	3.00
…: Fragile Creature 1-4 (2.50, 6/91- 2/92)	0.50	1.00	2.50
…: Land And Sea (2/89, 2.95)-r/1, 2	0.60	1.20	3.00
…: Odd Jobs 1 (7/90, 3.50)-r/5, 6	0.70	1.40	3.50

CONCRETE: KILLER SMILE
July, 1994-No. 4, Oct, 1994 (2.95, color, limited series)
Dark Horse Comics

1–4	0.60	1.20	3.00

COSMIC POWERS
Mar, 1994-No. 6, Aug, 1994 (2.50, color, limited series)
Marvel Comics

1-Featuring Thanos; Ron Lim-c/a(p)	0.50	1.00	2.50
2-6: 2-Terrax. 3-Jack of Hearts, Ganymede app.			
	0.50	1.00	2.50

COSMIC POWERS UNLIMITED
May 1995- (3.95, color, Quarterly)
Marvel Comics

1–	0.80	1.60	4.00

COYOTE
June, 1983-No. 16, Mar, 1986
Epic Comics (Marvel)

	Good	Fine	N-Mint
1-16: 11-1st McFarlane-a. 12-14-McFarlane-a			
	0.20	0.40	1.00

CRAZYMAN
May, 1993-No. 4, Jan, 1994 (2.50, color)
Continuity Comics

	Good	Fine	N-Mint
V2#1-Total book die cut	0.50	1.00	2.50
2-4: 2-(12/93)-Adams-c(p) & part scripts. 3-(12/93). 4-Indicia says #3,			
Jan. 1993	0.50	1.00	2.50

CREATURES ON THE LOOSE (Formerly Tower of Shadows)
No. 10, Mar, 1971-No. 37, Sept, 1975
Marvel Comics

	Good	Fine	N-Mint
10-First King Kull story; Wrightson-a	3.90	11.60	27.00
11-37: 16-Origin Warrior of Mars (1st app?) by G. Kane. 21, 22-Steranko-c.			
30-Manwolf begins	0.50	1.00	2.50

CREED
Jun 1995-Present (2.75, B&W)
Lightning Comics

	Good	Fine	N-Mint
1–	0.60	1.10	2.75

CREEPY (Also see Eerie)
1964-No. 145, Feb, 1983; No. 146, 1985 (B&W, Magazine)
Warren Publishing

	Good	Fine	N-Mint
1-Frazetta art (last story in comics)	11.00	32.00	75.00
2-Frazetta-c & 1 pg. strip (also in #7)	6.00	17.10	40.00
3-13: 3-7, 9-11-Frazetta-c	3.00	8.00	18.00
14-Adams' 1st Warren work	3.10	9.40	22.00
15-25: 15-17-Frazetta-c	1.70	4.20	10.00
26-31, 33-40: 27-Frazetta-c	1.50	4.00	9.00
32-Harlan Ellison story; Frazetta-c	1.30	3.00	8.00
41-47, 49-54, 56-61: 61-Wertham parody	1.30	3.30	8.00
48, 55, 65 (1973-75 Annuals)	1.50	4.00	9.00
62-64, 66-112,114-145: 125-All Adams-r issue. 139-All Toth-r issue.			
144-2.25-c giant; Frazetta-c	1.20	2.90	7.00
113-All Wrightson reprint issue	1.50	4.00	9.00
146-(2.95)	1.50	3.80	9.00
Year Book 1968, 1969	1.70	4.20	10.00
Yearbook 1970-Adams, Ditko-a	2.00	5.00	12.00
Annual 1971, 1972	1.70	4.20	10.00
1993 Fearbook ('93, 3.95)-Harris Publ.	1.20	2.40	6.00

CRISIS ON INFINITE EARTHS
Apr, 1985-No. 12, Mar, 1986 (12 issue maxi-series)
DC Comics

1	0.80	1.60	4.00
2-6	0.40	0.80	2.00
7-Death of Supergirl, double size	0.80	1.60	4.00
8-Death of Flash	1.00	2.00	5.00
9-11	0.40	0.80	2.00
12-Double size, Kid Flash becomes Flash	0.80	1.60	4.00

CRITTERS
1986-No. 50, 1989 (1.70/2.00, B&W)
Fantagraphics Books

1-Cutey Bunny, Usagi Yojimbo app.	0.50	1.00	2.50
2-11	0.40	0.80	2.00
12-22, 24-49	0.30	0.70	1.70
23-(3.95)-Alan Moore Flexi-disc	0.80	1.60	4.00
50-(4.95, 84 pgs.)	1.00	2.00	5.00
Special 1 (1/88, 2.00)	0.40	0.80	2.00

CROW, THE (See Caliber Presents)
Feb, 1989-No. 4, 1989 (1.95, B&W, mini-series)
Caliber Press

1	9.00	28.00	65.00
1-3-2nd printings	2.00	4.00	10.00
2, 4	5.00	13.00	30.00
2-3rd printing	2.00	4.00	10.00
3-Scarcer	4.60	13.70	32.00

CROW, THE
Jan, 1992-No. 3, 1992 (4.95, B&W, 68 pgs.)
Tundra Publishing, Ltd.

1-3-Reprints	2.00	5.00	12.00

CRUCIBLE
Feb, 1993-No. 6, July, 1993 (1.25, color)
DC Comics

1-(99¢)-Quesada-c(p) & layouts begin	0.20	0.40	1.00
2-6: 2-Last Quesada-c. 4-Last Quesada layouts			
	0.30	0.50	1.25

CRY FOR DAWN
1989-No. 9 (2.25, B&W, adult)

	Good	Fine	N-Mint
Cry For Dawn Pub.			
1	10.00	30.00	70.00
1-2nd, 3rd printing	1.00	2.00	5.00
2	10.00	25.00	60.00
2-2nd printing	0.60	1.20	3.00
3	5.80	14.60	35.00
4–6	4.00	8.00	20.00
7–9	1.60	3.20	8.00

CRYPT OF SHADOWS
Jan, 1973-No. 21, Nov, 1975
Marvel Comics

	Good	Fine	N-Mint
1-Wolverton-r/Advs. Into Terror #7	0.80	1.60	4.00
2-21: 2-Starlin/Everett-c	0.40	0.80	2.00

CURSE OF DREADWOLF
Sept, 1994 (2.75, B&W)
Lightning Comics

	Good	Fine	N-Mint
1	0.60	1.10	2.75

CURSE OF RUNE
May 1995-Present (2.50, color)
Malibu Comics

	Good	Fine	N-Mint
1-Two covers form one image	0.50	1.00	2.50

CURSE OF THE WEIRD
Dec, 1993-No. 4, Mar, 1994 (1.25, color, mini-series)
Marvel Comics

	Good	Fine	N-Mint
1-5: 1-Ditko/Heath/Wolverton pre-code horror/sci-fi-r. 4-Zombie-r by Everett. Wolverton r-1,3,4	0.30	0.50	1.25

CYBERFORCE
Oct, 1992-No. 4, 1993 (1.95, color, mini-series)
Image Comics

	Good	Fine	N-Mint
1-Coupon for Image #0; Silvestri-c/a in all	1.20	2.40	6.00
1-With coupon missing	0.40	0.80	2.00
2 (3/93)	0.40	0.80	2.00
3,4: 3-Pitt-c/story. 4-Foil-c; Stryke Force back-up (1st in comics)	0.40	0.80	2.00
0-(9/93, 1.95)-Walt Simonson-c/a/script	0.50	1.00	2.50

CYBERFORCE
Nov, 1993-Present (1.95, color)

Cyberforce #6 © Marc Silvestri

Cyberforce Universe #1 © Marc Silvestri

Image Comics
1-14: 1-7-Silvestri/Williams-c/a. 8-McFarlane-c;

10-variant painted-c	0.40	0.80	2.00
1-Goil logo	2.00	4.00	10.00
2-Silver embossed	2.00	4.00	10.00
3-Gold embossed	2.00	4.00	10.00

CYBERFORCE ORIGINS
Jan 1995(2.50, color)
Image Comics

1-Cyblade	0.50	1.00	2.50
2-Stryker	0.50	1.00	2.50

CYBERFORCE UNIVERSE SOURCEBOOK
Aug 1994 - Present (2.50, color)
Image Comics

1-(8/94) Silvestri-c	0.50	1.00	2.50
2-(2/95) Silvestri-c	0.50	1.00	2.50

D

DAMAGE
Apr, 1994-Present (1.75/1.95, color)
DC Comics

1–4	0.40	0.70	1.75
5,6: 5-Begin 1.95-c. 6-(9/94)-Zero Hour	0.40	0.80	2.00
0,7-12: 0-(10/94). 7-(11/94)	0.40	0.80	2.00
13-Begin 2.25-c; 14-Ray app. 15–	0.50	0.90	2.25

DANGER TRAIL
Apr, 1993-No. 4, July, 1993 (1.50, color, mini-series)
DC Comics

1-4: Gulacy-c	0.30	0.60	1.50

DANGER UNLIMITED
Feb, 1994-No. 4, May, 1994 (2.00, color, mini-series)
Dark Horse Comics (Legend imprint)

1-4: 1-1st app. Thermal; Byrne scripts; intro Torch of Liberty & Golgotha in back up. 2-Byrne-a. 3,4-Byrne-a/stories	0.40	0.80	2.00

DAREDEVIL (Also see Giant-Size Daredevil)
April, 1964-Present
Marvel Comics Group

1-Origin & 1st app. Daredevil; Everett-c/a	150.00	450.00	1350.00
2-Fantastic Four cameo; 2nd app. Electro (Spidey villain); Thing guest stars; Kirby c-2-4, 5p	40.00	119.00	395.00
3-Origin & 1st app. The Owl	28.00	83.00	275.00
4	27.00	80.00	265.00
5-Minor costume change; Wood-c/a begins	17.00	51.00	170.00
6, 8-10: 8-Origin & 1st app. Stiltman	10.00	36.00	120.00
7-Battles Sub-Mariner; new red costume	17.00	51.00	170.00
11-15: 12-Romita's 1st art at Marvel	7.00	22.00	65.00
16, 17-Spider-Man x-over in both. 16-1st Romita-a on Spider-Man (5/66)	8.00	24.00	80.00
18-20: 18-Origin/1st app. Gladiator	4.40	13.00	44.00
21-26, 28-30	4.00	8.00	30.00
27-Spider-Man x-over	3.50	11.00	35.00
31-40: 38-F.F. x-over. 39-1st app. Exterminator	2.20	7.00	22.00
41-49: 41-Death of Mike Murdock. 43-Origin partially retold; D.D. battles Capt. America	2.00	6.00	17.00
50-52: B. Smith art	2.00	6.00	20.00

132

53-Origin retold; last 12¢ issue	3.70	9.00	22.00
54-56, 58-60	1.70	4.20	10.00
57-Reveals identity to Karen Page	1.80	5.00	11.00
61-99: 81-Black Widow begins (11/71)	1.50	3.80	9.00
100-Origin retold	3.70	9.00	22.00
101-104, 106, 108-113, 115-120: 113-1st app. Deathstalker (cameo)			
	1.20	2.90	7.00
105-Origin Moondragon by Starlin (12/73); Thanos cameo in flashback			
(early app.)	1.40	4.00	10.00
107-Starlin-c; Thanos cameo	1.00	3.00	6.00
114-1st full app. Deathstalker	1.20	2.90	7.00
121-130, 133-137: 124-1st Copperhead	0.80	1.60	4.00
131-Origin/1st app. new Bullseye (see Nick Fury #15)			
	4.20	10.00	25.00
132-Bullseye app.	1.10	2.20	5.50
138-Byrne-a, Ghost Rider c/story; Death's Head app. (early)			
	1.70	5.10	12.00
139-157: 146-Bullseye app.	0.80	1.60	4.00
158-Frank Miller art begins (5/79)	5.70	17.00	40.00
159	2.40	7.30	17.00
160, 161	1.30	3.00	8.00
162-Ditko-c/a; no Miller-a	0.60	1.20	3.00
163, 164: 164-Origin retold; Wood-c(i)	1.20	2.90	7.00
165-167, 170	1.10	2.20	5.50
168-Intro/Origin Elektra	3.90	11.60	27.00
169-Elektra app.	1.30	3.00	8.00
171-175: 174, 175-Elektra	0.80	1.60	4.00
176-180: Elektra in all. 178-Cage app.	0.60	1.20	3.00
181-(52 pgs.)-Death of Elektra	1.30	3.00	7.50
182-184: Punisher app. by Miller	1.50	4.00	9.00
185-191: 190-(1.00, 52 pgs.)	0.40	0.80	2.00
192-195, 197-210: 197, 200-Bullseye app.	0.30	0.60	1.50
196-Wolverine app.	1.70	5.00	12.00
211-225	0.20	0.40	1.00
226-Frank Miller plots begin	0.40	0.80	2.00
227-Miller scripts begin	0.70	1.30	3.25
228-233: Last Miller scripts	0.50	0.90	2.25
234-237, 239, 240, 242-247: 234,235-Ditko-p			
	0.20	0.40	1.00
238-Mutant Massacre; Sabretooth-c/app.	1.00	2.50	6.00
241-Todd McFarlane art(p)	0.60	1.20	3.00
248, 249-Wolverine app.	1.00	2.50	6.00
250, 251, 253, 258: 250-1st Bullet	0.20	0.40	1.00

	Good	Fine	N-Mint
252-(52 pgs.)-Fall Of The Mutants	0.60	1.20	3.00
254-Origin/1st app. Typhoid Mary (5/88)	1.40	4.00	10.00
255-2nd app. Typhoid Mary	0.80	2.10	5.00
256-3rd app. Typhoid Mary	0.80	1.60	4.00
257-Punisher app. (x-over w/Punisher #10)	1.90	5.60	13.00
259, 260-Typhoid Mary app. 260-(52 pgs.)	0.60	1.20	3.00
261-291, 294, 296-299: 297-Typhoid Mary app. 264-Ditko-a(p)			
	0.20	0.40	1.00
292, 293-Punisher app. 292-Chichester scripts begin			
	0.40	0.80	2.00
295-Ghost Rider app.	0.50	1.00	2.50
300-(2.00, 52 pgs.)-Part 4 of Last Rites	0.60	1.20	3.00
301-318: 309-Punisher-c/story	0.30	0.50	1.25
319-Prologue "Fall From Grace;" Elektra app.	1.40	4.30	10.00
319-2nd printing w/black-c	0.30	0.50	1.25
320-"Fall from Grace" chapter 1, ends #325	1.30	3.00	8.00
321-(1.25)-Regular ed.; "Fall from Grace," chapter 2; 1st new costume;			
Venom app.	0.60	1.50	3.50
321-(2.00)-Glow-in-the-dark ed.	1.00	3.00	7.00
322-"Fall from Grace" chapter 3; Ed Brock app.			
	1.00	2.00	5.00
323, 324-"Fall from Grace" Ch. 4 & Ch. 5. 323-Vs. Venom-c/story.			
324-Morbius-c/story	0.40	0.80	2.00
325-(2.50, 52 pgs.)-Bound-in poster	0.50	1.00	2.50
326, 327: 326-New logo	0.30	0.50	1.25
328-343: 328-Begin 1.50-c; bound-in card sheet. 330-Gambit app.			
	0.30	0.60	1.50
Special 1 (9/67)-New story	4.00	12.00	28.00
Special 2, 3 (2/71, 1/72)-Reprints. 2-Wood-i	1.70	4.00	10.00
Annual 4 (10/76)	1.00	2.00	5.00
Annual 4 (#5, 1989)-Atlantis Attacks	0.50	1.00	2.50
Annual 6 ('90, 2.00)	0.40	0.80	2.00
Annual 7 ('91, 2.00)	0.40	0.80	2.00
Annual 8 ('92, 2.25)	0.50	0.90	2.25
Annual 9 ('93, 2.95)-Polybagged w/card	0.60	1.20	3.00
Annual 10 ('94, 2.95, 68 pgs.)	0.60	1.20	3.00
Daredevil/Punisher trade PB (4.95)	1.00	2.50	6.00
Daredevil/Punisher TPB, 2nd, 3rd prints	1.00	2.00	5.00
...: Fall from Grace TPB (19.95)-r/#319-325	2.90	8.60	20.00

DAREDEVIL THE MAN WITHOUT FEAR
Oct, 1993-No. 5, Feb, 1994 (2.95, color, mini-series)
Marvel Comics

1-5-Foil embossed etched-c; Miller scripts; Romita Jr/Williamson-c/a

| | 0.80 | 1.60 | 4.00 |

DARK, THE
Nov, 1990-No. 4, Feb, 1993; V2#1, May, 1993-V2#7 (1.95, color)
Continum Comics/August House

1-(2.00)-Bright-p; Panosian, Hanna-i; Stroman-c	0.40	0.80	2.00
2-(1/92, 2.25)-Stroman-c/a(p)	0.50	0.90	2.25
3,4-(2.50): 4-Perez-c & part-i	0.50	1.00	2.50
V2#1-Red foil Bart Sears-c	0.40	0.80	2.00
V2#1-Red non-foil variant-c	0.40	0.80	2.00
V2#1-2nd printing w/blue foil Sears-c	0.40	0.80	2.00
V2#2-6: 2-Stroman/Bryant-a. 3-6-Foil-c. 3-Perez-c(i). 4-Perez-c & part-i;			
bound-in trading cards. 5,6-Perez-c(i)	0.40	0.80	2.00
V2#7-(B&W)-Perez-c(i)	0.40	0.80	2.00
V#3-1-2:1-Foil-c w/bound in Foodang trading card w/Sears/a			
	0.50	1.00	2.50
…Convention Book 1 (Fall 1994, 2.00)-Perez-c			
	0.40	0.80	2.00
…Convention Book 2 (10/94, 2.00)-Perez-c(i)			
	0.40	0.80	2.00

DARKER IMAGE
Mar, 1993 (2.50, color, mini-series intended)
Image Comics

1-The Maxx by Kieth begins; 1st app. Bloodwulf by Liefeld & Deathblow			
by Lee & begin series; polybagged w/1 of 3 cards by Liefeld, Lee or Kieth			
	0.50	1.00	2.50
1-B&W interior pages w/silver foil logo	1.70	4.00	10.00

DARK FANTASIES
1994 (2.95, color)
Dark Fantasy

1-Test print run (3,000)-Linsner-c	1.70	4.00	10.00
1-Linsner-c	0.80	2.00	5.00
2-4-Deluxe, 4-(3.95)	0.80	2.00	5.00
2-4-Regular	1.20	1.00	3.00

DARKHAWK
Mar, 1991- Apr 1995 (1.00/1.25, color)
Marvel Comics
1-Origin/1st app. Darkhawk; Hobgoblin cameo

	Good	Fine	N-Mint
	0.70	2.10	5.00
2,3-Spider-Man, Hobgoblin app.	0.40	1.00	3.00
4–8; 6-Capt. America & D.D. x-over	0.30	0.80	2.00
9-Punisher x-over	0.30	0.80	2.00
10–12	0.40	0.80	2.00
13, 14-Venom-c/stories	0.40	0.80	2.00
15-24, 26-38: 23-25-Origin. 35-37-Venom 3 part story			
	0.30	0.50	1.25
25-(2.95, 52 pgs.)-Red foil-c w/double gatefold poster; origin of armor			
revealed	0.60	1.20	3.00
39-49: 39-Begin 1.50-c; bound-in card sheet; 48- Intro Overhawk			
	0.30	0.60	1.50
50-(2.50, 52 pgs)	0.50	1.00	2.50
Annual 1 ('92, 2.25)-Vs. Iron Man	0.50	1.00	2.50
Annual 2 ('93, 2.95)-Polybagged w/card	0.60	1.20	3.00
Annual 3 ('94, 2.95)	0.60	1.20	3.00

DARKHOLD: Pages From The Book of Sins
Oct, 1992-No. 16, Jan, 1994 (1.75, color)
Marvel Comics (Midnight Sons imprint #15 on)

1-(2.75, 52 pgs.)-Polybagged w/poster	0.60	1.10	2.75
2-10, 12-16: 3-Reintro Modred the Mystic. 15, 16-Siege of Darkness Pt. 4			
& 12. 15-Spot varnish-c	0.40	0.70	1.75
11-(2.25)-Outer-c is a Darkhold envelope made of black parchment			
w/gold ink	0.50	0.90	2.25

DARK HORSE COMICS
Aug, 1992-Present (2.50, color)
Dark Horse Comics

1-Dorman double gatefold-c; begin 3-part Timecop story, 1st app.			
	0.60	1.20	3.00
2-6, 11-25: 17-Begin 3 part Star Wars: Droids story; Droids-c. 19-Begin			
2-part X story plus-c. 25-Flip book	0.50	1.00	2.50
7-Begin Star Wars: Tales of the Jedi	1.00	2.00	5.00
8-1st app. X and begins	1.00	2.00	5.00
9, 10: 9-Star Wars ends. 10-X ends	0.60	1.20	3.00

DARK HORSE DOWN UNDER
June, 1994-No. 3, Oct, 1994 (2.50, B&W, limited series)
Dark Horse Comics

1–3	0.50	1.00	2.50

DARK HORSE PRESENTS

July, 1986-Present (1.50/2.25/2.50, B&W, mature)
Dark Horse Comics

1-1st app. Concrete	2.50	6.00	15.00
1-2nd printing ('88, 1.50)	0.50	1.00	2.50
1-3rd printing ('92, 2.25)	0.50	0.90	2.25
2-Concrete app.	1.20	3.00	7.00
3-Concrete app.	1.00	2.00	5.00
4, 5-Concrete app.	0.80	1.60	4.00
6-9: 6,8-Concrete app.	0.60	1.20	3.00
10-Mask	1.00	2.00	5.00
11-19,21-23: 11–19,21-Mask stories. 17-All Roachmill issue			
	0.40	0.80	2.00
20-(2.95, 68 pgs.)-Concrete, Flaming Carrot, Mask			
	0.60	1.20	3.00
24-Origin Aliens-c/story (11/88)	2.90	8.60	20.00
25-31, 33: 28-(2.95)	0.60	1.20	3.00
32-(3.50, 68 pgs.)-Annual	0.80	1.60	4.00
34- Aliens-c/story	0.80	2.00	5.00
35-Predator-c/story	0.80	2.00	5.00
36-1st Aliens vs. Predator story; painted-c	1.30	3.00	8.00
36-Line drawn-c version	1.00	2.50	6.00
37-39, 41, 44, 45, 47	0.40	0.80	2.00
40-(2.95, 52 pgs.)	0.60	1.20	3.00
42, 43-Aliens-c/stories	1.00	2.00	5.00
46-Prequel to new Predator II mini series	0.80	1.60	4.00
48-50: Contain trading cards	0.40	0.80	2.00
51-53: 51-Sin City by Frank Miller thru #62	0.60	1.20	3.00
54-Next Men by Byrne begins (9/91, 1st app.)			
	1.30	3.30	8.00
55-2nd app. Next Men	0.80	1.60	4.00
56-(3.95, 68 pgs.)-Annual; part I Aliens	0.80	1.60	4.00
57-(3.50, 52 pgs.)-Cover swipe/D.D. 1	0.70	1.40	3.50
58-66, 68-84-(2.25): 72-1st Eudaemon by Nelson, ends #74			
	0.50	0.90	2.25
67-(3.95, 68 pgs.)-Begin 3 part prequel to Predator: Race War			
	0.80	1.60	4.00
85-98: 85-Begin 2.50-c; 92,93,95-Too Much Coffee Man			
	0.50	1.00	2.50
Fifth Anniversary Special nn (4/91, 9.95)-Part 1 of Sin City by Frank Miller; Aliens, Aliens vs. Predator	1.70	4.00	10.00
...: Aliens Platinum Edition (1992)-r/DHP #24, 42, 43, 56 & Special			
	3.30	9.90	23.00

	Good	Fine	N-Mint

DARKMAN
Apr, 1993-No. 6, Sept, 1993 (2.95, color)
Marvel Comics

	Good	Fine	N-Mint
V2#1 (3.95, 52 pgs.)	0.80	1.60	4.00
2–6	0.60	1.20	3.00

DARK MANSION OF FORBIDDEN LOVE, THE
Sept-Oct, 1971-No. 4, Mar-Apr, 1972
National Periodical Publications

	Good	Fine	N-Mint
1	2.50	6.30	15.00
2-4: 2-Adams-c. 3-Jeff Jones-c	1.00	2.50	6.00

DARK SHADOWS
March, 1969-No. 35, Feb, 1976 (Photo covers, 1-7)
Gold Key

	Good	Fine	N-Mint
1-(30039-903)-With pull-out poster	27.00	81.00	190.00
1-Without pull-out poster	9.00	27.00	62.00
2	10.00	30.00	70.00
3-With pull-out poster attached	14.00	41.00	95.00
3-Without pull-out poster	6.60	20.00	46.00
4-7: Last photo covers	8.00	24.00	56.00
8–10	6.00	18.00	42.00
11–20	4.60	14.00	32.00
21-35	3.00	9.40	22.00
Story Digest (6/70)-Photo cover	7.90	24.00	55.00

DARK SHADOWS
June, 1992-No. 4, Spr, 1993 (2.50, color, mini-series)
Innovation

Dark Horse Comics #1 © DH

Darkman #3 © MEG

1-Based on 1991 NBC TV mini-series	0.60	1.20	3.00
2–4	0.50	1.00	2.50

DARK SHADOWS: BOOK TWO
1993-No. 4, July, 1993 (2.50, color, mini-series)
Innovation

1-4-Painted-c	0.50	1.00	2.50

DARK SHADOWS: BOOK THREE
Nov, 1993 (2.50, color)
Innovation

1-(Whole #9)	0.50	1.00	2.50

DARKSTARS, THE
Oct, 1992-Present (1.75/1.95, color)
DC Comics

1-Larry Stroman-c/a	0.50	1.00	2.50
2-21: 4-7-Travis Charest-a. 18-20-Flash app.	0.40	0.70	1.75
22-24: 22-Begin 1.95-c. 24-(9/94)-Zero Hour	0.40	0.80	2.00
0,25-30: 0-(10/94). 25-(11/94). 26-Starfire app.			
30-Green Lantern app.	0.40	0.80	2.00
31-vs. Darkseid, 32-Green Lantern app.;33,	0.50	0.90	2.25

DAWN
June, 1995-Present (2.95, color)
Sirius Entertainment

1-	0.60	1.20	3.00

DAZZLER, THE (See X-Men #130)
Mar, 1981-No. 42, Mar, 1986
Marvel Comics Group

1,2: X-Men app.	0.40	0.80	2.00
3-37, 39-42	0.20	0.40	1.00
38-Wolverine c/app.; X-Men app.	0.80	2.10	5.00

DC COMICS PRESENTS
July-Aug, 1978-No. 97, Sept, 1986
DC Comics

1-12, 14-25, 27-40, 42-71, 73-76, 79-84, 86-97: 1,2-4th Superman/Flash			
race	0.40	0.80	2.00
13-Legion Of Superheroes	0.40	0.80	2.00
26-1st app. New Teen Titans (10/80)	1.20	3.00	7.00

	Good	Fine	N-Mint
41-Superman/Joker-c/story	0.50	1.00	2.50
72-Joker/Phantom Stranger	0.50	1.00	2.50
77, 78-Animal Man app.	0.60	1.20	3.00
85-Swamp Thing by Alan Moore	0.60	1.20	3.00
Annual 1-4 (9/82-10/85)	0.20	0.50	1.20

DC 100 PAGE SUPER SPECTACULAR
1971-No. 13, 6/72; No. 14, 2/73-No. 22, 11/73
National Periodical Publications

	Good	Fine	N-Mint
4-Weird Mystery Tales	0.80	1.60	4.00
5-Love Stories (scarcer)	1.20	2.40	6.00
6-JLA, JSA app.; Adams-c	0.80	1.60	4.00
7-13: See individual titles for values			
14-Batman-r/Detective #31, 32	1.00	2.50	6.00
15-22: 20-Batman-r. 21-r/Brave & Bold #54	0.40	0.80	2.00

DC SILVER AGE CLASSICS
1992 (1.00, color)
DC Comics

	Good	Fine	N-Mint
...Action Comics 252; r/1st Supergirl	0.20	0.40	1.00
...Adventure Comics 247; r/1stLegion of SH	0.20	0.40	1.00
...Brave And The Bold 28; r/1st JLA	0.20	0.40	1.00
...Detective Comics 225; r/1stM.Manhunter	0.20	0.40	1.00
...Detective 327; r/1st new look Batman	0.20	0.40	1.00
...Green Lantern 76;r/1stAdams Gr. Lantern	0.20	0.40	1.00
...House Of Secrets 92; r/1st Swamp Thing	0.20	0.40	1.00
...Showcase 4; r/1st S.A. Flash	0.20	0.40	1.00
...Showcase 22; r/1st S.A. Green Lantern	0.20	0.40	1.00
...Sugar And Spike 99; two new stories	0.20	0.40	1.00

DC SPECIAL (Also see Super DC Special)
10-12/68-No. 15, 11-12/71; No. 16, Spr/75-No. 29, 8-9/77
National Periodical Publications

	Good	Fine	N-Mint
1-Batman-r; 25¢, 68 pg. Giant	1.30	3.30	8.00
2-15: 25¢, 68 pg. Giants. 15-(52 pgs.)	1.00	2.50	6.00
16-29: 25-27-Oversized. 27-Untold origin JSA. 29-Secret origin JSA			
	0.60	1.20	3.00

DC SPECIAL SERIES
Sept, 1977-No. 16, Fall, 1978; No. 17, Aug, 1979- No. 27, Fall, 1981
National Periodical Publications/DC Comics

	Good	Fine	N-Mint
1	0.60	1.20	3.00
2-r/Swamp Thing 1, 2 by Wrightson	0.60	1.20	3.00

3-20, 22-24: 16-Death of Jonah Hex. 19-Origin Batman/Superman team-r

	0.40	0.80	2.00
16-Death of Jonah Hex	1.60	3.20	8.00
21-1st Batman by Frank Miller	1.70	5.00	12.00
25, 26 (2.95)-Superman in each	0.60	1.20	3.00
27-(2.50)-Batman vs. Incredible Hulk	1.00	2.00	5.00

DC SUPER-STARS
March, 1976-No. 18, Winter, 1978 (#3-18: 52 pgs.)
National Periodical Publications/DC Comics

1-(68 pgs.)-Re-intro Old Teen Titans (predates Teen Titans #44, 11/76); tryout issue; also T.T. reprint	0.90	1.70	4.25
2-(68 pgs.)-r/Mystery in Space #90	0.20	0.40	1.00
3-7,9,11-14,16,18	0.20	0.40	1.00
8-r/1st Space Ranger/Showcase 15	0.70	1.40	3.50
10-Batman/Joker-c/story	0.80	1.60	4.00
15-Batman Spec.; Golden & Rogers-a	0.50	1.00	2.50
17-Secret Origins of Super-Heroes	0.40	0.80	2.00

DC UNIVERSE: TRINITY
Aug, 1993-No. 2, Sept, 1993 (2.95, color, 52 pgs.)
DC Comics

1,2-Foil covers; Gr. Lantern, Darkstars, Legion			
	0.60	1.20	3.00

DEADLY DUO, THE
Nov, 1994- Jan, 1995 (2.50, color, limited series)
Image Comics

1-3: 1-1st app. Kill Cat and Kid Avenger	0.50	1.00	2.50

DEADLY FOES OF SPIDER-MAN (See Lethal Foes of...)
May, 1991-No. 4, Aug, 1991 (1.00, color, mini-series)
Marvel Comics

1-4: 1-Punisher, Kingpin, Rhino app.	0.20	0.40	1.00

DEADLY HANDS OF KUNG-FU, THE (See Master of Kung-Fu)
Apr, 1974-No. 33, Feb, 1977 (B&W, Magazine, 75¢)
Marvel Comics

1-Shang-Chi, Master of Kung-Fu begins, Bruce Lee photo pin-up inside; ties for 3rd app. of Shang-Chi			
w/Master of Kung-Fu #17 (same date)	0.80	1.60	4.00
2, 3, 5	0.40	0.80	2.00
4-Bruce Lee-c by N. Adams, 8 pg. Lee biog.	0.60	1.20	3.00

	Good	Fine	N-Mint

DC Universe: Trinity #1 © DC

Deadpool #2 © MEG

6-15: 15-(Annual 1, Summer '75)-Origin Iron Fist; pre-dates Iron Fist #1
	0.40	0.80	2.00
16-19, 21-27, 29-33	0.30	0.60	1.50
20-Origin White Tiger, Perez-a	0.40	0.80	2.00

28-Origin Jack of Hearts; Bruce Lee life story
| | 0.60 | 1.20 | 3.00 |

Special Album Edition 1 (Summer, '74)-Iron Fist-c/story (3rd app.);
| Adams-i | 0.40 | 0.80 | 2.00 |

DEAD OF NIGHT
Dec, 1973-No. 11, Aug, 1975
Marvel Comics
| 1-Horror reprints | 0.60 | 1.20 | 3.00 |
| 2-11:11-Intro Scarecrow;Kane/Wrightson-c | 0.40 | 0.80 | 2.00 |

DEADPOOL
Aug, 1994-No. 4, Nov, 1994 (2.50, color, limited series)
Marvel Comics
| 1 | 1.00 | 2.00 | 5.00 |
| 2-4 | 0.60 | 1.20 | 3.00 |

DEADPOOL: THE CIRCLE CHASE (See The New Mutants #98)
Aug, 1993-No. 4, Nov, 1993 (2.00, color, mini-series)
Marvel Comics
| 1-(2.50)-Embossed-c | 0.50 | 1.00 | 2.50 |
| 2–4 | 0.40 | 0.80 | 2.00 |

DEADWORLD
Dec, 1986-No. 28?, 1992 (1.50, B&W)
Arrow Comics/Caliber Comics

1	0.80	1.60	4.00
2	0.60	1.20	3.00
3, 4	0.40	0.80	2.00
5-11: Normal-c	0.30	0.70	1.70
5-11: Graphic-c	0.40	0.80	2.00
12-28: Normal-c or Graphic-c	0.40	0.80	2.00
...Archives 1 (1992, 2.50)	0.40	0.80	2.00

DEATHBLOW (See Darker Image)
May, 1993 (April inside)-Present (1.75/1.95, color)
Image Comics

1-(2.50)-Red foil stamped logo on black varnish-c; Jim Lee-c/a; flip-book side has Cybernary-c/story	0.50	1.00	2.50
1-(1.95)-Newsstand ed. w/o foil & varnish	0.40	0.80	2.00
2-4: 2-Lee/Choi-a; Cybernary on flip side plus bound-in poster. 4-Jim Lee-c	0.40	0.70	1.75
2-(1.75)-Newsstand ed. w/o poster	0.40	0.70	1.75
3-low dist.	1.00	2.00	5.00
5-9-Jim Lee-c: 5-Begin 1.95-c	0.40	0.80	2.00
5-Alternate Portacio-c; cover forms larger picture when combined w/alternate Portacio-c for Gen 13 #5, Kindred #3, Stormwatch #10, Union #0, Wetworks #2, WildC.A.T.s #11 & Team 7 #1	1.40	4.00	10.00
10-16-(2.50-c) w/pinup poster by Tim Sale			
13-w/pinup poster by T.Sale & Jim Lee	0.50	1.00	2.50
16-(1.95)-Newsstand, WildStorm Rising pt.6	0.40	0.80	2.00
16-(2.50)-Direct Market, WildStorm Rising pt. 6	0.50	1.00	2.50

DEATHLOK (See Astonishing Tales)
July, 1990-No. 4, Oct, 1990 (3.95, limited series, 52 pgs.)
Marvel Comics

1-4	0.70	2.00	5.00

DEATHLOK
July, 1991-Present (1.75, color)
Marvel Comics

1-Silver ink cover	0.60	1.20	3.00
2-5: 5-X-Men, FF x-over	0.60	1.10	2.75
6-10: 6, 7-Punisher. 9, 10-Ghost Rider	0.40	0.80	2.00
11-18, 20-24, 26-34: 17-Jae Lee-c. 22-Black Panther. 27-Siege app.	0.40	0.70	1.75
19-(2.25)-Foil-c	0.50	0.90	2.25

	Good	Fine	N-Mint
25-(2.95, 52 pgs.)-Holo-grafx foil-c	0.60	1.20	3.00
Annual 1 ('92, 2.50)-Quesada-c(p)	0.50	1.00	2.50
Annual 2 ('93, 2.95)-Polybagged w/card; intro Tracer			
	0.60	1.20	3.00

DEATHLOK SPECIAL
May, 1991-No. 4, Late June, 1991 (Bi-weekly mini-series)
Marvel Comics

1-4: r/Deathlok 1-4 w/new covers	0.50	1.00	2.50
1-2nd printing (white cover)	0.50	0.90	2.25

DEATHMATE
Sept, 1993-Feb, 1994 (2.95, color, limited series)
Valiant/Image

Preview-(7/93, 8 pgs.)	0.20	0.40	1.00
Prologue (#1)-Silver foil; Lee/Layton-c; B. Smith/Lee-a; Liefeld-a(p)			
	0.60	1.20	3.00
Prologue-Special gold foil edition	1.40	4.00	10.00
Black (#2)-(9/93, 4.95, 52 pgs.)-Silvestri/Jim Lee-c; 1st app. Gen 13			
	1.00	2.00	5.00
Black-Special gold foil edition	2.10	6.00	15.00
Yellow (#3)-(10/93, 4.95, 52 pgs.)-Yellow foil-c; Indicia says Prologue			
Sept 1993 by mistake; 3rd app. Ninjak	0.80	1.60	4.00
Yellow-Special gold foil edition	1.40	4.00	10.00
Blue (#4)-(10/93, 4.95, 52 pgs.)-Thibert blue foil-c(i)			
	0.80	1.60	4.00
Blue-Special gold foil Edition	1.40	4.00	10.00
Red (#5)	0.80	1.60	4.00
Epilogue (#6)-(2/94, 2.95)-Silver Foil; Quesada/Silvestri-c;			
Silvestri-a(p)	0.60	1.20	3.00

DEATH RACE 2020
Apr, 1995- (2.50, color)
Roger Corman's Cosmic Comics

1,2-Sequel to Movie	0.50	1.00	2.50

DEATH RATTLE
1986-?
Kitchen Sink

1-7	0.40	0.80	2.00
8-(12/86)-1st app. Xenozoic Tales/Cadillacs & Dinosaurs by Mark Schultz			
	1.00	2.00	5.00

DEATH'S HEAD (See Dragon's Claws & The Incomplete...)
Dec, 1988-No. 10, Sept, 1989 (1.75, color)
Marvel Comics UK, Ltd.

1-Dragon's Claws spinoff	0.70	2.00	5.00
2-Dragon's Claws x-over	0.80	1.60	4.00
3–10: 9-Simonson-c(p); F.F. guests	0.40	0.80	2.00
…Gold 1 (1/94, 3.95, 68 pgs.)-Gold foil-c	0.80	1.60	4.00

DEATH'S HEAD II
Mar, 1992-No. 4, June, 1992 (1.75, color, mini-series)
Marvel Comics UK, Ltd.

1	1.20	3.00	7.00
1, 2-Silver 2nd printings (1.75-c)	0.40	0.70	1.75
2–4	0.80	1.60	4.00

DEATH'S HEAD II
Dec, 1992-Present (1.75/1.95, color)
Marvel Comics UK, LTD.

V2#1-5: 1-4-X-Men app.	0.40	0.70	1.75
V2#6-13,15,16: 6-Begin 1.95-c	0.40	0.80	2.00
14-(2.95)-Foil flip-c w/Death's Head II Gold #0			
	0.60	1.20	3.00

DEATHSTROKE: THE TERMINATOR
(…, The Hunted #0 on)
(See Marvel & DC..., New Teen Titans & Tales of the Teen Titans)
Aug, 1991-Present (1.75, color)
DC Comics

1-Mike Zeck c-1-28	1.00	2.00	5.00
1-Gold 2nd printing	0.30	0.60	1.50
2	0.60	1.20	3.00
3–5	0.40	0.80	2.00
6-37: 7,9-Batman-c/story. 9-1st new Vigilante (cameo). 10-1st full app.			
Vigilante (female)	0.40	0.70	1.75
38-40: 38-Begin 1.95-c. 40-(9/94)	0.40	0.80	2.00
0,41-47: 0-(10/94)-Begin Deathstroke, The Hunted. 41-(11/94)			
	0.40	0.80	2.00
48-Begin 2.25-c, 49–	0.50	0.90	2.25
50-(3.50)	0.70	1.40	3.50
Annual 1 ('92, 3.50)-New Vigilante app.	0.70	1.40	3.50
Annual 2 ('93, 3.50)-Bloodlines Deathstorm	0.70	1.40	3.50
Annual 3 ('94, 3.95, 68 pgs.)-Elseworlds-story			
	0.80	1.60	4.00

	Good	Fine	N-Mint
Annual 4 ('95, 3.95)-Year One story	0.80	1.60	4.00

DEATH: THE HIGH COST OF LIVING (See Books of Magic & Sandman #8)
March, 1993-No.3, May, 1993 (1.95, color)
DC Comics (Vertigo)

1-Neil Gaiman scripts in all	1.00	2.50	6.00
1-Platinum	7.10	21.00	50.00
2	1.40	2.80	7.00
3-Pgs. 19 & 20 out of sequence	0.80	1.60	4.00
3-Corrected version w/no price & contains ads for Sebastion O & the Geek			
	0.60	1.20	3.00
TPB (6/94, 12.95)-r/1-3 & Death Talks about Life; prism-c; published by Titan Books	1.90	5.60	13.00

DEATHWISH
Dec, 1994-Present (2.50, color)
DC Comics

1-4	0.50	1.00	2.50

DEFENDERS, THE (See Marvel Feature & Secret Defenders)
Aug, 1972-No. 152, Feb, 1986
Marvel Comics Group

1-Hulk, Dr. Strange, Sub-Mariner begin	9.00	28.00	65.00
2-Silver Surfer x-over	4.60	14.00	32.00
3-5: 3-Silver Surfer x-over	3.00	9.00	21.00
6-9: 6, 8-Silver Surfer x-over	2.30	6.90	16.00
10-Thor vs. Hulk Battle	4.00	10.70	25.00
11-14: 11-Surfer x-over. 12-Last 20¢ issue	1.50	3.80	9.00
15, 16-Magneto app.	1.70	5.00	12.00
17-20: 17-Power Man x-over (11/74)	1.20	3.00	7.00
21-25: 24, 25-Son of Satan app.	1.00	2.50	6.00
26-29: Guardians Of The Galaxy app. 28-1st full app. Starhawk (#27 is a cameo). 29-Starhawk joins Guardians	1.60	4.70	11.00
30-50: 47-49-Early Moon Knight app. (5-7/77)			
	0.90	1.80	4.50
51-60	0.80	1.60	4.00
61-75: 73-75-Foolkiller app.	0.70	1.40	3.50
76-95, 97-124, 126-149, 151: 101-Silver Surfer app. 105-Son of Satan joins. 122-Final app. Son of Satan	0.40	0.90	2.20
96-Ghost Rider app.	0.90	1.80	4.50
125-Double size; Intro new Defenders	0.60	1.20	3.00
150-Double size	0.60	1.20	3.00
152-Double-size; X-Factor app.	0.60	1.20	3.00

Annual 1 (1976)-All new story and art	0.80	1.60	4.00

Giant Size 1-5: See Giant-Size listing

DEMOLITION MAN
Nov, 1993-No. 4, Feb, 1994 (1.75, color, mini-series)
DC Comics

1-4-Movie adaptation	0.40	0.70	1.75

DEMON, THE
Aug-Sept, 1972-No. 16, Jan, 1974
National Periodical Publications

1-Origin; Kirby-c/a in all	4.30	12.90	30.00
2–5	2.50	6.30	15.00
6–16	1.70	4.20	10.00

DEMON, THE
Nov–Feb 1986 (.75, color, limited series)
DC Comics

1–4-Matt Wagner	0.40	0.80	2.00

DEMON, THE
July, 1990-Present (1.50/1.95, color)
DC Comics

1-Grant scripts begin	0.40	0.70	1.80
2-18, 20,21,23-27: 12-Bisley-c. 12-15,21-Lobo app.	0.30	0.60	1.60
19 (2.50, 44 pgs.)-With Lobo mini-poster	0.60	1.20	3.00
22-Matt Wagner	0.40	0.80	2.00
28-47 (1.75-c): 31, 33-39-Lobo app. 46-Haunted Tank-c/story; also in #47, 48	0.40	0.70	1.75
48,49,51: 48-Begin 1.95-c. 51-(9/94)	0.40	0.80	2.00
50-(2.95, 52 pgs.)	0.60	1.20	3.00
0,52-57: 0-(10/94). 52-(11/94)	0.40	0.80	2.00
Annual 1 ('92, 3.00)-Eclipso-c/story	0.60	1.20	3.00
Annual 2 ('93, 3.50)	0.70	1.40	3.50

DEMONIQUE
Oct, 1994 (3.00, B&W, limited series: 4, Adult)
London Night Studios

1-4	0.60	1.20	3.00

DESTROYER, THE
Apr 1995 - Present (2.95, color))

	Good	Fine	N-Mint
Valiant			
#0-Indicia indicates issue #1	0.60	1.20	3.00

DESTROYER DUCK
Feb, 1982-No. 7, May, 1984
Eclipse Comics

	Good	Fine	N-Mint
1-1st app. Groo the Wanderer; D.D. origin	0.60	1.20	3.00
2-7: Kirby c/a-1-5. 7-Miller-c	0.20	0.40	1.00

DETECTIVE COMICS
No. 217, Mar, 1955-Present
National Periodical Publications/DC Comics

	Good	Fine	N-Mint
217-224: 217-1st code approved issue	34.00	101.00	235.00
225-Origin&1st app.Martian Manhunter	270.00	800.00	4000.00
226-Manhunter origin cont. (2nd app.)	130.00	390.00	910.00
227-229:Martian Manhunter stories in all	51.00	154.00	360.00
230-1st app. Mad Hatter	53.00	159.00	370.00
231-Brief origin recap Martian Manhunter	33.00	99.00	230.00
232, 234, 237-240: 239-Grey tone-c	31.00	92.00	215.00
233-Origin & 1st app. Batwoman	132.00	396.00	925.00
235-Origin Batman and his costume	60.00	170.00	390.00
236-John Jones talks to Mars & parents	36.00	109.00	255.00
241-260	25.00	75.00	175.00
261-264, 266, 269, 270	19.00	58.00	135.00
265-Batman origin retold w/new data	29.00	88.00	205.00
267-Origin & 1st app. Batmite	26.00	79.00	185.00
268, 271-Manhunter origin retold	19.00	57.00	132.00
272, 274-280: 276-2nd Batmite	14.30	43.00	100.00
273-J'onn J'onnz id revealed for 1st time	15.00	46.00	108.00
281-292, 294-297: 287-Origin J'onn J'onzz retold.			
297-Last 10¢ issue(11/61)	11.00	33.00	78.00
293-(7/61)-Aquaman begins (pre #1)	12.00	36.00	85.00
298-1st modern Clayface	24.00	71.00	165.00
299, 300: 300-(2/62)-Aquaman ends	8.00	24.00	55.00
301-Manhunter returns home to Mars (3/62); 1st since stranded on Earth			
6 years before	7.40	22.00	52.00
302-326, 329, 330	5.40	16.00	38.00
327-1st new look Batman w/new costume (5/64); Elongated Man begins,			
ends #383	11.00	32.00	75.00
328-Death of Alfred	9.00	28.00	65.00
331, 333-340, 342-358, 360-364, 366-368, 370: 362, 364-Early S.A.			
Riddler app.	3.60	10.70	25.00
332,341,365-Joker-c/stories	4.60	14.00	32.00

359-Intro/origin new Batgirl (1/67)	6.60	20.00	46.00
369-N. Adams-a; 3rd app. SA Catwoman (cameo, 11/67); leads into			
Batman #197; 4th app. new Batgirl	6.00	17.00	40.00
371-1st new Batmobile fromTVshow(1/68)	3.60	10.70	25.00
372-386, 389, 390: 377-Early S.A. Riddler app.			
	2.10	6.00	15.00
387-Reprints 1st Batman story from Detective 27; Joker-c			
	5.40	16.00	38.00
388-Joker-c/story; last 12¢ issue	4.00	10.70	25.00
391-394, 396, 398, 399	2.00	5.00	12.00
395, 397-Adams-a	2.40	7.30	17.00
400-Origin/1st app. Man Bat; Adams-a	5.70	17.00	40.00
401, 403, 405, 406, 409	1.80	4.60	11.00
402, 404, 407, 408, 410: Adams-a	2.10	6.40	15.00
411-420: 413-Last 15¢ issue	1.70	4.20	10.00
421-436: 428, 434-Hawkman begins, ends #467			
	1.50	3.80	9.00
437-New Manhunter begins, ends #443	1.60	5.00	11.00
438-445: 100 Page Super Spectaculars	2.50	6.00	15.00
446-460: 457-Origin retold & updated	1.30	3.00	7.50
461-465, 469, 470, 480	1.20	2.40	6.00
466-468, 471-474, 478, 479: Rogers-a	1.90	6.00	13.00
475, 476-Joker-c/stories; Rogers-a	4.00	10.70	25.00
477-Adams, Rogers-a	2.30	6.90	16.00
481-Begin 1.00-c issues; Rogers-a	1.80	5.00	11.00
482-Starlin/Russell/Golden-a	1.30	3.00	7.50
483-40th anniversary issue; origin retold	1.50	3.80	9.00
484-499: 484-Origin Robin	0.90	1.80	4.50
500-(1.50, 52 pgs.)-Kubert Hawkman story; cover states in error that this			
is 500th anniversary of Det. Comics(see #572)			
	1.80	4.60	11.00
501-503, 505-523	0.80	1.60	4.00
504-Joker-c/story	1.20	2.90	7.00
524-2nd app. Jason Todd (cameo)	1.00	2.00	5.00
525-Jason Todd app. (3rd)	0.80	1.60	4.00
526-(1.50, 68 pgs.)-Batman's 500th app. in Detective Comics;			
Joker-c/story	2.60	7.70	18.00
527-531, 533, 534, 536-568, 571, 573	0.60	1.10	2.75
532, 569, 570-Joker-c/stories	1.20	2.40	6.00
535-Intro new Robin (Jason Todd); first appeared in Batman			
	1.00	2.00	5.00
572-(3/87, 1.25, 60 pgs.)-50th anniv. Detective			
	0.70	1.40	3.50

	Good	Fine	N-Mint

Detective Comics #604 © DC   Detective Comics #677 © DC

	Good	Fine	N-Mint
574-Origin Batman & Jason Todd retold	1.00	2.00	5.00
575-Year 2 begins	2.00	6.00	14.00
576-578: McFarlane-c/a; last Year 2	1.70	5.00	12.00
579-597, 601-610: 604, 607-Batman poster	0.30	0.60	1.50
598-(2.95, 84 pgs.)-Blind Justice begins	1.00	2.50	6.00
599	0.80	1.60	4.00
600-(5/89, 2.95)-50th Anniv. of Batman	1.00	2.50	6.00
611-625, 628-658: 644-Last 1.00-c	0.30	0.50	1.25
626-Batman's 600th app. in Det. Comics	0.30	0.50	1.25
627-(2.95, 84 pgs.)-r/1st story Detective #27 supposedly celebrating			
Batman's 600th app. in Det.	0.70	1.40	3.50
659-Knightfall Pt. 2; Kelley Jones-c (also 661, 663-675)			
	1.40	2.80	7.00
660-Knightfall Pt. 4; Bane-c by Kieth	1.20	2.90	7.00
661-664-Knightfall Pts. 6,8,10,12: 661-Brief Joker, Riddler app. 662-Riddler			
app.; Kieth-c. 664-Bane-c/sty; Joker app.; cont'd in Showcase 93 #'s 7, 8			
	0.80	1.60	4.00
665,666-Knightfall Pt. 16 & 18. 666-Bane-c/sty			
	0.50	1.00	2.50
667, 668: 667-Begin Knightquest: the Crusade			
	0.40	0.70	1.75
669-675: 669-Knightquest; cont'd in Robin #1. 673-Joker-c/story			
	0.40	0.70	1.75
675-(2.95)-Collectors Ed. w/foil-c	0.60	1.20	3.00
676-(2.50, 52 pgs.)-KnightsEnd Pt.3	0.50	1.00	2.50
677,678: 677-KnightsEnd Pt. 9. 678-(9/94)-Zero Hour			
	0.30	0.60	1.50
0,679-684: 0-(10/94). 679-(11/94) 682-Troika Pt. 3			
	0.30	0.60	1.50
682-(2.50) Embossed-c Troika Pt. 3	0.50	1.00	2.50

686-Begin 1.95-c; 687,688–	0.40	0.80	2.00
Annual 1 ('88, 1.50)	1.00	2.00	5.00
Annual 2 ('89, 2.00, 68 pgs.)	0.80	1.60	4.00
Annual 3 ('90, 2.00, 68 pgs.)	0.40	0.80	2.00
Annual 4 ('91, 2.00, 68 pgs.)	0.40	0.80	2.00
Annual 5 ('92, 2.50)-Sam Kieth-c; Joker-c/sty			
	0.50	1.00	2.50
Annual 6 ('93, 2.50)-Bloodlines; Azrael as Batman in new costume			
	0.50	1.00	2.50
Annual 7 ('94, 2.95, 68 pgs.)-Elseworlds story			
	0.60	1.20	3.00
Annual 8 ('95, 3.95, 68 pgs.)-Year One	0.80	1.60	4.00

DETONATOR
Dec 1994 (2.95, color, Limited series:2)
Chaos Comics

1-2-Pulido/s - S.Hughes/a	0.60	1.20	3.00

DEVIL DINOSAUR
April, 1978-No. 9, Dec, 1978
Marvel Comics Group

1-9: Kirby/Royer-a in all; Kirby-c all	0.60	1.20	3.00

DINO (TV)(The Flintstones)
Aug, 1973-No. 20, Jan, 1977 (Hanna-Barbera)
Charlton Publications

1	1.10	2.70	6.50
2–20	0.70	1.40	3.50

DIATOM
Apr 1995–Present (4.95, limited series)
Photographics

1-Photo/computer-a	1.00	2.00	5.00

DISNEY AFTERNOON, THE
Nov, 1994-Present (1.50, color)
Marvel Comics
1-9: 3-w/bound in Power Ranger Barcode Card

	0.30	0.60	1.50

DISNEY'S ALADDIN
Oct, 1994-Present (1.50, color)
Marvel Comics

	Good	Fine	N-Mint
1–11	0.30	0.60	1.50

DISNEY'S BEAUTY AND THE BEAST
Sept, 1994-Present (1.50, color)
Marvel Comics

| 1–12 | 0.30 | 0.60 | 1.50 |

DISNEY'S POCAHONTAS
1995 (4.95, color)
Marvel Comics

| 1–Movie Adaptation | 1.00 | 2.00 | 5.00 |

DISNEY'S THE LION KING
July, 1994-No. 2, July, 1994 (1.50, color)
Marvel Comics

| 1,2: 2-part story | 0.30 | 0.60 | 1.50 |
| 1-(2.50, 52 pgs)-Complete story | 0.50 | 1.00 | 2.50 |

DISNEY'S THE LITTLE MERMAID
Sept, 1994-Present (1.50, color)
Marvel Comics

| 1–12 | 0.30 | 0.60 | 1.50 |

DISNEY'S THE THREE MUSKETEERS
Jan, 1994-No. 2, Feb, 1994 (1.50, limited series)
Marvel Comics

| 1, 2-Movie adaptation; Spiegle-a | 0.30 | 0.60 | 1.50 |

DIVISION 13
Sept, 1994-Present (2.50, color)
Dark Horse Comics

| 1-4: 1-Art Adams-c | 0.50 | 1.00 | 2.50 |

DOC SAVAGE
Nov, 1966
Gold Key

| 1-Adapt. of the Thousand-Headed Man | 9.00 | 26.00 | 60.00 |

DOC SAVAGE (Also see Giant-Size Doc Savage)
Oct, 1972-No. 8, Jan, 1974
Marvel Comics Group

| 1 | 1.30 | 3.00 | 8.00 |
| 2-8: 2, 3-Steranko-c | 1.00 | 2.00 | 5.00 |

DOC SAVAGE
Aug, 1975-No. 8, Spring, 1977 (B&W, magazine)
Marvel Comics Group

1-Cover from movie poster	0.80	1.60	4.00
2–8	0.50	1.00	2.50

DOC SAVAGE
Nov, 1987-No. 4, Feb, 1988 (1.75, color, mini-series)
DC Comics

1–4	0.40	0.70	1.75

DOC SAVAGE
Nov, 1988-No. 24, Oct, 1990 (1.75/2.00 #13 on, color)
DC Comics

1–24	0.40	0.80	2.00
Annual 1 (1989, 3.50, 68 pgs.)	0.70	1.40	3.50

DOCTOR SOLAR, MAN OF THE ATOM
(Also see The Occult Files of Dr. Spektor & Solar)
10/62-No. 27, 4/69; No. 28 4/81-No. 31, 3/82
Gold Key/Whitman No. 28-on (Painted-c No. 1-27)

1-(#10000-210)-Origin/1st app. Dr. Solar (1st original Gold Key character)	40.00	120.00	280.00
2-Prof. Harbinger begins	13.00	39.00	90.00
3,4	9.00	26.00	60.00
5-Intro Man of Atom in costume	9.00	27.00	63.00
6–10	5.70	17.00	40.00
11-14, 16-20	4.70	14.00	33.00
15-Origin retold	6.30	19.00	44.00
21-27: 27-(1969)	3.00	9.40	22.00
28-31: 28-(1981). 29-Magnus begins	1.70	4.20	10.00

DOCTOR SOLAR, MAN OF THE ATOM
1990-No. 2, 1991 (7.95, color, card stock-c, high quality)
Valiant Comics

1,2-Reprints Gold Key Series	1.30	3.30	8.00

DOCTOR STRANGE (Formerly Strange Tales; see Giant-Size...)
No. 169, 6/68-No. 183, 11/69; No. 1, 6/74-No. 81, 2/87
Marvel Comics

169-Origin retold (1st series)	18.00	54.00	125.00
170-176	6.00	18.00	42.00
177-New Costume	5.30	16.00	37.00
178-183: 179-Spider-Man-r; B. Smith-c	4.90	15.00	34.00

	Good	Fine	N-Mint
1-(2nd series, 6/74)	4.60	14.00	32.00
2: Brunner a-1-5; c-1-6	2.40	7.30	17.00
3-5: 4-Neal Adams-a(i)	1.30	3.00	8.00
6-10: 8-10-G. Kane-c(p)	1.00	2.50	6.00
11-20: 14-Dracula app.	1.00	2.00	5.00

21-26: 21-Origin-r/169. 23,26-Starlin-a. 25,26-Starlin-c

	0.80	1.60	4.00

27-77, 79-81: 56-Origin retold. 58-Reintro Hannibal King (cameo).
  59-Full app. Hannibal King. 59-62-Darkhold storyline w/Dracula app.
  61,62-Dr. Strange, Blade, Hannibal King & Frank Drake team up to battle
  Dracula. 62-Death of Dracula & Lilith

	0.30	0.60	1.50
78-New costume	0.50	1.00	2.50
Annual 1 (1976)-New Russell-a	0.80	1.60	4.00
.../Silver Dagger Special Edition 1 (3/83, 2.50)			
	0.50	1.00	2.50

DOCTOR STRANGE/GHOST RIDER SPECIAL
Apr, 1991 (1.50, color)
Marvel Comics

1-Same cover/contents as D.S.S.S #28	0.80	1.60	4.00

DOCTOR STRANGE, SORCERER SUPREME (3rd series)
Nov, 1988-Present (1.25/1.50/1.95, color)
Marvel Comics (Midnight Sons imprint #60 on)

1	0.80	1.60	4.00

2-9, 12-14, 16-27, 29, 30: 14-18-Morbius 5-part story

	0.30	0.60	1.50
10-Re-intro Morbius w/new costume (11/89)			
	0.40	0.80	2.00
11-Hobgoblin app.	1.00	2.00	5.00

Doctor Strange #169 © MEG

Doctor Strange Sorcerer Supreme #69 © MEG

15-Unauthorized Amy Grant photo cover	0.80	2.10	5.00
28-Ghost Rider app.; has same cover & contents as Dr. Strange/Ghost Rider Special	0.80	1.60	4.00
31-36-Infinity Gauntlet x-over: 33-Thanos-c. 36-Warlock app.	0.60	1.20	3.00
37-49, 51-64: 41-Wolverine-c/sty. 52,53-Morbius-c/sty. 60, 61-Siege of Darkness Pt. 7 & 15. 60-Spot varnish-c. 61-New Dr. Strange begins (cameo). 62-Dr. Doom & Morbius app.	0.40	0.70	1.75
50-(2.95, 52 pgs.)-Holo-grafx foil-c	0.60	1.20	3.00
65-74, 76-79: 65-Begin 1.95-c; bound-in card sheet. 72-Silver ink-c	0.40	0.80	2.00
75-(2.50)	0.50	1.00	2.50
75-(3.50)-Foil cover	0.70	1.40	3.50
...Ashcan ('95, .75)	0.20	0.30	0.75
Annual 2 ('92, 2.25)-Return Of The Defenders	0.50	0.90	2.25
Annual 3 ('93, 2.95)-Polybagged w/card	0.60	1.20	3.00
Annual 4 ('94, 2.95, 68 pgs.)	0.60	1.20	3.00

DR. STRANGE VS. DRACULA
Mar, 1994 (1.75, color, 52 pgs.)
Marvel Comics

1-r/Tomb of Dracula #44 & Dr. Str. #14	0.40	0.70	1.75

DR. WEIRD SPECIAL
Feb, 1994 (3.95, B&W, one-shot, 68 pgs.)
Big Bang Comics

1-Origin-r by Starlin; Starlin-c	0.80	1.60	4.00

DOMINIQUE: KILLZONE
May 1995-Present (2.95, B&W)
Caliber Comics

1	0.60	1.20	3.00

DONATELLO
Aug, 1986 (1.50, B&W, one-shot)
Mirage Studios

1	0.80	2.00	5.00

DONNA MATRIX
Aug, 1993 (2.95, color, 52 pgs.)
Reactor, Inc.

1-Computer generated 3-D effects	0.60	1.20	3.00

	Good	Fine	N-Mint

DON SIMPSON'S BIZARRE HEROES
May, 1994-Present (2.95, B&W, adult)
Fiasco Comics

	Good	Fine	N-Mint
1-10: 1,2-Megaton Man-c/story	0.60	1.20	3.00
#0-r/Bizarre Heroes #1 (1990)	0.60	1.20	3.00

DOOM PATROL, THE (Formerly My Greatest Adventure)
Mar, 1964-No. 124, June-July, 1973
National Periodical Publications

	Good	Fine	N-Mint
86	12.60	38.00	88.00
87-99: 99-Intro Beast Boy who later became The Changeling			
	8.00	25.00	58.00
100-Origin Beast Boy (12/65)	9.00	28.00	65.00
101-110	4.60	14.00	32.00
111-120	3.60	10.70	25.00
121-Death of Doom Patrol (9-10/68)	10.00	30.00	70.00
122-124: Reprints (1973)	0.50	1.00	2.50

DOOM PATROL
Oct, 1987-Present
DC Comics (Vertigo imprint #64 on)

	Good	Fine	N-Mint
1	0.40	0.80	2.00
2–18	0.20	0.40	1.00
19-New format and Morrison scripts begin	1.40	4.30	10.00
20-25	1.00	2.50	6.00
26-30	0.80	1.60	4.00
31-40	0.40	0.80	2.00
41-49, 51-56, 58-60: 53-Steacy-a	0.40	0.70	1.80
50, 57-(2.50, 52 pgs.)	0.50	1.00	2.50
61-65 (1.75-c): 64, 75-Bolland-c	0.40	0.70	1.80
66-87: 66-Begin 1.95-c. 70-Photo-c. 73-Death cameo (2 panels)			
	0.40	0.80	2.00
Annual 1 ('88, 1.50, 52 pgs.)	0.30	0.60	1.60
Annual 2 ('94,3.95,68 pgs.)-Children's Crusade			
	0.80	1.60	4.00
...And Suicide Squad Special 1 (1988, 1.50, 52 pgs.)-No Morrison scripts			
	0.30	0.60	1.60

DOOMSDAY + 1 (See Charlton Bullseye)
July, 1975-No. 6, June, 1976; No. 7, June, 1978-No. 12, May, 1979
Charlton Comics

	Good	Fine	N-Mint
1: 1-5 are 25¢ issues: Byrne-c/a in all	1.20	2.90	7.00
2	1.00	2.00	5.00

Doom 2099 #21 © MEG

Dracula #1 © Malibu

3-6: 4-Intro Lor. 6-Begin 30¢ issues	0.60	1.20	3.00
V3#7-12: Reprints #1-6	0.30	0.60	1.60
Modern Comics Reprint 5 (1977)	0.20	0.40	1.00

DOOM'S IV
July, 1994-Present (2.50, color)
Image Comics

1-4: 1,2-Liefeld story	0.50	1.00	2.50
1,2-Two alternate Liefeld-c each; 4 covers form one picture			
	1.00	2.00	5.00

DOOM 2099 (See Marvel Comics Presents #118)
Jan, 1993-Present (1.25/1.50, color)
Marvel Comics

1-(1.75)-Silver foil stamped-c	0.60	1.20	3.00
1-2nd printing (1.75)	0.40	0.70	1.75
2-16: 14-Ron Lim-c(p)	0.30	0.50	1.25
17-24, 26-28: 17-Begin 1.50-c; bound-in card sheet			
	0.30	0.60	1.50
25-(2.25-c, 52 pgs)	0.50	0.90	2.25
25-(2.95-c, 52 pgs) Foil embossed cover	0.60	1.20	3.00
29-32-(1.95-c)	0.40	0.80	2.00
29-acetate cover (3.50)	0.70	1.40	3.50

DOUBLE-DARE ADVENTURES
Dec, 1966-No. 2, March, 1967 (35¢-25¢, 68 pgs.)
Harvey Publications

1-Origin Bee-Man, Glowing Gladiator & Magic-Master; Simon & Kirby-a			
	5.10	15.00	36.00
2-Williamson/Crandall-a	3.70	11.00	26.00

	Good	Fine	N-Mint

DOUBLE IMPACT
Mar 1995-Present (3.95, color)
High Impact Studios

	Good	Fine	N-Mint
1—Chromium cover	0.70	2.00	5.00
2-Regular and Nude-c	0.40	1.00	3.00

DOUBLE LIFE OF PRIVATE STRONG
June, 1959-No. 2, Aug, 1959
Archie Publications (Radio Comics)

	Good	Fine	N-Mint
1-Origin & re-intro The Shield, Simon & Kirby art; 1st app. The Fly; 1st S.A. super-hero for Archie Pub.	59.00	176.00	410.00
2-S&K-a; The Fly app. (2nd or 3rd app.)	37.00	111.00	260.00

DR. WEIRD
Oct, 1994-Present (2.95, B&W)
Big Bang Comics

	Good	Fine	N-Mint
1-Frank Brunner-c, 2–	0.60	1.20	3.00

DRACULA (Also see Frankenstein & Werewolf)
10-12/62; No. 2, 11/66-No. 4, 3/67; No. 6, 7/72-No. 8, 7/73 (No #5)
Dell Publishing Co.

	Good	Fine	N-Mint
12-231-212 (#1)-Dell Movie Classic	4.20	12.50	25.00
2-Origin/1st app. Dracula (super hero)	2.40	6.50	13.00
3, 4: 4-Intro Fleeta	1.30	4.00	8.00
6-Reprints #2 w/origin	1.00	2.00	5.00
7, 8-Reprint #3 & 4	0.80	1.60	4.00

DRACULA CHRONICLES
Apr, 1995-June 1995 (2.50, color, limited series)
Topps Comics

	Good	Fine	N-Mint
1-3-Linser-c	0.50	1.00	2.50

DRACULA LIVES!
1973-No. 13, July, 1975 (75¢, B&W magazine)
Marvel Comics Group

	Good	Fine	N-Mint
1-Neal Adams a-2, 3i, 10i	0.90	2.30	5.50
2, 3: 2-Origin; Starlin-a	0.80	1.60	4.00
4-Ploog-a	0.50	1.00	2.50
5 (V2#1)-13: 5-Dracula series begins	0.40	0.80	2.00
Annual 1 (Sum/75, 1.25)-N. Adams-r/#2, 3	0.50	1.00	2.50

DRACULA VERSUS ZORRO
Oct, 1993-No. 2, Nov, 1993 (2.95, color, limited series)

Topps Comics
1, 2: 1-Spot varnish & red foil-c. 2-Polybagged w/Zorro #0
| | 0.60 | 1.20 | 3.00 |

DRACULA: VLAD THE IMPALER (Also see Bram Stoker's Dracula)
Feb, 1993-No. 3, Apr, 1993 (2.95, color, mini-series)
Topps Comics
1-3-Polybagged w/3 cards ea.

| | 0.60 | 1.20 | 3.00 |

DRAGON, THE: BLOOD & GUTS
Mar 1995-May 1995 (2.50, color, limited series)
Image Comics
1–3

| | 0.50 | 1.00 | 2.50 |

DRAGONFORCE
1988-No. 13, 1989 (2.00, color)
Aircel

1-Dale Keown c/a & scripts in #'s 1-12	0.80	1.60	4.00
2, 3	0.70	1.40	3.50
4–6	0.50	1.00	2.50
7–12	0.40	0.80	2.00
13-No Keown-a	0.40	0.80	2.00

DRAGON QUEST
Dec, 1986-No. 3, 1987 (1.50, B&W)
Silverwolf Comics

1-Tim Vigil-c/a in all	1.50	3.80	9.00
2, 3	0.90	2.30	5.50

DRAGON'S CLAWS
July, 1988-No. 10, Apr, 1989 (1.50/1.75, color)
Marvel Comics UK, Ltd.
1-4: 3-Death's Head full pg. strip on back-c (1st app.). 4-Silhouette of

Death's Head on last page; last 1.50-c	0.30	0.60	1.50
5-1st full app. Death's Head	1.00	2.50	6.00
6–10	0.40	0.70	1.75

DRAGON STRIKE
Feb 1994 (1.25, color)
Marvel Comics

1-Adaptation of TSR role playing game	0.30	0.50	1.25

	Good	Fine	N-Mint

DRAMA
June 1994 (2.95, color, one-shot, mature)
Sirius

	Good	Fine	N-Mint
1-1st full color Dawn app.	1.60	3.20	8.00
1-Limited ed. (1400 copies); signed & numbered; fingerprint authenticity			
	2.00	5.00	12.00

DREADSTAR
Nov 1982-No. 64, Mar, 1991
Epic Comics/ First Comics (No. 27 on)

	Good	Fine	N-Mint
1-64: 1-Starlin art begins	0.30	0.50	1.25
Annual 1 (12/83)-Reprints The Price	0.40	0.70	1.75

DREADSTAR
Apr 1994- Jan 1995 (2.50, color, limited series)
Malibu Comics

	Good	Fine	N-Mint
1-6-Peter David scripts: 1,2-Starlin-c	0.50	1.00	2.50

Note: Issues #1-6 will contain Bravura stamps.

DROPSIE AVENUE: THE NEIGBORHOOD
June, 1995 (15.95, B&W)
Kitchen Sink Press

	Good	Fine	N-Mint
NN-Will Eisner	2.40	6.70	16.00

DRUID
May 1995-Present (2.50, color)
Marvel Comics

	Good	Fine	N-Mint
1-4	0.50	1.00	2.50

DUCKMAN
Nov, 1994-Present (2.50, color, bi-monthly)
Topps Comics

	Good	Fine	N-Mint
1-5:1-w/coupon #A for Duckman trading card			
2-w/Duckman 1st season episode guide	0.50	1.00	2.50

DUCKMAN: THE MOB FROG SAGA
Nov 1994- Feb 1995 (2.50, color, limited series)
Topps Comics

	Good	Fine	N-Mint
1-3:1 -w/coupon #B for Duckman trading card, S.Shaw!-c			
	0.50	1.00	2.50

DUCKTALES (Disney's...)
Oct, 1988-No. 13, May, 1990 (1.50/1.95, color)

V2#1, June, 1990-No. 18, Nov, 1991 (1.50, color)
Gladstone/Disney Comics

1	1.00	1.90	4.75
2-11	0.40	0.80	2.00
12, 13-(1.95, 68 pgs.)	0.40	0.90	2.20
V2#1-1st Disney issue	0.60	1.10	2.75
V2#2-18	0.30	0.60	1.60

DUDLEY DO-RIGHT (TV)
Aug, 1970-No. 7, Aug, 1971 (Jay Ward)
Charlton Comics

1	6.40	19.00	45.00
2-7	4.00	12.00	28.00

DYNAMO (Also see T.H.U.N.D.E.R. Agents)
Aug, 1966-No. 4, June, 1967 (25¢ giants)
Tower Comics

1-Crandall/Wood-a, Ditko/Wood art	4.90	15.00	34.00
2-4: Wood-c/a in all	3.30	9.90	23.00

DYNOMUTT (TV)
Nov, 1977-No. 6, Sept, 1978 (Hanna-Barbera)
Marvel Comics Group

1-The Blue Falcon app. in all	0.60	1.10	2.75
2-6: 3-Scooby Doo story	0.30	0.60	1.60

ECLIPSO (See Brave & the Bold #64, House of Secrets #61)
Nov,1992-No. 18, Apr, 1994 (1.25, color)
DC Comics
1-14: 3-6, 9, 11-13-Creeper app. 10-Darkseid app.

	0.30	0.50	1.25
15-18-(1.50): 18-Spectre-c/story	0.30	0.60	1.50
Annual 1 ('93, 2.50)-Intro Prism	0.50	1.00	2.50

ECLIPSO: THE DARKNESS WITHIN
July, 1992-No. 2, Oct, 1992 (2.50, color)
DC Comics

1-Purple gem attached to cover	0.60	1.20	3.00
1-Newsstand version without gem	0.50	1.00	2.50
2-Concludes storyline from annuals	0.50	1.00	2.50

ECTOKID (See Razorline) (Created by Clive Barker)
Sept, 1993-No. 9, May, 1994 (1.75, color)
Marvel Comics

1-(2.50)-Foil embossed-c	0.50	1.00	2.50
2-9: 2-Origin. 5-Saint Sinner x-over	0.40	0.70	1.75
...: Unleashed! 1 (10/94, 2.95, 52 pgs.)	0.60	1.20	3.00

EDDIE CAMPBELL'S BACCHUS
May 1995-Present (2.95, B&W)
Eddie Campbell Comics

1-Cerebus app., 2–	0.60	1.20	3.00

EDEN MATRIX, THE
1994 (2.95, color)
Adhesive Comics
1,2-Two variant covers; alternate-c on inside back-c

	0.60	1.20	3.00

EDGAR RICE BURROUGHS' TARZAN: A TALE OF MUGAMBI
1995 (2.95, color, one-shot)
Dark Horse Comics

1	0.60	1.20	3.00

EDGAR RICE BURROUGHS' TARZAN: THE LOST ADVENTURE
Jan 1995 - Present (2.95, B&W, limited series:4)
Dark Horse Comics

1-4- Tarzan adapted by J.Lansdale   0.60   1.20   3.00

EDGE
July, 1994-Present (2.50, color, limited series:4)
Malibu Comics
1-3 -S.Grant-sty, Gil Kane-c/a; w/Bravura stamp
                                      0.50   1.00   2.50

EERIE (Magazine)(See Creepy)
Sept, 1965, No. 2, Mar, 1966-No. 139, Feb, 1983
Warren Publishing
1-First printing (see Annual Guide)	32.00	96.00	225.00
1-Second printing (see Annual Guide)	13.00	39.00	90.00
2-Frazetta-c	6.00	18.00	42.00
3-Frazetta-c	4.00	12.90	30.00
4-10: 5, 7, 8-Frazetta-c	2.60	7.70	18.00
11-22, 24, 25	2.00	5.00	12.00
23-Frazetta-c	2.00	5.00	12.00
26-41, 43-45	1.20	2.90	7.00
42 (1973 Annual)	1.50	3.80	9.00
46-50, 52, 53, 56-59, 61-78	1.20	2.40	6.00
51 (1974 Annual)	1.50	3.80	9.00
54, 55-Color Spirit story by Eisner	1.30	3.30	8.00
60-Summer Giant (1.25-c)	1.30	3.00	8.00
79, 80-Origin/1st app. Darklon The Mystic by Starlin			
	1.20	2.40	6.00
81-139	0.80	1.60	4.00
Yearbook 1970, 1971-Reprints in each	2.00	5.00	12.00
Yearbook 1972-Reprints	1.50	3.80	9.00

EGYPT
August, 1995-Present (2.50, color, limited series, mature)
DC Comics (Vertigo)
1   0.50   1.00   2.50

80 PAGE GIANT
Aug, 1964-No. 15, Oct, 1965 (Continued in regular series)
National Periodical Publications
1-Superman Annual (on cover; originally planned as Superman Annual
   #9, 8/64)   21.00   63.00   250.00
2-Jimmy Olsen   13.00   39.00   155.00
3, 4: 3-Lois Lane. 4-Flash (G.A.-r)   11.00   32.00   126.00
5-Batman,25th Anniv. Special;Catwoman-r11.00 33.00   130.00

	Good	Fine	N-Mint

6, 7: 6-Superman. 7-Sgt. Rock's Prize Battle Tales; Kubert-c/a

	9.00	26.00	105.00

8-More Secret Origins; origin JLA, Aquaman, Robin, Superman retold;
(also see Secret Origins, 1961)   22.00   66.00   265.00

9-14: 9-Flash-r/Flash 106,117,123 & Showcase 14. 10-Superboy.
11-Superman; all Luthor issue. 12-Batman. 13-Jimmy Olsen. 14-Lois Lane

	9.00	26.00	105.00

15-Superman & Batman; Joker-c/story   9.00   26.00   105.00

ELEKTRA
Mar 1995 - Present (2.95, color, limited series)
Marvel Comics

1-4-Embossed-c	0.60	1.20	3.00

ELEKTRA: ASSASSIN
Aug, 1986-No. 8, June, 1987 (Limited series)
Marvel Comics

1-Miller scripts in all	0.80	1.60	4.00
2	0.60	1.20	3.00
3–7	0.40	0.80	2.00
8	0.70	1.70	4.00

ELEKTRA SAGA, THE (Also see Daredevil #168)
Feb, 1984-No. 4, June, 1984
Marvel Comics

1-4: Frank Miller reprints from Daredevil	0.80	1.60	4.00

ELEMENTALS, THE (See Justice Machine)
June, 1984-No. 29, Sept, 1988
V2#1, March, 1989-No. 28 (1.95, color)

Eerie #14 © Warren

Elementals #7 © Comico

Comico			
1	0.80	1.60	4.00
2	0.50	1.00	2.50
3–10	0.40	0.80	2.00
11–29	0.30	0.60	1.50
V2 #1-28: 4-Begin 2.50-c	0.40	0.80	2.00
Special 1 (3/86)	0.40	0.70	1.75
Special 2 (1/89)	0.40	0.80	1.90

ELEVEN OR ONE
Apr 1995 (2.95, color)
Sirius

1–Linsner-c/a	0.80	1.60	4.00

ELFQUEST (Also see Fantasy Quarterly)
No. 1, April, 1979, No. 2, Aug, 1978-No. 21, Feb, 1985
WaRP Graphics (Magazine size, B&W)

1 (1st printing,1.00-c)	5.00	15.00	35.00
(2nd printing, 1.25-c)	1.80	4.60	11.00
(3rd printing, 1.50-c)	1.00	2.00	5.00
(4th printing, 1989)	0.30	0.60	1.50
2-5: (1st printings, 1.00-c)	3.10	9.40	22.00
(2nd printings, 1.25-c)	1.00	2.00	5.00
(3rd, 4th printings, 1.50-c)	0.60	1.20	3.00
6-9: (1st printings, 1.00-c)	1.50	3.80	9.00
(2nd printings, 1.25-c)	0.80	1.60	4.00
(3rd, 4th printings, 1.50-c)	0.40	0.80	2.00
10-14 (1st printings, 1.50-c)	1.00	2.50	6.00
(2nd printings)	0.30	0.60	1.50
15-21 (only one printing of each)	1.00	2.50	6.00

ELFQUEST
Aug, 1985-No. 32, Mar, 1988
Epic Comics (Marvel)

1	0.60	1.20	3.00
2–32	0.40	0.80	2.00

ELFQUEST: BLOOD OF TEN CHIEFS
July, 1993-Present (2.00, color)
Warp Graphics

1–15	0.50	0.90	2.25
16-begin 2.50-c; 17-	0.50	1.00	2.50

	Good	Fine	N-Mint

ELFQUEST : JINK
Nov 1994 (2.25, color)
Warp Graphics

	Good	Fine	N-Mint
1-3-Back-c-W.Pini/J. Byrne	0.50	0.90	2.25
4-begin 2.50-c; 5–	0.50	1.00	2.50

ELFQUEST: KINGS OF THE BROKEN WHEEL
June, 1990-No. 9, Feb, 1992 (2.00, B&W)
WaRP Graphics

	Good	Fine	N-Mint
1-9: 3rd Elfquest saga (#1 has 2nd printing)	0.40	0.80	2.00

ELFQUEST: NEW BLOOD
Aug, 1992-Present (2.00/2.25, color)
Warp Graphics

	Good	Fine	N-Mint
1-(3.95, 68 pgs.)-Byrne-a/scripts (16pgs.)	0.80	1.60	4.00
2–17	0.50	0.90	2.25
18-26: 18-Begin 2.25-c	0.50	0.90	2.25
27-begin 2.50-c; 28–	0.50	1.00	2.50

ELFQUEST: THE REBELS
Nov, 1994- (2.25/2.50, color)

	Good	Fine	N-Mint
1-3	0.50	0.90	2.25
4-Begin 2.50-c; 5–6	0.50	1.00	2.50

ELFQUEST:SHARDS
Aug, 1994-Present (2.25/2.50, color)
Warp Graphics

	Good	Fine	N-Mint
1–8	0.50	0.90	2.25
9-begin 2.50-c	0.50	1.00	2.50

ELFQUEST: SIEGE AT BLUE MOUNTAIN
Mar, 1987-No. 8, Dec, 1988 (1.75/1.95, B&W, mini-series)
Warp Graphics/Apple Comics

	Good	Fine	N-Mint
1-Begin 2nd Elfquest saga	1.00	2.00	5.00
1-2nd print	0.40	0.80	2.00
2	0.70	1.40	3.50
2-2nd print	0.40	0.70	1.75
3–8	0.40	0.80	2.00

ELFQUEST: WAVE DANCERS
Dec, 1993-Present (2.00/2.25, color)
Warp Graphics

1, 2: 1-Foil cover & poster	0.50	1.00	2.50
3-6: 3-Begin 2.25-c	0.50	0.90	2.25

ELIMINATOR
Apr, 1995 (2.50/2.95, color, 44pgs.)
Malibu

0-(2.95)-Mike Zeck-a	0.60	1.20	3.00
1,2	0.50	1.00	2.50
1–Black Cover Ed. (3.95)	0.80	1.60	4.00

ELVEN
No. 0, Oct, 1994-Present (2.50, color)
Malibu Comics

0-(2.95)-Prime app.	0.60	1.20	3.00
1-4; 2,4-Prime app. 3-PrimeEvil app.	0.50	1.00	2.50
1-Limited Foil Edition-no price on cover	0.50	1.00	2.50

ELVIRA MISTRESS OF THE DARK
May, 1993-Present (2.50, B&W)
Claypool Comics (Eclipse)

1-25-Photo-c: 1-Austin-i. 1-6-Spiegle-a	0.50	1.00	2.50
26-Satirizes Batman Animated Series	0.50	1.00	2.50

ELVIRA'S HOUSE OF MYSTERY
Jan, 1986-No. 11, Jan, 1987
DC Comics

1-(1.50)	0.30	0.60	1.50
2-11: 9-Photo-c. 11-Dave Stevens-c	0.30	0.50	1.25
Special 1 (3/87, 1.25)	0.30	0.50	1.25

E-MAN
Oct, 1973-No. 10, Sept, 1975
Charlton Comics

1-Origin E-Man, Staton-c/a in all	1.70	5.10	12.00
2-4: 2, 4-Ditko-a	1.00	2.50	6.00
5-Miss Liberty Belle app. by Ditko	0.80	2.10	5.00
6, 7, 9, 10-Byrne-a in all	1.00	3.00	6.00
8-Nova becomes E-Man's partner	1.20	2.90	7.00
1-4, 9, 10 (Modern Comics reprints)	0.20	0.40	1.00

EMERALD DAWN
1991 (4.95, color, squarebound)
DC Comics

	Good	Fine	N-Mint
nn-r/Green Lantern: Emerald Dawn #1-6	1.00	2.00	5.00

EMERGENCY
June, 1976-No. 4, Jan, 1977 (B&W, magazine)
Charlton Comics

	Good	Fine	N-Mint
1-Neal Adams-c/a	0.50	1.00	2.50
2,4: 2-N. Adams-c	0.30	0.60	1.60
3-Neal Adams-a	0.40	0.70	1.80

EMERGENCY (TV)
June, 1976-No. 4, Dec, 1976 (Color)
Charlton Comics

1-Byrne-a; Staton-c	0.50	1.00	2.50
2-4: 2-Staton-c	0.30	0.60	1.50

ENEMY
May, 1994-No. 5, Sept, 1994 (2.50, color, limited series)
Dark Horse Comics

1–5	0.50	1.00	2.50

ENEMY ACE SPECIAL (Also see Star Spangled War Stories)
1990 (1.00, color)
DC Comics

1-r/Our Army At War #151, 153	0.30	0.60	1.50

ENIGMA
Mar, 1993-No. 8, Oct, 1993 (2.50, color)
DC Comics/ Vertigo

1-8: Milligan scripts	0.50	1.00	2.50

ETERNALS, THE
July, 1976-No. 19, Jan, 1978
Marvel Comics Group

1-Origin, Jack Kirby-c/a in all	0.80	1.60	4.00
2-19: 14, 15-Cosmic powered Hulk-c/story	0.50	1.00	2.50
Annual 1 (10/77)	0.50	1.00	2.50

ETERNAL WARRIOR (Also see Solar #10)
Aug, 1992-Present (2.25, color)
Valiant

1-Origin Eternal Warrior & Armstrong; Miller-c; B. Smith/Layton-a			
	1.10	3.40	8.00
1-(Gold Logo)	2.00	6.00	15.00

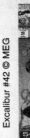

Eternal Warrior #28 © Voyager

Excalibur #42 © MEG

1-(Gold Foil Logo)	3.00	9.00	20.00
2: 1, 2-Unity x-overs	0.50	1.00	3.00
3-Archer & Armstrong x-over	0.50	1.30	3.00
4-1st app. Bloodshot (cameo)(See Rai #0)	0.70	2.10	5.00
5-2nd full app. Bloodshot	0.50	1.30	3.00
6, 7: 6-2nd app. Master Darque	0.60	1.10	2.75
8-Combined w/Archer & Armstrong #8	0.80	2.10	5.00

9-25, 27-34: 9-1st Book of Geomancer & 1st Dr. Image. 14-16-Bloodshot
app. 18-Dr. Mirage cameo. 19-Dr. Mirage app. 22-w/bound in trading
card. 25-Archer & Armstrong app. cont'd from A&A #25

	0.50	0.90	2.25
35-(2.50)-Double cover; 36-42	0.50	1.00	2.50
Year Book 1 ('93, 3.95)	0.80	1.60	4.00
Year Book 2 ('94, 3.95)	0.80	1.60	4.00

EUDAEMON, THE (See Dark Horse Presents #72-74)
Aug, 1993-No. 3, Nov, 1993 (2.50, color, mini-series)
Dark Horse Comics

1-3: All have Nelson-a, painted-c & scripts	0.50	1.00	2.50

EVIL ERNIE
Dec, 1991-No. 5, 1992 (2.50, B&W, mini-series)
Eternity Comics

1-1st app. Lady Death by Steven Hughes (12,000 print run); Lady Death

appears in all issues	10.00	30.00	70.00

2—3: 2-1st Lady Death-c. 2, 3-(7,000 print run)

	8.30	20.80	50.00
3,4; 4-(8,000 print run)	5.80	14.60	35.00
5	3.00	7.50	18.00
...Youth Gone Wild ! (9.95)-TPB r/#1-5	1.70	4.20	10.00

	Good	Fine	N-Mint

EVIL ERNIE THE RESURRECTION
1993
Chaos

	Good	Fine	N-Mint
1	1.70	4.20	10.00
1A-Gold	5.80	14.60	35.00
2-4	1.00	2.50	6.00

EVIL ERNIE: REVENGE
Oct, 1994- Feb 1995 (2.95, color, limited series)
Chaos! Comics

	Good	Fine	N-Mint
1;1-Glow in dark-c;Lady Death app.;1-3-flip book w/Killzone Preview			
(series of 3)	1.20	2.40	6.00
2–4	0.80	1.60	4.00

EXCALIBUR
Apr, 1988 (3.25, color, one-shot)
Oct, 1988-Present (1.50, color)
Marvel Comics Group

	Good	Fine	N-Mint
Special Edition nn (4/88)-The Sword is Drawn; 1st Excalibur book			
	1.30	3.30	8.00
Special Edition-2nd print (10/88, 3.50)	0.70	1.40	3.50
Special Edition-3rd print (12/89, 4.50)	0.90	1.80	4.50
...The Sword Is Drawn (4/92, 4.95)	1.00	2.00	5.00
1-(10/88, 1.50)-Series begins	1.20	2.90	7.00
2	0.70	1.40	3.50
3, 4	0.50	1.00	2.50
5–10	0.50	0.90	2.25
11–15	0.40	0.80	1.90
16-23	0.30	0.60	1.50
24-40, 42-49, 51-70, 72-74,76 : 52,57,58-X-Men-c/stories. 53-Spider-			
Man-c/story. 61-Phoenix returns	0.30	0.60	1.50
41-X-Men, Wolverine app.; Cable cameo	0.40	0.80	2.00
50-(2.75, 56 pgs.)	0.50	1.00	2.50
71-(3.95, 52 pgs.)-Hologram cover	0.80	1.60	4.00
75-(2.25, 52 pgs.)-Regular edition	0.50	0.90	2.25
75-(3.50, 52 pgs.)-Collectors ed. w/prism foil-c			
	0.70	1.40	3.50
77-81: 77-Begin 1.95-c; bound-in card sheet	0.40	0.80	2.00
82-(2.50)-Newsstand edition	0.50	1.00	2.50
82-(3.50)-Enhanced edition	0.70	1.40	3.50
83-86-(1.95)-Deluxe edition	0.40	0.80	2.00

83-86-(1.50)-Standard edition	0.30	0.60	1.50
87-88; 87–Return from "Age of Apocalypse"	0.40	0.80	2.00
Annual 1 ('93, 2.95)-1st app. Khaos	0.60	1.20	3.00
Annual 2 ('94, 2.95, 68 pgs.)-X-Men and Psylocke app.			
	0.60	1.20	3.00
...Air Apparent (12/91, 4.95)	0.80	1.60	4.00
...Mojo Mayhem (12/89, 4.50)-A. Adams-c	0.80	1.60	4.00
...: The Possession (7/91, 2.95)	0.50	1.00	2.50
...: XX Crossing (7/92, 2.50)-Vs. X-Men	0.40	0.80	2.00

EXILES
Aug, 1993-No. 4, Nov, 1993(1.95, color)
Malibu Comics (Ultraverse)

1,2,4: 1,2-Bagged copies exist of each	0.40	0.80	2.00
3-(2.50, 44 pgs.)-Rune Flip-c/story by B. Smith			
	0.50	1.00	2.50
1-Full cover holographic edition	4.00	13.00	30.00

EX-MUTANTS
Nov, 1992-Present (1.95/2.25/2.50, color)
Malibu Comics

1-10	0.40	0.80	2.00
11-14-(2.25): 11-Polybagged w/Skycap	0.50	0.90	2.25
15-18-(2.50)	0.50	1.00	2.50

EXOSQUAD (TV)
Jan, 1994 (1.25, color)
Topps Comics

0-(1.00, 20 pgs.)-1st app.; Staton-a(p); wraparound-c			
	0.20	0.40	1.00

Ex-Mutants #18 © Malibu

Exosquad #0 © Topps

	Good	Fine	N-Mint

EXTREME JUSTICE
Jan, 1995 (1.50, color)
DC Comics

	Good	Fine	N-Mint
1–5	0.30	0.60	1.50
6-begin 1.75-c; 7–	0.50	0.90	2.25

EXTREME SACRIFICE PRELUDE
Jan 1995 (2.50, color)
Image Comics

	Good	Fine	N-Mint
1-Liefeld wraparound-c; polybagged w/trading card	0.50	1.00	2.50

EXTREME SUPER CHRISTMAS SPECIAL
Dec 1994 (2.95, color)
Image Comics

	Good	Fine	N-Mint
1	0.60	1.20	3.00

EXTREMES OF VIOLET
1995 (2.95, color, bimonthly)
Blackout Comics

	Good	Fine	N-Mint
#0-2:#0-w/8 pg pin-up section	0.60	1.20	3.00

EXTREMIST, THE
Sept, 1993-No. 4, Dec, 1993 (1.95, color, mini-series)
DC Comics (Vertigo)

	Good	Fine	N-Mint
1-4-Milligan scripts	0.50	1.00	2.50
1-Platinum Edition	3.00	8.00	18.00

F

FACE
Jan, 1995 (4.95, color)
DC Comics

1	0.90	1.80	4.50

FACTOR X
Mar 1995 - Present (1.95, color)
Marvel Comics

1-Age of Apocalypse	0.80	1.60	4.00
2–4	0.40	0.80	2.00

FALLEN EMPIRES ON THE WORLD OF MAGIC: THE GATHERING
Sep 1995-Present (2.75, color)
Armada (Acclaim)

1-bagged with Fallen Empires Booster Pack; 2–polybagged			
	0.60	1.10	2.75

FAMILY AFFAIR (TV)
Feb, 1970-No. 4, Oct, 1970 (25¢)
Gold Key

1-With pull-out poster; photo-c	4.00	12.00	28.00
1-With poster missing	1.70	5.00	12.00
2-4: 3,4-photo-c	2.60	7.70	18.00

FAMILY MAN
1995 (4.95, B&W, limited series:3)
Paradox Press

1-3	1.00	2.00	5.00

FAMOUS FIRST EDITION
1974-No. 8, Aug, 1975; C-61, Sept, 1978
(1.00-c; 10x13 1/2 - Giant Size) (72 pgs.; No. 6-8: 68 pgs)
National Periodical Publications/DC Comics

C-26 Action 1	1.20	4.00	12.00
C-28 Detective 27	3.50	11.00	35.00
C-28 Hardcover edition	6.80	20.00	68.00
C-30 Sensation 1 (1974)	1.20	4.00	12.00
F-4 Whiz 2 (No. 1) (10-11/74)	1.20	4.00	12.00
F-5 Batman 1 (F-6 on inside)	2.50	8.00	25.00
F-6 Wonder Woman 1	1.20	4.00	12.00
F-7 All Star Comics 3	1.20	4.00	12.00

	Good	Fine	N-Mint

Fantastic Four #244 © MEG

Fantasy Masterpieces #4 © MEG

	Good	Fine	N-Mint
F-8 Flash 1 (8-9/75)	1.20	4.00	12.00
C-61 Superman 1 (9/78)	1.20	4.00	12.00
Hardbound editions w/dust jackets ($5.00) (Lyle Stuart, Inc.)			
C-26, 30, (F) 4, 6 known	2.00	6.00	17.00

FANTASTIC FORCE
Nov, 1994-Present (1.75, color)
Marvel Comics

	Good	Fine	N-Mint
1-(2.50)-Foil wraparound-c; intro Fantastic Force w/Huntara, Devlor, Psi-Lord & Vibraxas	0.50	1.00	2.50
2-10	0.40	0.70	1.75

FANTASTIC FOUR (See Giant-Size... & Marvel Milestone Ed.)
Nov, 1961-Present
Marvel Comics Group

	Good	Fine	N-Mint
1-Origin & 1st app. The Fantastic Four; Marvel's first super hero effort since the G.A.	1090.00	3270.00	13750.00
1-Golden Record reprint (1966)	17.00	51.00	120.00
With Golden Record ('66)	29.00	86.00	200.00
2-Last 10¢ issue; Vs. The Skrulls	230.00	680.00	2250.00
3-FF dons costumes & establishes headquarters; intro the Fantasti-Car	160.00	480.00	1600.00
4-1st Silver Age Sub-Mariner app.	190.00	570.00	1900.00
5-Origin & 1st app. Doctor Doom	230.00	690.00	2300.00
6-Dr. Doom/Sub-Mariner team up; first Marvel villain team-up; 2nd app. S.A. Sub-Mariner	125.00	375.00	875.00
7-10: 8-1st app. Puppet Master and Alicia Masters. 9-3rd app. Sub-Mariner	81.00	242.00	565.00
11-Origin/1st app. The Impossible Man	65.00	195.00	455.00

12-FF vs. The Hulk (1st Hulk x-over, 3/63)(ties w/Amazing Spider-Man #1			
as 1st Marvel x-over)	82.00	246.00	575.00
13-1st app. The Watcher	50.00	150.00	350.00
14-19: 16-1st Ant-Man x-over (7/63)	33.00	99.00	230.00
20-Origin/1st app. The Molecule Man	38.00	114.00	265.00
21-1st Sgt. Fury x-over (12/63)	24.00	73.00	170.00
22-24	15.00	45.00	105.00
25, 26-1st Thing vs. The Hulk battle. 25-3rd Avengers x-over (1st time w/			
Capt. America (cameo, 4/64); 2nd app. Capt. America, takes place between			
Avengers #4 & 5. 26-4th Avengers x-over; see TOS #49 for 1st x-over			
	46.00	137.00	320.00
27-1st Dr. Strange x-over (6/64)	17.00	52.00	122.00
28-Early X-Men x-over (7/64)	23.00	69.00	160.00
29, 30: 30-Intro Diablo	12.00	36.00	85.00
31-40: 31-Early Avengers x-over (10/64)	10.00	30.00	70.00
41-47: 45-1st app. The Inhumans-c/sty(12/65)			
	6.90	21.00	48.00
48-1st app./partial origin Silver Surfer (3/66) & Galactus; 1st of 3 part			
story; Galactus cameo in last panel	75.00	225.00	750.00
49-2nd app. Silver Surfer & Galactus	17.00	50.00	165.00
50-Silver Surfer battles Galactus	18.00	54.00	180.00
51, 54: 54-Inhumans cameo	4.00	11.00	38.00
52-1st app. Black Panther (7/66)	7.00	20.00	65.00
53-Origin Black Panther	5.00	16.00	54.00
55-Thing battles Silver Surfer-c/story (10/66); 4th app. Silver Surfer			
	6.00	17.00	55.00
56-60: Silver Surfer x-over	5.00	14.00	46.00
61-65, 68-70: 61-Sandman-c/story	3.00	10.00	32.00
66-(9/67)-Partial origin Him (no app.)	8.00	24.00	80.00
67-Partial origin & 1st app. Him (cameo on last page) (see Thor			
#163-166)	9.00	27.00	90.00
71, 73, 78-80: 73-Spider-Man x-over	3.00	8.00	25.00
72-Silver Surfer-c/story (3/68); pre-dates Silver Surfer #1 (#77 is same			
date as Silver Surfer #1)	3.00	8.00	28.00
74-77: Silver Surfer app. (5/68-8/68)	3.00	8.00	28.00
81-88: 88-Last 12¢ issue	2.00	6.00	20.00
89-99	1.00	4.00	13.00
100-(7/70)	6.00	19.00	62.00
101, 102-F.F. vs. Sub-Mariner	1.00	4.00	14.00
103-111: 104-Magneto-c/story	2.00	5.00	11.00
112-Hulk vs. The Thing	6.40	19.00	45.00
113-115: 115-Last 15¢ issue	1.80	5.00	11.00
116-120: 116-(52 pgs.)	1.40	3.50	8.50

	Good	Fine	N-Mint
121-123: Silver Surfer-c/stories	2.00	5.00	12.00
124, 125, 127, 129-149	1.30	3.00	7.50
126-Origin retold; cover swipe FF #1	1.50	3.80	9.00
128-4 pg. glossy insert FF Friends & Foes	1.50	3.80	9.00
150-Crystal & Quicksilver wed	1.50	3.80	9.00
151-154, 158-160	1.20	2.90	7.00
155-157: Silver Surfer app.	1.30	3.00	8.00
161-180: 168-170-Cage app.	0.60	1.20	3.00
181-199: 190,191-FF breaks up	0.40	0.80	2.00
200-(11/78, 52 pgs.)-FF reunited	1.20	2.40	6.00
201-208, 219, 222-231: 207-H. Torch vs. Spidey-c/story			
	0.30	0.60	1.50
209-216, 218, 220, 221: Byrne-a	0.40	0.80	2.00
217-Dazzler app. by Byrne	0.60	1.20	3.00
232: Byrne-a begins	0.70	1.40	3.50
233-235, 237-249, 251-260-All Byrne art: 252-Bound-in tattooz			
	0.50	1.00	2.50
236-(11/81, 68 pgs.)-20th Ann.; Byrne-c/a	0.70	1.40	3.50
250-(52 pgs.)-Byrne; Spider-Man x-over	0.70	1.40	3.50
261-285: 262-Origin Galactus. 274-Early app. Spidey's alien costume (1/85, 2 pgs.). 280-(7/85)-"July 1984" in indicia			
	0.50	1.00	2.50
286-X-Factor (2nd app. cont. from Avengers 263; story cont. in X-Factor #1)	1.00	2.00	5.00
287-295: 293-Last Byrne-a	0.30	0.60	1.50
296-(1.50)-Thing rejoins	0.40	0.80	2.10
297-305, 307-318, 320-330: 311-Re-intro The Black Panther (2/88)			
	0.30	0.60	1.50
306-New team begins	0.30	0.70	1.70
319-Double size	0.50	1.00	2.50
331-346: 337-Simonson art begins	0.30	0.60	1.50
347-Ghost Rider/Wolverine app.	1.00	2.30	5.50
347-2nd print	0.50	1.00	2.50
348, 349: Ghost Rider/Wolverine app.	0.70	1.40	3.50
348-Gold 2nd printing	0.30	0.60	1.50
350-(1.50, 52 pgs.)	0.60	1.20	3.00
351-357, 359, 360: 356-Vs. New Warriors	0.30	0.60	1.50
358-(2.25, 88 pg.)-Die-cut-c; 30th Anniversary			
	0.60	1.20	3.00
361-368,370,372-374,376-380,382-386: 374-Secret Defenders app.			
	0.30	0.60	1.50
369-Infinity War; Thanos app.	0.50	1.00	2.50
371-(2.00)-All-white, embossed-c	0.80	1.60	4.00

371-All-red 2nd printing (2.00)	0.50	1.00	2.50
375-(2.95, 52 pg.)-Holo-grafx foil-c; ann. iss.			
	0.60	1.20	3.00
381-"Death" of Reed Richards & Dr. Doom	0.80	1.60	4.00
387-(1.25)-Newsstand Edition	0.30	0.50	1.25
387-(2.95)-Collectors Edition; die cut & foil-c			
	0.60	1.20	3.00
388-397: 388-Bound-in card sheet; begin 1.50-c. 390-c is re-creation of			
FF #48. 394-White logo. 395-Wolverine app.			
	0.30	0.60	1.50
394-(2.95)-Polybagged w/16 pg. Marvel Action Hour book and acetate			
print; pink logo	0.60	1.20	3.00
398,399-Rainbow Foil-c	0.50	1.00	2.50
398,399-Newstand-c	0.30	0.60	1.50
400-Rainbow Foil-c	0.70	1.40	3.50
401-402-Atlantis Rising	0.30	0.60	1.50
Annual 1 ('63)-Origin retold; Ditko-i	46.00	137.00	455.00
Annual 2 ('64)-Dr. Doom origin & c/story	30.00	89.00	295.00
Annual 3 ('65)-Reed & Sue wed-r/#6,11,1	12.00	36.00	120.00
Special 4 (11/66)-1st S.A. app. G.A. Torch; origin retold; Torch vs. Torch			
battle	7.00	21.00	70.00
Special 5 (11/67)-1st solo Silver Surfer story; Inhumans app.			
	8.00	23.00	75.00
Special 6 (11/68)-New story & art	4.00	12.00	40.00
Special 7 (11/69)-Reprints	2.90	8.60	20.00
Special 8, 9, 10 (12/70-'73)-Reprints	1.70	4.20	10.00
Annual 11-14 ('76-'79)-11-Begin new-a	1.00	2.50	6.00
Annual 15-20 ('80-'87)	0.80	1.60	4.00
Annual 21 ('88, 1.75)-Evolutionary War	0.80	1.60	4.00
Annual 22-24 ('89-'91): 22-Atlantis Attacks	0.50	1.00	2.50
Annual 25 ('92, 2.25) Moondragon back-up	0.50	1.00	2.50
Annual 26 ('93, 2.95)-Polybagged w/card	0.70	1.40	3.50
Annual 27 ('94, 2.95)	0.60	1.20	3.00
Special Edition 1-(5/84)-r/Ann. 1; Byrne-c/a	0.50	1.00	2.50
FF Roast (5/82)- X-Men, Ghost Rider cameo	0.80	1.60	4.00
...Monsters Unleashed ('92, 5.95)-r/347-349	1.00	2.50	6.00
...Nobody Gets Out Alive ('94,15.95)TPB r/#387-392			
	2.30	6.90	16.00

FANTASTIC FOUR: ATLANTIS RISING COLLECTOR'S PREVIEW
May, 1995 (2.25, color, 52 pgs.)

1-One-shot	0.30	1.00	2.25

	Good	Fine	N-Mint

FANTASTIC FOUR: ATLANTIS RISING
June 1995-July 1995 (3.95, color, limited series)
Marvel Comics

	Good	Fine	N-Mint
1,2-acetate cover	0.60	1.70	4.00

FANTASTIC FOUR UNLIMITED
Mar, 1993-Present (3.95, color, 68 pgs.)
Marvel Comics

	Good	Fine	N-Mint
1-9: 1-Black Panther app. 4-Thing vs. Hulk battle. 5-Vs. The Frightful Four. 6-vs. Namor. 7,9,10-Wraparound-c	0.80	1.60	4.00

FANTASTIC FOUR VS X-MEN
Feb, 1987-No. 4, June, 1987 (Mini-series)
Marvel Comics

	Good	Fine	N-Mint
1	0.70	1.30	3.25
2–4	0.50	0.90	2.25

FANTASTIC GIANTS (Formerly Konga #1-23)
V2#24, September, 1966 (25¢, 68 pgs)
Charlton Comics

	Good	Fine	N-Mint
V2#24- Special Ditko issue; origin of Konga & Gorgo-r plus 2 new Ditko stories	5.70	17.00	40.00

FANTASTIC VOYAGE (TV)
Aug, 1969-No. 2, Dec, 1969
Gold Key

	Good	Fine	N-Mint
1, 2	2.60	8.00	18.00

FANTASTIC VOYAGES OF SINDBAD, THE
Oct, 1965; No. 2, June, 1967
Gold Key

	Good	Fine	N-Mint
1, 2-Painted-c	4.00	11.00	25.00

FANTASY MASTERPIECES (Marvel Super Heroes No. 12 on)
Feb, 1966-No. 11, Oct, 1967 (All contain S.A. & G.A. reprints)
Marvel Comics Group

	Good	Fine	N-Mint
1-Photo of Stan Lee inside FC	5.00	15.00	35.00
2-Last 12¢ issue; r/1st Fin Fang Foom/Str. Tales	2.50	6.30	15.00
3-G.A. Capt. America-r begin; 1st 25¢ issue	2.10	6.00	15.00
4-6: Captain America reprints	2.10	6.00	15.00
7-Begin G.A. Sub-Mariner, Torch reprints	2.10	6.00	15.00
8-Torch battles the Sub-Mariner-r/M.M. #9	2.10	6.00	15.00

9-Origin Human Torch r/Marvel Comics #1	2.40	7.30	17.00
10-Reprints 1st All Winners Squad	2.50	6.30	15.00
11-r/origin Toro from Human Torch #1 (GA)			
	2.50	6.30	15.00

FANTASY MASTERPIECES (Second series)
Dec, 1979-No. 14, Jan, 1981
Marvel Comics Group

V2#1-(75¢, 52 pgs.)-r/Silver Surfer #1	0.90	1.80	4.50
2-14: r/Silver Surfer #2-14	0.60	1.20	3.00

FANTASY QUARTERLY (See Elfquest)
Spring, 1978 (B&W, one-shot)
Independent Publishers Syndicate

1-1st app. Elfquest; Dave Sim-a (6 pgs.)	5.60	17.00	39.00

FAST FORWARD
1992-No. 3, 1993 (4.95, color, 68 pgs.)
Piranha Press (DC)

1-3: 1-Morrison script/McKean-c/a. 3-Sam Kieth-a			
	1.10	2.20	5.50

FATE
No. 0, Oct, 1994-Present (1.95, color)
DC Comics

0–7	0.40	0.80	2.00
8-begin 2.25-c; 9–	0.50	0.90	2.25

FATMAN, THE HUMAN FLYING SAUCER
Apr, 1967-No. 3, Aug-Sept, 1967 (68 pgs.)
Lightning Comics (Written by Otto Binder)

1-Origin Fatman & Tinman by C. C. Beck	5.30	16.00	37.00
2-Beck art	3.60	11.00	25.00
3-(Scarce)-Beck art	6.00	18.00	42.00

FAUST
1989-No. 12 (B&W, adult, violent)
Northstar/Rebel Studios

1-Tim Vigil-c/a in all	5.00	14.00	33.00
1-2nd print	1.10	3.00	8.00
1-3rd print	0.60	1.10	2.75
2	3.40	10.30	24.00
2-2nd & 3rd prints	0.60	1.10	2.75

	Good	Fine	N-Mint
3	2.00	6.00	14.00
3-2nd print	0.60	1.10	2.75
4	0.80	2.00	5.00
5-10: 7-Begin Rebel Studios series	0.70	1.30	3.25

FEAR (Adventures into...)
Nov, 1970-No. 31, Dec, 1976 (No. 1-6; Giant Size)
Marvel Comics Group

	Good	Fine	N-Mint
1-Reprints Fantasy and Sci-Fi stories	1.50	3.80	9.00
2-6	1.00	2.00	5.00
7-9	0.60	1.20	3.00
10-Man-Thing begins (10/72), ends #19	1.50	3.80	9.00
11, 12: 11-Adams-c. 12-Starlin-a	0.80	1.60	4.00
13, 14, 16-18 (See Savage Tales #1)	0.60	1.20	3.00
15-1st full length Man-Thing story	1.00	2.00	5.00
19-Intro Howard the Duck	2.10	6.40	15.00
20-Morbius series begins; Gulacy-a(p) in all	2.90	9.00	20.00
21-25	1.70	4.20	10.00
26-31: Morbius solo series ends	1.30	3.30	8.00

FELICIA HARDY: THE BLACK CAT
July, 1994-No. 4, Oct, 1994 (1.50, color, mini-series)
Marvel Comics

	Good	Fine	N-Mint
1-4: 1,4 -Spider-Man app.	0.30	0.60	1.50

FEMFORCE (...Western Jam No. 7)
April, 1985-Present (Color 1-15, B&W 16-on)
Americomics

	Good	Fine	N-Mint
1	0.90	2.30	5.50
2	0.70	1.40	3.50
3-30	0.60	1.20	3.00
31-35, 37-49, 51-80: 51-Movie photo-c	0.50	1.00	2.50
36-(2.95, 52 pgs.)	0.50	1.00	2.50
50-(2.95, 52 pgs.)	0.50	1.00	2.50
Special #1- (Fall, 1984, B&W)	0.40	0.80	2.00
Frightbook 1 ('92, 2.95)	0.60	1.20	3.00
In The House Of Horror (2.50, B&W)	0.50	1.00	2.50
Night Of The Demon (2.75, B&W)	0.60	1.10	2.75
Out Of The Asylum Special 1 (1.95, B&W)	0.40	0.80	2.00
Pin-Up Portfolio	0.40	0.80	2.00

FERRET (See The Protectors)
Sept, 1992; May, 1993-No. 10, Feb, 1994 (1.95, color)

Malibu Comics

1-One-shot, 1992	0.40	0.80	2.00
1 (2.50)-Completely die-cut book	0.50	1.00	2.50
2-4-(2.50)-Coll. ed. w/poster	0.50	1.00	2.50
2-4-Newsstand ed. w/o poster & diff.-c	0.40	0.80	2.00
5-8 (2.25): 5-Polybagged w/Skycap	0.50	0.90	2.25
9,10: 9-Begin 2.50-c	0.50	1.00	2.50

FIGHTING AMERICAN
Oct, 1966 (25¢ giant)
Harvey Publications
1-Origin Fighting American & Speedboy-r by Simon & Kirby

	2.40	7.30	17.00

FIGHTING AMERICAN
Feb, 1994-No. 6, July, 1994 (1.50, color, limited series)
DC Comics

1–6	0.30	0.60	1.50

FIGHTIN' FIVE (Formerly Space War; see Peacemaker)
July, 1964-No. 41, Jan, 1967; No. 42, Oct, 1981-No. 49, Dec, 1982
Charlton Comics

V2#28-Origin/1st app. Fightin' Five	3.00	9.00	21.00
29-39, 41	2.30	5.80	14.00
40-Peacemaker begins (1st app.)	3.10	9.00	22.00
42-49: Reprints	0.40	0.80	2.00

FIGHT THE ENEMY
Aug, 1966-No. 3, Mar, 1967 (25¢, 68 pgs.)
Tower Comics

Firearm #13 © Malibu

The Flash #104 © DC

	Good	Fine	N-Mint
1-Lucky 7 & Mike Manly begin	3.00	9.00	21.00
2-Boris Vallejo & McWilliams-a	2.40	7.30	17.00
3-Wood-a (1/2 pg.); McWilliams-a	2.40	7.30	17.00

FIREARM (See The Night Man #4)
Sept, 1993-Present (1.95, color)
Malibu Comics (Ultraverse)

1-(1.95)-Direct sale ed. w/o card	0.40	0.80	2.00
1-(2.50)-Newsstand ed. bagged w/card	0.50	1.00	2.50
1-Ultra Limited silver foil-c	1.70	5.10	12.00
2-(2.50, 44 pgs.)-Rune flip-c/story by B. Smith			
	0.50	1.00	2.50

3-10,12-17: 1-4-Chaykin-c; Hamner/Lowe-a. 5-Origin Prime. 6-Brereton-c;
   Prime app. 10-1st app. Candle. 13, 16-Rafferty Saga Pt. 1& Pt. 4

15-Night Man & Freex app.	0.40	0.80	2.00
11-(3.50, 68 pgs)-Flip book w/Ultraverse Premiere #5			
	0.70	1.40	3.50
0-Came with video tape containing first part of story (book has 2nd half)			
(Set priced at $14.95)	2.10	6.40	15.00
18-Last Robinson issue	0.40	1.10	2.50

FIRESTAR
March, 1986-No. 4, June, 1986 (75¢)
Marvel Comics Group

1-X-Men & New Mutants app.	0.70	1.30	3.25
2-Wolverine-c; Arthur Adams-a(p)	1.00	2.50	6.00
3, 4: 3-Art Adams/Seinkiewicz-c. 4-B. Smith-c			
	0.50	0.90	2.25

FIRESTORM
March, 1978-No. 5, Oct-Nov, 1978
DC Comics

1-Origin/1st app.	0.60	1.20	3.00
2–5	0.40	0.80	2.00

1ST ISSUE SPECIAL
April, 1975-No. 13, April, 1976
National Periodical Publications

1-7, 9-12: 1-Intro Atlas; Kirby-c/a/scripts. 5-Manhunter; Kirby-c/a/scripts.

7-Creeper by Ditko (c/a)	0.50	1.00	2.50
8-Origin/1st app. Warlord; Grell-c/a (12/73)			
	0.90	2.60	6.00

13-Return of the New Gods; Darkseid app.; 1st new costume Orion;

| pre-dates New Gods #12 (try-out issue) | 0.80 | 1.60 | 4.00 |

FLAMING CARROT (...Comics #6 on; also see Teenage Mutant Ninja
Turtles/Flaming Carrot...)
May, 1984-Present? (1.70, B&W)
Aardvark-Vanaheim/Renegade Press/Dark Horse

1	5.00	15.00	35.00
2	3.00	8.60	20.00
3	1.90	5.60	13.00
4-6	1.10	3.40	8.00
7-9	0.80	2.10	5.00
10-12	0.80	1.60	4.00
13-15	0.60	1.20	3.00
15-Variant w/out cover price	0.80	2.10	5.00
16-20: 18-1st Dark Horse issue	0.60	1.20	3.00
21-23, 25: 25-Trading cards	0.40	0.80	2.00
24-(2.50-c)	0.50	1.00	2.50
26-28: 26, 27-TMNT app. 27-McFarlane-c	0.50	0.90	2.25
29-31-(2.50-c)	0.50	1.00	2.50

FLAMING CARROT COMICS
Summer-Fall, 1981 (1.95, one-shot, B&W, over-sized)
Killian Barracks Press

1- Serially numbered to 6500	10.00	24.00	60.00

FLASH, THE (See Showcase #4, 8, 13, 14)
No. 105, Feb-Mar, 1959-No. 350, Oct, 1985
National Periodical Publications/DC Comics

105-Origin Flash retold	350.00	1050.00	3500.00
106-Origin Grodd & Pied Piper; begin trilogy			
	89.00	267.00	800.00
107-Part 2 of Grodd trilogy	52.00	155.00	465.00
108-Grodd trilogy ends	48.00	145.00	435.00
109-2nd Mirror Master	41.00	122.00	365.00
110-Origin & intro Kid Flash who later becomes Flash; part 1 of 3 part			
"Showcase style" tryout	100.00	300.00	700.00
111-2nd Kid Flash tryout; Cloud Creatures			
	34.00	101.00	235.00
112-Intro & Origin Elongated Man	36.00	109.00	255.00
113-Origin & 1st app. Trickster	34.00	103.00	240.00
114-Capt. Cold app. (see Showcase 8)	27.00	81.00	190.00
115, 116, 118-120: 120-Flash & Kid Flash team-up for 1st time			
	21.00	62.00	145.00

	Good	Fine	N-Mint
117-Origin/1st app. Capt. Boomerang	28.00	84.00	195.00
121, 122: 122-Origin/1st app. The Top	15.00	45.00	105.00
123-Re-intro GA Flash; 1st mention Earth II			
	74.00	221.00	735.00
124-Last 10¢ issue	13.00	39.00	90.00
125-128, 130-136, 138, 140: 127-Return of Grodd-c/sty. 131-Early Green			
Lantern x-over (9/62)	12.00	36.00	85.00
129-2nd Golden Age Flash x-over; JSA app. (cameo flashback)			
	31.00	94.00	220.00
137-G.A. Flash x-over; JSA team decides to re-form; 1st S.A. app. JSA			
(cameo); 1st app. G.A. Johnny Thunder in S.A.			
	46.00	137.00	320.00
139-Origin/1st app. Prof. Zoom	14.00	41.00	95.00
141-150: 142-Trickster app.	8.00	24.00	55.00
151-GA Flash vs. The Shade	9.00	28.00	75.00
152-159	5.30	16.00	37.00
160-Giant G-21	8.30	25.00	58.00
161-168,170: 170-GA Flash app.	4.60	14.00	32.00
169-Giant G-34; new facts about origin	8.30	25.00	58.00
171-174, 176, 177, 179, 180: 173-G.A. Flash x-over			
	3.70	11.00	26.00
175-2nd Superman/Flash race (12/67)	16.00	36.00	90.00
178-Giant G-46	5.40	16.00	38.00
181-186, 188-195, 197-200	4.00	5.10	12.00
187, 196-Giants G-58 & G-70	4.00	12.90	30.00
201-204, 206-213, 216, 220: 201-New GA Flash story. 208-Begin 52 pg.			
issues, ends 213, 215, 216	1.20	2.90	7.00
205-Giant G-82	2.40	7.30	17.00
214-Giant DC-11; r/origin Metal Men/Showcase 37			
	2.00	5.00	12.00
215-(52 pgs.)-r/Flash from Showcase 4	1.70	5.00	12.00
217-219: N. Adams-a. 217-Green Lantern/Green Arrow series begins (9/72).			
219-Green Arrow ends	1.70	5.10	12.00
221-225, 227, 228, 230, 231, 233	1.00	2.50	6.00
226-N. Adams art	1.50	3.80	9.00
229, 232: 100 page issues	1.30	3.00	8.00
234-274, 277-288, 290: 246-Last Gr. Lantern			
	0.60	1.20	3.00
275, 276-Iris West Allen dies	0.60	1.20	3.00
289-1st Perez DC-a;Firestorm begins-ends 304			
	1.10	2.20	5.50
291-299, 301-305: 294-296-Starlin back-up-a			
	0.50	1.00	2.50

300-(52 pgs.)-Origin Flash retold	0.80	1.60	4.00
306-Dr. Fate by Giffen begins	0.50	1.00	2.50
307-313: Giffen art. 309-Origin Flash retold. 313-Last Dr. Fate			
by Giffen	0.40	0.80	2.00
314-349: 344-Origin Kid Flash	0.40	0.80	2.00
350: Double-size	0.90	2.30	5.50
Annual 1 (10-12/63, 84 pgs.)	31.00	92.00	305.00

FLASH
June, 1987-Present
DC Comics

1-New Teen Titans x-over	1.00	2.00	5.00
2, 3: 3-Intro Kilgore	0.60	1.20	3.00
4-10: 5-Intro Speed McGee	0.50	1.00	2.50
11-20: 12, 19-Contain free 16 pg. inserts	0.40	0.80	2.00
21-30: 28-Capt. Cold app.	0.40	0.80	2.00
31-49, 51-65: 65-Last 1.00-c issue	0.40	0.80	2.00
50-(1.75-c, 52 pgs.)	0.40	0.80	2.00
66-78: 73-Re-intro Barry Allen & begin saga (Barry Allen revealed as			
Reverse Flash in #78)	0.40	0.80	2.00
79-(2.50, 68 pgs.)-Barry Allen saga ends	0.50	1.00	2.50
80-84: 81, 82-Nightwing & Starfire app. 84-Razer app.			
	0.40	0.80	2.00
80-(2.50)-Foil cover edition	0.50	1.00	2.50
85-94: 85-Begin 1.50-c. 94-(9/94)-Zero Hour			
	0.40	0.80	2.00
0,95-99, 101: 0-(10/94). 95-(11/94)	0.40	0.80	2.00
92-1st Impulse	1.20	2.40	6.00
100-(2.50)-Newstand	0.50	1.00	2.50
100-(3.50)-Foil-c	0.80	1.60	4.00
102-Begin 1.75-c; 103-104	0.40	0.70	1.75
Annual 1 ('87, 1.25)	0.40	0.80	2.00
Annual 2, 3: 2-('88, 1.50). 3-('89, 1.75)	0.40	0.70	1.75
Annual 4 ('91, 2.00)-Armageddon 2001	0.40	0.80	2.00
Annual 5, 6: ('92-'93, 2.50, 68 pgs.)	0.50	1.00	2.50
Annual 7 ('94, 2.95)-Elseworlds story	0.60	1.20	3.00
Annual 8 ('95, 3.50)-Year One story	0.70	1.40	3.50
Special 1 ('90, 2.95)-50th anniversary	0.60	1.20	3.00
TV Special 1 ('91, 3.95)-Photo-c	0.80	1.60	4.00

FLASH GORDON
June, 1965 (Painted-c)
Gold Key

	Good	Fine	N-Mint
1-Reprint from 1947	2.90	9.00	20.00

FLASH GORDON
9/66-No. 11, 12/67; No. 12, 2/69-No. 18, 1/70; No. 19,
10-11/78-No. 37, 3/82 (Painted c-19-30, 34)
King Comics #1-11/Charlton #12-18/Gold Key #19-23/Whitman #28 on

	Good	Fine	N-Mint
1-Williamson-c/a(2); Mandrake story	4.70	9.00	25.00
1-Army giveaway (1968); same as regular #1, but without Mandrake			
story & back-c	2.10	6.00	15.00
2-Mandrake story; Bolle, G. Kane-c	2.10	6.00	15.00
3-Williamson-c	2.10	6.00	15.00
4-Secret Agent X-9 begins; Williamson-c/a(3)			
	2.10	6.00	15.00
5-Williamson-c/a(2)	2.10	6.00	15.00
6, 8-Crandall-a. 8-Secret Agent X-9 reprint	2.90	9.00	20.00
7-Mac Raboy-a	2.60	8.00	18.00
9, 10-Raymond-r. 10-Buckler's 1st-a (11/67)	2.60	7.70	18.00
11-Crandall-a	1.90	6.00	13.00
12-Crandall-c/a	2.10	6.00	15.00
13-Jeff Jones-a (15 pgs.)	2.60	8.00	18.00
14-17: 17-Brick Bradford story	1.40	4.00	8.50
18-Kaluta-a (3rd pro work?)	1.70	4.20	10.00
19-30: 19-1st G.K. issue	0.70	1.40	3.50
30-2nd printing (7/81)	0.40	0.80	2.00
31-33: Movie adaptation; Williamson-a	0.40	0.80	2.00
34-37: Movie adaptation	0.40	0.80	2.00

FLASH GORDON
June 1995-July 1995 (2.95, color, limited series)
Marvel Comics

	Good	Fine	N-Mint
1,2-Shultz-s/Williamson-a	0.60	1.20	3.00

FLESH CRAWLERS
Aug 1993-Present (2.50, B&W, limited series:3, Adult)
Kitchen Sink Press

	Good	Fine	N-Mint
1-(8/93)	0.50	1.00	2.50
2-(1/95)	0.50	1.00	2.50

FLINTSTONES, THE (TV)
July, 1961; No. 2, Nov-Dec, 1961-No. 60, Sept, 1970 (Hanna-Barbera)
Dell Publ. Co./Gold Key No. 7 (10/62) on

	Good	Fine	N-Mint
Dell Giant #48 (#1, 7/61)	17.00	50.00	250.00
2	9.00	28.00	65.00

3-6 (7-8/62)	7.10	21.00	50.00
7 (10/62; 1st GK)	6.30	19.00	44.00
8-10: Mr. & Mrs. J. Evil Scientist begin?	5.40	16.00	38.00
11-1st app. Pebbles (6/63)	8.00	24.00	55.00
12-15, 17-20	4.70	14.00	33.00
16-1st app. Bamm Bamm (1/64)	6.40	19.00	45.00
21-30: 24-1st app. The Grusomes	3.90	12.00	27.00
31-33, 35-40: 33-Meet Frankenstein & Dracula			
	3.60	10.70	25.00
34-1st app. The Great Gazoo	4.60	14.00	32.00
41-60: 45-Last 12¢ issue	3.00	9.40	22.00
At N.Y. World's Fair ('64)-JW Brooks (25-cents)-1st printing; no date on-c			
(29 cent version exists, 2nd print?)	5.00	15.00	35.00
At N.Y. World's Fair (1965 on-c; re-issue)	1.00	2.50	6.00
Bigger and Boulder 1(#30013-211)(Gold Key Giant, 11/62, 25¢, 84 pgs.)			
	9.00	28.00	66.00
Bigger and Boulder 2(25¢)(1966)-Reprints B & B No. 1			
	8.00	24.00	55.00
....With Pebbles & Bamm Bamm(100 pgs., GK.)-30028-511			
(paper-c, 25¢)(11/65)	8.00	24.00	55.00

FLINTSTONES, THE (TV)(...& Pebbles)
Nov, 1970-No. 50, Feb, 1977 (Hanna-Barbera)
Charlton Comics

1	5.00	15.00	35.00
2	2.60	7.70	18.00
3-7,9,10	1.70	5.00	12.00
8-"Flintstones Summer Vacation" (Summer,1977, 52 pgs.)			
	2.10	6.40	15.00
11–20	1.80	4.60	11.00
21-50: 36-Early Zeck illos. 37-Early Byrne illos			
	1.80	4.60	11.00

FLINTSTONES, THE (TV)
Oct, 1977-No. 9, Feb, 1979 (Hanna-Barbera)
Marvel Comics

1-9: Yogi Bear app. 4-The Jetsons app.	0.40	0.80	2.00

FLOATERS
Sep 1993-No. 5 Jan 1994 (2.50, B&W, limited series)
Dark Horse Comics

1–5	0.50	1.00	2.50

	Good	Fine	N-Mint

FLOOD RELIEF
Jan, 1994 (Color, 36 pgs.)(Ordered thru mail w/$5.00 to Red Cross)
Malibu Comics (Ultraverse)

	Good	Fine	N-Mint
1-Hardcase, Prime & Prototype app.	1.00	2.00	5.00

FLY, THE (See Adventures of..., Mighty Comics & Mighty Crusaders)
May, 1983-No. 9, Oct, 1984
Archie Enterprises, Inc.

	Good	Fine	N-Mint
1-9: 1-Origin Shield. 1,2-Steranko-c. 2-9-Ditko-a	0.20	0.40	1.00

FLYING SAUCERS
Apr, 1967-No. 4, Nov, 1967; No. 5, Oct, 1969
Dell Publishing Co.

	Good	Fine	N-Mint
1	1.80	4.60	11.00
2–5	1.00	2.50	6.00

FLY MAN (Formerly Adventures Of The Fly)
No. 32, July, 1965- No. 39, Sept, 1966
Mighty Comics Group (Radio Comics) (Archie)

	Good	Fine	N-Mint
32, 33-Comet, Shield, Black Hood, The Fly & Flygirl. 33-1st S.A. app. Wizard & Hangman (re-intro)	3.70	11.10	26.00
34-39: 34-Shield begins. 35-Origin Black Hood. 36-Re-intro/origin Web (1st S.A. app.). 39-1st S.A. app. Steel Sterling	2.40	7.30	17.00

FOODANG
July, 1994 - Present (1.95/2.50, B&W)
Continum Comics/August House

	Good	Fine	N-Mint
1-Perez foil-c(i) w/bound in card of The Dark B.Sears/a	0.40	0.80	2.00
2-(2.50)	0.50	1.00	2.50

FOOLKILLER (See Amaz. Spider-Man 225, Man-Thing & Omega)
Oct, 1990-No. 10, Oct, 1991 (1.75, color, limited series)
Marvel Comics

	Good	Fine	N-Mint
1-Origin	0.40	0.80	2.00
2-7, 9,10	0.40	0.70	1.75
8-Spider-Man x-over	0.50	1.00	2.50

FORBIDDEN TALES OF DARK MANSION
(Dark Mansion Of Forbidden Love #1-4)
No. 5, May-June, 1972-No. 15, Feb-Mar, 1974

National Periodical Publications
5-15: 13-Kane/Howard art   1.00   2.00   5.00

FORBIDDEN WORLDS
No. 35, Aug, 1955-No. 145, Aug, 1967
American Comics Group
35-(Scarce)-1st code approved issue   7.90   24.00   55.00
36-62   5.00   15.00   35.00
63, 69, 76, 78-Williamson-a   6.00   18.00   42.00
64, 66-68, 70-72, 74, 75, 77, 79-85, 87-90 4.60   13.70   32.00
65-Record fan mail response   5.30   16.00   37.00
73-1st app. Herbie by Whitney   27.00   81.00   190.00
86-Flying saucer-c by Schaffenberger   5.00   15.00   35.00
91-93, 95-100   3.00   9.40   22.00
94-Herbie app.   7.00   20.00   46.00
101-109, 111-113, 115, 117-120   2.60   7.70   18.00
110, 114, 116-Herbie app. 114-1st Herbie-c 4.10   12.40   29.00
121-124: 124-Magic Agent app.   2.60   7.70   18.00
125-Magic Agent app.; intro & origin Magicman series, ends 141
                                            2.90   9.00   20.00
126-130   2.40   7.30   17.00
131-139: 133-Origin/1st app. Dragonia(1-2/66)
                                            2.10   6.00   15.00
140-Mark Midnight app. by Ditko   2.40   7.30   17.00
141-145   2.00   5.00   12.00

FORCE WORKS
July, 1994-Present (1.50, color)
Marvel Comics
1-(3.95)-Fold-out pop-up-c; Iron Man, Wonder Man, Spider-Woman, U.S.
    Agent & Scarlet Witch (new costume)   0.80   1.60   4.00
2–11, 13–14: 5-Blue logo 9-Intro Dreamguard
                                            0.30   0.60   1.50
5-(2.95)-Pink logo; polybagged w/16-pg Marvel Action Hour Preview &
    acetate print   0.60   1.20   3.00
12-(2.50)-Flip book w/War Machine 13-Avengers app.
                                            0.50   1.00   2.50

FOREVER PEOPLE
Feb-Mar, 1971-No. 11, Oct-Nov, 1972
National Periodical Publications
1-1st app. Forever People; Kirby-c/a in all; Darkseid app. (1st full app.;
    see Superman's Pal... #134, 135)   5.70   17.00   40.00

	Good	Fine	N-Mint

Freak Force #7 © Eric Larson

Freex #5 © Malibu

	Good	Fine	N-Mint
2-5: Darkseid storyline in #1-8	4.00	10.70	25.00
6-11: 9,10-Deadman x-over	1.70	4.20	10.00

FRANK
Apr (Mar. inside), 1994-No. 4, July, 1994 (1.75, color, limited series)
Nemesis Comics

1-(2.50)-Foil cover edition	0.50	1.00	2.50
1-(1.75)-Cowan-a(p) in all	0.40	0.70	1.75
2-4-(2.50)-Direct Edition	0.50	1.00	2.50
2-4-(1.75)-Newsstand Edition	0.40	0.70	1.75

FRANKENSTEIN (See Dracula, Universal Monsters & Werewolf)
Aug-Oct, 1964; No. 2, Sept, 1966-No. 4, Mar, 1967
Dell Publishing Co.

1(12-283-410)	2.30	6.90	16.00
2-Intro & origin super-hero character	1.70	4.20	10.00
3,4	1.30	3.00	8.00

FRANKENSTEIN (Monster Of...)
Jan, 1973-No. 18, Sept, 1975
Marvel Comics Group

1-Ploog-c/a begins, ends #6	2.30	6.90	16.00
2-5, 8, 9: 8, 9-Dracula app. (death of in 9)	1.50	3.80	9.00
6, 7, 10	1.00	2.00	5.50
11–18	0.60	1.20	3.00
Power Record giveaway (16 pgs., Adams art)			
	1.70	4.00	10.00

FRANKENSTEIN/DRACULA WAR, THE
Feb 1995 - Present (2.50, color,limited series:3)
Topps Comics

| 1-3 | 0.50 | 1.00 | 2.50 |

FRANKENSTEIN, JR. (...& The Impossibles)(TV)
Jan, 1967 (Hanna-Barbera)
Gold Key

| 1-Super heroes | 2.30 | 6.90 | 16.00 |

FRANKENSTEIN: OR THE MODERN PROMETHEUS
1994 (2.95, color, Oneshot)
Caliber Press

| 1 | 0.60 | 1.20 | 3.00 |

FREAK FORCE
Dec, 1993-Present (1.95/2.50, color)
Image Comics

1-7: Superpatriot & Mighty Man in all; Larsen scripts. 4-Vanguard app.
| | 0.40 | 0.80 | 2.00 |
8-17-w/centerfold pinup: 8-Begin 2.50-c. 9-CyberForce-c & app.
| | 0.50 | 1.00 | 2.50 |

FREEDOM AGENT (Also see John Steele)
Apr, 1963 (12¢)
Gold Key

| 1 (10054-304)-Painted-c | 1.80 | 5.00 | 11.00 |

FREEDOM FIGHTERS
Mar-Apr, 1976-No. 15, July-Aug, 1978
National Periodical Publ./DC Comics

1-Uncle Sam, Ray, Black Condor, Doll Man, Human Bomb & Phantom
    Lady begin | 0.40 | 0.80 | 2.00 |
2-15: 14, 15-Batgirl & Batwoman app. | 0.20 | 0.40 | 1.00 |

FREEX
July, 1993-Present (1.95, color)
Malibu Comics (Ultraverse)

1-3, 5-14, 16, 17: 1-Bagged w/trading card & coupon for Ultraverse
    Premiere #0. 1st app. Boom Boy,Anything,Pressure, Sweetface and Plug
    2-Some came bagged w/card. 6-Night Man-c/story. 7-Origin Hardcase
    17-Rune app. | 0.40 | 0.80 | 2.00 |
1-Full cover Hologram ed. | 4.30 | 13.00 | 30.00 |
1-Ultra 5,000 limited ed. w/silver ink-c | 2.90 | 9.00 | 20.00 |
4-(2.50, 48 pgs.)-Rune flip-c/story by Smith; 3 pg. Night Man preview
    | 0.50 | 1.00 | 2.50 |

	Good	Fine	N-Mint
15-(3.50) w/Ultraverse Premiere #9 flip book			
	0.70	1.40	3.50
Giant Size… 1 (7/94, 2.50, 44 pgs.)-Prime app.			
	0.50	1.00	2.50

FROM BEYOND THE UNKNOWN
Oct-Nov, 1969-No. 25, Nov-Dec, 1973
National Periodical Publications

1	1.20	2.90	7.00
2-10: N. Adams c-3,6,8,9	0.90	1.80	4.50
11-25: Space Museum in 23-25	0.60	1.10	2.75

F-TROOP (TV)
Aug, 1966- No. 7, Aug, 1967 (All have photo-c)
Dell Publishing Co.

1	7.90	24.00	55.00
2-7	3.60	11.00	25.00

FUGITOID
Jan, 1985 (B&W, one-shot, magazine size)
Mirage Studios

1-Ties-in w/TMNT #4 & 5	1.00	3.00	6.00

FUN-IN (TV)
2/70-No. 10, 1/72; No. 11, 4/74-No. 15, 12/74 (Hanna-Barbera)
Gold Key

1-Dastardly & Muttley; Perils of Penelope Pitstop			
	2.40	7.30	17.00
2-4, 6: 2-4-Cattanooga Cats app.	1.30	3.00	8.00
5,7-Motormouse & Autocat; Dastardly & Muttley			
	1.70	4.20	10.00
8,10-Harlem Globetrotters. 10-Dastardly & Muttley			
	1.30	3.00	7.50
9-Where's Huddles?, Dastardly & Muttley, Motormouse & Autocat app.			
	1.70	4.20	10.00
11-15: 12,15-Speed Buggy	1.00	2.50	6.00

FUNKY PHANTOM, THE (TV)
Mar, 1972-No. 13, Mar, 1975 (Hanna-Barbera)
Gold Key

1	1.90	6.00	13.00
2-5	1.10	2.70	6.50
6-13	0.80	1.50	3.75

FUNTASTIC WORLD OF HANNA-BARBERA, THE (TV)
Dec, 1977-No. 3, June, 1978 (1.25, oversized)
Marvel Comics Group
1-3: 1-The Flintstones Christmas Party. 2-Yogi Bear's Easter Parade.
  3-Laff-a-lympics   1.00   2.00   5.00

FURY
May, 1994 (2.95, color, one-shot)
Marvel Comics
1-Ironman, Red Skull, FF, Hatemonger, Logan, Scorpio app.; origin Nick
  Fury   0.60   1.20   3.00

FURY OF FIRESTORM (Becomes Firestorm the Nuclear Man No. 65 on)
June, 1982-No. 64, Oct, 1987
DC Comics
1   0.40   0.80   2.00
2-64: 24-1st app. Blue Devil   0.20   0.40   1.00
61-Test cover, Superman logo   4.00   12.00   28.00
Annual 1-4 (1983-1986)   0.30   0.50   1.25

FURY OF HELLINA
Jan 1995- Present (2.75, B&W)
Lightning Comics
1   0.60   1.10   2.75

FURY OF SHIELD
Apr 1995-July 1995 (1.95, color, limited series)
Marvel Comics
1-(2.50)-foil-c   0.50   1.00   2.50
2–4; 4-bagged with decoder   0.40   0.80   2.00

FUTURIANS
Aug 1995-Present (2.95, color)
Aardwolf
1-Dave Cockrum   0.60   1.20   3.00

G

Gen Roddenberry's Lost Universe #6 © Big Ent.

Gen 13 #4 © Aegis Ent.

	Good	Fine	N-Mint
GALACTIC GUARDIANS			
July, 1994-No. 4, Oct, 1994 (1.50, color, mini-series)			
Marvel Comics			
1–4	0.30	0.50	1.25
GAMBIT (See X-Men #266 & X-Men Annual #14)			
Dec, 1993-No. 4, Mar, 1994 (2.00, color, mini-series)			
Marvel Comics			
1-(2.50)-Gold foil stamped-c	1.00	2.00	5.00
1–Gold	6.00	12.00	30.00
2–4	0.60	1.20	3.00
GAMBIT AND THE X-TERNALS			
Mar 1995 (1.95 color)			
Marvel Comics			
1-Age of Apocalypse	0.80	1.60	4.00
2-4	0.40	0.80	2.00
GARGOYLES			
Feb 1995 - Present (2.50, color)			
Marvel Comics			
1-6-based on animated TV series	0.50	1.00	2.50
GARRISON'S GORILLAS (TV)			
Jan, 1968-No. 4, Oct, 1968: No. 5, Oct, 1969 (Photo-c)			
Dell Publishing Co.			
1	3.60	11.00	25.00
2-5: 5-Reprints #1	2.40	7.30	17.00

GASP!
March, 1967-No. 4, Aug, 1967 (12¢)
American Comics Group
1	3.30	9.90	23.00
2-4	2.00	6.00	14.00

GEEK, THE (See Brother Power... & Vertigo Visions)

GENE RODDENBERRY'S LOST UNIVERSE
Apr, 1995 (1.95, color)
Tekno Comix
1-3-w/bound in game piece and trading card			
	0.40	0.80	2.00
4-bound in trading card, 5-7	0.40	0.80	2.00

GENERATION NEXT
Mar 1995 (1.95, color)
Marvel Comics
1- Age of Apocalypse	0.80	1.60	4.00
2-4	0.40	0.80	2.00

GENERATION X
Oct, 1994-Present (1.50, 1.95, color)
Marvel Comics
...Collectors Preview (1.75)	0.40	0.70	1.75
..."Ashcan" Edition	0.20	0.30	0.75
1-(3.95)-Wraparound chromium-c	1.00	2.00	5.00
2-4-(1.95)-Deluxe edition	0.40	0.80	2.00
2-4-(1.50)-Standard edition	0.30	0.60	1.50
5-(1.95-c) Return from "Age of Apocalypse"; 6–			
	0.40	0.80	2.00

GEN 13
Feb, 1994-July, 1994 (1.95, color, limited series)
Image Comics
1-(2.50)-Created by Jim Lee; pull-out poster			
	4.30	8.60	30.00
2-(2.50)	4.20	10.40	25.00
3-4: 3,4-Pitt-c & story. 4-Wraparound-c	3.00	6.00	15.00
5-	1.00	2.00	5.00
5-Alternate Portacio-c, see Deathblow #5	2.00	4.00	10.00
0-(2.50)-Ch. 1 w/Jim Lee-p; Ch. 4 w/Charest-p			
	0.60	1.20	3.00

	Good	Fine	N-Mint
...Collected Edition ('94, 12.95) r/#1-5	1.90	5.60	13.00
...Rave-(1.50, 3/95)-Wraparound-c	0.80	1.60	4.00

GEN 13
Mar, 1995-Present (2.50, color)
Image Comics
(Note: #1's all have 2.95-c)

	Good	Fine	N-Mint
1-A-(Charge)-a-J. Scott Campbell/Alex Garner			
	0.60	1.20	3.00
1-B-(Thumbs Up)-a-J. Scott Campbell/Alex Garner			
	0.60	1.20	3.00
1-C-(Li'l GEN 13)-a-Art Adams	2.40	4.80	12.00
1-D-(Barbari-GEN)-a-Simon Bisley	2.40	4.80	12.00
1-E-(Your Friendley Neighborhood Grunge)-a-John Cleary			
	2.40	4.80	12.00
1-F-(GEN 13 Goes Madison Ave.)-a-Michael Golden			
	2.40	4.80	12.00
1-G-(Lin-GEN-re)-a-Michael Lopez	3.60	7.20	18.00
1-H-(GEN-et Jackson)-a-Jason Pearson	3.60	7.20	18.00
1-I-(That's the Way We Became GEN 13)-a-J. Scott Campbell/Chuck Gibson			
	2.40	4.80	12.00
1-J-(All Dolled Up)-a-J. Scott Campbell/Tom McWeeney			
	2.40	4.80	12.00
1-K-(Verti-GEN)-a-Joe Dunn	2.40	4.80	12.00
1-L-(Picto-Fiction)	2.40	4.80	12.00
1-M-(Do-It-Yourself-Cover)	2.40	4.80	12.00
2-(1.95)-Newstand, WildStorm Rising pt.4			
	0.40	0.80	2.00
2-(2.50)-Direct Market, WildStorm Rising pt. 4, bound-in card			
	0.50	1.00	2.50

GEOMANCER
Nov, 1994-Present (2.25, color)
Valiant

	Good	Fine	N-Mint
1-(3.75)-Chromium wraparound-c; Eternal Warrior app.			
	0.80	1.50	3.75
2-8	0.50	0.90	2.25

GEORGE OF THE JUNGLE (TV)
Feb, 1969-No. 2, Oct, 1969 (Jay Ward)
Gold Key

	Good	Fine	N-Mint
1	8.60	26.00	60.00
2	7.10	21.00	50.00

GET SMART (TV)
June, 1966-No. 8, Sept, 1967 (All have Don Adams photo-c)
Dell Publishing

1	10.00	30.00	70.00
2-Ditko-a	6.40	19.00	45.00
3-8: 3-Ditko-a(p)	5.70	17.00	40.00

GHOST
Apr, 1995-Present (2.50, color)
Dark Horse Comics

1-Adam Hughes-a	0.40	1.00	3.00
2,3-Hughes-a	0.40	1.00	2.50

GHOSTDANCING
Mar 1995 - Present (1.95, color, limited series:6)
DC Comics

1–5-Case-a	0.40	0.80	2.00

GHOST IN THE SHELL
Mar 1995-Present (3.95, color & B&W, limited series:8))
Dark Horse Comics

1–4	0.80	1.60	4.00

GHOST RIDER (See Night Rider & Western Gunfighters)
Feb, 1967-No. 7, Nov, 1967 (Western)
Marvel Comics Group

1-Origin Ghost Rider; Kid Colt reprint	5.00	15.00	35.00
2–7	2.00	6.00	14.00

GHOST RIDER (See The Champions & Marvel Spotlight #5)
Sept, 1973-No. 81, June, 1983 (Motorcycle hero)
Marvel Comics Group

1-Johnny Blaze (Ghost Rider) begins; 1st app. Daimon Hellstrom (Son of Satan) in cameo	11.00	34.00	80.00
2-1st full app. Daimon Hellstrom; cont. in Marvel Spotlight #12	4.60	14.00	32.00
3-5: 3-Ghost Rider gets new cycle; Son/Satan app.	3.30	9.90	23.00
6-10: 10-Reprints origin & 1st app.	2.10	6.40	15.00
11–19	1.70	5.10	12.00
20-Byrne-a; Death's Head app.; see Daredevil #138	2.30	6.90	16.00

	Good	Fine	N-Mint
21-30: 29, 30-G.R. battles Dr. Strange	1.20	2.90	7.00
31-49	1.00	2.50	6.00
50-Double size	1.20	3.00	7.00
51-67, 69-76, 78-80	0.90	1.80	4.40
68, 77-Origin retold	1.00	2.50	6.00
81-Death of Ghost Rider	1.50	3.80	9.00

GHOST RIDER
May, 1990-Present (1.50/1.75, color)
Marvel Comics (Midnight Sons imprint #44 on)

	Good	Fine	N-Mint
V2#1-(1.95, 52 pgs.)-Origin	1.40	4.00	10.00
1-2nd printing (not gold)	1.00	1.70	4.00
2	1.40	4.00	10.00
3-Kingpin app.	1.40	4.00	10.00
4-Scarcer	2.10	6.40	15.00
5-Punisher app.	1.40	4.30	10.00
5-Gold 2nd print	1.20	2.90	7.00
6-Punisher app.	0.80	2.10	5.00
7-10	0.70	1.40	3.50
11-14: 14-Johnny Blaze vs. Ghost Rider	0.50	1.00	2.50
15-Glow In The Dark cover; begin 1.75-c	0.90	2.30	5.50
15-Gold 2nd printing (1.75-c)	0.50	0.90	2.25
16, 17- Spider-Man/Hobgoblin-c/story	0.60	1.20	3.00
18-24, 29, 30, 32-39: 37-Archangel app.	0.30	0.60	1.60
25-(2.75)-Contains pop-up scene insert	0.50	0.90	2.25
26, 27-X-Men x-over, Jim Lee-c(p)	0.50	0.90	2.25
28-(2.50, 52 pgs.)-Polybagged w/poster	0.70	1.40	3.50
31-(2.50, 52 pgs.)-Polybagged w/poster	0.40	0.80	2.00
40-(2.25)-Outer-c is a Darkhold envelope made-c black parchment w/gold ink; Midnight Massacre; Demogoblin app.	0.40	0.80	1.90
41-48: 41-Lilith & Centurious app. 41-43-Neon ink-c. 44-Spot varnish-c. 44, 45-Siege of Darkness Pt. 2 & Pt. 10. 46-Intro new Ghost Rider. 48-Spider-Man app.	0.40	0.70	1.75
49,51-60, 62-64: 49-Begin 1.95-c; bound-in trading card sheet; Hulk app. 55-Werewolf by Night app.	0.40	0.80	2.00
50-(2.50, 52 pgs.)-Regular edition	0.50	1.00	2.50
50-(2.95, 52 pgs.)-Collectors ed. die cut foil-c	0.60	1.20	3.00
61-(2.50)	0.50	1.00	2.50
Annual 1 ('93, 2.95)-Polybagged w/card	0.50	1.00	2.50
Annual 2 ('94, 2.95, 68 pgs.)	0.50	1.00	2.50

Ghost Rider and Cable #1 (9/92, 3.95)-r/Marvel Comics #90-98 with new

Ghost Rider #53 © MEG

Ghost Rider 2099 #5 © MEG

Kieth-c	0.70	1.40	3.50
Ghost Rider/Captain America: Fear nn (10/92, 5.95, 52 pgs.)-Gatefold-c;			
Williamson-i	1.00	2.50	6.00
Ghost Rider;Wolverine;Punisher:The Dark Design			
(12/94, 5.95) Gatefold-c	1.00	2.50	6.00

GHOST RIDER/BLAZE: SPIRITS OF VENGEANCE
Aug, 1992-No. 23, June, 1994 (1.75, color)
Marvel Comics (Midnight Sons imprint #17 on)

1-(2.75, 52 pgs.)-Polybagged w/poster	0.60	1.10	2.75
2-11, 14-16: 5, 6-Spirits of Venom parts 2 & 4. 14-17-Neon ink-c;			
15-Intro Blaze's new costume & powers	0.40	0.70	1.75
12-(2.95)-Glow-in-the-dark-c	0.60	1.20	3.00
13-(2.25)-Outer-c is a Darkhold envelope made of black parchment			
w/gold ink	0.50	0.90	2.25
17-21: 17-Spot varnish-c. 17,18-Siege of Darkness Pt. 8 & Pt. 13			
	0.40	0.70	1.75
22, 23: 22-Begin 1.95-c; bound-in card sheet			
	0.40	0.80	2.00

GHOST RIDER 2099
May, 1994-Present (1.50, color)
Marvel Comics

1-(2.25)-Collectors Ed. foil-c w/bound-in trading card sheet			
	0.60	1.20	3.00
1-(1.50)-Newsstand Ed. w/bound-in card sheet			
	0.30	0.60	1.50
2–12: 7-Spider-Man 2099-c & app.	0.30	0.60	1.50
13-16; 13-begin 1.95-c	0.40	0.80	2.00

	Good	Fine	N-Mint
GHOST RIDER; WOLVERINE; PUNISHER: HEARTS OF DARKNESS			
Dec, 1991 (4.95, color, one-shot, 52 pgs.)			
Marvel Comics			
1-Double gatefold-c; Romita, Jr.-c/a(p)	1.00	2.00	5.00
GHOSTS			
Sept-Oct, 1971-No. 112, May, 1982 (#1-5: 52 pgs.)			
National Periodical Publications			
1	1.70	4.00	10.00
2-Wood-a	0.80	1.60	4.00
3-5: 5-Last 52-pg. issue	0.60	1.20	3.00
6–20	0.40	0.80	2.00
21-96: 95-99,101-Dr. 13 Ghostbreaker back-ups			
	0.30	0.60	1.50
97-99: Spectre app.; 97, 98 Spectre-c	0.40	0.80	2.00
100-112: 100-Infinity-c	0.20	0.40	1.00
GHOST SPECIAL			
July, 1994 (3.95, color, 48 pgs., one-shot)			
Dark Horse Comics			
1	1.20	2.40	6.00
GIANT-SIZE...			
May, 1974-Dec, 1975 (35-50¢, 52-68 pgs.) (Some titles quarterly)			
Marvel Comics Group			
Avengers 1 (8/74)	1.30	3.30	8.00
Avengers 2, 3	1.20	2.40	6.00
Avengers 4, 5	1.00	2.00	5.00
Captain America 1 (12/75)-r/origin T.O.S. 63			
	1.70	4.20	10.00
Captain Marvel 1 (12/75)	1.50	4.00	9.00
Chillers 1 (6/74)	0.80	1.60	4.00
Chillers 1 (2/75)	0.60	1.20	3.00
Chillers 2 (5/75)	0.60	1.20	3.00
Chillers 3 (8/75)-Wrightson-c/a	0.80	1.60	4.00
Conan 1 (9/74)-1st app. Belit	1.20	2.90	7.00
Conan 2 (12/74)	1.00	2.50	6.00
Conan 3-5 (1975)	0.80	1.60	4.00
Creatures 1 (5/74)-Werewolf app.; becomes Giant-Size Werewolf			
	1.00	2.00	5.00
Daredevil 1 (1975)	1.30	3.30	8.00
Defenders 1 (7/74)-Silver Surfer app.; Starlin-a			
	1.80	4.60	11.00

Defenders 2 (10/74)-Son of Satan app.	1.00	2.50	6.00
Defenders 3-5: 3-Starlin-a. 5-Guardians app.			
	1.00	2.00	5.00
Doc Savage 1 (1975)-Reprints 1&2	0.80	1.60	4.00
Doctor Strange 1 (11/75)-r/Strange Tales #164-168			
	1.00	2.90	7.00
Dracula 2 (9/74)-Formerly G-S Chillers	1.00	2.00	5.00
Dracula 3 (12/74)	0.80	1.60	4.00
Dracula 4 (3/75)-Ditko-r	0.60	1.20	3.00
Dracula 5 (6/75)-1st Byrne art at Marvel	1.00	2.50	6.00
Fantastic Four 2-4 (8/74-2/75)-Formerly Giant-Size Super-Stars #1			
	1.70	4.20	10.00
Fantastic Four 5 (5/75), 6 (10/75)	1.30	3.30	8.00
Hulk 1 (1975)	2.00	5.00	12.00
Invaders 1 (6/75)-Origin	1.00	2.50	6.00
Iron Man 1 (1975)-Ditko-r	1.50	3.80	9.00
Kid Colt 1-3 (1975)	0.80	1.60	4.00
Man-Thing 1 (8/74)-New Ploog-c/a	1.00	2.50	6.00
Man-Thing 2, 3: 2-Buscema-c/a(p)	0.80	1.60	4.00
Man-Thing 4, 5 (1975)-Howard The Duck app.			
	1.00	2.50	6.00
Marvel Triple Action 1, 2 (1975)	0.60	1.20	3.00
Master Of Kung Fu 1 (9/74)-Yellow Claw-r	1.20	2.90	7.00
Master Of Kung Fu 2 (12/74)-Yellow Claw-r	0.80	1.60	4.00
Master Of Kung Fu 3 (3/75)-Yellow Claw-r	0.80	1.60	4.00
Master Of Kung Fu 4 (6/75)-Yellow Claw-r	0.80	1.60	4.00
Power Man 1 (1975)	1.00	2.50	6.00
Spider-Man 1 (7/74)-Dracula-c/story; Kirby/Ditko & Byrne-r plus new-a			
	3.60	11.00	25.00
Spider-Man 2, 3: 3-Byrne-r	1.70	4.20	10.00
Spider-Man 4 (4/75)-3rd app. Punisher	8.00	24.00	55.00
Spider-Man 5, 6 (1975): 5-Byrne-r	1.50	4.00	9.00
Super-Heroes Featuring Spider-Man 1 (6/74)-Spidey vs. Man-Wolf; Morbius app.	5.70	17.00	40.00
Super-Stars 1 (5/74)-Thing vs. Hulk; becomes Giant-Size Fantastic Four; F.F. app.	2.10	6.40	15.00
Super-Villain Team-Up 1 (3/75)	1.20	2.90	7.00
Super-Villain Team-Up 2 (6/75)-Dr. Doom & Sub-Mariner			
	1.00	2.00	5.00
Thor 1 (7/75)	1.00	2.90	7.00
Werewolf 2 (10/74)-Frankenstein app.; formerly G.S. Creatures			
	0.80	1.60	4.00
Werewolf 3, 5 (1/75 & 7/75)	0.80	1.60	4.00

	Good	Fine	N-Mint
Werewolf 4 (4/75)-Morbius app.	1.00	2.00	5.00
X-Men 1 (Summer, 1975)-1st app. New X-Men; 2nd full app. of			
Wolverine after Hulk #181	41.00	120.00	290.00
X-Men 2 (11/75)-N. Adams-r(51 pgs.)	5.70	17.10	40.00

G. I. COMBAT
No. 44, Jan, 1957-No. 288, Mar, 1987
National Periodical Publications/DC Comics

	Good	Fine	N-Mint
44-Early DC grey-tone-c	29.00	86.00	285.00
45	21.00	64.00	150.00
46-50	14.00	43.00	100.00
51-60 : 51-Grey-tone cover	11.00	34.00	80.00
61-66, 68-80: 75-109-Grey-tone covers	8.60	26.00	60.00
67-1st Tank Killer	11.00	34.00	80.00
81, 82, 84-86,88-90: 90 last 10¢ issue	6.40	19.00	45.00
83-1st Big Al, Little Al, Charlie Cigar	7.10	21.00	50.00
87-1st Haunted Tank	22.00	66.00	155.00
91-100: 91-1st Haunted Tank cover	4.60	14.00	32.00
101-110: 108-1st Sgt. Rock x-over	3.90	11.60	27.00
111-113, 115-120 : 113-Grey-tone-c	3.10	9.40	22.00
114-Origin Haunted Tank	8.60	26.00	60.00
121-137, 139, 140: 136-Last 12¢ issue	2.90	8.60	20.00
138-Intro the Losers in Haunted Tank (Capt. Storm, Gunner & Sarge,			
Johnny Cloud)	2.90	9.00	20.00
141-200: 146-148-(68-pg. issues)	1.00	2.00	5.00
201-288: 260-281-(52 pgs.)	0.60	1.20	3.00

G. I. JOE, A REAL AMERICAN HERO
June, 1982-No. 155, Dec, 1994
Marvel Comics Group

	Good	Fine	N-Mint
1	1.00	2.00	5.00
2	1.00	1.90	4.75
3-10	0.60	1.20	3.00
11-20	0.30	0.60	1.60
21, 22, 26, 27	0.40	0.80	2.00
23-25,28-30	0.40	0.70	1.80
31-134, 139-143: 139-142-New Transformers app.			
	0.30	0.60	1.60
135-138-(1.75)-Polybagged w/trading card	0.40	0.70	1.75
144-149,151,152-(1.25): 144-Origin Snake-Eyes			
	0.30	0.50	1.25
150-(2.00, 52 pgs.)	0.40	0.80	2.00
153-155: 153-Begin 1.50-c	0.30	0.60	1.50

Any 2nd printings	0.20	0.40	1.00
Special Treasury Edition-('82)-r/#1	0.60	1.20	3.00
Yearbook 1-(3/85)-r/#1	0.40	0.80	2.00
Yearbook 2-(3/86)-Golden-c/a	0.40	0.70	1.80
Yearbook 3-(3/87)	0.40	0.70	1.80
Yearbook 4-(2/88)	0.30	0.60	1.50

GIRL FROM U.N.C.L.E, THE (TV)
Jan, 1967-No. 5, Oct, 1967 (All 12¢ issues)
Gold Key
1-Stephanie Powers photo cover front & back & pin-ups (no ads)

	6.90	21.00	48.00
2-5: Photo covers	4.60	13.70	32.00

GIVE ME LIBERTY
June, 1990-No. 4, Apr, 1991 (4.95, mini-series)
Dark Horse Comics

1-4: Miller story/Dave Gibbons art	1.00	2.00	5.00

GLORY
Mar, 1995-Present (2.50, color)
Image Comics

1-Deodato Jr.-a,	0.60	1.20	3.00
1a–variant cover	0.60	1.20	3.00
2, 3–Deodato-a	0.50	1.00	2.50

GOBBLEDYGOOK
1984-No. 2, 1984 (B&W, no price on cover)(1st Mirage book)
Mirage Studios
1, 2-1st app. Teenage Mutant Ninja Turtles (24 pgs.)

	31.00	94.00	220.00

GOBBLEDYGOOK
Dec, 1986 (3.50, one-shot, B&W, 100 pgs.)
Mirage Studios

1-New 8-pg. TMNT story	0.90	1.80	4.50

GOD'S COUNTRY
1994 (6.95, color)
Marvel comics

nn-P. Craig Russell-i	1.20	3.00	7.00

	Good	Fine	N-Mint

GODDESS
June 1995-Present (2.95, color, limited series)
DC Comics

| 1-3 -Garth Ennis-s | 0.50 | 1.00 | 3.00 |

GODWHEEL
Jan 1995 - Present (2.50, color, limited series:4)
Malibu Comics
#0-3:#0-Flip-c, 1-Primevil 1st app. 1-panel Thor cameo

| 3- G.Perez/p-Ch.3-Thor app. | 0.50 | 1.00 | 2.50 |

GODZILLA
August, 1977-No. 24, July, 1979
Marvel Comics Group

1-Based on movie series	1.30	3.30	8.00
2-10: 3-Champions app.	1.00	2.00	5.00
11-24: 20-Fantastic Four app.	0.80	1.60	4.00

GODZILLA
May, 1988-No. 6, 1988 (1.95, B&W, mini-series)
Dark Horse

1	1.00	2.50	6.00
2-6	0.60	1.20	3.00
Color Special 1 (Sum/92, 3.50)-Art Adams-c/a			
	0.70	1.40	3.50
King Of The Monsters Spec. (8/87, 1.50)	0.60	1.20	3.00
...Vs. Barkley nn (12/93, 2.95, color)-Dorman painted-c			
	0.60	1.20	3.00

GODZILLA
May 1995-Present (2.50, color)
Dark Horse Comics
0,1; 0-reprints from Dark Horse Comics #10,11

| | 0.50 | 1.00 | 2.50 |

GO-GO
June, 1966-No. 9, Oct, 1967
Charlton Comics

1-Miss Bikini Luv begins; Rolling Stones, Elvis, Sonny & Cher, Bob Dylan; Sinatra parody; Herman Hermits pin-ups	3.70	11.10	26.00
2-David McCallum, Beatles photos on-c; Beatles story and photos			
	3.70	11.10	26.00
3,4: 3-Blooperman begins, ends #6	2.30	6.90	16.00

5-9: 5-Super Hero & TV satire begins. 6-Petula Clark photo-c. 8-Monkees photo on-c & photo inside b/c	2.30	6.90	16.00

GOLDEN AGE, THE
1993-No. 4, 1994 (4.95, color, mini-series, 52 pgs.)
DC Comics (Elseworlds)

1-4-Gold foil embossed-c; Robinson-s	1.00	2.00	5.00

GOMER PYLE (TV)
July, 1966-No. 3, Jan, 1967
Gold Key

1-Photo front/back-c	5.70	17.00	40.00
2, 3	5.00	15.00	35.00

GORGO (Based on movie)(See Return of...)
May, 1961-No.23, Sept, 1965
Charlton Comics

1-Ditko-a (22 pgs.)	24.00	70.00	170.00
2,3-Ditko-c/a	12.00	36.00	85.00
4-10: 4-Ditko-c	7.00	21.00	50.00
11, 13-16-Ditko-a	5.70	17.00	40.00
12, 17-23: 12-Reptisaurus x-over	2.90	9.00	20.00
Gorgo's Revenge ('62)-Becomes Return of..5.00		15.00	35.00

GRAVESTONE
July, 1993-No. 7, Feb, 1994 (2.25, color)
Malibu Comics

1-6: 3-Polybagged w/Skycap	0.50	0.90	2.25
7-(2.50)	0.50	1.00	2.50

Godzilla #1 © DH

Golden Age #1 © DC

	Good	Fine	N-Mint
GREAT GAZOO, THE (The Flintstones)(TV)			
Aug, 1973-No. 20, Jan, 1977 (Hanna-Barbera)			
Charlton Comics			
1	1.20	2.90	7.00
2–10	0.80	1.60	4.00
GREAT GRAPE APE, THE (TV)			
Sept, 1976-No. 2, Nov, 1976 (Hanna-Barbera)			
Charlton Comics			
1, 2	1.10	2.70	6.50
GREEN ARROW (See Brave & the Bold #50 & 85)			
May, 1983-No. 4, Aug, 1983 (Mini-series)			
DC Comics			
1-Origin	0.80	1.60	4.00
2–4	0.60	1.20	3.00
GREEN ARROW			
Feb, 1988-Present (1.00/1.95, color)			
DC Comics			
1-Grell scripts in all; c-most	0.70	1.70	4.00
2	0.50	1.00	2.50
3-49, 51-74, 76-86: 68-Last 1.50-c. 85-Deathstroke-c/story.			
86-Catwoman-c/story w/Jim Balent layouts	0.40	0.70	1.75
50, 75-(2.50, 52 pgs.)-Ann. issues	0.50	1.00	2.50
87-90: 87-Begin 1.95-c. 88-Wonder Woman-c. 90-(9/94)-Zero Hour			
	0.40	0.80	2.00
0,91-96: 0-(10/94)-Aparo-a(p). 91-(11/94)	0.40	0.80	2.00
97–begin 2.25-c; 98-99	0.50	0.90	2.25
Annual 1 ('88, 2.00)-No Grell scripts	0.40	0.80	2.00
Annual 2 ('89, 2.50, 68 pgs.)	0.50	1.00	2.50
Annual 3 ('90, 2.95)	0.60	1.20	3.00
Annual 4 ('91, 2.95)-50th Ann. issue	0.40	0.80	2.00
Annual 5 ('92, 3.00)-Batman, Eclipso app.	0.60	1.20	3.00
Annual 6 ('93, 3.50)-Bloodlines; Hook app.	0.70	1.40	3.50
GREEN ARROW: THE LONG BOW HUNTERS			
Aug, 1987-No. 3, Oct, 1987 (2.95, color, mini-series)			
DC Comics			
1-Grell-c/a in all	1.30	3.00	7.50
1,2-2nd printings	0.40	0.80	2.00
2	0.80	1.60	4.00
3	0.60	1.20	3.00

GREEN ARROW: THE WONDER YEAR
Feb, 1993-No. 4, May, 1993 (1.75, color, mini-series)
DC Comics

1-4: By Grell/Morrow	0.40	0.70	1.75

GREEN HORNET, THE (TV)
Feb, 1967-No. 3, Aug, 1967
Gold Key

1-Bruce Lee photo-c on all	18.00	54.00	125.00
2, 3	14.00	40.00	95.00

GREEN HORNET, THE
Nov, 1989-No. 14, Feb, 1991 (1.75, color)
Now Comics

1-(2.95, 52 pgs.)-Steranko painted-c	1.10	3.00	8.00
1-2nd print ('90, 3.95)-New cover	0.80	1.60	4.00
2	0.80	2.00	5.00
3-5: 5-Death of original ('30s) Green Hornet	0.50	1.30	3.00
6-8: 6-Dorman painted-c	0.60	1.20	3.00
9–14	0.40	0.80	2.00

GREEN HORNET
V2#1, Sept, 1991-Present (1.95, color)
Now Comics

V2#1-11, 13-21, 24-26, 28-37,39: 1-Butler painted-c			
	0.40	0.80	2.00
12-(2.50)-Bagged w/color Gr. Hornet button	0.50	1.00	2.50
22, 23-(2.95)-Bagged w/color hologravure card			
	0.60	1.20	3.00
27-(2.95)-Newsstand; bagged w/multi-dimensional card (1993			
anniversary special on-c)	0.60	1.20	3.00
27-(2.95)-Direct; bagged w/multi-dimensional card; cover variation			
	0.60	1.20	3.00
31,38: 31-(2.50)-Newsstand bagged w/card			
	0.50	1.00	2.50
1-(2.50)-Polybagged w/button (same as #12)			
	0.50	1.00	2.50
2, 3 (1.95)-Same as #13 & 14	0.40	0.80	2.00
Annual 1 (12/92, 2.50)	0.50	1.00	2.50
Annual 1994 (10/94 , 2.95)	0.60	1.20	3.00

GREEN HORNET: SOLITARY SENTINEL, THE
Dec, 1992-No. 3, 1993 (2.50, color, mini-series)

	Good	Fine	N-Mint
Now Comics			
1–3	0.50	1.00	2.50

GREEN LANTERN (...Corps No. 206 on)(See Showcase #22-24)
July-Aug, 1960-No. 205 (indicia), Oct, 1986
National Periodical Publications/DC Comics

	Good	Fine	N-Mint
1-Origin retold	217.00	650.00	1950.00
2-1st Pieface	74.00	221.00	590.00
3	40.00	130.00	355.00
4, 5: 5-Origin/1st app. Hector Hammond	34.00	103.00	275.00
6-10: 8-Grey tone-c. 9-Last 10¢ issue	24.00	71.00	190.00
11, 12	18.60	60.00	130.00
13-Flash x-over (also #20)	23.00	69.00	160.00
14-20: 16-Origin/1st app. Star Sapphire	17.00	51.00	120.00
21-30: 29-JLA cameo	14.00	43.00	100.00
31-39	11.00	34.00	80.00
40-1st app. Crisis; 2nd solo GA Green Lantern in Silver Age (10/65); see			
Showcase #55	50.00	150.00	400.00
41-44, 46-50	7.00	21.00	48.00
45-2nd SA app. GA Green Lantern in title(6/66)			
	11.00	32.00	75.00
51, 53-58	5.00	15.00	35.00
52-GA Green Lantern x-over (9/67)	5.70	17.00	40.00
59-1st app. Guy Gardner (3/68)	24.00	70.00	170.00
60, 62-69: 69-Last 12¢ issue	3.00	9.00	21.00
61-GA Green Lantern x-over	4.60	13.70	32.00
70-75	2.60	7.70	18.00
76-Begin Green Lantern/Green Arrow series (4/70); ends #122 (see			
Flash #217); Adams-a #76-87,89	17.00	51.00	120.00
77	6.00	18.00	42.00
78-80	4.60	14.00	32.00
81-84: 84-Last 15¢ issue	3.70	11.00	26.00
85, 86: (52 pgs.)-Anti-Drug issues	5.40	16.00	38.00
87-(12-1/71-72, 52 pgs.)-2nd app. Guy Gardner (cameo); 1st app. John			
Stewart (3rd Gr. Lantern)	3.40	10.30	24.00
88-(52 pgs.)-r/Showcase 23 & unpubbed G.A. Green Lantern story; 1 pg.			
Neal Adams-a plus-c	1.00	2.50	6.00
89-(4-5/72, 52 pgs.)-Last G.L./G. A. by Adams; Green Lantern & Green			
Arrow move to Flash #217 (9/72)	1.80	5.00	11.00
90-99: 90-(8/76)-Grell-a begins, ends 111	0.60	1.20	3.00
100-(Giant, 1/78)-1st app. Air Wave II	1.00	2.50	6.00
101-111, 113-115, 117-119: 108-110-(44 pgs.). 111-Origin retold			
	0.50	1.00	2.50

112-GA Green Lantern origin retold	1.00	2.50	6.00
116-(5/79)-1st app. Guy Gardner as Green Lantern			
	3.60	10.70	25.00
120, 121, 124-135, 138-140, 142-149: 132-Adam Strange series begins,			
ends #147	0.40	0.70	1.80
122-Last GL/Green Arrow teamup	0.50	0.90	2.25
123-2nd Guy Gardner as G. L.	1.00	2.50	6.00
136,137-1st app. Citadel; Space Ranger app.	0.60	1.10	2.75
141-1st app. Omega Men (6/81)	0.60	1.10	2.75
150-(52 pgs.)-Anniversary issue	0.60	1.10	2.75
151-193, 196-199, 201-205	0.40	0.70	1.80
194-Hal Jordan/Guy Gardner battle	1.00	2.10	5.00
195-Guy Gardner becomes Green Lantern	1.70	5.10	12.00
200-Double Size	0.60	1.10	2.75
Special 1, 2 (1988, 1989, 1.50, 52 pgs.)	0.50	1.00	2.50
Note: Annual #1 listed under Tales Of The…			

GREEN LANTERN
June, 1990-Present (1.00/1.25, color)
DC Comics

1-Hal Jordan, John Stewart, Guy Gardner	0.60	1.20	3.00
2, 3	0.40	0.80	2.00
4–8	0.20	0.50	1.20
9-12: Guy Gardner solo story	0.50	1.00	2.50
13-(1.75, 52 pgs.)	0.40	0.80	2.00
14-18, 20-24, 26: 18-Guy Gardner solo story			
	0.20	0.40	1.00
19-(1.75, 52 pgs.)-50th Anniversary issue	0.40	0.70	1.75
25-(1.75,52 pgs)-Hal Jordan/G. Gardner battle			
	0.40	0.80	2.00
27-45, 47: 42-Deathstroke-c/story	0.30	0.50	1.25
46-Superman app. cont'd in Superman #82			
	1.00	2.00	5.00
48,49: 48-Begin 1.50-c; Emerald Twilight begins			
	0.60	1.20	3.00
50-(2.95, 52 pgs.)-Glow-in-the-dark-c; intro new GL, death of Sinestro;			
Emerald Twilight ends	0.60	1.20	3.00
51-55: 51-New GL & new costume. 53-Superman-c/sty. 55-(9/94)-			
Zero Hour	0.30	0.60	1.50
0,56-62: 0-(10/94). 56-(11/94)	0.30	0.60	1.50
63-(begin 1.75-c) 63,64-vs. Hal Jordan,65-New Titans app.			
	0.40	0.70	1.75
Annual 1 ('92, 2.50)	0.50	1.00	2.50

Grendel #3 © Comico/Matt Wagner

Grifter #1 © Aegis Ent.

	Good	Fine	N-Mint
Annual 2 ('93, 2.50)-Intro Nightblade	0.50	1.00	2.50
Annual 3 ('94, 2.95)-Elseworlds story	0.60	1.20	3.00
…Emerald Twilight nn ('94, 5.95)-r/#48-50	1.00	2.50	6.00
…Ganthet's Tale nn ('92, 5.95)-Foil logo; Byrne-c/a			
	1.00	2.50	6.00
…/Green Arrow Collection, Volume 2-r/GL #84-87,89 & Flash #217-219 & GL/GA #5-7 by O'Neil/Adams/Wrightson			
	1.90	5.60	13.00

GREEN LANTERN CORPS
No. 206, Nov, 1986-No. 224, June, 1986
DC Comics

	Good	Fine	N-Mint
206-223	0.20	0.40	1.00
224-Double-size final issue	0.30	0.60	1.50
Annual 2 (12/86)-A. Moore scripts	0.30	0.60	1.50
Annual 3 (8/87)-Moore scripts, Byrne art	0.30	0.60	1.50

GREEN LANTERN CORPS QUARTERLY
Summer, 1992-No. 8, Spring, 1994 (2.50, color, 68 pgs.)
DC Comics

	Good	Fine	N-Mint
1–8	0.50	1.00	2.50

GREEN LANTERN: EMERALD DAWN
Dec, 1989-No. 6, May, 1990 (1.00, color, mini-series)
DC Comics

	Good	Fine	N-Mint
1-Origin retold	0.80	1.60	4.00
2	0.60	1.20	3.00
3, 4	0.40	0.80	2.00
5, 6	0.30	0.60	1.50

GREEN LANTERN: EMERALD DAWN II
Apr, 1991-No. 6, Sept, 1991 (1.00, color, mini-series)
DC Comics (Emerald Dawn II #s 1, 2)

1	0.30	0.60	1.50
2–6	0.20	0.40	1.00

GREEN LANTERN/GREEN ARROW
Oct, 1983-No. 7, Apr, 1984 (2.50, color, deluxe format)
DC Comics

1-7: Adams-r/G.L. 76-89	0.60	1.20	3.00

GREEN LANTERN: MOSAIC
June, 1992-No. 18, Nov, 1993 (1.25, color)
DC Comics

1-18: Featuring John Stewart	0.30	0.50	1.25

GRENDEL (See Primer, Mage)
Mar,1983-No.3, Feb, 1984 (B&W)
Comico

1	7.10	21.00	50.00
2, 3	5.70	17.00	40.00

GRENDEL
Oct, 1986-No. 40, Feb, 1991 (Color)
Comico

1-New series begins	0.70	1.50	5.00
1,2-2nd printings	0.30	0.60	1.60
2	0.60	1.20	3.00
3-10: 4-Dave Stevens-c(i)	0.40	0.80	2.00
11–15	0.40	0.70	1.75
16-Reintro Mage; series begins, ends #19	0.70	1.40	3.50
17-32: (18-26: 1.75-c; 27-32: 1.95-c)	0.40	0.80	2.00
33-(2.75, 44 pgs.)	0.60	1.10	2.75
34-40: (2.50-c)	0.50	1.00	2.50

GRENDEL: DEVIL BY THE DEED
July, 1993 (3.95, color, one-shot, mature readers)
Dark Horse Comics

nn-r/Grendel back-ups/Mage #6-14	1.00	2.00	5.00

GRENDEL TALES: DEVILS AND DEATHS
Oct, 1994-Nov 1994 (2.95, color, limited series, mature readers)
Dark Horse Comics

	Good	Fine	N-Mint
1–2	0.60	1.20	3.00

GRENDEL TALES: DEVIL'S CHOICES
Mar 1995-June 1995 (2.95, color, limited series, mature readers)
Dark Horse Comics

1–4	0.60	1.20	3.00

GRENDEL TALES: FOUR DEVILS, ONE HELL
Aug, 1993-No. 6, Jan, 1994 (2.95, color, limited series, mature readers)
Dark Horse Comics

1-6: Wagner painted-c	0.60	1.20	3.00
TPB (12/94, 17.95)	2.60	7.70	18.00

GRENDEL TALES: HOMECOMING
Dec 1994 -Feb 1995 (2.95, color, Limited series, mature readers)
Dark Horse Comics

1–3	0.60	1.20	3.00

GRENDEL TALES: THE DEVIL IN OUR MIDST
May, 1994-No. 5, Sept, 1994 (2.95, color, limited series, mature readers)
Dark Horse Comics

1-5-Wagner painted-c	0.60	1.20	3.00

GRENDEL TALES: THE DEVIL'S HAMMER
Feb, 1994 -No. 3, Apr, 1994 (2.95, color, limited series, mature readers)
Dark Horse Comics

1–3	0.60	1.20	3.00

GRENDEL: WAR CHILD
Aug, 1992-No. 10, June, 1993 (2.50, color, limited series, mature readers)
Dark Horse Comics

1-9: Bisley painted c-1-4; Wagner c-5-10	0.80	1.60	4.00
10-(3.50, 52 pgs.)	1.00	2.00	5.00

GRIFTER: ONE SHOT
Jan 1995 (4.95, color, one shot)
Image Comics

1-Flip-c	1.00	2.00	5.00

GRIFTER
May 1995-Present (1.95, color)
Image Comics

1-(1.95)-Newsstand, WildStorm Rising pt.5	0.40	1.00	2.00

1-(2.50)-Direct Market, WildStorm Rising pt. 5, bound-in card			
	0.50	1.20	2.50
2	0.50	1.20	2.50

GRIMJACK
Aug, 1984-No. 81, Apr, 1991
First Comics

1	0.40	0.80	2.00
2–25	0.30	0.60	1.50
26-2nd color Teenage Mutant Ninja Turtles	0.80	1.60	4.00
27-74, 76-81 (later issues 1.95, 2.25): 73, 74-Kelley Jones-a			
	0.30	0.50	1.25
75-(5.95, 52 pgs.)-With map	1.00	2.50	6.00

GRIPS
Sept, 1986-No. 4, Dec, 1986 (1.50, B&W, adult)
Silverwolf Comics

1-Tim Vigil art in all issues	2.10	6.40	15.00
2	1.40	4.30	10.00
3	1.30	3.90	9.00
4	1.30	3.00	8.00

GROO (Sergio Aragones'...)
Dec 1994 - Present (1.95, color)
Image Comics

1-7: 2-indicia reads #1 Jan 1995	0.40	0.80	2.00

GROO CHRONICLES, THE (Sergio Aragones)
June, 1989-No. 6, Feb, 1990 (3.50, color)
Epic Comics (Marvel)

Book 1-6: Reprints early Pacific issues	0.70	1.40	3.50

GROO SPECIAL
Oct, 1984 (One-shot)
Eclipse Comics

1	5.00	15.00	35.00

GROO, THE WANDERER (See Destroyer Duck #1 & Starslayer #5)
Dec, 1982-No. 8, Apr, 1984
Pacific Comics

1	3.90	11.60	27.00
2	2.00	7.30	17.00
3-7: 5-Deluxe paper, 1.00-c	2.00	6.00	14.00

	Good	Fine	N-Mint
8	2.00	4.70	11.00

GROO THE WANDERER (Sergio Aragones'...)
March, 1985- Jan, 1995
Epic Comics (Marvel)

	Good	Fine	N-Mint
1	1.70	4.00	10.00
2	1.20	2.40	6.00
3–10	0.80	1.60	4.00
11–20	0.50	1.00	2.50
21-30	0.40	0.80	2.00
31-86	0.30	0.50	1.25
87-99, 101-120: 87-Begin direct sale, 2.25-c, 120-Last Marvel edition			
	0.50	0.90	2.25
100-(2.95, 52 pgs.)	0.60	1.20	3.00
Marvel Graphic Novel 32: Death Of Groo	1.20	2.90	7.00
Death of Groo 2nd printing (5.95)	1.00	2.50	6.00
Groo Garden, The (4/94, 10.95)-r/25-28	1.60	4.70	11.00

GROOVY (Cartoon Comics, not code approved)
March, 1968-No. 3, July, 1968
Marvel Comics Group

	Good	Fine	N-Mint
1-Monkees, Ringo Starr photos	3.40	10.00	24.00
2, 3	2.60	7.70	18.00

GUARDIANS OF METROPOLIS
Nov, 1994-Present (1.50, color, mini-series:4)
DC Comics

	Good	Fine	N-Mint
1-4: 1-Superman & Granny Goodness app.	0.30	0.60	1.50

GUARDIANS OF THE GALAXY
(See Marvel Super Heroes #18 for 1st app.)
June, 1990-Present (1.00, color)
Marvel Comics

	Good	Fine	N-Mint
1	0.70	2.00	4.00
2, 3	0.60	1.20	3.00
4-6: 5-McFarlane-c(i)	0.60	1.20	3.00
7-10: 9-Liefeld-c(i). 10-Jim Lee-c(i)	0.40	0.80	2.00
11, 12, 15: 15-Starlin-c(i)	0.40	0.80	2.00
13, 14-Spirit of Vengeance (futuristic Ghost Rider) app.			
	0.50	1.30	3.00
16-(1.50, 52 pgs.)-Starlin-c(i)	0.40	0.80	2.00
17-23, 26-38, 40-47: 26-Origin. 43-Intro Woden, son of Thor			
	0.30	0.50	1.25

24-Silver Surfer-c/story; Ron Lim-c	0.60	1.20	3.00
25-(2.50)-Prism foil-c; Silver Surfer-c/story			
	0.70	1.40	3.50
25-Without foil-c (newsstand copy)	0.40	0.80	2.00
39-(2.95, 52 pgs.)-Embossed, holo-grafx foil-c			
	0.60	1.20	3.00
48,49,51-62: 48-Begin 1.50-c; bound-in card sheet. 55-Ripjak app.			
	0.30	0.60	1.50
50-(2.00, 52 pgs.)-Newsstand ed.	0.40	0.80	2.00
50-(2.95, 52 pgs.)-Collectors ed. w/foil embossed-c			
	0.60	1.20	3.00
Annual 1 ('91, 2.00, 68 pg.)-2 pg. origin	0.50	1.00	2.50
Annual 2 ('92, 2.25)-Spirits of Vengeance-c/sty			
	0.50	0.90	2.25
Annual 3 ('93, 2.95)-Polybagged w/card	0.60	1.20	3.00
Annual 4 ('94, 2.95)	0.60	1.20	3.00

GUMBY'S...
July, 1987; Dec, 1988 (2.50, color)
Comico

Summer Fun Special 1-A. Adams-a; B. Burden story			
	0.50	1.00	2.50
Winter Fun Special 1-Art Adams-a	0.50	1.00	2.50

GUNFIRE (See Deathstroke the Terminator Annual #2 & Showcase 94)
May, 1994-Present (1.75/1.95, color)
DC Comics

1-4: 2-Ricochet-c/story	0.40	0.70	1.75
5,0,6-12: 5-(9/94)-Begin 1.95-c. 0-(10/94). 6-(11/94)			

Guardians of the Galaxy #52 © MEG

Gunfire #5 © DC

	Good	Fine	N-Mint
	0.40	0.80	2.00
13-begin 2.25-c	0.50	0.90	2.25

GUY GARDNER (…: Warrior #17 on)
Oct, 1992-Present (1.25/1.50, color)
DC Comics

1-15: 6-Guy vs. Hal Jordan. 8-Vs. Lobo-c/story: 15-JLA app.			
	0.30	0.60	1.50
16-24: 16-Begin 1.95-c. 18-Splash page x-over GL #50. 18-21-Vs. Hal			
Jordan. 24-(9/94)-Zero Hour	0.30	0.60	1.50
0,26-30: 0-(10/94), 27: Intro Sledge	0.30	0.60	1.50
25-(11/94, 2.50, 52 pgs)	0.50	1.00	2.50
29-(2.95)-Gatefold-c	0.60	1.20	3.00
29-variant-c (Edward Hopper's Nighthawks)	0.30	0.60	1.50
31-begin 1.75-c; 32-33	0.40	0.70	1.75
Annual 1('95, 3.50)-Year One story	0.70	1.40	3.50

GUY GARDNER REBORN
1992-No. 3, 1992 (4.95, color, mini-series)
DC Comics

1-3: 1-Lobo cameo. 2, 3-Lobo-c/story	1.00	2.00	5.00

H

HAIR BEAR BUNCH, THE
Feb, 1972-No. 9, Feb, 1974 (Hanna-Barbera)
Gold Key
1	1.40	3.50	8.50
2–9	1.00	2.00	5.00

HAMMER OF GOD: BUTCH
May, 1994-No. 3, Aug, 1994 (2.50, color, limited series)
Dark Horse Comics
1–3	0.50	1.00	2.50

HAMMER OF GOD: PENTATHLON
Jan, 1994 (2.50, color, one-shot)
Dark Horse Comics
1-Character from Nexus	0.50	1.00	2.50

HANNA-BARBERA BAND WAGON (TV)
Oct, 1962-No. 3, April, 1963
Gold Key
1, 2-Giants (84 pgs.)	8.00	24.00	55.00
3-Regular size	5.00	15.00	35.00

HANNA-BARBERA PARADE (TV)
Sept, 1971-No. 10, Dec, 1972
Charlton Comics
1	4.60	14.00	32.00
2-10: 7-"Summer Picnic" (52 pgs.)	2.60	7.70	18.00

HANNA-BARBERA SUPER TV HEROES (TV)
Apr, 1968-No. 7, Oct, 1969
Gold Key
1-Herculoids, Birdman, Mighty Mightor, Young Samson & Goliath, & Moby Dick begin	12.00	36.00	85.00
2-Shazzan begins; 12 & 15¢ versions exist	10.00	29.00	78.00
3-7: The Space Ghost app. in 3, 6, 7	10.00	31.00	72.00

HAPPY BIRTHDAY MARTHA WASHINGTON
Mar 1995 (2.95, color, One shot)
Dark Horse Comics
1-F.Miller/s D. Gibbons/a	0.60	1.20	3.00

	Good	Fine	N-Mint

HARBINGER
Jan, 1992-Present (1.95/2.50, color)
Valiant

	Good	Fine	N-Mint
0-(Advance)	6.00	17.00	40.00
1-1st app. Harbinger	4.00	11.00	25.00
2–3	1.40	4.00	10.00
4-Low print run	2.10	6.00	15.00
5, 6	1.10	3.40	8.00
7-9: 8,9-Unity x-overs. 8-Miller-c	0.70	2.10	5.00
10-1st app. H.A.R.D. Corps. (10/92)	0.80	2.00	5.00
11-16: 14-1st Stronghold	0.60	1.10	2.75

17-24, 26-41: 18-Intro Screen. 19-1st Stunner. 22-Archer & Armstrong app.
   26-Intro New Harbingers. 29-w/bound-in trading card. 30-H.A.R.D. Corps
   app. 32-Eternal Warrior app. 33-Dr. Eclipse app.

	Good	Fine	N-Mint
	0.50	1.00	2.50
25-(3.50, 52 pgs.)	0.70	1.40	3.50

Trade Paperback (11/92, 9.95-c)-Reprints #1-4 & comes polybagged
   with copy of Harbinger #0 w/new-c   3.60   11.00   25.00
Note: Issues 1-6 have coupon redeemable for Harbinger #0 plus origin of
Harada.

HARBINGER FILES
Aug, 1994-Present (2.50, color)
Valiant

	Good	Fine	N-Mint
1,2	0.50	1.00	2.50

HARDCASE (Also see Flood Relief)
June, 1993-Present (1.95, color)
Malibu Comics (Ultraverse)

1-Intro Hardcase; Dave Gibbons-c, Jim Callahan-a(p) begin, end #3
   has coupon for Ultraverse Premiere #0   0.80   1.60   4.00

	Good	Fine	N-Mint
1-With coupon missing	0.30	0.60	1.50
1-Platinum Edition	1.40	4.00	10.00

1-Full cover holographic edition, 1st of kind along w/Prime #1 &
   Strangers #1   2.90   9.00   20.00

	Good	Fine	N-Mint
1- Ultra Limited silver foil-c	1.40	4.00	10.00
2,3-Callahan-a	0.60	1.10	2.75

2-(2.50)-Newsstand ed. bagged w/trading card

	Good	Fine	N-Mint
	0.50	1.00	2.50

4, 6-15, 17-19: 4-Strangers app. 7-Break-Thru x-over. 8-Solution app.
   9-Vs. Turf 12-Silver foil logo, wraparound-c, 17- Prime app.

	Good	Fine	N-Mint
	0.40	0.80	2.00
5-(2.50, 48 pgs.)-Rune flip-c/story by Smith	0.50	1.00	2.50

16-(3.50, 68 pgs) Rune pin-up	0.70	1.40	3.50
20-24-(2.50); 23-Loki app.	0.50	1.00	2.50

H.A.R.D. CORPS (See Harbinger #10)
Dec, 1992-Present (2.25, color)
Valiant

1-(Advance)	4.00	11.00	25.00
1-(2.50)-Gatefold-c by Jim Lee & Bob Layton			
	0.60	1.20	3.00
1-Gold variant	1.40	4.00	10.00
2-6: 5-Bloodshot-c/story cont'd/Bloodshot #3			
	0.50	0.90	2.25
5-Variant ed.; came w/Comic Defense System			
	0.90	1.80	4.50
7-30: 10-Turok app. 17-Vs. Armorines. 18-w/bound in trading card.			
20-Harbinger app.	0.50	0.90	2.25

HARDWARE
Apr, 1993-Present (1.50/1.75, color)
DC Comics (Milestone)

1-(2.95)-Collector's Ed.; polybagged w/poster & trading card			
(direct sale only)	0.60	1.20	3.00
1-Platinum	1.10	3.00	8.00
1-15,17-19: 11, 14-Simonson-c. 17-Worlds Collide Pt. 2. 18-Simonson-c;			
Worlds Collide Pt. 9	0.30	0.60	1.50
16-(3.95, 52 pgs.)-Gatefold 2nd-c by J. Byrne; new armor; Icon app.			
	0.80	1.60	4.00
16-(2.50, 52 pgs.)-Newsstand Edition	0.50	1.00	2.50
20-24, 26-28: 20-Begin 1.75-c	0.40	0.70	1.75
25-(2.95, 52 pgs)	0.60	1.20	3.00

Harbinger #9 © Voyager

H.A.R.D. Corps #20 © Voyager

	Good	Fine	N-Mint
29,30 (2.50)	0.50	1.00	2.50

HARLAN ELLISON'S DREAM CORRIDOR SPECIAL
Jan 1995 (4.95, color)
Dark Horse Comics

	Good	Fine	N-Mint
1- adaptation of Ellison stories	1.00	2.00	5.00

HARLAN ELLISON'S DREAM CORRIDOR
Mar, 1995-Present (2.95, color)

1-4 adaptations-Byrne-a	0.60	1.20	3.00

HARRIERS
June 1995–Present (6.95, color)
Entity Comics

1–Foil-c; polybagged with PC Game	1.40	2.80	7.00

HARSH REALM
1994-Present (2.95, color)
Harris Comics

1-4-Painted-c	0.60	1.20	3.00

HAVOK AND WOLVERINE - MELTDOWN
Mar, 1989-No. 4, Oct, 1989 (3.50, color, mini-series)
Epic Comics (Marvel)

1–4	1.00	2.00	5.00

HAWK AND DOVE
Oct, 1988-No. 5, Feb, 1989 (1.00, color, mini-series)
DC Comics

1-Liefeld-c/a(p) in all; early DC work	0.70	1.40	3.50
2–5	0.40	0.80	2.00
TPB-(1993, 9.95)-r/1-5	1.70	4.00	10.00

HAWK AND DOVE
June, 1989-No. 28, Oct, 1991 (1.00, color)
DC Comics

1–28	0.20	0.40	1.00
Annual 1 ('90, 2.00)-Liefeld pin-up	0.40	0.80	2.00
Annual 2 ('91)-Armageddon 2001 x-over	0.40	0.80	2.00

HAWK AND THE DOVE (See Showcase #75)
Aug-Sept, 1968-No. 6, June-July, 1969
National Periodical Publications

1-Ditko-c/a #1, 2	6.00	18.00	42.00
2-6: 3-6-Kane-c/a	4.60	14.00	32.00

HAWKEYE
Jan, 1994-No. 4, Apr, 1994 (1.75, color, mini-series)
Marvel Comics

1–4	0.40	0.70	1.75

HAWKMAN (Also See Atom #7, Brave & the Bold & Mystery in Space)
Apr-May, 1964-No. 27, Aug-Sept, 1968
National Periodical Publications

1	53.00	159.00	425.00
2	20.00	60.00	160.00
3, 5	11.00	34.00	90.00
4-Origin/1st app. Zatanna	14.00	41.00	110.00
6-10: 9-Atom cameo	8.00	22.00	58.00
11–15	6.00	18.00	42.00
16-27: 25-GA Hawkman-r	4.30	12.90	30.00

HAWKMAN
Aug, 1986-No. 17, Oct, 1987
DC Comics

1–17	0.20	0.40	1.00
Special 1 (1986, 1.25)	0.30	0.60	1.50

HAWKMAN
Sept, 1993-Present (1.75, color)
DC Comics

1-(2.50)-Gold foil embossed-c; new costume & powers

	0.50	1.00	2.50

2-11: 3-Airstryke app. 4-Wonder Woman app.

	0.40	0.70	1.75

12,13: 12-Begin 1.95-c. 13-(9/94)-Zero Hour 0.40 0.80 2.00
0,14-20: 0-(10/94). 14-(11/94). 15-Aquaman-c & app.

	0.40	0.80	2.00

21-begin 2.25-c; 22–23, 23-Wonder Woman app.

	0.50	0.90	2.25

Annual 1 ('93, 2.50)-Bloodlines Earthplague

	0.50	1.00	2.50

HAWKWORLD
1989-No. 3, 1989 (3.95, prestige format)
DC Comics

	Good	Fine	N-Mint
1-3-Tim Truman-a in all	0.80	1.60	4.00

HAWKWORLD
June, 1990-No. 32, March, 1993 (1.50, color)
DC Comics

1	0.50	1.00	2.50
2–32	0.40	0.70	1.75
Annual 1-3 ('90-'92, 2.95): 1-Flash app.	0.60	1.20	3.00

HEART OF THE BEAST, THE
1994 (19.95, color, one-shot, adult)
DC Comics

1-Hardcover	3.00	8.60	20.00

HEARTS OF DARKNESS
Dec, 1992 (4.95, color; double gatefold-c)
Marvel Comics

1-Ghost Rider, Punisher, Wolverine app.	1.00	2.00	5.00

HECKLE AND JECKLE (TV)
11/62-No. 4, 8/63; No. 1, 5/66; No. 2, 10/66; No. 3, 8/67
Gold Key/Dell Publishing Co.

1 (11/62; Gold Key)	7.10	21.00	50.00
2–4	2.40	7.30	17.00
1 (5/66; Dell)	3.00	9.40	22.00
2, 3	2.40	7.30	17.00

HELLBLAZER (See Swamp Thing #37)
Jan, 1988-Present (1.25/1.50, color, mature)
DC Comics (Vertigo imprint #63 on)

1-(44 pgs.)-John Constantine	2.40	7.00	17.00
2–5	1.30	3.30	8.00
6-10: 9, 10-Swamp Thing cameo	0.80	1.60	4.00
11-20: 19-McKean-c	0.70	1.40	3.50
21-30: 24- Shocker movie poster. 25, 26-Morrison scripts.			
	0.60	1.20	3.00
27-McKean-a; Gaiman scripts	1.60	3.20	8.00
31-39,41-49: 44-Begin 1.75-c	0.50	1.00	2.50
40-(2.25-c, 52 pgs.)-McKean-a	0.60	1.20	3.00
50-(3.00, 52 pgs.)	0.60	1.20	3.00
51-65: 62-Special Death insert by McKean	0.40	0.70	1.75
66-74,76-88: 66-Begin 1.95-c	0.40	0.80	2.00
75-(2.95, 52 pgs.)	0.60	1.20	3.00

Hellblazer #70 © DC

Hellina #1 © Lighting Comics

89-begin 2.25-c; 90–92	0.50	0.90	2.25
Annual 1 (1989, 2.95, 68 pages)	0.90	1.80	4.50
Special 1 ('93, 3.95, 68 pages)-w/pin-ups	0.80	1.60	4.00

HELLBOY: SEED OF DESTRUCTION
Mar, 1994-No. 4, June, 1994 (2.50, color, limited series)
Dark Horse Comics (Legend imprint)

1-4-Mignola-a; Byrne scripts; Monkeyman & O'Brien back up story (origin			
parts 1 & 2) by A. Adams	0.80	1.60	4.00
TPB (10/94, 17.95)-r/#1-4	2.60	8.00	18.00

HELLHOUNDS(...: Panzer Cops #3-6)
1994-No. 6, July, 1994 (2.50, B&W, limited series)
Dark Horse Comics

1,3-5: 1-Hamner-c. 3-(4/94)	0.50	1.00	2.50
2,6-(2.95, 52 pgs.): 2-Joe Phillips-c	0.60	1.20	3.00

HELLINA
Sept, 1994 (2.75, B&W)
Lightning Comics

1-Origin; pin-up gallery	0.60	1.10	2.75
1–Nude ed. (9.95)	2.00	4.00	10.00

HELLINA: TAKING BACK THE NIGHT
Apr, 1995-Present (2.75, B&W)
Lightning Comics

1-	0.60	1.10	2.75

HELLSHOCK
July, 1994-Present (1.95, color, limited series:4)

	Good	Fine	N-Mint
Image Comics			
1-4-Jae Lee-story/a 4-Variant-c	0.40	0.80	2.00

HELLSTORM: PRINCE OF LIES (See Ghost Rider 1 & Marvel Spotlight 12)
Apr, 1993-Present (2.00, color)
Marvel Comics

1-(2.95)-Parchment-c w/red thermographic ink			
	0.60	1.20	3.00
2-21: 14-Bound-in trading card sheet. 18-P. Craig Russell-c			
	0.40	0.80	2.00

HERBIE (Also see Forbidden Worlds & Unknown Worlds)
Apr-May, 1964-No. 23, Feb, 1967
American Comics Group

1	16.00	49.00	115.00
2-4	8.00	25.00	58.00
5-Beatles, Dean Martin, F. Sinatra app.	11.00	33.00	78.00
6, 7, 9, 10	7.00	20.00	46.00
8-Origin/1st app. The Fat Fury	8.00	25.00	58.00
11-23:17,23-R/ForbiddenWorlds #(94&73)	4.60	14.00	32.00

HERCULES
Oct, 1967-No. 13, Sept, 1969; Dec, 1968
Charlton Comics

1-Thane of Bagarth begins; Glanzman art	1.50	3.80	9.00
2-13	1.00	2.50	6.00
8-(Low distribution)-(12/68, 35 cents, B&W)-magazine format;			
new Hercules story & r/#1	2.40	7.00	17.00

HERCULES
Sept, 1982-No. 4, Dec, 1982;
V2 #1, Mar, 1984-No. 4, June, 1984
Marvel Comics Group

| 1-4 | 0.30 | 0.60 | 1.60 |
| V2#1-4 | 0.20 | 0.40 | 1.00 |

HERCULES UNBOUND
Oct-Nov, 1975-No. 12, Aug-Sept, 1977
National Periodical Publications

| 1-Wood inks in #1-8; c-7i, 8i | 0.30 | 0.60 | 1.40 |
| 2-12: 10-Atomic Knights x-over | 0.20 | 0.50 | 1.20 |

HERMES VS. THE EYEBALL KID

Dec 1994 - Feb 1995 (2.95, B&W, Limited series)
Dark Horse Comics

1-3	0.60	1.20	3.00

HEROES FOR HOPE STARRING THE X-MEN
Dec, 1985 (1.50, one-shot, 52 pgs.)
Marvel Comics Group

1-Arthur Adams-c; Starlin back-c	0.60	1.20	3.00

HERO FOR HIRE (Power Man No. 17 on)
June, 1972-No. 16 Dec, 1973
Marvel Comics Group

1-Origin/1st app. Luke Cage	4.30	13.00	30.00
2–5	1.70	5.00	12.00
6–10	1.00	2.50	6.00
11-16: 14-Origin retold	0.90	2.30	5.50

HERO ZERO
Sept, 1994-Present (2.50, color)
Dark Horse Comics

#0	0.50	1.00	2.50

HEX
Sept, 1985-No. 18, Feb, 1987
DC Comics

1-10, 14-18: 1-Origin; cont'd from Jonah Hex 92			
	0.40	0.80	2.00
11-13: Future Batman storyline	0.50	1.00	2.50

Note: Mark Texeira a-1, 2p, 3p, 5-7p, 9p, 11-14p; c-1, 2, 4-7, 12.

HI-ADVENTURE HEROES (TV)
May, 1969-No. 2, Aug, 1969 (Hanna-Barbera)
Gold Key

1-Three Musketeers, Gulliver, Arabian Knights			
	2.90	9.00	20.00
2-Three Musk., Micro-Venture, Arab. Knights			
	2.40	7.30	17.00

HILLY ROSE'S SPACE ADVENTURES
May 1995-Present (2.95, B&W)
Astro Comics

1	0.60	1.20	3.00

	Good	Fine	N-Mint

House of Mystery #77 © DC

House of Mystery #267 © DC

HOGAN'S HEROES (TV)(No. 1-7 have photo-c)
June, 1966- No. 8, Sept, 1967, No. 9, Oct, 1969
Dell Publishing

	Good	Fine	N-Mint
1	8.00	24.00	55.00
2,3-Ditko-a(p)	5.00	15.00	35.00
4-9: 9-Reprints #1	3.60	10.70	25.00

HOKUM & HEX (See Razorline)
Sept, 1993-No. 9, May, 1994 (1.75, color)
Marvel Comics

	Good	Fine	N-Mint
1-(2.50)-Foil embossed-c; Clive Barker	0.50	1.00	2.50
2-8: 5-Hyperkind app.	0.40	0.70	1.75
9-(1.95)	0.40	0.80	2.00

HONG KONG PHOOEY (TV)
June, 1975-No. 9, Nov, 1976 (Hanna-Barbera)
Charlton Comics

	Good	Fine	N-Mint
1	2.00	5.00	12.00
2	1.00	2.00	5.00
3–9	0.60	1.20	3.00

HOT WHEELS (TV)
Mar-Apr, 1970-No. 6, Jan-Feb, 1971
National Periodical Publications

	Good	Fine	N-Mint
1-Toth-a in #1-5	5.40	16.00	38.00
2, 4, 5	2.60	7.70	18.00
3-Neal Adams-c	3.70	11.10	26.00
6-Neal Adams-c/a	4.30	12.90	30.00

HOUSE OF MYSTERY, THE
No. 36, Mar, 1955-No. 321, Oct, 1983

National Periodical Pub./DC Comics

36-49: 36-1st code approved issue	13.00	40.00	80.00
50-Text of Orson Welles' War Of The World broadcast			
	11.00	34.00	80.00
51-60	9.00	28.00	65.00
61, 63, 65, 66, 70, 72, 76, 84, 85: Kirby-a	9.00	27.00	62.00
62, 64, 67-69, 71, 73-75, 77-83, 86-99	5.60	17.00	39.00
100 (7/60)	9.00	26.00	52.00
101-116: 116-Last 10¢ issue	3.00	8.00	28.00
117-119, 121-130	3.00	8.00	28.00
120-Toth art	2.90	9.00	29.00
131-142	2.00	7.00	23.00
143-Jonn J'onnz begins (6/64), ends 173; story cont'd from			
Detective 326	20.00	70.00	215.00
144	12.00	36.00	107.00
145-155, 157-159	8.00	23.00	70.00
156-Origin & 1st app. Robby Reed in Dial H For Hero (11-12/65) (Robby			
Reed in 156-173)	9.00	26.00	78.00
160-Robby Reed becomes Plastic Man for 1 issue (1st S.A. Plastic Man,			
7/66) (try-out issue)	11.00	32.00	95.00
161-173: 173-Last Martian Manhunter	5.00	14.00	42.00
174-177, 182: 174-Mystery format begins. 182-Toth-a			
	2.00	5.00	12.00
178-Adams art	2.00	6.00	16.00
179-Adams/Orlando-a; 1st pro Wrightson-a	6.00	17.00	45.00
180, 181, 183-Wrightson-a. 180-Last 12¢ issue			
	2.00	5.00	13.00
184-Kane/Wood art, Toth art	1.00	4.00	11.00
185-Williamson/Kaluta art	1.00	4.00	11.00
186-Adams & Wrightson art	1.00	4.00	11.00
187, 190: 190-Toth art reprints	1.00	3.00	7.00
188, 191, 195-Wrightson art	2.00	5.00	12.00
189, 192-194, 196-198: 189-Wood art	1.00	3.00	7.00
199-(52 pgs.)-Wood & Kirby-a (2/72)	1.00	3.00	8.00
200-203: 25¢, 52 pgs.; 1/3-r	1.20	2.40	6.00
204-Wrightson-c/a (9 pgs.)	1.20	2.40	6.00
205-220: 207-Wrightson, Starlin, Redondo art			
	1.00	2.00	5.00
221-223, 225, 227; 221-Wrightson/Kaluta art			
	1.00	2.00	5.00
224-Begin 100 pg. iss.; Adams-i, Wrightson-a			
	1.60	3.20	8.00
226-Wrightson/Redondo art	1.10	2.20	5.50

	Good	Fine	N-Mint
228-Adams inks; Wrightson reprint	1.20	2.40	6.00
229-235, 237-321: 229-Last 100 pgs. 251-259: 84 pgs. 251-Wood-a;			
Adams-c. 282-(68 pgs.)-Extra Starlin-a	1.10	2.20	5.50
236-Ditko-a(p); Adams-i; Wrightson-c	1.20	2.40	6.00

HOUSE OF SECRETS
11-12/56-No. 80, 9-10/66; No. 81, 8-9/69-No. 140, 2-3/76;
No. 141, 8-9/76-No. 154, 10-11/78
National Periodical Publ./DC Comics

	Good	Fine	N-Mint
1	65.00	195.00	650.00
2	36.00	107.00	320.00
3-Kirby-c/a	26.00	77.00	230.00
4, 8-Kirby-a	16.00	48.00	145.00
5-7, 9-11	12.00	35.00	105.00
12-Kirby-c/a	13.00	38.00	115.00
13-15: 14-Flying saucer-c	8.00	25.00	75.00
16-20	7.00	22.00	65.00
21, 22, 24-30	7.00	20.00	60.00
23-1st app. Mark Merlin	8.00	23.00	70.00
31-50: 48-Toth-a. 50-Last 10¢ issue	4.00	13.00	40.00
51-60 : 58-1st told origin Mark Merlin	4.00	13.00	35.00
61-1st Eclipso (7-8/63) and begin series	16.00	49.00	130.00
62	8.00	24.00	64.00
63-65, 67: Toth-a	6.00	19.00	50.00
66-1st Eclipso-c	9.00	26.00	70.00
68-80: 73-Mark Merlin becomes Prince Ra-Man. 76-Eclipso vs. Prince			
Ra-Man. 80-Last Eclipso&Prince Ra-Man	4.00	13.00	35.00
81-91: 81-Mystery format begins	1.00	2.00	6.00
92-1st app. Swamp Thing-c/story by Bernie Wrightson (8 pgs.) (6-7/71)			
	39.00	116.00	425.00
93-100: 94-Wrightson-a(i)	1.10	2.20	5.50
101-154	0.60	1.10	2.75

HOWARD THE DUCK
Jan, 1976-No. 31, May, 1979; No. 32, Jan, 1986-No. 33, Sept, 1986
Marvel Comics Group

	Good	Fine	N-Mint
1-Spider-Man x-over; Brunner-c/a	1.30	3.00	8.00
2-11: 2-Brunner-c/a	0.40	0.80	2.00
12-1st app. Kiss (cameo, 3/77)	0.80	1.60	4.00
13-1st full app. Kiss; Son of Satan app.	0.90	1.80	4.50
14-33: 14-Son of Satan app.; Howard as Son of Satan-c/story.			
22, 23-Man-Thing-c/story	0.20	0.40	1.00
Annual 1 (1977, 52 pgs.)	0.20	0.40	1.00

H. R. PUFNSTUF (TV)
Oct, 1970-No. 8, July, 1972
Gold Key

1-Photo-c	12.00	36.00	85.00
2–8	5.00	15.00	30.00

HUCKLEBERRY HOUND (TV)
No. 990, 5-7/59-No. 43, Oct, 1970 (Hanna-Barbera)
Dell/Gold Key No. 18 (10/62) on
4 Color 990 (#1)-1st app. Huck, Yogi Bear & Pixie & Dixie & Mr. Jinx

	10.00	30.00	70.00
4 Color 1050, 1054 (12/59)	7.50	23.00	45.00
3 (1-2/60) - 7 (9-10/60)	7.50	23.00	45.00
4 Color 1141 (10/60)	7.50	23.00	45.00
8-10	5.50	17.00	33.00
11-17 (6-8/62)	4.70	14.00	28.00
18, 19 (84 pgs.)	6.90	21.00	55.00
20-30	3.30	10.00	20.00
31-43: 37-Reprints	2.70	8.00	16.00

HUCKLEBERRY HOUND (TV)
Nov, 1970-No. 8, Jan, 1972 (Hanna-Barbera)
Charlton Comics

1	2.30	6.90	16.00
2–8	1.80	4.60	11.00

HUEY, DEWEY AND LOUIE JUNIOR WOODCHUCKS
Aug, 1966-No. 81, 1984 (Disney)
Gold Key

1	5.00	15.00	35.00
2, 3 (12/68)	2.90	8.60	20.00
4, 5(4/70)-Barks-r	3.70	11.10	26.00
6-17-Written by Barks	5.00	15.00	35.00
18, 27-30	1.70	4.20	10.00
19-23, 25-Barks scripts. 22, 23, 25-Barks-r	3.30	8.00	20.00
24, 26-Barks-r	2.20	5.00	13.00
31-57, 60-81: 41, 70, 80-Reprints	1.20	2.40	6.00
58, 59-Barks-r	1.20	2.40	6.00

HULK (Formerly The Rampaging Hulk)
No. 11, Oct, 1978-No. 27, June, 1981 (1.50, color, magazine)
Marvel Comics Group

	Good	Fine	N-Mint
11-Moon Knight begins	1.00	1.90	4.75
12-15: Moon Knight app.	0.70	1.30	3.25
16, 19	0.40	0.80	2.00
17, 18, 20-Moon Knight app.	0.60	1.20	3.00
21, 22, 24-27: 25-27-B&W issues	0.40	0.80	1.90
23-Banner is attacked, last full-color issue	0.60	1.10	2.75

HULK: FUTURE IMPERFECT
Jan, 1993-No. 2, Dec, 1992 (in error) (5.95, color)
Marvel Comics

	Good	Fine	N-Mint
1, 2-Embossed-c; Perez-c/a	1.00	2.50	6.00
	0.30	0.60	1.50

HULK 2099
Dec, 1994-Present (1.50, color)
Marvel Comics

	Good	Fine	N-Mint
1-(2.50)-Green foil-c	0.50	1.00	2.50
2-6: 2-A. Kubert-c	0.30	0.60	1.50
7-begin 1.95-c; 8–9	0.40	0.80	2.00

HUMAN FLY, THE
Sept, 1977-No. 19, Mar, 1979
Marvel Comics Group

	Good	Fine	N-Mint
1-Origin; Spider-Man app.	0.80	1.60	4.00
2-Ghost Rider app.	0.80	2.00	4.75
3-19: 9-Daredevil x-over	0.40	0.70	1.80

HUMAN TORCH, THE
No. 36, Apr, 1954-No. 38, Aug, 1954
Atlas Comics

	Good	Fine	N-Mint
36-38-Sub-Mariner in all	61.00	182.00	425.00

HUMAN TORCH
Sept, 1974-No. 8, Nov, 1975
Marvel Comics Group

	Good	Fine	N-Mint
1: 1-8 reprint Str. Tales 101-108 plus GA-r	1.00	2.00	5.00
2-8: 7-Vs. Sub-Mariner	0.60	1.20	3.00

HUNTER'S HEART
June 1995-Present (5.95, B&W, Limited series)
Paradox Press

	Good	Fine	N-Mint
1	1.20	2.40	6.00

HUNTRESS, THE (See Brave & the Bold #62)
June, 1994-No. 4, Sept, 1994 (1.50, color, mini-series)
DC Comics
1-4-Netzer-c/a: 2-Batman app.   0.30   0.60   1.50

HYBRIDS
Jan, 1994-Present (2.50, color)
Continuity Comics
1-Neal Adams-c(p) & part-i; embossed-c 0.50   1.00   2.50

HYBRIDS DEATHWATCH 2000
Apr, 1993-No. 3, Aug, 1993 (2.50, color)
Continuity Comics
0-Foil-c; Neal Adams-c(i) & plots
1-3: 1-Bagged w/card; die-cut-c; Adams-c(i). 2-Thermal-c by Adams-(i).
   3-Bagged w/card; indestructible-c   0.50   1.00   2.50

HYBRIDS ORIGIN
1993-Present (2.50, color)
Continuity Comics
1-5: 2, 3-Neal Adams-c. 4, 5-Valeria the She-Bat app.; Adams-c(i)
                                       0.50   1.00   2.50

HYDE-25
Apr, 1995-Present (2.95, color)
Harris Publications
0-coupon for poster-reprint Vampirella first app.
                                       0.60   1.20   3.00

HYPERKIND (See Razorline)
Sept, 1993-No. 9, May, 1994 (1.75, color)
Marvel Comics
1-(2.50)-Foil embossed-c; Clive Barker 0.50   1.00   2.50
2-9   0.40   0.70   1.75

Icon #13 © Milestone Media

Incredible Hulk #418 © MEG

	Good	Fine	N-Mint
ICE AGE ON THE WORLD OF MAGIC: THE GATHERING			
July 1995-(2.50, color, limited series)			
Armada			
1-2 bound-in Magic card; 3-bound-in insert			
	0.50	1.00	2.50
ICON			
May, 1993-Present (1.50/1.75, color)			
DC Comics (Milestone)			
1-(2.95)-Collector's Ed.; polybagged w/poster & trading card;			
(direct sale only)	0.60	1.20	3.00
1-14: 9-Simonson-c	0.30	0.60	1.50
15-24,26-(1.75)-Worlds Collide Pt. 4 & 11. 15-Superboy app.			
16-Superman-c/story	0.40	0.70	1.75
25-(2.95, 52pgs.)	0.60	1.20	3.00
27,28-(2.50, 32 pgs.)	0.50	1.00	2.50
I DREAM OF JEANNIE (TV)			
April, 1965-No. 2, Dec, 1966 (Photo-c)			
Dell Publishing			
1, 2-Barbara Eden photo-c	10.00	36.00	70.00
I LOVE LUCY COMICS (TV)(Also see The Lucy Show)			
No. 536, Feb, 1954-No. 35, Apr-June, 1962 (All photo-c)			
Dell Publishing Co.			
4-Color 535(#1)	39.00	120.00	270.00
4-Color 559(#2, 5/54)	26.00	80.00	185.00
3(8-10/54)-5	17.00	51.00	120.00

6–10	13.00	39.00	90.00
11–20	11.00	34.00	80.00
21-35	10.00	30.00	70.00

IMAGES OF SHADOWHAWK
Sept, 1993-No. 3, 1994 (1.95, color, limited series)

Image Comics	0.40	0.80	2.00
1-3-Giffen-c/a			

IMAGE ZERO
1993 (Received thru mail w/coupons from Image books)
Image Comics
0-Troll, Savage Dragon, Stormwatch, Shadowhawk, & Strykeforce; 1st app.
  Troll; 1st app. McFarlane's Freak, Blotch, Sweat and Bludd

	2.10	6.40	15.00

IMPULSE
Apr 1995-Present (1.50, color)
DC Comics

1-Brief origin retold; 2-4	0.30	0.60	1.50
5-Max Mercury app.; Begin 1.75-c.	0.40	0.70	1.75

INCREDIBLE HULK, THE (Formerly Tales to Astonish; see Giant-Size...)
May, 1962 - No. 6, Mar, 1963; No. 102, Apr, 1968-Present
Marvel Comics Group

1-Origin & 1st app. Hulk (Grey); Kirby-a(p)			
	708.00	2125.00	8500.00
2-Ditko-a & Kirby/Ditko-a; 1st Green Hulk			
	180.00	540.00	1800.00
3-Origin retold; 1st app. Ringmaster; Kirby-a(p)			
	119.00	358.00	1075.00
4, 5-Kirby-a(p). 4-Brief origin retold	94.00	283.00	850.00
6-Intro Teen Brigade; only all Ditko-a issue			
	158.00	475.00	1425.00
102-Story continued from Tales To Astonish #101; origin retold			
	24.00	73.00	170.00
103	9.00	27.00	64.00
104-Rhino app.	8.00	25.00	58.00
105-108: 105-1st Missing Link	7.00	21.00	48.00
109, 110: 109-Ka-Zar app.	4.60	14.00	32.00
111-117: 117-Last 12¢ issue	3.60	10.70	25.00
118-Hulk vs. Sub-Mariner	2.90	8.60	20.00
119-121, 123-125	2.50	6.30	15.00

	Good	Fine	N-Mint
122-Hulk Battles Thing (12/69)	3.30	10.00	23.00
126-140: 131-Hulk vs. Iron Man	1.30	3.30	8.00
141-1st Doc Samson	1.30	3.30	8.00
142-144, 146-157, 159-161	1.00	2.50	6.00
145-(52 pgs.)-Origin retold	1.30	3.30	8.00
158-Warlock cameo (12/72)	1.00	2.50	6.00
162-1st app. Wendigo; Beast app.	1.30	3.00	8.00
163-171,173-175	1.00	2.50	6.00
165-Variant w/4 extra pgs. ads on slick paper			
	1.00	2.50	6.00
172- X-Men cameo	1.50	3.80	9.00
176-Warlock cameo, 2 panels only, same date as StrangeTales #178			
(6/74)	0.80	2.10	5.00
177-1st actual death of Warlock (last panel only, 7/74)			
	1.00	3.00	7.00
178-Rebirth of Warlock	1.70	5.10	12.00
179-No Warlock	1.00	2.00	5.00
180-1st Wolverine (cameo on last pg.,10/74)			
	9.00	27.00	62.00
181-1st full Wolverine story (11/74)	40.00	120.00	290.00
182-Wolverine cameo cont. from issue #181; see Giant-Size X-Men #1			
for next app.	6.90	21.00	48.00
183-199	0.70	1.40	3.50
200-Silver Surfer app.; anniversary issue	4.00	10.70	25.00
201-240: 234-(4/79)-1st app. Quasar	0.60	1.20	3.00
241-249,251-299: 243-Cage app.	0.40	0.80	2.00
250-(Giant size)-Silver Surfer app.	1.40	3.50	8.50
300-(11/84, 52 pgs.)-Black Spidey-c/cameo		1.60	4.00
301-313: 312-Origin Hulk retold	0.50	1.00	2.50
314-Byrne art begins	1.00	1.90	4.75
315-319: 319-Last Byrne art	0.50	1.00	2.50
320-323, 325, 327-329	0.40	0.80	2.00
324-1st app. Grey Hulk since #1 (1962)	1.80	4.60	11.00
326-Grey vs. Green Hulk	1.00	1.90	4.75
330-1st McFarlane issue (c/a)(p)	3.00	7.70	18.00
331-Grey Hulk series begins	1.70	5.10	12.00
332-334, 336-339	1.30	3.90	9.00
335-No McFarlane-a	0.60	1.20	3.00
340-Hulk battles Wolverine by McFarlane	5.70	17.00	40.00
341-344	1.20	3.00	7.00
345-(1.50, 52 pgs.)	1.30	3.30	8.00
346-Last McFarlane issue	1.00	2.50	6.00
347-349, 351-358, 360-366	0.60	1.20	3.00

350-Hulk/Thing battle	0.80	1.60	4.00
359-Wolverine app. (illusion only)	0.90	1.80	4.50
367-1st Dale Keown-a in Hulk	2.10	6.40	15.00
368-Sam Kieth-c/a	1.90	5.60	13.00
369, 370-Keown-a	1.80	4.60	11.00
371, 373-376: Keown-a; 376-Green vs. Grey			
	1.10	2.70	6.50
372-Green Hulk app.; Keown-c/a	2.10	6.00	15.00
377-Fluorescent-c;1st all-new Hulk; Keown-a	2.40	7.00	17.00
377-Fluorescent green-c; 2nd printing	1.00	2.30	5.50
378, 380, 389-No Keown-a	0.60	1.20	3.00
379-Keown-a	0.80	2.00	5.00
381-388, 390-392: Keown-c/a	1.00	2.00	5.00
393-Green foil stamped-c; Keown-c/a	0.80	2.00	5.00
393-(2.50) 2nd printing	0.60	1.20	3.00
394-No Keown-a	0.40	0.80	2.00
395, 396-Keown-c/a; Punisher-c/stories	0.40	0.80	2.00
397-Begin 4 part Ghost of the Past; Keown-c/a			
	0.40	0.80	2.00
398, 399: Ghost Of The Past cont.	0.30	0.60	1.60
400 (2.50-c)-Holo-grafx foil-c; Ditko-r	0.80	1.60	4.00
401-416: 402-Return of Doc Samson	0.30	0.60	1.60
417-424, 426: 417-Begin 1.50-c; bound-in trading card sheet. 418-Death app.			
420-Death of Jim Wilson. 421-Peter David-sty			
	0.30	0.60	1.50
418-(2.50-c)-Gatefold die cut-c	0.50	1.00	2.50
425-(2.25, 52 pgs)	0.50	0.90	2.25
425-(3.50, 52 pgs)-Holographic cover	0.80	1.60	4.00
426-432-(1.95)-Deluxe edition, 427-428-Man-Thing app.			
431-432-Abomination app.	0.40	0.80	2.00
Special 1 (10/68)-Hulk battles The Inhumans (early app.); Steranko-c			
	9.00	26.00	60.00
Special 2 (10/69)-Origin retold	5.00	15.00	35.00
Special 3 (1/71)	1.30	3.00	8.00
Special 4 (1/72)	1.00	2.50	6.00
Annual 5 (1976)	1.00	2.00	5.00
Annual 6 (1977)	0.60	1.20	3.00
Annual 7 (1978)-Byrne-a; Iceman, Angel app.			
	0.80	1.60	4.00
Annual 8-17 ('79-'86, '90, '91): 11-Miller-a (5 pgs.); Spider-Man &			
Avengers x-over; 17-Origin retold; no Keown			
	0.40	0.80	2.00
Annual 18 ('92, 2.25)-Return/Defenders pt. 1			

	Good	Fine	N-Mint
	0.50	0.90	2.25
Annual 19 ('93, 2.95)-Polybagged w/card	0.60	1.20	3.00
Annual 20 ('94, 2.95, 68 pgs.)	0.60	1.20	3.00
...And Wolverine 1 (10/86, 2.50)-r/1st app. #180,181			
	1.40	4.00	10.00
...Ground Zero ('95, 12.95) r/#340-346	1.90	6.00	13.00
...Versus Quasimodo 1 (3/83)-(TV cartoon)		0.60	1.60
...Vs. Venom 1 (4/94, 2.50)-Embossed-c 2/red foil logo			
	0.50	1.00	2.50

INDIANA JONES AND THE ARMS OF GOLD
Feb, 1994-No. 4, May, 1994 (2.50, color, limited series)
Dark Horse Comics

1-4	0.50	1.00	2.50

INDIANA JONES AND THE FATE OF ATLANTIS
Mar, 1991-No. 4, Sept, 1991 (2.50, color, limited series)
Dark Horse Comics

1-4: Dorman painted-c. 1,2-w/trading cards		1.00	2.50
1-2nd printing (10/91)	0.50	1.00	2.50

INDIANA JONES AND THE GOLDEN FLEECE
June, 1994-July, 1994 (2.50, color, limited series)
Dark Horse Comics

1,2	0.50	1.00	2.50

INDIANA JONES AND THE IRON PHOENIX
Dec 1994 - Mar 1995 (2.50, color, limited series)
Dark Horse Comics

1-4	0.50	1.00	2.50

INDIANA JONES AND THE SHRINE OF THE SEA DEVIL
Sept, 1994 (2.50, color, one-shot)
Dark Horse Comics

1	0.50	1.00	2.50

INDIANA JONES AND THE SPEAR OF DESTINY
Apr 1995-Present (2.50, color, limited series)

1–3	0.50	1.00	2.50

INDIANA JONES: THUNDER IN THE ORIENT
Sept, 1993-No. 6, April, 1994 (2.50, color, limited series)
Dark Horse Comics

1-6: Barry-a & scripts. 1-Dorman painted-c 0.50   1.00   2.50

INFERIOR FIVE, THE (See Showcase #62, 63, 65)
Mar-Apr, 1967-No. 12, Oct-Nov, 1972
National Periodical Publications
1-4th app. Inferior Five	4.70	14.00	33.00
2-Plastic Man, F.F. app.	2.40	7.30	17.00
3-12: 11, 12-r/Showcase 62, 63	1.70	5.10	12.00

INFINITY CRUSADE, THE
June, 1993-No. 6, Nov, 1993 (2.50, color, mini-series, 52 pgs.)
Marvel Comics
1-6-By Starlin/Lim   0.50   1.00   2.50

INFINITY GAUNTLET (Also see Warlock & The Infinity Watch)
July, 1991-No. 6, Dec, 1991 (2.50, color, 52 pgs.)
Marvel Comics
1-Perez painted-c; Starlin scripts in all	0.80	2.10	5.00
2-Thanos-c/stories in all	0.60	1.20	3.00
3-6: 5, 6-Ron Lim-c/a	0.50	1.00	2.50

INFINITY, INC.
Mar, 1984-No. 53, Aug, 1988
DC Comics
1	0.30	0.60	1.50
2-13, 38-49, 51-53	0.20	0.50	1.20
14-Todd McFarlane art (5/85)	0.50	1.00	2.50
15-37: Todd McFarlane art	0.40	0.70	1.80
50-(2.50, 52 pgs.)	0.50	1.00	2.50
Annual 1 (12/85), 2 (1988): 1-McFarlane-a	0.40	0.80	2.00
Special 1 (1987, 1.50)	0.30	0.60	1.50

INFINITY WAR, THE
June, 1992-No. 6, Nov, 1992 (2.50, color, mini-series)
Marvel Comics
1-Starlin scripts; Ron Lim-a(p)	0.90	1.70	4.25
2–6	0.50	1.00	2.50

INHUMANS, THE (Also see Amazing Adventures)
Oct, 1975-No. 12, Aug, 1977
Marvel Comics Group
1	1.20	2.40	6.00
2-12: 9-r/Amazing Advs. #1, 2 ('70)	0.60	1.20	3.00

	Good	Fine	N-Mint
Special 1 (4/90, 1.50, 52 pgs.)	0.40	0.80	2.00

INHUMANS:THE GREAT REFUGE
May, 1995- (2.95, color)
Marvel Comics

| 1 | 0.60 | 1.20 | 3.00 |

INVADERS, THE (TV)
Oct, 1967-No. 4, Oct, 1968 (All have photo-c)
Gold Key

| 1-Spiegle-a in all | 7.10 | 21.00 | 50.00 |
| 2–4 | 5.70 | 17.10 | 40.00 |

INVADERS, THE (Also see Giant-Size Invaders)
Aug, 1975-No. 41, Sept, 1979
Marvel Comics Group

1-Capt. America, Human Torch, Sub-Mariner begin			
	1.70	4.20	10.00
2-10: 3-Battle issue; Cap vs. Namor vs. Torch			
	1.00	2.50	6.00
11–19	1.00	2.00	5.00
20-Reprints 1st Sub-Mariner story from Motion Pictures Funnies			
Weekly (1939) w/brief history	1.00	2.50	6.00
21-Reprints Marvel Mystery #10	0.80	1.60	4.00
22, 23, 25-40	0.60	1.20	3.00
24-Reprints Marvel Mystery #17	0.60	1.20	3.00
41-Double size final issue	0.60	1.20	3.00
Annual 1 (1977)-Schomburg-c/a (1st since G.A.); Avengers app.;			
re-intro The Shark	0.60	1.20	3.00

Inhumans #6 © MEG

Iron Man #262 © MEG

INVADERS, THE (See Namor #12)
May, 1993-No. 4, Aug, 1993 (1.75, color, mini-series)
Marvel Comics
1–4	0.40	0.70	1.75

INVISIBLES, THE
Sept, 1994-Present (1.95, color, mature)
DC Comics
1-(2.95, 52 pgs)-G. Morrison story	0.70	1.40	3.50
2-8: 4-w/bound-in trading card	0.40	0.80	2.00
9-begin 2.50-c; 10-11	0.50	1.00	2.50

IRON FIST (See Deadly Hands of Kung-Fu, Marvel Premiere & Power Man)
Nov, 1975-No. 15, Sept, 1977
Marvel Comics Group
1-Battles Iron Man (Byrne-a in all 1-15)	3.90	12.00	27.00
2	2.40	7.30	17.00
3–5	2.00	5.00	12.00
6-10: 6-Last 25¢ issue. 8-Origin retold	2.00	5.00	12.00
11-13: 12-Capt. America app.	1.20	3.00	7.00
14-1st app. Sabretooth (30¢ & 35¢ versions)			
	17.00	51.00	120.00
15-New X-Men app.; Byrne-a (30¢ & 35¢ versions exist)			
	3.90	12.00	27.00

IRON MAN (Also see Giant-Size Iron Man & Tales Of Suspense)
May, 1968-Present
Marvel Comics Group
1-Origin; story cont'd from Iron Man & Sub-Mariner #1			
	46.00	139.00	325.00
2	14.00	40.00	100.00
3	10.00	30.00	70.00
4, 5	6.30	19.00	50.00
6-10: 9-Iron Man battles Hulk-like android	5.00	15.00	40.00
11-15: 15-Last 12¢ issue	3.00	9.00	25.00
16-20	3.00	8.00	19.00
21-24, 26-42: 42-Last 15¢ issue	1.80	5.00	14.00
25-Iron Man battles Sub-Mariner	2.90	8.00	20.00
43-Giant-size, 25¢-c	1.80	5.00	14.00
44-46, 48-50	1.00	3.00	10.00
47-Origin retold; Smith art	2.00	6.00	15.00
51-53: 53-Starlin pencils (part)	1.20	2.90	7.00
54-Iron Man battles Sub-Mariner; 1st app. of Moondragon			

	Good	Fine	N-Mint
(as Madame MacEvil) (1/73)	2.10	5.00	15.00
55-1st app. Thanos (cameo) & Drax (2/73); Starlin-c/a			
	11.00	34.00	90.00
56-Starlin-a(p)	3.00	7.20	18.00
57-67, 69, 70: 67-Last 20¢ issue	1.20	2.90	7.00
68-Starlin-c; origin retold; Sunfire app.	1.70	4.00	10.00
71-99: 88-Thanos app. 89-Last 25¢ issue	0.80	2.10	5.00
100-Starlin-c (7/77)	1.70	4.00	10.00
101-117: 110-Origin Jack of Hearts retold	0.90	2.30	5.50
118-Byrne art	1.10	2.70	6.50
119, 120, 123-128: Tony Stark recovers from alcoholism			
	1.00	1.90	4.75
121, 122, 129-149: 122-Origin retold. 131, 132-Hulk x-over			
	0.60	1.10	2.75
150-Double size	0.80	1.60	4.00
151-168: 152-New armor	0.50	1.00	2.50
169-New Iron Man begins	1.50	3.80	9.00
170	0.90	1.80	4.50
171	0.80	1.60	4.00
172-199	0.50	0.90	2.25
200-Tony Starks returns as new Iron Man	1.00	1.90	4.75
201-224	0.40	0.70	1.80
225-(1.25, 52 pgs.)	1.00	1.90	4.75
226-243, 245-249: 231-Intro new Iron Man	0.40	0.70	1.80
244-(1.50, 52 pgs.)-New armor	0.90	1.80	4.50
250-(1.50, 52 pgs.)	0.40	0.70	1.80
251-274, 276-281,283, 285-287,289, 291-299: 281-1st app. War Machine			
(cameo).	0.30	0.50	1.25
282-1st full app. War Machine (also in #283)			
	1.00	2.00	5.00
275-(1.50, 52 pgs.)	0.40	0.80	2.00
284-Death of Tony Stark	0.60	1.20	3.00
288-(2.50, 52 pgs)-Silver foil stamped-c	0.50	1.00	2.50
290-(2.95, 52 pgs.)-Gold foil stamped-c	0.60	1.20	3.00
300-(3.95, 68 pgs.)-Coll. Ed.; foil embossed-c			
	0.80	1.60	4.00
300-(2.50, 68 pgs.)-Newsstand Ed.; War Machine-c/story			
	0.50	1.00	2.50
301-303: 302-Venom-c/story (cameo #301)		0.50	1.25
304-316, 318– : 304-Begin 1.50-c; bound-in card sheet. 310-Orange logo			
312-w/ bound in Power Ranger Barcode Card			
	0.30	0.60	1.50
310-(2.95)-Polybagged w/16 pg. Marvel Action Hour preview			

317-(2.50)-Flip book	0.50	1.00	2.50
and acetate print; white logo	0.60	1.20	3.00
Special 1 (8/70)-Sub-Mariner x-over	2.60	7.70	18.00
Special 2 (11/71)	1.30	3.30	8.00
Annual 3 ('76)-Man-Thing x-over	0.80	1.60	4.00
King Size 4 ('77)-Champions (Ghost Rider) app.			
	0.60	1.20	3.00
Annual 5-9 (1982-87): 8-X-Factor app.	0.40	0.80	2.00
Annual 10 ('89)-Atlantis Attacks	0.50	1.00	2.50
Annual 11 ('90)-Ditko-a. Annual 12 ('91)	0.40	0.80	2.00
Annual 13 ('92, 2.25)-Darkhawk app.	0.50	1.00	2.50
Annual 14 ('93, 2.95)-Polybagged w/card	0.60	1.20	3.00
Annual 15 ('94, 2.95, 68 pgs.)	0.60	1.20	3.00
Manual 1 ('93, 1.75)-Operations Handbook	0.40	0.70	1.75
...2020 (6/94, 5.95)	1.00	2.50	6.00
...: Collectors' Preview 1 (11/94, 1.95)-Wraparound-c; text & illos -			
no comics	0.40	0.80	2.00
...Vs. Dr. Doom (12/94, 12.95) r/#149-150, #249-250 J.Bell-c			
	1.90	5.60	13.00

IRON MAN & SUB-MARINER
April, 1968 (One-shot, 12¢)
Marvel Comics Group

1-Pre-dates Iron Man #1 and Sub-Mariner #1; first story is an Iron Man story which continues from TOS 99 and continues in Iron Man #1. Second story is a Sub-Mariner story which continues from TTA #101 and is completed in Sub-Mariner #1	21.00	64.00	150.00

I SPY (TV)
Aug, 1966-No. 6, Sept, 1968 (Photo-c)
Gold Key

1-Bill Cosby, Robert Culp photo covers	23.00	70.00	160.00
2-6: 3,4-Mcwilliams-a	15.00	45.00	105.00

ITCHY & SCRATCHY COMICS (Simpson's TV show)
1993-Present (1.95, color, three times yearly)
Bongo Comics Group

1-(2.25)-Pull out poster	0.50	1.00	2.50
2-(1.95)	0.40	0.80	2.00
3-(2.25)-w/decoder screen trading card	0.50	0.90	2.25
Holiday Special ('94, 1.95)	0.40	0.80	2.00

Secret City Saga # 0 © Jack Kirby

Next Men #21 © John Byrne

JACKIE GLEASON AND THE HONEYMOONERS (TV)
June-July, 1956-No. 12, Apr-May, 1958
National Periodical Publications

1	75.00	225.00	525.00
2	50.00	160.00	375.00
3–11	39.00	118.00	275.00
12 (Scarce)	58.00	176.00	410.00

JACK KIRBY'S SECRET CITY SAGA
No. 0, Apr, 1993; No. 1, May, 1993-No. 4, Aug, 1993 (2.95, color, mini-series)
Topps Comics

0-(No cover price, 20 pgs.)-Simonson-c/a	0.40	0.80	2.00
1-4-Polybagged w/3 trading cards; Ditko-c/a: 1-Ditko/A. Adams-c.			
2-Ditko/Byrne-c. 3-Dorman poster	0.60	1.20	3.00

Note: Issues 1-4 contain coupons for Amberchrome version of #0.

JACK KIRBY'S SILVER STAR (Also see Silver Star)
Oct, 1993 (2.95, color)(Intended as 4-issue mini-series)
Topps Comics

1-Polybagged w/3 cards; silver ink-c	0.60	1.20	3.00

JACK KIRBY'S TEENAGENTS (See Satan's Six #4)
Aug, 1993-No. 3, Oct, 1993 (2.95, color)(Intended as 4-issue limited series)
Topps Comics

1-3-Polybagged w/3 trading cards; Austin-c(i)			
	0.60	1.20	3.00

JAMES BOND 007: A SILENT ARMAGEDDON
Mar, 1993-No. 2, May, 1993 (2.95, color)

Dark Horse/Acme
1, 2	0.60	1.20	3.00

JAMES BOND 007: SERPENT'S TOOTH
July, 1992-No. 3, Sept, 1992 (4.95, color, mini-series)
Acme Comics/Dark Horse Comics
1-3: Paul Gulacy-c/a	1.00	2.00	5.00

JAMES BOND 007: SHATTERED HELIX
1994-No. 2, July, 1994 (2.50, color, limited series)
Dark Horse Comics
1,2	0.60	1.20	3.00

JAMES BOND 007: THE QUASIMODO GAMBIT
Jan 1995-May 1995 (3.95, color, limited series:3)
Dark Horse Comics
1-3	0.80	1.60	4.00

JAMES BOND: PERMISSION TO DIE
1989-No. 3, 1991 (3.95/4.95, color, deluxe format)
Eclipse Books
1-3: Written & illus. by Mike Grell	1.00	2.00	5.00

JAR OF FOOLS
1994 (5.95, B&W)
Penny Dreadful Press
1–Jason Lutes s/a	1.20	2.40	6.00

JAR OF FOOLS
1994 (6.95, B&W)
Black Eye Productions
1–reprint of earlier ed. Jason Lutes s/a	1.40	2.80	7.00

JET DREAM (...& Her Stunt-Girl Counterspies)
June, 1968 (12¢)
Gold Key
1-Painted-c; see Man From U.N.C.L.E. #7	2.40	7.30	17.00

JETSONS, THE (TV)
Jan, 1963-No. 36, Oct, 1970 (Hanna-Barbera)
Gold Key
1	20.00	60.00	180.00
2	10.00	30.00	90.00
3–10	8.00	25.00	75.00

	Good	Fine	N-Mint
11–20	6.00	17.00	50.00
21-36	4.00	13.00	40.00

JETSONS (TV)
Nov, 1970-No. 20, Dec, 1973
Charlton Comics

1	7.70	23.00	54.00
2	3.90	12.00	27.00
3–10	3.10	9.00	22.00
11–20	2.00	6.00	14.00

JIGSAW (Big Hero Adventures)
Sept, 1966-No. 2, Dec, 1966
Harvey Publications

1-Origin & 1st app.; Crandall-a (5 pgs.)	1.30	3.00	8.00
2	1.00	3.00	6.00

JOHN BYRNE'S NEXT MEN (Also see Dark Horse Presents)
Jan, 1992-Present (2.50, color, mature)
Dark Horse Comics (Legend imprint #19 on)

1-Foil embossed-c; Byrne-c/a/scripts begins	1.20	3.00	7.00
1-2nd printing w/gold ink logo	0.70	1.40	3.50
0 (2/92)-r/1st 4 chapters from DHP w/new-c			
	1.00	2.00	5.00
2	0.70	1.40	3.50
3, 4	0.60	1.20	3.00

5-29: 7-10-MA #1-4 mini-series on flip side. 16-Origin of Mark IV.
   17-Miller-c. 18-Last issue reg. series. 19-22-Faith storyline Pt. 1-4.
   23-26-Power storyline Pt.1-4. 27-30-Lies storyline Pt. 1-4

	0.50	1.00	2.50
...Parallel, Book 2-(16.95)-TPB; r/#7-12	2.00	7.00	18.00
...Fame, Book 3 (16.95)-TPB r/#13-18	1.90	7.00	17.00
...Faith, Book 4 (14.95)-TPB r/#19-22			

Note: #1-6 contain certificates redeemable for an exclusive Next Men
trading card set by Byrne. Prices are for complete books.

JOHN CARTER OF MARS
April, 1964-No. 3, Oct, 1964
Gold Key

1(10104-404)-r/F.C. 375	4.00	8.00	28.00
2,3(10104-407 & 10104-410)-r/F.C. 437 & 488			
	2.20	7.00	20.00

JOHN CARTER, WARLORD OF MARS
June, 1977-No. 28, Oct, 1979
Marvel Comics Group

1-17, 19-28	0.20	0.40	1.00
18-Miller-a(p)	0.30	0.60	1.50
Annual 1-3: 1(10/77), 2('78), 3 ('79)	0.20	0.40	1.00

JOHN JAKES' MULKON EMPIRE
Sep 1995-Present (1.95, color)
Tekno•Comix

1–2	0.40	0.80	2.00

JOHNNY DYNAMITE
Sept 1994 - Dec 1994 (2.95, B&W & red, limited series)
Dark Horse Comics

1-4	0.60	1.20	3.00

JOHNNY THUNDER
Feb-Mar, 1973-No. 3, July-Aug, 1973
National Periodical Publications

1-All have 1950s-r from All-American West.		0.40	1.00
2,3		0.40	1.00

JOHN STEELE SECRET AGENT (Also see Freedom Agent)
Dec, 1964
Gold Key

1-Freedom Agent	9.00	27.40	64.00

JOKER, THE
May, 1975-No. 9, Sept-Oct, 1976
National Periodical Publications

1-Two-Face app.	2.10	6.40	15.00
2, 3	1.30	3.00	8.00
4-6: 4-Green Arrow-c/story	1.00	2.50	6.00
7-9: 7-Lex Luthor-c/sty. 9-Catwoman-c/sty			
	1.00	2.00	5.00

JONAH HEX (See All-Star Western & DC Special Series #16)
Mar-Apr, 1977-No. 92, Aug, 1985 (Also see Weird Western Tales)
National Periodical Publications/ DC Comics

1	5.00	15.00	35.00
2-6, 9, 10: 9-Wrightson-c	1.70	4.20	10.00
7, 8-Explains Hex's face disfigurement	1.70	4.20	10.00
11-20: 12-Starlin-c	1.00	2.00	5.00

	Good	Fine	N-Mint
21-50: 31, 32-Origin retold	0.80	1.60	4.00
51-92: 89-Mark Texeira-a(p). 92-Story cont'd in Hex #1			
	0.60	1.20	3.00

JONAH HEX : RIDERS OF THE WORM AND SUCH
Mar 1995-July 1995 (2.95, color, limited series: 5)
DC Comics

	Good	Fine	N-Mint
1-Lansdale/s, Truman/a , S. Glansman/i	0.80	1.60	4.00
2-5-Lansdale/s, Truman/a , S. Glansman/i	0.60	1.20	3.00

JONAH HEX: TWO-GUN MOJO
Aug, 1993-No. 5, Dec, 1993 (2.95, color, mini-series)
DC Comics (Vertigo)

	Good	Fine	N-Mint
1-Truman/Glanzman-a in all	1.20	2.90	7.00
1-Silver Ink ed. w/no price on-c	2.40	7.30	17.00
2–5	0.80	1.60	4.00
nn ('94, 12.95, TPB)-r/#1-5	1.90	5.60	13.00

JONNY DEMON
May, 1994-No. 3, July, 1994 (2.50, color, limited series)
Dark Horse Comics

	Good	Fine	N-Mint
1–3	0.50	1.00	2.50

JONNY QUEST (TV)
Dec, 1964 (Hanna-Barbera)
Gold Key

	Good	Fine	N-Mint
1 (10139-412)-TV tie-in	24.00	72.00	240.00

JOURNEY
1983-No. 27, July, 1986 (B&W)
Aardvark-Vanaheim/First

	Good	Fine	N-Mint
1	1.00	2.00	5.00
2	0.60	1.20	3.00
3-27: 20-Sam Kieth-a	0.30	0.50	1.25

JOURNEY INTO MYSTERY (1st Series) (Thor No. 126 on)
June, 1952-No. 48, Aug, 1957; No. 49, Nov, 1958-No. 125, Feb, 1966
Marvel Comics Group

	Good	Fine	N-Mint
1	130.00	400.00	1600.00
2	67.00	201.00	535.00
3, 4	51.00	150.00	410.00
5–11	33.00	98.00	260.00
12-20, 22: 22-Last pre-code iss. (2/55)	27.00	81.00	215.00

21-Kubert-a	28.00	84.00	225.00
23-32, 35-38, 40: 38-Ditko-a	17.00	51.00	135.00
33-Ditko, Williamson-a	19.00	56.00	150.00
34, 39: 34-Krigstein-a. 39-Wood-a	18.00	53.00	140.00
41-Crandall-a	14.00	41.00	110.00
42, 48-Torres-a	14.00	41.00	110.00
43, 44-Williamson/Mayo in both	15.00	45.00	120.00
45, 47, 52, 53	12.00	36.00	95.00
46-Torres, Krigstein-a	14.00	41.00	110.00
49-Matt Fox-a	14.00	43.00	115.00
50, 54:50-Davis-a;Ditko-a begins, ends#96	9.00	27.00	90.00
51-Kirby/Wood-a	10.50	32.00	105.00
55-61, 63-65, 67-69, 71, 72, 74, 75: 58-F.F. #1 cover prototype.			
75-Last 10¢ issue	9.50	29.00	95.00
62-1st app. Xemnu (Titan) called The Hulk (Hulk prototype)			
	15.00	50.00	150.00
66-Return of Xemnu (Hulk prototype)	13.00	39.00	130.00
70-Sandman prototype (7/61)	12.00	36.00	120.00
73-Spider-Man prototype (10/61)	16.00	50.00	155.00
76, 77, 80-82	8.50	26.00	85.00
78-The Sorceror; Dr. Strange prototype (3/62)			
	14.00	42.00	140.00
79-Mr. Hyde prototype	12.00	35.00	115.00
83-Origin & 1st app. Thor & begin series; Kirby-a (8/62); Thor-c begin			
	330.00	990.00	3300.00
83-(Reprint)	9.00	26.00	70.00
With Golden Records ('66)	18.00	53.00	140.00
84-2nd app. Thor	93.00	278.00	740.00
85-1st app. Loki & Heimdall; 1 panel cameo Odin			
	47.00	141.00	375.00

Journey into Mystery #7 © MEG

Judge Dredd #2 © DC

	Good	Fine	N-Mint
86-1st full app. Odin	30.00	90.00	260.00
87-89: 89-origin retold	20.00	60.00	175.00
90-No Kirby art	13.00	38.00	105.00
91, 92, 94-96: Sinnott art	12.00	36.00	95.00
93, 97-Kirby art. 97-Tales of Asgard begins			
	16.00	47.00	125.00
98-100: 98-Origin/1st app. Human Cobra	11.00	32.00	85.00
101-108, 110: 101-(2/64)-2nd Avengers x-over (w/o Capt. America)(see T.O.S. #49 for 1st x-over). 107-1st app. Grey Gargoyle. 108-Early Dr. Strange & Avengers app. (9/64)	7.00	21.00	56.00
109-Magneto-c/app. (10/64); 1st x-over	11.00	32.00	85.00
111, 113, 114, 116-125: 124-Hercules-c/story			
	7.00	21.00	55.00
112-(1/65)-Thor vs. Hulk, origin Loki 112, 113			
	16.00	47.00	125.00
115-Origin Loki	8.00	23.00	60.00
Annual 1 (1965)-New Thor vs. Hercules-c/story; 1st app. Hercules			
	14.00	43.00	115.00

JOURNEY INTO MYSTERY (2nd Series)
Oct, 1972-No. 19, Oct, 1975
Marvel Comics Group

1-Robert Howard adaptation	1.00	2.50	6.00
2, 3, 5-Bloch adaptations	0.60	1.20	3.00
4, 6-19: 4-H.P. Lovecraft adapt.	0.40	0.80	2.00

JUDGE DREDD (Judge Dredd Classics #62 on)
Nov, 1983-No. 35, 1986; V2#1, Oct, 1986-No. 77, 1993
Eagle Comics/Quality Comics No. 33 on

1-Bolland c/a-1-10, 15; Antrax	1.70	4.20	10.00
2–35	0.80	1.60	4.00
V2#1-New look begins	0.60	1.20	3.00
2–6	0.40	0.80	2.00
7-21/22: 20-Begin 1.50-c	0.40	0.80	2.00
23/24-2 issues in one	0.30	0.60	1.50
25-38	0.30	0.60	1.50
39-50: 1.75-c	0.40	0.70	1.75
51-77: 1.95-c begin	0.40	0.80	2.00
Special No. 1	0.40	0.80	2.00

JUDGE DREDD (3rd Series)
Aug, 1994-Present (1.95, color)
DC Comics

1–11	0.40	0.80	2.00
12–begin 2.25-c; 13–	0.50	0.90	2.25

JUDGE DREDD: LEGENDS OF THE LAW
Dec, 1994-Present (1.95, color)
DC Comics

1-5-Dorman-c 6-7	0.40	0.80	2.00
8-begin 2.25-c	0.50	0.90	2.25

JUDGMENT DAY
Sept, 1993-No. 8, Apr, 1994 (2.95, color)
Lightning Comics

1-(3.50)-Red prism-c	0.70	1.40	3.50
1-Gold prism-c	1.60	5.00	11.00
1-Purple-c	0.80	2.10	5.00
2-8: 2-1st app. War Party; polybagged w/trading card. 7-Origin			
	0.60	1.20	3.00

JUDOMASTER (See Sarge Steel & Special War Series)
No. 89, May-June, 1966-No. 98, Dec, 1967
Charlton Comics

89	2.40	7.30	17.00
90-98: 89-3rd app.? 91-Sarge Steel begins	1.90	6.00	13.00
93, 94, 96, 98 (Modern Comics reprints)	0.20	0.40	1.00

JUGHEAD AS CAPTAIN HERO (See Archie as Pureheart...)
Oct, 1966-No. 7, Nov, 1967 (Also see Life With Archie)
Archie Publications

1-Super-hero parody	3.85	11.50	28.00
2	2.60	7.70	18.00
3–7	1.70	5.10	12.00

JUNGLE ACTION (See Black Panther)
Oct, 1972-No. 24, Nov, 1976
Marvel Comics Group

1	1.00	2.50	6.00
2-4: (1-4: all reprints)	0.60	1.20	3.00
5-Black Panther begins (origin in #8)	1.00	2.50	6.00
6-18: All new stories	0.60	1.20	3.00
19-24	0.40	0.80	2.00

JURASSIC PARK(...Adventures #5 on)
June, 1993-No. 4, Aug, 1993 (Color, mini-series, movie adaptation)

	Good	Fine	N-Mint

Jurassic Park #1 © Topps

Justice #1 © MEG

No. 5, Oct, 1994-Present (1.95, on-going series)
Topps Comics

	Good	Fine	N-Mint
1 -(2.50)-Newsstand ed.; Kane/Perez-a	0.80	1.60	4.00
1-(2.95)-Polybagged Collectors Ed. w/3 cards			
	1.00	2.50	6.00
1-Amberchrome Edition no price/no ads	2.40	7.00	17.00
2-4-(2.50)-Newsstand editions	0.50	1.00	2.50
2, 3-(2.95)-Bagged Collectors Ed. w/3 cards	0.60	1.20	3.00
4-(2.95)-Polybagged w/1 of 4 action hologram cards			
	0.60	1.20	3.00
5-10:10-Last issue (2/95)	0.40	0.80	2.00
Annual 1 (May 1995, 3.95)	0.80	1.60	4.00
Jurassic Park TPB w/#0-Polybagged	1.70	4.20	10.00

JURASSIC PARK: RAPTOR
Nov, 1993-No. 2, Dec, 1993 (2.95, color, limited series)
Topps Comics

	Good	Fine	N-Mint
1,2-Bagged w/3 trading cards. 1-Contains Zorro #0			
	0.60	1.20	3.00

JURASSIC PARK: RAPTORS ATTACK
Mar, 1994-No. 4, June, 1994 (2.50, color, limited series)
Topps Comics

	Good	Fine	N-Mint
1-4-Michael Golden-c/frontispiece	0.50	1.00	2.50

JURASSIC PARK: RAPTORS HIJACK
July, 1994-No. 4, Oct, 1994 (2.50, color, limited series)
Topps Comics

	Good	Fine	N-Mint
1-4: 1-3-Michael Golden-c/frontispiece. 4-Golden-c			
	0.50	1.00	2.50

JUSTICE: FOUR BALANCE
Sept, 1994-No. 4, Dec, 1994 (1.75, color, limited series)
Marvel Comics

1-4: 1-Thing and Firestar app.	0.40	0.70	1.75

JUSTICE LEAGUE (...International No. 7 -25) (...America #26 on)
(See Legends #6 for 1st app.)
May, 1987-Present
DC Comics

1	0.80	2.00	5.00
2	0.80	1.60	4.00
3-Regular cover, white background	0.60	1.20	3.00
3-Limited-c; yellow background & Superman logo			
	14.00	41.00	95.00
4-6: 4-Booster Gold joins	0.50	1.00	2.50
7-(1.25, 52 pgs.)-Capt. Atom joins	0.60	1.20	3.00
8-10	0.30	0.60	1.50
11-23: 18-21: Lobo app.	0.20	0.50	1.20
24-(1.50)-1st app. JL Europe	0.30	0.60	1.50
25-49, 51-62: 58-Lobo app. 61-New team	0.20	0.40	1.00
50-(1.75, 52 pgs.)	0.40	0.70	1.75
63-68, 72-82: 80-Intro new Booster Gold	0.30	0.50	1.25
69-Doomsday battle issue	1.70	5.10	12.00
69,70-2nd printings	0.30	0.50	1.25
70-Funeral For A Friend pt 1;red 3/4 outer-c	1.30	3.00	8.00
70-Newsstand version w/o outer-c	0.90	1.80	4.50
71-Direct sale version w/black outer-c	0.40	0.80	2.00
71-Newsstand ed. w/o outer-c	0.30	0.50	1.25
83-92: 82,83-Guy Gardner-c/s. 83-Begin 1.50-c. 92-(9/94)-Zero Hour			
	0.30	0.60	1.50
0-(10/94)-New membership - Hawkman, Wonder Woman, Metamorpho, Flash, Nuklon, Crimson Fox, Obsidian & Fire			
	0.30	0.60	1.50
93-99: 93-(11/94)	0.30	0.60	1.50
100-(3.95, 52 pgs. foil-c)	0.80	1.60	4.00
100-(2.95, Newstand)	0.60	1.20	3.00
101-begin 1.75-c; 102–	0.40	0.70	1.75
Annual 1-5 (1987-1991)	0.40	0.80	2.00
Annual 5 (91, 2.00)-Silver ink 2nd print	0.40	0.80	2.00
Annual 6, 7 ('92, '93, 2.50): 7-Bloodlines	0.50	1.00	2.50
Annual 8 ('94, 2.95, 68 pgs.)-Elseworlds story			
	0.60	1.20	3.00

	Good	Fine	N-Mint
Annual 9 ('95, 3.50)-Year One story	0.70	1.40	3.50
Special 1 ('90, 1.50, 52 pgs.)	0.30	0.60	1.50
Special 2 ('91, 2.95)	0.60	1.20	3.00
...Spectacular 1 ('92, 1.50)-Intro new team	0.30	0.60	1.50
...:A New Beginning (TPB, 1989, 12.95)	1.90	6.00	13.00

JUSTICE LEAGUE EUROPE (Becomes Justice League International #51 on)
Apr, 1989-No. 68, Sept, 1994 (Color)
DC Comics

	Good	Fine	N-Mint
1	0.40	0.80	2.00
2-49, 51-57: 33, 34-Lobo vs. Despero. 37-New Team begins			
	0.30	0.50	1.25
50-(2.50, 68 pgs.)-Battles Sonar	0.50	1.00	2.50
58-68: 58-Begin 1.50-c. 68-Zero Hour	0.30	0.60	1.50
Annual 1 ('90, 2.00). Annual 2 ('91, 2.00)	0.40	0.80	2.00
Annual 3, 4 ('92, '93, 2.50): 4-Intro Lionheart			
	0.50	1.00	2.50
Annual 5 ('94, 2.95)-Elseworlds story	0.60	1.20	3.00

JUSTICE LEAGUE OF AMERICA (See Brave & the Bold #28-30)
Oct-Nov, 1960-No. 261, Apr, 1987
National Periodical Publications/DC Comics

	Good	Fine	N-Mint
1-Origin/1st app. Despero	260.00	780.00	2600.00
2	81.00	242.00	645.00
3-Origin & 1st app. Kanjar Ro; x-over app. in Mystery in Space #75			
	56.00	168.00	505.00
4-Green Arrow joins JLA	37.00	110.00	330.00
5-Origin/1st app. Dr. Destiny	33.00	99.00	265.00
6-8, 10: 7-Last 10¢ issue	27.00	81.00	215.00
9-Origin JLA (1st origin)	39.00	118.00	355.00
11-15: 12-Origin & 1st app. Dr. Light. 14-Atom joins JLA			
	21.00	62.00	145.00
16-20	17.00	51.00	120.00
21-Reintro of JSA in JLA (see Flash #129)			
	37.00	111.00	260.00
22-JSA cont. from #21	34.00	103.00	240.00
23-28: 28-Robin app.	8.00	24.00	57.00
29,30-JSA x-over	10.00	31.00	72.00
29-1st SA app. Starman	11.00	32.00	75.00
31-Hawkman joins JLA (11/64)	7.10	21.00	50.00
32-Intro & origin Brainstorm	4.00	12.00	33.00
33,35,36,40,41: 40-3rd SA Penguin app.	3.00	10.00	27.00
34-Joker-c/story	4.00	13.00	34.00

Justice League of America #178 © DC

Justice League #91 © DC

37, 38-JSA x-over. 37-1st SA app. Mr. Terrific

	7.00	17.00	48.00
39-Giant G-16	8.00	20.00	72.00
42-45	2.00	7.00	17.00

46-(8/66)-JSA x-over; 1st S.A. Sandman; 1st SA app. GA Spectre & Wildcat
alongside JSA

	7.00	21.00	57.00
47-JSA x-over	4.00	8.00	25.00
48-Giant G-29	4.00	8.00	27.00
49-54, 57, 59, 60	2.10	5.00	15.00
55-1st SA app of GA Robin; JSA x-over	5.00	11.00	32.00
56-JLA vs. JSA	2.10	6.00	17.00
58-Giant G-41	2.00	6.00	17.00
61-63, 66, 68-72: 72-Last 12¢ issue	1.60	4.00	10.00
64, 65-JSA story. 64-(8/68)	1.00	3.00	11.00
67-Giant G-53	1.00	3.00	14.00

73-1st SA app. GA Superman; 1st SA app. of Black Canary

	1.00	3.00	11.00
74-Black Canary joins	1.00	2.00	6.00
75-2nd Green Arrow in new costume	1.00	2.00	7.00
76-Giant G-65	1.00	2.00	9.00
77-80: 78-Reintro Vigilante	1.00	2.00	6.00
81-84, 86-92: 83-Death of Spectre	1.00	2.00	5.00
85, 93-Giants G-77 & G-89	1.00	2.00	9.00

94-Adams art; r/origin Sandman from Adv. #40 & origin/1st app. Starman/
Adv. #61 (94-99: 25¢, 52 pgs.)

	3.00	8.00	25.00
95-r/origin Dr. Fate & Dr. Midnight	1.00	3.00	8.00
96-r/origin Hourman (Adventure 48)	1.00	3.00	8.00
97-Origin JLA retold	1.00	2.00	6.00
98, 99: Golden Age reprints	1.00	2.00	6.00

	Good	Fine	N-Mint
100-(8/72)	1.00	2.00	7.00
101, 102-JSA x-over	1.00	2.00	7.00
103-106, 109	0.80	1.60	4.00
107, 108-JSA x-over	1.20	2.90	7.00
110-116: 100 pg. issues	1.00	2.00	5.00
117-190: 137-Superman battles G.A. Capt. Marvel. 139-Begin 52 pg. issues, ends #157. 144-Origin retold	0.50	1.00	2.50
191-199: 193-1st app. All-Star Squadron	0.40	0.80	2.00
200-Double size anniversary issue	0.70	1.30	3.25
201-250:233-New JLA. 250-Batman rejoins	0.40	0.70	1.80
251-260	0.30	0.50	1.25
261-Final issue	0.60	1.10	2.75
Annual 1 (1983)	0.60	1.10	2.75
Annual 2 (1984)-Intro new JLA	0.40	0.70	1.80
Annual 3 (1985)-Crisis x-over	0.40	0.70	1.80

JUSTICE LEAGUE TASK FORCE
June, 1993-Present (1.25/1.50, color)
DC Comics

1-7: Aquaman, Nightwing, Flash, J'onn J'onzz & Gypsy. 5, 6-Knightquest tie-ins (new Batman cameo #5, 1 pg.)	0.30	0.50	1.25
8-16: 8-Begin 1.50-c. 16-(9/94)-Zero Hour	0.30	0.60	1.50
0,17-23: 0-(10/94). 17-(11/94)	0.30	0.60	1.50
24-begin 1.75-c; 25–26; 26-Impulse app.	0.40	0.70	1.75

JUSTICE MACHINE
June, 1981-No. 5, Nov, 1983
Noble Comics/Texas Comics (Annual 1)

1-Magazine size, Byrne cover	1.10	2.70	6.50
2-Magazine size	0.90	1.80	4.50
3-Magazine size	0.60	1.20	3.00
4, 5	0.50	1.00	2.50
Annual 1 (1/84)-1st app. The Elementals	0.70	1.70	4.00

KABUKI
Nov, 1994-Present (3.50, B&W)
Caliber Press

1-Intro Kabuki	1.00	2.00	5.00

KABUKI: DANCE OF DEATH
Jan 1995 (3.00, B&W, One shot)
London Night Studios

1-David Mack s/a	1.00	2.00	5.00

KABUKI:CIRCLE OF BLOOD
Jan 1995 - Present (2.95, B&W)
Caliber Press

1-3 David Mack s/a; 3-#1 on inside indicia	0.60	1.20	3.00

KAMANDI: AT EARTH'S END
June, 1993-No. 6, Nov, 1993 (1.75, color, limited series)
DC Comics

1-6-Elseworlds storyline	0.40	0.70	1.75

KAMANDI THE LAST BOY ON EARTH
Oct-Nov, 1972-No. 59, Sept-Oct, 1978
National Periodical Publications

1-Origin/1st app.; Kirby-a in #1-40	5.30	16.00	37.00
2	2.90	8.60	20.00
3–5	1.70	5.10	12.00
6–10	1.30	3.00	8.00
11–20	1.20	2.40	6.00
21-40: 32-(68 pgs.)-r/#1 plus new Kirby-s	0.80	1.60	4.00
41-59: 59-Return Of Omac back-up by Starlin (c/a); Kamandi story cont'd in B&B #157	0.60	1.20	3.00

KARATE KID
Mar-Apr, 1976-No. 15, July-Aug, 1978
National Periodical Publications/DC Comics

1	0.40	0.80	2.00
2-15: 15-Continued in Kamandi #58	0.40	0.70	1.80

KA-ZAR (See X-Men #10)
Aug, 1970-No. 3, Mar, 1971 (Giant Size, 25¢, 68 pgs.)
Marvel Comics Group

	Good	Fine	N-Mint
1-Kirby c/a; X-Men app.	1.90	6.00	13.00
2,3-Daredevil app.(r) in both: 2-Kirby c/a	1.50	3.80	9.00

KA-ZAR
Jan, 1974-No. 20, Feb, 1977 (Regular size)
Marvel Comics Group

1	0.60	1.10	2.75
2–20	0.40	0.80	2.00

KA-ZAR THE SAVAGE
Apr, 1981-No. 34, Oct, 1984 (Regular size)
Marvel Comics Group

1-34: 29-Double size	0.20	0.40	1.00

KID ETERNITY
1991-No. 3, Nov, 1991 (4.95, mini-series)
DC Comics

1-3: Grant Morrison scripts	1.00	2.00	5.00

KID ETERNITY
May, 1993-Present (1.95, color, mature)
DC Comics (Vertigo)

1-16: 1-Gold ink-c. 6-photo-c	0.40	0.80	2.00

KILL YOUR BOYFRIEND
June 1995 (4.95, color one-shot)
DC Comics

1-Grant Morrison-s	1.00	2.00	5.00

Kid Eternity #16 © DC

Kill Your Boyfriend #1 © DC

KILROY: THE SHORT STORIES
1995 (2.95, B&W)
Caliber Press

1	0.60	1.20	3.00

KILROY IS HERE
1995 (2.95, B&W)
Caliber Press

1	0.60	1.20	3.00

KINDRED, THE
Mar, 1994-Present (1.95 , color)
Image Comics

1-(2.50)-Has bound-in trading card; Booth-c/a			
	1.00	2.00	5.00
2,3-(1.95)	0.60	1.10	2.75
2-Variant cover	2.10	6.40	15.00
3-Alternate-c by Portacio, see Deathblow #5			
	1.60	3.20	8.00
4-(2.50-c)	0.50	1.00	2.50

Note: First four issues will contain coupons redeemable for a Jim Lee
Grifter/Backlash print.

...Collected Edition (2/95, 9.95)	1.70	4.20	10.00

KING CONAN (Becomes Conan the King #20 on)
March, 1980-No. 19, Nov, 1983
Marvel Comics Group

1	0.50	1.00	2.50
2-19: 7-1st Paul Smith-a (1 pg. pin-up)	0.40	0.70	1.75

KITTY PRYDE AND WOLVERINE
Nov, 1984-No. 6, Apr, 1985 (Mini-series)
Marvel Comics Group

1-X-Men spin-off	0.80	1.60	4.00
2–6	0.50	1.00	2.50

KNIGHTMARE
Feb, 1995-Present (2.50, color)
Image Comics

1–2	0.50	1.00	2.50

KNIGHTHAWK
Sep 1995-Present (2.50, color)

	Good	Fine	N-Mint
Windjammer (Acclaim)			
1–4	0.50	1.00	2.50

KNIGHT WATCHMAN: GRAVEYARD SHIFT
Late 1994-Present (2.95, B&W)
Caliber Press

1-2-Ben Torres-a	0.60	1.20	3.00

KOBALT
June, 1994-Present (1.75, color)
DC Comics (Milestone)

1-12: 1-Byrne-c. 4-intro Page	0.40	0.70	1.75
13-15-(2.50); 15-Long Hot Summer	0.50	1.00	2.50

KOBRA
Feb-Mar, 1976-No. 7, Mar-Apr, 1977
National Periodical Publications

1-1st app; art plotted by Kirby	0.60	1.20	3.00
2-7: 3-Giffen-a. 4-Kubert-c	0.40	0.80	2.00

KONA (...Monarch of Monster Isle)
Feb-Apr, 1962-No. 21, Jan-Mar, 1967 (Painted-c)
Dell Publishing Co.

4-Color 1256 (#1)	6.40	19.00	45.00
2-10: 4-Anak begins	2.90	8.60	20.00
11–21	2.50	6.30	15.00

KONGA (Fantastic Giants #24)(See Return of...)
1960; No. 2, Aug, 1961-No. 23, Nov, 1965
Charlton Comics

1 (1960)-Based on movie	27.00	81.00	190.00
2-Giordano-c	13.00	39.00	90.00
3–5	11.00	32.00	75.00
6–15	6.90	21.00	48.00
16-23	5.00	15.00	35.00

Note: Ditko a-1, 3-15; c-4, 6-9.

KONGA'S REVENGE (Formerly Return of Konga)
No. 2, Summer, 1963; No. 3, Fall, 1964; Dec, 1968
Charlton Comics

2,3: 2-Ditko-c/a	5.00	15.00	35.00
1 (12/68)-Reprints Konga's Revenge #3	2.60	7.70	18.00

KONG THE UNTAMED
June-July, 1975-No. 5, Feb-Mar, 1976
National Periodical Publications
1-1st app.; Wrightson-c	0.30	0.60	1.50
2-5: 2-Wrightson-c	0.20	0.40	1.00

KORAK, SON OF TARZAN
Jan, 1964-No. 45, Jan, 1972
Gold Key
1-Russ Manning-a	5.70	17.00	40.00
2-11-Russ Manning-a	3.00	9.40	22.00
12-21: 12, 13-Tufts-a. 21-Manning-a	2.30	6.90	16.00
22-30	1.70	4.20	10.00
31-45	1.30	3.00	8.00

KORAK, SON OF TARZAN
No. 46, 5-6/72-No. 56, 2-3/74; No. 57, 5-6/75-No. 59, 9-10/75
National Periodical Publications
46-(52 pgs.)-Carson of Venus begins (origin)	0.80	1.50	3.75
47-59: 49-Origin Korak retold	0.40	0.80	2.00

KRUSTY COMICS
1995 (2.25, color, limited series:3)
Bongo Comics
1–3	0.50	0.90	2.25

KULL AND THE BARBARIANS
May, 1975-No. 3, Sept, 1975 (1.00, B&W, magazine, 84 pgs.)
Marvel Comics Group
1-Andru/Wood-r/Kull #1; Gil Kane(p)	0.20	0.40	1.00
2, 3: 2-Red Sonja by Chaykin begins. 3-Origin Red Sonja; Adams-a in #1, 2	0.20	0.40	1.00

KULL THE CONQUEROR (...the Destroyer No. 11 on)
June, 1971 - No. 29, Oct, 1978
Marvel Comics Group
1-Origin Kull; 15¢ issue	1.50	3.80	9.00
2-5: 2-Last 15¢ issue	0.90	1.70	4.25
6–10	0.70	1.30	3.25
11-29: 11-15-Ploog-a. 13-Last 20¢ issue	0.50	0.90	2.25

LA PACIFICA
1994 - 1995(4.95, B&W, Mature readers, limited series)
Paradox Press

1-3	1.00	2.00	5.00

LADY DEATH (See Evil Ernie)
Jan, 1994-No. 3, Mar, 1994 (2.75, color, limited series)
Chaos! Comics

1-(3.50)-Chromium-c; S. Hughes-c/a in all	8.90	27.00	62.00
1-Commemorative	7.10	21.00	50.00
2	4.70	12.00	28.00
3	5.00	10.00	25.00
...Swimsuit Special #1-(2.50)-Wraparound-c	1.00	2.00	5.00
...Swimsuit Special #1-red velvet-c	7.00	21.40	50.00
....:The Reckoning (7/94, 6.95)-r/1-3	1.20	3.00	7.00

LADY DEATH: BETWEEN HEAVEN & HELL
Mar 1995-Present (3.50, color, limited series:4)
Chaos Comics

1-Chromium wraparound-c; Evil Ernie cameo			
	1.00	2.00	5.00
1-Black velvet-c	9.00	19.30	45.00
2–3	0.60	1.30	3.00

LADY VAMPRE
June 1995–Present (2.95, color)
Blackout Comics

0,1	0.60	1.30	3.00

LAST OF THE VIKING HEROES, THE (See Silver Star #1)
Mar, 1987-No. 12 (1.50, color)
Genesis West Comics

1–4	0.50	1.00	2.50
5A-Kirby/Dave Stevens-c	0.70	1.30	3.25
5B,6	0.40	0.80	2.00
7-Art Adams-c	0.60	1.20	3.00
8-12: 9, 10, 12-(2.50-c)	0.50	1.00	2.50
Summer Special 1-3: 1-Frazetta-c	0.60	1.20	3.00

LAST ONE, THE
July, 1993-No. 6, Dec, 1993 (2.50, color, limited series, mature)

DC Comics (Vertigo)

1–6	0.50	1.00	2.50

LAST TEMPTATION, THE
May, 1994-Present (4.95, color, limited series)
Marvel Comics

1–3-Gaiman story	1.00	2.00	5.00

LEGEND OF MOTHER SARAH
Apr, 1995-Present (2.50, color, limited series)
Dark Horse Comics

1-3-Katsuhiro Otomo-s	0.50	1.00	2.50

LEGEND OF SUPREME
Dec, 1994 - Feb, 1995 (2.50, color, limited series)
Image Comics

1–3	0.50	1.00	2.50

LEGENDS
Nov, 1986-No. 6, Apr, 1987 (Mini-series)
DC Comics

1-1st app. New Captain Marvel	0.50	0.90	2.25
2-5: 3-1st app. new Suicide Squad	0.40	0.80	2.00
6-Intro./1st app. New Justice League	0.50	1.00	2.50

LEGENDS OF NASCAR
Nov, 1990-No. 14? (Color)
Vortex Comics

1-Bill Elliott bio; Trimpe-a, 1.50-c	1.30	3.00	8.00
1-2nd print, 2.00-c (11/90)	0.80	1.50	3.75
1-3rd print, 3.00-c; includes Maxx racecards (3rd print, says 2nd in indicia)	0.90	1.80	4.50
2-(2.00)-Richard Petty	0.60	1.20	3.00
3-14: 3-Ken Schrader. 4, 7-Spiegle-a(p)	0.40	0.80	2.00
1-13-Hologram-c versions. 2-Hologram shows Bill Elliott's car by mistake (all numbered & limited)	1.00	1.90	4.75
2-Hologram corrected version	1.00	1.90	4.75

LEGENDS OF THE WORLD'S FINEST
1994-No. 3, 1994 (4.95, color, limited series)
DC Comics

1-3: Embossed foil logos; Brereton-c/a	1.00	2.00	5.00
TPB ('95, 14.95)	2.10	6.00	15.00

	Good	Fine	N-Mint

L.E.G.I.O.N.
Feb, 1989-No. 70, Sept, 1994 (1.50/1.75, color)
DC Comics

	Good	Fine	N-Mint
1	0.40	0.80	2.00
2-22: 3-Lobo app. #3-on. 5-Lobo joins	0.30	0.60	1.50
23-(2.50, 52 pgs.)-LEGION '91 begins	0.50	1.00	2.50
24-47: 35-LEGION '92 begins	0.30	0.60	1.50
48,49,51-69: 48-Begin 1.75-c. 63-LEGION '94 begins; Superman app;			
	0.40	0.70	1.75
50-(3.50, 68 pgs)	0.70	1.40	3.50
70-(2.50, 52 pgs.)-Zero Hour	0.50	1.00	2.50
Annual 1-3 ('90-'92, 2.95, 68 pgs.)	0.60	1.20	3.00
Annual 4 ('93, 3.50, 68 pgs.)	0.70	1.40	3.50
Annual 5 ('94, 3.50, 68 pgs.)-Elseworlds story; Lobo app.			
	0.70	1.40	3.50

LEGIONNAIRES (See Legion of Super-Heroes #41)
Apr, 1992-Present (1.25, color)
DC Comics

	Good	Fine	N-Mint
1-8: 1-Polybagged w/Skybox trading card	0.40	0.80	2.00
9-18: 9-Begin 1.50-c. 18-(9/94)-Zero Hour	0.30	0.60	1.50
0,19-25: 0-(10/94). 19-(11/94)	0.30	0.60	1.50
26-begin 1.75-c; 27,28–	0.40	0.70	1.75
Annual 1 ('94, 2.95)-Elseworlds story	0.60	1.20	3.00

LEGION OF MONSTERS (See Marvel Premiere #28 & Marvel Preview #8)
Sept, 1975 (1.00, B&W magazine, 76 pgs.)
Marvel Comics Group

	Good	Fine	N-Mint
1-Origin & 1st app. Legion of Monsters; Neal Adams painted-c; origin & only app. The Manphibian; Frankenstein by Val Mayerik; Bram Stoker's Dracula adaptation	1.00	2.00	5.00

LEGION OF SUPER-HEROES (See Action Comics & Adventure Comics #247
Feb, 1973-No. 4, July-Aug, 1973
National Periodical Publications

	Good	Fine	N-Mint
1-Legion & Tommy Tomorrow-r begin	1.30	3.30	8.00
2–4	0.90	2.30	5.50

LEGION OF SUPER-HEROES (Formerly Superboy; Tales of the Legion #314 or
No. 259, Jan, 1980-No. 313, July, 1984
DC Comics

	Good	Fine	N-Mint
259 (#1)-Superboy leaves Legion; 1st non-reprint Legion solo title			
	0.60	1.20	3.00

260-270	0.40	0.80	2.00
271-284	0.30	0.60	1.60
285, 286-Giffen back up stories	0.40	0.80	2.00
287-Giffen art on Legion begins	0.60	1.10	2.80
288-290	0.40	0.80	2.00
291-293	0.30	0.60	1.60
294-Double size	0.40	0.70	1.80
295-299, 301-305: 297-Origin retold	0.30	0.60	1.60
300-Double size anniversary issue	0.40	0.80	2.00
306-313 (75¢ cover)	0.20	0.40	1.00
Annual 1 (1982)-Giffen-c/a; origin/1st app.			
new Invisible Kid who joins Legion	0.40	0.80	2.00
Annual 2, 3 ('83-84): 2-Giffen-c	0.30	0.60	1.60
Trade Paperback (1989, 17.95)	2.60	8.00	18.00

LEGION OF SUPER-HEROES
Aug, 1984-No. 63, Aug, 1989 (Color)
DC Comics

1	0.40	0.80	2.00
2-10: 4-Death of Karate Kid	0.30	0.60	1.60
11-14: 14-Intro new members	0.20	0.50	1.20
15-18: Crisis tie-ins	0.30	0.60	1.60
19-25	0.20	0.50	1.20
26-36, 39-44	0.20	0.40	1.10
37, 38-Death Of Superboy	1.40	4.30	10.00
45-(2.95, 68 pgs.)-Anniversary issue	0.60	1.20	3.00
46-49, 51-62	0.20	0.40	1.10
50-(2.50, double size)	0.50	1.00	2.50
63-Final issue	0.30	0.60	1.40
Annual 1 (10/85)-Crisis tie-in	0.40	0.70	1.80

Legion of Superheroes #0 © DC

Leonard Nimoy's Primortals #3 © Big Ent.

	Good	Fine	N-Mint
Annual 2 ('86). Annual 3 ('87, 2.25)	0.30	0.60	1.60
Annual 4 ('88, 2.50)	0.40	0.80	2.00

LEGION OF SUPER-HEROES
Nov, 1989-Present (1.75/1.95, color)
DC Comics

	Good	Fine	N-Mint
1-49, 51-53,55-58: 8-Origin. 13-Free poster		0.70	1.75
50-(3.50, 68 pgs)	0.70	1.40	3.50
54-(2.95)-Die-cut foil cover	0.60	1.20	3.00
59-61: 59-Begin 1.95-c. 61-(9/94)-Zero Hour			
	0.40	0.80	2.00
0,62-68: 0-(10/94). 62-(11/94)	0.40	0.80	2.00
69-begin 2.25-c; 70–71	0.50	0.90	2.25
Annual 1-4 ('90-'93, 3.50): 4-Bloodlines	0.70	1.40	3.50
Annual 5 ('94, 3.50)-Elseworlds story	0.70	1.40	3.50
Annual 6 ('95, 3.95)-Year One	0.80	1.60	4.00

LEONARD NIMOY'S PRIMORTALS
Mar, 1995-Present (1.95, color)
Tekno•Comix

	Good	Fine	N-Mint
1-3-Concept by Leonard Nimoy & Isaac Asimov; w/bound-in game piece			
& trading card	0.40	0.80	2.00
4-7: 4-w/Teknophage Steel Edition coupon	0.40	0.80	2.00

LEONARDO
Dec, 1986 (1.50, B&W, one-shot)
Mirage Studios

	Good	Fine	N-Mint
1-Member of Teenage Mutant Ninja Turtles	1.00	2.50	6.00

LETHAL FOES OF SPIDERMAN, THE
Sept, 1993-No. 4, Dec, 1993 (1.75, color, mini-series)
Marvel Comics

	Good	Fine	N-Mint
1-4-Sequel to Deadly Foes of...	0.20	0.40	1.00

LETHAL STRYKE
June 1995-Present (3.00, color)
London Night

	Good	Fine	N-Mint
1–polybagged w/card	0.60	1.20	3.00

LIFE OF CAPTAIN MARVEL, THE
Aug, 1985-No. 5, Dec, 1985 (2.00, Baxter paper)
Marvel Comics Group

	Good	Fine	N-Mint
1: 1-5 reprint Thanos saga/Capt. Marvel, etc.		0.80	2.00

2-5: 4-New Thanos back-c by Starlin	0.40	0.80	2.00

LIFE WITH ARCHIE
Sept, 1958-No. 290, 1981
Archie Publications

1	22.00	65.00	215.00
2 (9/59)	14.00	40.00	100.00
3-5: 3-(7/60)	10.00	30.00	70.00
6-10	5.00	15.00	35.00
11–20	3.00	9.40	22.00
21-30	2.40	7.30	17.00
31-41	1.70	4.20	10.00
42-45: 42-Pureheart begins (1st app?, 1965?)			
	1.30	3.00	8.00
46-Origin Pureheart	1.70	5.10	12.00
47-59: 50-United Three begin (Pureheart/Archie, Superteen/Betty,			
Capt. Hero/Jughead). 59-Last Pureheart	1.00	2.50	6.00
60-100: 60-Archie band begins	0.60	1.20	3.00
101-290: 279-Intro Mustang Sally	0.30	0.50	1.25

LIGHTNING COMICS PRESENTS
May, 1994 (3.50, color, one-shot)
Lightning Comics

1-Red foil-c dist. by Diamond	0.70	1.40	3.50
1-Black/yellow/blue-c dist. by Capital	0.70	1.40	3.50
1-Red/yellow-c dist. through H. World	0.70	1.40	3.50
1-Platinum	0.70	1.40	3.50

LIPPY THE LION AND HARDY HAR HAR (TV)
March, 1963 (12¢, Hanna-Barbera)
Gold Key

10049-303 (#1)	9.20	27.50	55.00

LISA COMICS
1995 (2.25, color, Annual)
Bongo Comics

1- Lisa in Wonderland	0.50	0.90	2.25

LOBO (See Omega Men)
Nov, 1990-No. 4, Feb, 1991 (99¢/1.50, mini-series)
DC Comics

1-(99¢)-Legion '89 spinoff	1.00	2.00	5.00
2	0.60	1.20	3.00

	Good	Fine	N-Mint
3, 4	0.50	1.00	2.50
Annual 1 ('93, 3.50)-Bloodlines begins	0.70	1.40	3.50
Blazing Chain of Love 1 (9/92, 1.50)-By Grant			
	0.30	0.60	1.50
Convention Special 1 ('93, 1.75)	0.40	0.70	1.75
Paramilitary Christmas Spec. ('91, 2.39)	0.50	1.00	2.50
Portrait of a Victim 1 ('93, 1.75)	0.40	0.70	1.75

LOBO
Dec, 1993-Present (1.75/1.95, color)
DC Comics

	Good	Fine	N-Mint
1-(2.95)-Foil enhanced-c; Alan Grant scripts	0.70	1.40	3.50
2-7-Alan Grant scripts	0.40	0.70	1.75
8,9: 8-Begin 1.95-c. 9-(9/94)	0.40	0.80	2.00
0,10-15: 0-(10/94)-Origin retold. 10-(11/94)	0.40	0.80	2.00
16-begin 2.25-c; 17-18	0.50	0.90	2.25
Annual 2-('94, 3.50)-21 artists (20 listed on cover); Alan Grant script;			
Elseworlds story	0.70	1.40	3.50
Lobocop 1 (2/94, 1.95)-Alan Grant scripts; painted-c			
	0.40	0.80	2.00
....:Big Babe Spring Break Special (Spring '95, 1.95, Mature readers)			
Alan Grant/s Jim Balent/a	0.40	0.80	2.00
....:Bounty Hunting for Fun and Profit ('95)-S.Bisley-c			
	1.00	2.00	5.00
.../Deadman: The Brave and the Bald (2/95,3.50)			
	0.70	1.40	3.50
...In the Chair 1 (8/94, 1.95, 36 pgs.)	0.40	0.80	2.00

LOBO: A CONTRACT ON GAWD
Apr, 1994-No. 4, July, 1994 (1.75, color, mini-series, mature)
DC Comics

	Good	Fine	N-Mint
1-4-Alan Grant scripts. 3-Groo cameo	0.40	0.70	1.75

LOBO/DEADMAN: THE BRAVE AND THE BALD
Feb, 1995 (3.50, color, one-shot)
DC Comics

	Good	Fine	N-Mint
1-Darkseid app.	0.70	1.40	3.50

LOBO INFANTICIDE
Oct, 1992-No. 4, Jan, 1993 (1.50, color, mini-series)
DC Comics

	Good	Fine	N-Mint
1-4: Giffen-c/a; Grant scripts	0.30	0.60	1.50

LOBO'S BACK
May, 1992-No. 4, Nov, 1992 (1.50, color, mini-series)
DC Comics

1-4: 1-Three outer covers. 3-Kieth-c	0.40	0.80	2.00
Trade paperback (1993, 9.95)-r/1-4	1.70	4.20	10.00

LOBO'S BIG BABE SPRING BREAK SPECIAL
Spring, 1995 (1.95, color, one-shot)
DC Comics

1-Jim Balent-a	0.30	0.80	2.00

LOBO: UNAMERICAN GLADIATORS
June, 1993-No. 4, Sept, 1993 (1.75, color, mini-series)
DC Comics

1-4: Mignola-c; Grant/Wagner scripts	0.40	0.70	1.75

LOGAN'S RUN
Jan, 1977-No. 7, July, 1977
Marvel Comics Group

1-Movie tie-in. 1-5 have Perez-c/a	0.70	1.40	3.50
2-5, 7	0.40	0.80	2.00
6-1st solo Thanos story (backup) by Zeck	1.40	4.30	10.00

LONE RANGER AND TONTO, THE
Aug, 1994-Nov, 1994 (2.50, color, limited series)
Topps Comics

1-4: 3-Origin of Lone Ranger; Tonto leaves	0.50	1.00	2.50
1–4-Silver Logo	1.00	2.00	5.00
...TPB (1/95, 9.95)	1.70	4.20	10.00

LONG, HOT SUMMER, THE
July 1995-Present (2.95/2.50, color)
DC Comics

1-(2.95)	0.50	1.30	3.00
2-(2.50)	0.40	1.00	2.50

LONGSHOT
Sept, 1985-No. 6, Feb, 1986 (Mini-series)
Marvel Comics Group

1-Art Adams/Whilce Portacio-c/a in all	1.40	4.00	10.00
2	1.50	4.00	9.00
3-5: 4-Spider-Man app.	1.20	2.90	7.00
6-Double size	1.30	3.30	8.00

	Good	Fine	N-Mint

LOONEY TUNES
April, 1975-No. 47, July, 1984
Gold Key

1	0.40	0.80	2.00
2-47: Reprints in #1-4, 16; 38-46(1/3-r)	0.20	0.40	1.00

LOONEY TUNES
Apr, 1994-Present (1.50, color)
DC Comics
1-17: 1-Marvin Martian-c/s; Bugs Bunny begins

	0.30	0.60	1.50

LOOSE CANNON
Jun, 1995-Present (1.75, color, limited series:4)
DC Comics

1–3,1-Superman app.	0.40	0.70	1.75

LORD PUMPKIN
Oct, 1994 (2.50/2.95, color)
Malibu Comics

#0	0.50	1.00	2.50

LORD PUMPKIN/NECROMANTRA
Apr, 1995- (2.95, color)
Malibu Comics

1–3;1-flip book	0.60	1.20	3.00

LOST IN SPACE
Aug, 1991-No. 12, 1992 (2.50, color, limited series)
Innovation Publishing

1-12: Bill Mumy scripts in all	0.50	1.00	2.50
Annual 1, 2 (1991-92, 2.95, 52 pgs.)	0.60	1.20	3.00

LOST IN SPACE: PROJECT ROBINSON
Nov, 1993 (2.50, color)(limited series of 2 intended)
Innovation

1	0.50	1.00	2.50

LOST IN SPACE: VOYAGE TO THE BOTTOM OF THE SOUL
No. 13, Aug, 1993-No. 18, 1994 (2.50, color)(12-issue limited series intended)
Innovation Publishing

13-(2.95)-Silver edition embossed logo	0.50	1.00	2.50
13-(4.95)-Gold collectors ed. bagged w/poster			

	1.00	2.00	5.00
14-18: (2.50)	0.50	1.00	2.50

LOVE AND ROCKETS
July, 1982-Present
Fantagraphics

1-B&W cover (July)	6.00	18.00	42.00
1-Color cover (Fall)	2.90	8.60	20.00
1-Color cover, 2nd/3rd print	0.60	1.10	2.75
2	1.40	4.30	10.00
3–5	1.30	3.00	7.50
6–10	0.90	1.70	4.25
11–40	0.60	1.10	2.75
2-11, 29-31-2nd printings	0.60	1.10	2.75

LUCY SHOW, THE (TV) (Also see I Love Lucy)
June, 1963-No. 5, June, 1964 (Photo c-1,2)
Gold Key

1	15.00	50.00	105.00
2	7.90	24.00	55.00
3-5: Photo back c-1, 2, 4, 5	6.40	19.00	45.00

LYCANTHROPE LEO
1994 -No. 7 (2.95, B&W, limited series, 44 pgs.)
Viz Communications

1	0.60	1.20	3.00

LYNCH MOB
June, 1994-No. 4, Sept, 1994 (2.50, color, limited series)
Chaos! Comics

1–4	0.50	1.00	2.50
1-Special Ed. full foil-c	2.90	8.60	20.00

Lynch Mob #2 © Brian Pulido

Madman Comics #1 © Mike Allred

	Good	Fine	N-Mint
MACHINE, THE Nov, 1994 (2.50, color) Dark Horse Comics			
1–4	0.50	1.00	2.50
MACHINE MAN April, 1978-No. 19, Feb, 1981 Marvel Comics Group			
1-Kirby-a #1-9	0.70	1.30	3.25
2-17: 10-19: Ditko-a	0.30	0.60	1.60
18-Wendigo, Alpha Flight ties into X-Men 140	0.90	2.30	5.50
19-Intro/1st app. Jack O'Lantern (Macendale); later becomes Hobgoblin II	2.40	7.30	17.00
MACHINE MAN Oct, 1984-No. 4, Jan, 1985 (Limited series) Marvel Comics Group			
1-Barry Smith-c/a(p) & colors in all	0.30	0.60	1.50
2–4	0.20	0.50	1.20
MADMAN Mar, 1992-No. 3, 1992 (3.95, duotone, 52 pgs.) Tundra Publishing			
1-Mike Allred-c/a in all	1.70	4.00	10.00
1-2nd printing	1.00	2.00	5.00
2, 3	1.60	3.20	8.00
MADMAN ADVENTURES 1992-No. 3, 1993 (2.95, color, mini-series, 52 pgs.) Tundra Publishing			
1-3-Mike Allred-c/a in all	1.00	2.00	5.00
MADMAN COMICS Apr, 1994-Present (2.95, color) Dark Horse Comics			
1-Allred-c/a: 1-Frank Miller back-c.	1.00	2.00	5.00
2-6-Allred c/a: 3-ALex Toth back-c. 4-Dave Stevens back-c. 6,7 Miller/Darrow-Big Guy app. 6-Bruce Timm back-c 7-Darrow back-c			
	0.60	1.20	3.00

MAGE (The Hero Discovered...)
Feb, 1984-No. 15, Dec, 1986 (1.50, color)
Comico

1-1st app.; 1st color Comico comic	1.00	3.00	6.00
2	1.00	2.00	5.00
3–5	0.60	1.20	3.00
6-Grendel begins; 1st time in color	2.10	6.40	15.00
7-1st new Grendel story	1.30	3.30	8.00
8–14	0.50	1.00	2.50
15-(2.95, double size)-W/pullout poster	0.60	1.20	3.00

MAGIC AGENT (See Forbidden Worlds & Unknown Worlds)
Jan-Feb, 1962-No. 3, May-June, 1962
American Comics Group

1-Origin & 1st app. John Force	2.60	7.70	18.00
2, 3	2.00	5.00	12.00

MAGIC:THE GATHERING-THE SHADOW MAGE
July 1995 (2.50, color)
Acclaim Comics

1-Polybagged w/Magic:The Gathering card; 2-4			
	0.50	1.00	2.50

MAGIK
Dec, 1983-No. 4, Mar, 1984 (Mini-series)
Marvel Comics Group

1-X-Men app.; Inferno begins	0.90	1.80	4.50
2-4: 2-Nightcrawler app. & X-Men cameo	0.70	1.40	3.50

MAGILLA GORILLA (TV)
May, 1964-No. 10, Dec, 1968 (Hanna-Barbera)
Gold Key

1	7.10	21.00	50.00
2-10: 3-Vs. Yogi Bear for President	4.30	12.90	30.00

MAGILLA GORILLA (TV)
Nov, 1970-No. 5, July, 1971 (Hanna-Barbera)
Charlton Comics

1	2.90	9.00	20.00
2–5	2.00	6.00	14.00

MAGNETO (See X-Men #1)
Sept, 1993 (Color, one-shot)
Marvel Comics

	Good	Fine	N-Mint
0-Giveaway, embossed foil-c by Sienkiewicz; reprints from Classic			
X-Men 19 & 12	1.00	2.00	5.00

MAGNUS, ROBOT FIGHTER
Feb, 1963- No. 46, Jan, 1977 (Painted covers)
Gold Key

	Good	Fine	N-Mint
1-Origin/1st app. Magnus; Aliens series begins (1st app.)			
	33.00	99.00	230.00
2, 3	17.00	51.00	120.00
4–10	10.00	29.00	68.00
11–20	6.40	19.00	45.00
21, 24-28: 28-Aliens ends	4.30	12.90	30.00
22, 23-12¢ and 15¢ versions exist. 22-Origin-r/#1			
	3.90	12.00	27.00
29-47: All reprints	1.70	5.10	12.00

MAGNUS ROBOT FIGHTER
May, 1991-Present (1.75/1.95/2.25, color)
Valiant Comics

	Good	Fine	N-Mint
1	2.00	6.40	15.00
2	1.40	4.00	10.00
3, 4: 4-Rai cameo	1.40	4.00	10.00
5-Origin & 1st full app. Rai (10/91); flip-book format; (flip side of #5-8			
are Rai #1-4 mini-series)	1.90	5.60	13.00
6-8: Rai-c/stories (on flip side). 6-1st Solar x-over. 7-Magnus vs.			
Rai-c/story; 1st X-O Armor. 8-Begin 1.95-c			
	1.30	3.30	8.00
0-Origin issue; ordered thru mail w/coupons from #1-8 & 50¢;			
w/B. Smith trading card	6.00	17.00	40.00
0-Sold thru shops without card	2.90	9.00	20.00
9-11: 11-Last 1.95-c	0.80	2.10	5.00
12-(3.25, 44 pgs.)-Reintro Turok-c/story; 1st app. in Valiant			
Universe (5/92)	4.30	13.00	30.00
13-20, 22-24, 26-48, 50-56: 13-Begin 2.25-c. 14-1st app. Isak.			
15-Unity x-over. 16-Magnus is born; Unity x-over. 24-Rai & Future Force			
prelude. 33-Timewalker app. 36-Bound-in trading card. 37-Rai &			
Starwatchers app. 44-Bound-in sneak peak card			
	0.50	0.90	2.25
21-New direction & new logo begins	0.60	1.20	3.00
21-Gold	1.40	4.00	10.00
25-(2.95)-Embossed silver foil-c; new costume			
	0.60	1.20	3.00
49-(2.50)	0.50	1.00	2.50

...Yearbook ('94, 3.95, 52 pgs.)	0.80	1.60	4.00
...Invasion ('94,9.95) r/Rai #1-4 & Magnus #5-8)			
	1.40	4.00	10.00

Note: 1-8 must have trading cards & coupons intact.

MAGNUS ROBOT FIGHTER 4000 A.D.
1990-No.2?, 1991 (7.95, high quality, card stock-c, 96 pgs.)
Valiant Comics

1,2: Russ Manning-r. 1-Origin-r	1.30	3.30	8.00

MAGNUS ROBOT FIGHTER/NEXUS
Dec, 1993-No. 2, Apr, 1994 (2.95, color, limited series)
Valiant

1, 2-Rude painted-c & pencils	0.60	1.20	3.00

MALIBU ASHCAN:RAFFERTY
Nov 1994 (.99, B&W)
Malibu Comics

1-Rafferty Saga preview	0.20	0.40	1.00

MAN-BAT (See Detective #400)
Dec-Jan, 1975-76-No. 2, Feb-Mar, 1976; Dec, 1984
DC Comics

1-Ditko-a (p); 1st app. She-Bat?	1.00	2.00	5.00
2-Aparo-c	0.70	1.30	3.25
1 (12/84, Baxter)-... Vs. Batman on-c; Adams-r			
	0.80	1.60	4.00

MAN CALLED AX, THE
Nov, 1994-Present (2.95, color, limited series:5)
Malibu Comics (Bravura)

1-4:1-"1A" on-c	0.60	1.20	3.00
#0-(2/95)	0.60	1.20	3.00

MANDRAKE THE MAGICIAN
Sept, 1966-No. 10, Nov, 1967 (All 12¢)
King Comics

1-Begin S.O.S. Phantom, ends #3	3.70	11.00	26.00
2-7, 9: 4-Girl Phantom app. 5-Flying saucer-c/s			
	2.00	6.00	14.00
8-Jeff Jones-a (4 pgs.)	2.90	9.00	20.00
10-Rip Kirby app.; Raymond-a (14 pgs.)	3.60	11.00	25.00

	Good	Fine	N-Mint
MANDRAKE THE MAGICIAN			
Apr 1995-Present (2.95, color, limited series:3)			
Marvel Comics			
1-Mike Barr/s; 2-	0.60	1.20	3.00
MAN FROM U.N.C.L.E., THE (TV)			
Feb, 1965-No. 22, April, 1969 (All have photo covers)			
Gold Key			
1	15.00	45.00	105.00
2-Photo back covers #2-8	9.30	28.00	65.00
3-10: 7-Jet Dream begins (1st app.)	5.70	17.00	40.00
11-22: 21, 22-Reprints	4.30	12.90	30.00
MANHUNTER			
No. 0, Oct, 1994-Present (1.95, color)			
DC Comics			
0-7	0.40	0.80	2.00
8-begin 2.25-c; 9–	0.50	0.90	2.25
MAN IN BLACK (See Thrill-O-Rama)			
Sept, 1957-No. 4, Mar, 1958			
Harvey Publications			
1-Bob Powell-c/a	9.00	27.90	65.00
2-4: Powell-c/a	6.40	19.00	45.00

MAN OF STEEL, THE (Also see Superman: The Man of Steel)
1986 (June)-No. 6, 1986 (75¢, mini-series)
DC Comics
1-6: Byrne-c/a/scripts in all. 2-Intro new Lois Lane & Jimmy Olsen. 3-Intro/
   origin new Magpie; Batman-c/story. 4-Intro new Lex Luthor

	Good	Fine	N-Mint
	0.30	0.60	1.50
Silver Edition 1, 2 (1993, 1.95)-Reprints	0.40	0.80	2.00
Limited Edition Softcover	4.30	13.00	30.00

MAN OF WAR (See the Protectors)
1993-No. 8, Feb, 1994 (1.95/2.25, color)
Malibu Comics

	Good	Fine	N-Mint
1-5-(1.95)-Newsstand ed. w/different-c	0.40	0.80	2.00
1-5-(2.50)-Collector's ed. w/poster	0.50	1.00	2.50
6-8 (2.25): 6-Polybagged w/Skycap	0.50	0.90	2.25

MAN-THING (Also see Fear #10, Giant-Size... & Savage Tales #1)
Jan, 1974-No. 22, Oct, 1975;

V2#1, Nov, 1979-V2 #11, July, 1981
Marvel Comics Group

1-2nd app. Howard The Duck	2.90	8.60	20.00
2	1.70	4.20	10.00
3-1st app. original Foolkiller	1.20	3.00	7.00
4-Origin & final app. Foolkiller	0.80	1.60	4.00
5-11: 5-11 have Ploog art	0.60	1.20	3.00
12-22: 21-Origin Man-Thing	0.50	1.00	2.50
V2#1 (1979)-11	0.30	0.50	1.30

MANTRA
July, 1993-Present (1.95, color)
Malibu Comics (Ultraverse)

1-Polybagged w/card & coupon for Ultraverse Premiere #0			
	0.90	1.80	4.50
1-Newsstand w/o card & coupon	0.70	1.30	3.25
1-Full cover holographic edition	3.60	11.00	25.00
1-Ultra limited silver foil-c	2.10	6.40	15.00
2, 3, 5, 6: 3-Intro Warstrike & Kismet. 6-Break-Thru x-over			
	0.50	0.90	2.25
2-(2.50)-Newsstand ed. bagged w/card	0.50	1.00	2.50
4, -(2.50, 48 pgs.)-Rune flip-c/sty by B. Smith			
	0.50	1.00	2.50
7-9,11-17: 7-Prime app.; origin Prototype (2 pgs.) by Jurgens/Austin.			
11-New costume. 13-Two variant covers exist 17-Intro NecroMantra and			
Pinnacle. Prelude to Godwheel	0.40	0.80	2.00
10-(3.50, 68 pgs.)-Flip cover w/Ultraverse Premiere #2			
	0.70	1.40	3.50
18-21; 18-begin 2.50-c	0.50	1.00	2.50
Giant Size 1 (7/94, 2.50, 44 pgs.)	0.50	1.00	2.50
Spear of Destiny 1-2 (4/95, 2.50, 36 pgs.)	0.50	1.00	2.50

MANY LOVES OF DOBIE GILLIS
May-June, 1960-No. 26, Oct, 1964
National Periodical Publications

1-TV tie-in series	21.00	64.00	170.00
2-5	11.00	34.00	90.00
6-10	8.10	24.00	65.00
11-26	7.00	21.00	55.00

MARC SPECTOR: MOON KNIGHT (Also see Moon Knight)
June, 1989-No. 60, Mar, 1994 (1.50, color)
Marvel Comics

	Good	Fine	N-Mint
1	0.60	1.20	3.00
2–7	0.40	0.80	2.00
8, 9-Punisher app.	0.70	2.00	4.00
10-18: 15-Silver Sable app.	0.50	0.90	2.25
19-21: Punisher & Spider-Man app.	0.80	2.10	5.00
22-24, 26-31, 34: 34-Last 1.50-c	0.40	0.70	1.80
25-(2.50, 52 pgs.)-Ghost Rider app.	0.70	1.30	3.25
32, 33-Hobgoblin II & Spider-Man app.	0.70	1.30	3.25
35-38: Punisher story	0.50	0.90	2.25
39-49, 51-54: 46-Demogoblin. 51,53-Gambit			
	0.40	0.70	1.75
50-(2.95, 56 pgs.)-Special die-cut-c	0.70	1.30	3.25
55-New look & Stephen Platt-c/a begins	1.60	5.00	11.00
56,57-Platt-c/a. 57-Spider-Man-c/story	0.80	1.60	4.00
58, 59-S. Platt-c only	0.40	0.80	2.00
60-S. Platt-c/a; death of Moon Knight	0.40	0.80	2.00
...: Divided We Fall (4.95, 52 pgs.)	1.00	2.00	5.00
Special 1 ('92, 2.50)	0.50	1.00	2.50

MARK, THE
Dec, 1993-No. 4, Mar, 1994 (2.50, color, limited series)
Dark Horse Comics

1–4	0.50	1.00	2.50

MARRIED... WITH CHILDREN
June, 1990-No. 7, Feb, 1991 (1.75, color)
V2#1, Sept, 1991-V2#12, 1992 (1.95, color)
Now Comics

1-Based on the Fox TV show	0.50	1.30	3.00
1-2nd printing	0.50	1.00	2.50
2-Photo-c	0.60	1.20	3.00
2-2nd printing	0.30	0.60	1.60
3	0.40	0.80	2.00
4–7	0.30	0.60	1.60
V2 #1-12 (1.95): 1, 4, 5, 9-Photo-c	0.40	0.80	2.00
...Buck's Tale (6/94, 1.95)	0.40	0.80	2.00
...1994 Annual (2/94, 2.50, 52 pgs.)-Flip book			
	0.50	1.00	2.50

MARS ATTACKS
May, 1994-No. 5, Sept, 1994 (2.95, color, mini-series)
Topps Comics

1-Special Edition	2.00	4.00	10.00
1-5-Flip books: 5-Tattoo	0.60	1.20	3.00

TPB (12/94, 12.95) r/#1-5 w/flip book new story
| | 1.90 | 5.60 | 13.00 |

MARSHAL LAW
Oct, 1987-No. 6, May, 1989 (1.95, color)
Epic Comics (Marvel)
| 1–6 | 0.40 | 0.80 | 2.00 |

M.A.R.S. PATROL TOTAL WAR (Formerly Total War)
No. 3, Sept, 1966-No. 10, Aug, 1969 (Painted-c)
Gold Key
| 3-Wood-a | 4.60 | 14.00 | 32.00 |
| 4–10 | 2.30 | 6.90 | 16.00 |

MARTHA WASHINGTON GOES TO WAR
May 1994-Nov, 1994 (2.95, color, limited series)
Dark Horse Comics
| 1-5-Miller-s, Gibbons-c/a | 0.60 | 1.20 | 3.00 |

MARVEL ACTION HOUR, FEATURING...
Nov, 1994-Present (1.50/2.95, color)
Marvel Comics
...Iron Man 1-8: 1-(11/94, 1.50)	0.30	0.60	1.50
...Iron Man 1-(2.95)-Polybagged w/16 pg. Marvel Action Hour Preview and acetate print	0.60	1.20	3.00
...The Fantastic Four 1-8: 1-(11/94, 1.50)	0.30	0.60	1.50
...F.F. 1 (2.95)-Polybagged w/16 pg. Marvel Action Hour Preview and acetate print	0.60	1.20	3.00

MARVEL ADVENTURES STARRING DAREDEVIL
Dec, 1975-No. 6, Oct, 1976 (...Adventure #4 on)
Marvel Comics Group
| 1-6: r/Daredevil 22-27 by Colan | 0.20 | 0.40 | 1.00 |

MARVEL AND DC PRESENT FEATURING THE UNCANNY X-MEN & THE NEW TEEN TITANS
1982 (2.00, one-shot, 68 pgs.)
Marvel Comics Group and DC Comics
| 1-3rd app. Deathstroke; Darkseid app. | 1.40 | 4.00 | 10.00 |

MARVEL CHILLERS (Also see Giant-Size Chillers)
Oct, 1975-No. 7, Oct, 1976
Marvel Comics Group

	Good	Fine	N-Mint
1, 2: 1-Intro Modred The Mystic, ends #2	0.70	1.30	3.25
3-7: 3-Tigra begins (origin), ends #7	0.40	0.80	2.00

MARVEL CLASSICS COMICS
1976-No. 36, Dec, 1978
Marvel Comics Group

1	0.80	1.50	3.75
2-27, 29-36	0.60	1.10	2.75
28-First Mike Golden-c/a	1.10	2.70	6.50

MARVEL COLLECTORS' ITEM CLASSICS (Marvel's Greatest #23 on)
Feb, 1965-No. 22, Aug, 1969 (All are 68 pgs.)
Marvel Comics Group

1-Early F.F., Spider-Man, Thor, Hulk, Iron Man reprints begin; Ditko, Kirby-r in all	6.60	20.00	46.00
2-4: 2-(4/66)	3.60	11.00	25.00
5-22: 22-r/1st Ant Man from TTA 27	1.70	4.00	10.00

MARVEL COMICS PRESENTS
Sept, 1988-Present (1.25/1.50/1.75, biweekly, color)
Marvel Comics (Midnight Sons imprint #143 on)

1-Wolverine begins, ends #10	1.40	4.00	10.00
2-5	1.00	2.00	5.00
6-10	0.80	1.50	3.75
11-32, 34-37: 25-Origin & 1st app. Nth Man. 32-McFarlane-a(p)	0.40	0.80	2.00
33-Jim Lee-a	0.60	1.10	2.75
38-Wolverine begins by Buscema	1.00	2.00	5.00
39-47, 51-53: 51-53-Wolverine by Liefeld	0.60	1.10	2.75
48-50: Wolverine/Spider-Man team up by E. Larsen-c/a; 49, 50-Savage			

Martha Washington Goes to War #5 © Frank Miller

Marvel Fanfare #10 © MEG

Dragon prototype app.	0.90	2.30	5.50
54-61: 8 part Wolverine/Hulk story	1.00	2.50	6.00
62-Deathlok, Wolverine	1.30	3.00	7.50
63-Wolverine	0.80	1.50	3.75
64-71: 8 part Wolverine/Ghost Rider story	0.80	1.60	4.00

72-Begin 13 part Weapon X story (Wolverine origin) by Barry Smith

(Prologue)	1.30	3.00	7.50
73-Part 1, Weapon X	1.00	2.00	5.00
74-Weapon X	0.80	1.50	3.75
75-80: Weapon X. 80,81-Capt. America	0.60	1.10	2.75

81-84: Weapon X ends. 83-Human Torch by Ditko

	0.50	0.90	2.25

85-Begin 8 part Wolverine series; 1st Kieth-a on Wolverine; begins 8 part

Beast story by Jae Lee(1st pro work, '91)1.20		3.00	7.00
86-89: Wolverine	0.80	1.50	3.75
90-Ghost Rider/Cable 8 part series begins	1.00	1.90	4.75
91-94 (1.25)-Ghost Rider/Cable story cont'd		1.10	2.75

95-98 (1.50): 97-Ghost Rider/Cable conclusion

	0.40	0.70	1.80

99, 101-107, 112-116: 112-Demogoblin story

	0.30	0.60	1.60

100-(1.50)-Special Anniversary issue; full length Ghost Rider/Wolverine

story by Kieth w/Tim Vigil	0.50	1.00	2.50
108-111: Thanos storyline by Starlin	0.40	0.80	2.00

117-1st Ravage 2099; begin 6 part Wolverine/Venom story with Kieth-a

	0.50	1.00	2.50
118-1st app. Doom 2099	0.50	1.00	2.50

119-142, 147-152: 129-Jae Lee back-c. 131-Cage app. 133-136-Iron Fist
vs. Sabretooth. 147-Begin 2 part Vengeance-c/sty w/new Ghost Rider. 149-
Vengeance-c/sty w/new Ghost Rider. 150-Silver ink-c; begin Bloody Mary
story w/Typhoid Mary, Wolverine, Daredevil, new Ghost Rider (ends #151);
intro Steel Raven. 152-Begin 4-part Wolverine, 4-part War Machine, 4-part

Vengeance & 3-part Moon Knight stories		0.70	1.80

143-146-Siege of Darkness Parts 3, 6, 11, 14. 143-Ghost Rider/Scarlet
Witch; intro new Werewolf (part 1 of 2); spot varnish-c

	0.40	0.70	1.75

153-175: 153-Begin 1.75-c. 153-155-Have bound-in Spider-Man trading

card sheet in each	0.40	0.70	1.75

...Colossus: God's Country ('94, 6.95)-r/10-17

	1.20	3.00	7.00

MARVEL COMICS SUPER SPECIAL
Sept, 1977-No. 41, Nov, 1986 (Magazine, 1.50)

	Good	Fine	N-Mint
Marvel Comics Group			
1-Kiss; 40 pgs. comics plus photos & features			
	8.00	25.00	58.00
2-Conan	0.30	0.60	1.50
3-Close Encounters	0.30	0.60	1.50
4-The Beatles Story (1978)	1.60	5.00	11.00
5-Kiss (12/78)-Includes poster	4.70	14.00	33.00
6-Jaws II	0.30	0.60	1.50
7-Does not exist; withdrawn from U.S. distribution (Sgt. Pepper)			
8-Battlestar Galactica	0.30	0.60	1.50
9, 10: 9-Conan. 10-Star Lord	0.30	0.60	1.50
11-13: Special copy limited print run, 25 copies each with gold seal			
& signed by artists	8.00	24.00	55.00
11-13: Regular issues	0.30	0.60	1.50
14-Meteor; Miller-c(p)	0.20	0.50	1.20
15-Star Trek; photos, pin-ups	0.20	0.50	1.20
15-Scarce $2.00-c version	0.40	0.80	2.00
16-41: All movie adaptations	0.40	0.70	1.75

MARVEL DOUBLE FEATURE
Dec, 1973- No. 21, Mar, 1977
Marvel Comics Group

	Good	Fine	N-Mint
1-r/TOS w/Capt. America & Iron Man begin	0.80	1.60	4.00
2-16, 20, 21: 3-Last 20¢ issue	0.40	0.80	2.00
17-Reprints Iron Man & Sub-Mariner #1	0.60	1.20	3.00
18, 19-Reprints Iron Man #1	0.80	1.60	4.00

MARVEL FANFARE
March, 1982-No. 60, Jan, 1992
Marvel Comics Group

	Good	Fine	N-Mint
1-Spider Man/Angel team-up	1.70	4.00	10.00
2-Origin Fantastic Four retold	0.90	2.30	5.50
3, 4: X-Men/Ka-Zar teamup; Deathlok app.	1.00	2.00	5.00
5-Dr. Strange by Rogers	0.60	1.20	3.00
6-32, 34-50: 18-Capt. America by Miller	0.50	1.00	2.50
33-X-Men, Wolverine app.	0.90	2.30	5.50
51-(2.95, 52 pgs.)-Silver Surfer, F.F. app.	0.60	1.20	3.00
52, 53, 56-60 (2.25-c)	0.50	1.00	2.50
54, 55-Wolverine backup stories	0.60	1.20	3.00

MARVEL FEATURE
Dec, 1971-No. 12, Nov, 1973
Marvel Comics Group (#1, 2 are 25¢ giants)

1-Origin/1st app. The Defenders; Dr. Strange solo story; pre-dates
  D.S.#1 (see Sub-Mariner #34, 35)   10.00   30.00   72.00
2,3-Defenders series ends   4.60   14.00   32.00
4-New Antman series begins (see Avengers #46) w/brief origin;
  Spider-Man x-over   1.90   5.60   13.00
5-10: Antman app.; 8-Starlin-a   0.90   2.30   5.50
10-(7/73)-Variant w/4 extra pgs. slick paper1.00   2.50   6.00
11-Hulk vs. Thing; Starlin-a;1st solo Thing bk
                                         1.30   3.00   7.50
12-Thanos, Iron Man story; Starlin-a(p) 1.70   4.00   10.00

MARVEL FEATURE
Nov, 1975-No.7 Nov, 1976
Marvel Comics Group
1-Red Sonja begins; Adams-r/Savage Sword #1 (Red Sonja gets her own
  book 1/77)   0.80   1.60   4.00
2-7: 7-Red Sonja battles Conan   0.50   0.90   2.25

MARVEL GRAPHIC NOVEL
1982-No. 38, 1990? (5.95/6.95)
Marvel Comics Group
1-Death of Capt. Marvel (1st print); Thanos battles Capt. Marvel by
  Starlin (c/a/scripts)   3.30   10.00   20.00
1-2nd & 3rd printings   1.20   3.00   5.00
2-Elric   1.60   5.00   9.00
3-Dreadstar   1.40   3.50   7.50
4-Origin & 1st app. The New Mutants ('82) 3.00   6.50   16.00
4, 5-2nd printings   1.20   3.00   5.50
5-X-Men ('82)   2.40   6.00   13.00
6–18   1.20   3.00   5.50
19-34, 36, 37: 22-Spider-Man (Hooky)   1.40   3.50   7.50
32-2nd printing (5.95)   1.20   3.00   6.00
35-Hitlers Diary/Shadow(12.95, hardbound)1.85   5.50   13.00
35-Softcover reprint (1990, 10.95)   1.60   4.70   11.00
38-Silver Surfer: Judgement Day (14.95) 2.10   6.40   15.00
Note: Prices listed are for 1st printings only.
Later printings are worth less than cover price.

MARVEL MASTERPIECES COLLECTION, THE
May, 1993-No. 4, Aug, 1993 (2.95, color, mini-series)
Marvel Comics
1-4: r/trading cards + new paintings by Jusko
                                         0.60   1.20   3.00

	Good	Fine	N-Mint

MARVEL MASTERPIECES 2 COLLECTION, THE
July, 1994-Present (2.95, color)
Marvel Comics
1-3: 1-Kaluta-c; r/trading cards; new Steranko centerfold

	Good	Fine	N-Mint
	0.60	1.20	3.00

MARVEL MILESTONE EDITION
1991-Present (Color, w/silver ink on-c)
Marvel Comics (all-r original w/original ads)

	Good	Fine	N-Mint
...X-Men 1 (2.95, silver ink-c)	0.60	1.20	3.00
...Giant-Size X-Men 1 (3.95)	0.80	1.60	4.00
...Fantastic Four #1 (11/91, 2.95)	0.60	1.20	3.00
...Incredible Hulk #1 (3/92, says 3/91)	0.60	1.20	3.00
...Amazing Fantasy 15 (3/92, 2.95)	0.60	1.20	3.00
...Fantastic Four #5 (11/92, 2.95)	0.60	1.20	3.00
...Amazing Spider-Man #129 (11/92, 2.95)	0.60	1.20	3.00
...Iron Man #55 (11/92, 2.95)	0.60	1.20	3.00
...Iron Fist #14 (11/92, 2.95)	0.60	1.20	3.00
...Amazing Spider-Man 1 (1/93, 2.95)	0.60	1.20	3.00
...Tales of Suspense #39 (3/93, 2.95)	0.60	1.20	3.00
...X-Men #9 (10/93, 2.95)	0.60	1.20	3.00
...Avengers #1 (9/93, 2.95)	0.60	1.20	3.00
...Avengers #16 (10/93, 2.95)	0.60	1.20	3.00
...Amazing Spider-Man #149 (11/94, 2.95)	0.60	1.20	3.00
...X-Men #28 (11/94, 2.95)	0.60	1.20	3.00
...Captain America #1 (3/95,3.95)	0.80	1.60	4.00
...Amazing Spider-Man #3 (3/95, 2.95)	0.60	1.20	3.00
...Avengers #4 (3/95, 2.95)	0.60	1.20	3.00
...Strange Tales r/Dr.Strange stories from #110,111,114 & #115			
	0.60	1.20	3.00

MARVEL PREMIERE
April, 1972-No. 61, Aug, 1981 (#1-14 are 20¢)
Marvel Comics Group

	Good	Fine	N-Mint
1-Origin Warlock (pre-#1) by Gil Kane	6.60	20.00	46.00
2-Warlock ends	3.60	10.70	25.00
3-Dr. Strange begins (pre-#1); Smith-a	3.90	11.60	27.00
4-Smith/Brunner art	1.60	4.70	11.00
5-9: 8-Starlin-c/a (p)	1.10	2.70	6.50
10-Death of Ancient One	1.50	3.80	9.00
11-14:14-Last Dr. Strange & last 20¢ issue	0.90	1.80	4.50
15-Intro & origin Iron Fist (5/74)	6.40	19.00	45.00
16-2nd app. Iron Fist; origin cont'd from #15			

	2.10	6.40	15.00
17-24: Iron Fist in all	1.90	5.60	13.00
25-Byrne-a (last Iron Fist issue)	2.30	6.90	16.00
26, 27: 26-Hercules. 27-Satana	0.90	1.80	4.50
28-Legion of Monsters w/Ghost Rider & Morbius			
	1.70	5.00	12.00
29-49,51-56,61: 47-Origin/1st new Antman	0.30	0.60	1.60
50-1st app. Alice Cooper (co-plotted-Cooper)			
	0.90	2.30	5.50
57-Dr. Who (1st U.S. app.)	0.70	1.40	3.50
58-60: Dr. Who	0.50	0.90	2.25

MARVEL PRESENTS
Oct, 1975-No. 12, Aug, 1977
Marvel Comics Group

1-Origin & 1st app. Bloodstone	1.00	1.90	4.75
2-Origin Bloodstone cont.	0.90	1.70	4.25
3-Guardians Of The Galaxy begins, ends #12 (1st solo book, 2/76)			
	2.00	7.30	17.00
4-7, 9-12: 9,10-Origin Starhawk	1.60	4.70	11.00
8-Reprints story from Silver Surfer #2	2.10	6.40	15.00

MARVEL PREVIEW
Feb (no month), 1975-No. 24, Winter, 1980 (Magazine, B&W)
Marvel Comics Group

1-Man-Gods; N. Adams-c & a(i)	0.40	0.80	2.00
2-1st origin The Punisher (1975)	19.00	56.00	130.00
3-7, 9-20, 22-24: 3-Blade, the Vampire Slayer. 11-Star-Lord; Byrne-a.			
14-Starlin painted-c	0.40	0.80	2.00
8-Legion of Monsters app. (Morbius)	1.40	3.50	8.50
21-Moon Knight app.; The Shroud by Ditko	1.00	2.00	5.00

MARVELS
Jan, 1994-No. 4, April, 1994 (5.95, color, mini-series)
Marvel Comics

1-4: Double cover w/acetate overlay	1.00	2.50	6.00
...Marvel Classic Collectors Pack-($11.90) Issues #1 & #2			
boxed-1st printings	1.70	5.00	12.00
0-(8/94, 2.95)	0.60	1.20	3.00
TPB (12/94, 19.95) r/#1-4 & #0	3.00	8.60	20.00

MARVELS: PORTRAITS
Mar 1995 - June, 1995 (2.95, color, limited series:4)

	Good	Fine	N-Mint

Marvel Premiere #47 © MEG

Marvel Team-Up #100 © MEG

Marvel Comics
1-4: Diff. artists renditions of Marvel characters   1.20   3.00

MARVEL'S GREATEST COMICS(Formerly Marvel Collectors' Item Classics)
No. 23, Oct,1969-No. 96, Jan, 1981
Marvel Comics Group

	Good	Fine	N-Mint
23-30: 23-Begin FF reprints	0.60	1.20	3.00
31-96: 35-37: r/FF #48-50	0.40	0.80	2.00

MARVEL SPECTACULAR
Aug, 1973-No. 19, Nov, 1975
Marvel Comics Group

	Good	Fine	N-Mint
1-Thor-r begin by Kirby	0.40	0.80	2.00
2–19	0.30	0.60	1.50

MARVEL SPOTLIGHT
Nov, 1971-No. 33, Apr, 1977;
V2#1, July, 1979-V2#11, Mar, 1981
Marvel Comics Group

	Good	Fine	N-Mint
1-Origin Red Wolf (1st solo book)	3.00	9.40	22.00
2-(25¢, 52 pgs.)-Origin & 1st app. Werewolf By Night by Ploog & begin series	5.70	17.00	40.00
3, 4-Werewolf By Night ends (6/72)	1.70	5.00	12.00
5-Origin/1st app. new Ghost Rider (8/72)	16.00	50.00	110.00
6-8: Last Ploog issue	7.10	21.00	50.00
9-11: 11-Last Ghost Rider; gets own title	5.70	17.00	40.00
12-(10/73)-Origin/2nd full app. Son of Satan (Daimon Hellstrom), story cont'd from Ghost Rider #2	1.70	4.20	10.00
12-Variant w/4 extra pgs. of ads on slick paper plus a Mark Jeweler pull-out centerfold ad	1.40	4.00	10.00

13-21, 23, 24: 13-Partial origin Son of Satan. 14-Last 20¢ issue.			
24-Son Of Satan ends (10/75)	0.80	1.60	4.00
22-Ghost Rider-c/cameo (5 panels)	1.50	3.70	9.00
25-27, 30, 31: 25-Contains pull-out Mark Jeweler centerfold ad			
	0.60	1.20	3.00
28, 29-1st solo app. Moon Knight (6/76)	1.70	4.00	10.00
32-1st app./part. origin Spider-Woman (2/77)			
	1.30	3.00	7.50
33-Deathlok app.; 1st app. Devil-Slayer	1.30	3.00	7.50
V2#1-11: 8-Miller art	0.20	0.40	1.00

MARVEL SUPER ACTION
Jan, 1976 (One-shot, B&W, magazine size)
Marvel Comics Group

1-Early Punisher app.	9.30	28.00	65.00

MARVEL SUPER ACTION
May, 1977-No. 37, Nov, 1981
Marvel Comics Group

1-Reprints Capt. America #100	0.50	1.00	2.50
2, 3, 5-13: All r/Cap. Am. 101, 102, 103-111		0.60	1.50
4-r/Marvel Boy #1 (1950)	0.30	0.60	1.50
14-37: Avengers reprints	0.20	0.40	1.00

MARVEL SUPER-HERO CONTEST OF CHAMPIONS
June, 1982-No. 3, Aug, 1982 (Mini-series)
Marvel Comics Group

1-3: 1st Marvel limited series	0.80	1.60	4.00

MARVEL SUPER HEROES
Oct, 1966 (25¢ giant, one-shot)
Marvel Comics Group

1-Reprints origin Daredevil from DD #1, Avengers from Avengers #2;			
first Marvel one-shot issue	10.00	29.00	68.00

MARVEL SUPER-HEROES (Fantasy Masterpieces 1-11)
No. 12, Dec, 1967-No. 105, Jan, 1982 (#12-20 are 25¢ giants)
Marvel Comics Group

12-Origin & 1st app. Captain Marvel	14.00	43.00	100.00
13-2nd app. Captain Marvel	7.00	21.00	50.00
14-Spidey story; new-a (5/68)	13.00	39.00	90.00
15-Black Bolt cameo in Medusa (new-a)	2.10	6.40	15.00
16-1st S.A. Phantom Eagle (new-a)	2.10	6.40	15.00

	Good	Fine	N-Mint
17-Origin Black Knight (new-a)	2.10	6.40	15.00
18-Origin & 1st app. Guardians Of The Galaxy (1/69)			
	9.00	26.00	60.00
19-New Ka-Zar story	1.70	5.00	12.00
20-New Dr. Doom story (5/69)	1.70	5.00	12.00
21-31: Giant Size issues; X-Men, D.D., Iron Man-r in all			
	0.90	2.30	5.50
32-105: 32-Hulk, Sub-Mariner-r from TTA begin. 56-Reprints origin Hulk/			
Incredible Hulk #102	0.20	0.40	1.00

Note: 12-20 contain at least one non-reprint story plus G.A. & S.A.-r.

MARVEL SUPER-HEROES (Special on cover)
May, 1990-Present? (2.95, 84 pgs., quarterly)
Marvel Comics

	Good	Fine	N-Mint
1-Moon Knight, Hercules, Black Panther, Magik, Brother Voodoo,			
Speedball & Hellcat	0.60	1.20	3.00
2, 4, 5: 2-Summer Special (7/90)	0.60	1.20	3.00
3-Retells Cap. origin w/new facts	0.60	1.20	3.00
6-9: 6-8: (2.25), 9-(2.50): 8-Larsen-c	0.50	1.00	2.50
10-(2.50)-Ms. Marvel/Sabretooth-c/story	0.50	1.00	2.50
11, 12-(2.50): 11-Original Ghost Rider-c/story			
	0.50	1.00	2.50
13-(2.75)-All Iron Man issue; 30th anniversary			
	0.60	1.10	2.75

MARVEL SUPER-HEROES SECRET WARS (See Secret Wars II)
May, 1984-No. 12, April, 1985
Marvel Comics Group

	Good	Fine	N-Mint
1	0.70	1.40	3.50
1-3 (2nd prints)-Sold in multi-packs	0.20	0.40	1.00
2-7, 9-12: 7-Intro new Spider-Woman	0.40	0.80	2.00
8-Spider-Man's black costume explained as alien costume; 1st app. Venom			
(as alien costume)	2.60	7.70	18.00

MARVEL TALES(...Annual #1, 2)
1964-Present (No. 1-32: 72 pg. giants)
Marvel Comics Group

	Good	Fine	N-Mint
1-Origin Spider-Man, Hulk, Antman/Giant-Man, Iron Man, Thor			
& Sgt. Fury reprinted	31.00	94.00	250.00
2-('65)-r/Origin X-Men, Dr. Strange, Avengers			
	11.00	32.00	75.00
3-(7/66)-Spider-Man, Strange Tales, JIM, TTA reprints begin; r/Strange			
Tales #101	5.00	15.00	35.00

4, 5	2.40	7.00	17.00
6-8, 10: 10-r/1st Kraven from A. S-M 15	1.70	4.20	10.00
9-Reprints Am. Spider-Man 14 w/cover	1.70	5.10	12.00

11-32: 22-r/Green Goblin-c/story. 30-New Angel story. 32-Last 72 pg.

issue	1.10	2.70	6.50
33-105	0.30	0.60	1.50
106-r/1st app. Punisher/Spider-Man 129	1.30	3.30	8.00

107-136: 111,112-Punisher-r. 126-128-r/clone story from Amazing

Spider-Man #149-151	0.20	0.40	1.00
137-r/Amazing Fantasy 15 w/original-c	0.90	1.80	4.50
138-Reprints Spider-Man #1	0.90	1.80	4.50
139-144: r/Spider-Man #2-7 with original-c	0.40	0.80	2.00

145-191, 193-199: 149-Contains skin "Tattooz" decals

	0.20	0.50	1.20
192-(52 pgs)-r/Amaz. Spidey 121, 122	0.40	0.80	2.00
200-(1.25, 52 pgs.)	0.30	0.60	1.50
201-208, 210-222: 211-222: Punisher-r	0.20	0.40	1.00
209-r/1st app. Punisher/Spider-Man 129	0.50	1.00	2.50
223-McFarlane-c begin, end #239	0.30	0.60	1.50

224-249, 251, 252, 254-257: 257-r/Am. Spidey #238. 252-r/Am.

Spidey #101 (Morbius); last 1.00-c	0.20	0.40	1.00
250-(1.50, 52 pgs.)-r/Marv. Team-up #100	0.30	0.60	1.50
253-(1.50, 52 pgs)-r/Am. Spidey #102	0.30	0.60	1.50

258-289: 262-X-Men vs. Sunstroke (new-a). 283, 284-r/Spidey #175

& 176 (Hobgoblin)	0.30	0.50	1.25

285-variant w/Wonder-Con logo on-c, no price (giveaway)

	0.20	0.40	1.00

286-(2.95)-Variant polybagged w/16-page insert & animation print

	0.60	1.20	3.00
290,291-(1.50)	0.30	0.60	1.50

NOTE: All are reprints with some new art. Ron Lim c-(p)-266-284.

MARVEL TEAM-UP
March, 1972-No. 150, Feb, 1985
Marvel Comics Group
NOTE: Spider-Man team-ups in all but Nos. 18, 23, 26, 29, 32, 35, 97, 104, 105, 137.

1-Spider-Man team-ups begin	11.00	32.00	75.00
2-Human Torch	3.90	11.60	27.00

3-Spider-Man/Human Torch battle Morbius; 3rd app. Morbius (7/72)

	5.70	17.00	40.00

4-Spider-Man/Original X-Men team-up; Pt. 2 Morbius battle story;

4th app. Morbius	7.10	21.00	50.00

	Good	Fine	N-Mint
5-10: 5-Vision. 8-Cat (4/73, early app.)	2.50	6.30	15.00
11-14, 16-20: 12-Werewolf by Night (8/73)	1.70	4.20	10.00
15-Ghost Rider app. (11/73)	2.10	6.40	15.00
21-30: 21-Dr. Strange. 27-Hulk	1.00	2.50	6.00
31-45, 47-50: 32-Son/Satan. 44-Moondragon			
	1.00	2.00	5.00
46-Spider-Man/Deathlok teamup	1.40	4.00	10.00
51, 52, 56, 57: 57-Black Widow	0.80	1.60	4.00
53-Hulk; 1st Byrne-a on New X-Men (1/77)	1.90	5.60	13.00
54, 59, 60: Byrne-a. 54-Hulk	1.00	2.50	6.00
55-Byrne-a; Warlock-c/story	1.30	3.30	8.00
58-Ghost Rider app.	1.00	2.50	6.00
61-70,75,79-Byrne-a: 63-Iron Fist. 69-Havok. 75-Cage app. 79-Clark			
Kent cameo, 1 panel (3/79)	0.60	1.20	3.00
71-74, 76-78, 80: 73-Daredevil	0.60	1.20	3.00
81-85, 87, 88, 90, 92-99	0.40	0.80	2.00
86-Guardians Of The Galaxy app.	0.80	1.60	4.00
89-Nightcrawler app.	0.60	1.20	3.00
91-Ghost Rider app.	1.00	2.00	5.00
100-(52 pgs.)-Origin & 1st Karma by Frank Miller; Byrne X-Men;			
origin Storm	1.30	3.30	8.00
101-116: 103-Ant-Man	0.30	0.60	1.50
117-Wolverine-c/story	1.70	5.00	12.00
118-140, 142-149: 118-Wolverine cameo	0.30	0.60	1.50
141-Same month as Am. Spider-Man 252; ties for 1st black costume			
	0.60	1.20	3.00
150-(1.00, 52 pgs.)-X-Men; B. Smith-c	0.70	1.40	3.50
Annual 1 (1976)-Early New X-Men app.	2.00	6.00	14.00
Annual 2-7: 2-('79)-Spider-Man/Hulk. 3-('80)-Hulk/Iron Fist. 4-D.D./Moon			
Knight. 6-('83)-Early New Mutants app.	0.40	0.80	2.00

MARVEL TRIPLE ACTION (Also see Giant-Size...)
Feb, 1972-No. 47, Apr, 1979
Marvel Comics Group

1-Giant (52 pgs.); FF reprints	0.60	1.20	3.00
2-47: 2-4: FF reprints. 5-47: Avengers reprints			
	0.20	0.40	1.00

MARVEL TWO-IN-ONE
January, 1974-No. 100, June, 1983
Marvel Comics Group

1-Thing team-ups begin; vs. Man-Thing	4.30	12.90	30.00
2-4: 2-Last 20¢ issue. 4-Capt. America app			

Mary Shelly's Frankrnstein #1
© Mary Shelly

The Mask Returns #4 © DH

	1.80	5.00	11.00
5-Guardians Of The Galaxy app. (9/74, 2nd app.?)			
	2.40	7.30	17.00
6-Dr. Strange (11/74)	2.40	7.30	17.00
7, 9, 10	1.20	2.90	7.00
8-Thing/Ghost Rider team-up (3/75)	1.70	5.10	12.00
11-20: 14-Early Son Of Satan. 17-Spidey	0.90	1.80	4.50
21-26, 28, 29, 31-40: 29-Spider-Woman cameo			
	0.70	1.40	3.50
27-Deathlok app.	1.00	2.50	6.00
30-2nd Spider-Woman app.	0.90	2.30	5.50
41, 42, 44-49: 46-Thing battles Hulk	0.30	0.60	1.50
43, 50, 53, 55: Byrne art	0.50	1.00	2.50
51-Miller-a(p)	0.60	1.20	3.00
52-Moon Knight app.	0.60	1.20	3.00
54-Death of Deathlok; Byrne-a	2.00	6.00	14.00
56-60,64-68, 70-79, 81, 82	0.20	0.40	1.00
61-63-"The Coming of Her" storyline (Warlock story). 61-Cover similar to			
FF #67. 63-Warlock revived briefly	0.40	0.80	2.00
69-Guardians Of The Galaxy	0.80	1.60	4.00
80-Ghost Rider app.	0.80	2.10	5.00
83, 84: 83-Sasquatch app. 84-Alpha Flight app.			
	0.40	0.80	2.00
85-99: 90-Spider-Man app. 96-X-Men-c, cameo			
	0.20	0.40	1.00
100-Double size	0.30	0.60	1.50
Annual 1 (1976)-Thing/Liberty Legion	0.40	0.80	2.00
Annual 2 (1977)-Thing/Spider-Man; 2nd Death of Thanos; Thanos saga ends;			
Warlock app.; Starlin-c/a	3.30	9.90	23.00
Annual 3, 4('78, '79): 3-Nova. 4-Black Bolt	0.30	0.60	1.50

	Good	Fine	N-Mint
Annual 5-7: 5-(1980)-Hulk. 6-(1981)-1st app. American Eagle. 7-(1982)- Colossus app. plus 1 pg. X-Men cameo	0.20	0.40	1.00

MARVEL X-MEN COLLECTION, THE
Jan, 1994-No. 3, Mar, 1994 (2.95, color, mini-series)
Marvel Comics

1-3-r/X-Men trading cards by Jim Lee	0.60	1.20	3.00

MARY SHELLY'S FRANKENSTEIN
Oct, 1994-Jan 1995 (2.95, color, limited series)
Topps Comics

1-4-Polybagged w/3 trading cards	0.60	1.20	3.00
1-4-(2.50)-Newsstand edition	0.50	1.00	2.50

MASK, THE
Aug, 1991-No. 4, Oct, 1991 (2.50, 36 pgs., mini-series)
Dark Horse Comics

1–4: 1-1st app. Lt. Kellaway as The Mask	1.00	2.00	5.00
0-(12/91, B&W, 56 pgs.)-r/Mayhem 1-4	1.00	2.00	5.00

MASK: OFFICIAL MOVIE ADAPTATION, THE
July, 1994-No. 2, Aug, 1994 (2.50, color)
Dark Horse Comics

1,2-Movie adaptation	0.50	1.00	2.50

MASK RETURNS, THE
Oct, 1992-No. 4, Mar, 1993 (2.50, 36 pgs., mini-series)
Dark Horse Comics

1-4: 1-"Mask" mask c-f; 4-"Walter" mask-f	0.70	1.40	3.50

MASK STRIKES BACK, THE
Feb 1995- June,1995 (2.50, color, limited series)
Dark Horse Comics

1-5	0.50	1.00	2.50

MASTER OF KUNG-FU (Formerly Special Marvel Edition; see Giant-Size…)
No. 17, April, 1974-No. 125, June, 1983
Marvel Comics Group

17-Starlin art; ties w/Deadly Hands of Kung-Fu #1 as 3rd app. of Shang Chi	2.40	7.30	17.00
18-20: 19-Man-Thing-c/story	1.50	3.80	9.00
21-23, 25-30	0.90	2.30	5.50
24-Starlin, Simonson-a	1.10	2.70	6.50
31-99: 43-Last 25¢ issue	0.60	1.20	3.00

100-Double size	0.70	1.40	3.50
101-117, 119-124	0.50	1.00	2.50
118, 125-Double size	0.60	1.20	3.00
Annual 1 (1976)-Iron Fist app.	0.90	1.80	4.50

MASTER OF KUNG-FU: BLEEDING BLACK
Feb, 1991 (2.95, 84 pgs., one shot)
Marvel Comics

1-The Return of Shang-chi	0.60	1.20	3.00

MAXX (Also see Darker Image & Primer #5)
Mar, 1993-Present (1.95, color)
Image Comics

1-Keith	1.00	2.00	5.00
1-Glow-in-the-dark variant	2.60	8.00	18.00
2-16-Sam Kieth-c/a/scripts. 6-Savage Dragon app. (1 pg.).			
7,8-Pitt-c & story	0.40	0.80	2.00
1/2	1.00	2.00	5.00

MAYHEM
May, 1989-No. 4, Sept, 1989 (2.50, B&W, 52 pgs.)
Dark Horse Comics

1-Four-part Stanley Ipkiss/Mask story begins; Mask-c			
	2.90	8.60	20.00
2–4: 2-Mask 1/2 back-c. 4-Mask-c	1.70	5.10	12.00

McHALE'S NAVY (TV)
May-July, 1963-No. 3, Nov-Jan, 1963-64 (All have photo-c)
Dell Publishing Co.

1	4.30	13.00	30.00
2, 3	3.00	10.00	24.00

M.D. GEIST
1995 (2.95, color, limited series)
CPM Comics

1	0.40	1.30	3.00

MECHA SPECIAL
May 1995 (2.95, color, one-shot)

1	0.40	1.00	3.00

MEDAL OF HONOR
Oct, 1994-Present (2.50, color, mini-series:5)

	Good	Fine	N-Mint

Dark Horse Comics
1-4:1-Simonson-c, 2- A.Adams-c

	Good	Fine	N-Mint
1-4:1-Simonson-c, 2- A.Adams-c	0.50	1.00	2.50
...Special 1 (1994, 2.50)-Kubert-c & 1st story-a	0.50	1.00	2.50

MEGATON
Nov, 1983; No. 2, Oct, 1985-No. 8, Aug, 1987
Megaton Pub.

	Good	Fine	N-Mint
1-Erik Larsen's 1st pro work; Vanguard begins (1st app.); 1st app. Megaton	1.70	4.20	10.00
2-Savage Dragon cameo (1 pg.) by Larsen; Guice-c/a in #1,2	1.30	3.30	8.00
3-1st full app. Savage Dragon by Erik Larsen; 1st comic work by Angel Medina (pin-up)	2.30	6.90	16.00
4-2nd app. Savage Dragon by Larsen	2.00	5.00	12.00
5-1st Liefeld-a (inside FC page, 6/86)	0.90	2.30	5.50
6, 7: 6-Larsen-c	0.60	1.20	3.00
8-1st Liefeld story-a (7 pg. super-hero story) plus 1 pg. Youngblood ad	0.60	1.20	3.00
Megaton Explosion ('87, color, 16 pg. preview comics); 1st app. of Youngblood by Rob Liefeld (2 pgs.)	3.10	9.40	22.00
Megaton Holiday Special #1-(1994, 2.95, color, 40 pgs.)-Gold foil logo bagged w/card (publ. by Entity Comics); shows unpublished-c to 1987 Youngblood #1 by Liefeld/Ordway	0.60	1.20	3.00

MEGATON MAN (See Don Simpson's Bizarre Heroes)
Nov, 1984-No. 10, 1986
Kitchen Sink Enterprises

	Good	Fine	N-Mint
1-10	0.40	0.80	2.00
1-2nd print (1989)	0.40	0.80	2.00
...Meets The Uncategorizable X-Thems 1 (4/89, 2.00)	0.40	0.80	2.00

MELTING POT
Dec, 1993-Present (2.95, color, mature)
Kitchen Sink Press

	Good	Fine	N-Mint
1-4-Eastman/Talbot/Bisley; Bisley painted-c	0.60	1.20	3.00

MEN OF WAR
Aug, 1977-No. 26, Mar, 1980 (#9, 10 are 44 pgs.)
DC Comics

	Good	Fine	N-Mint
1-Enemy Ace, Gravedigger (origin 1, 2) begin	0.50	1.00	2.50

| 2-26: 9-Unknown Soldier app. | 0.20 | 0.40 | 1.00 |

MEN'S ADVENTURES
No. 27, Mar, 1954-No. 28, July, 1954
Atlas Comics
27, 28-Captain America, Human Torch & Sub-Mariner app. in both

| | 66.00 | 200.00 | 465.00 |

MEPHISTO VERSUS...
Apr, 1987-No. 4, July, 1987 (1.50, mini-series)
Marvel Comics Group

| 1 | 0.40 | 0.70 | 1.75 |
| 2–4 | 0.30 | 0.60 | 1.60 |

MERCY
1993 (5.95, color, 68 pgs., mature)
DC Comics (Vertigo)

| nn | 1.00 | 2.50 | 6.00 |

METAL MEN (See Showcase #37-40)
Apr-May, 1963-No. 56, Feb-Mar, 1978
National Periodical Publications/DC Comics

1-5th app. Metal Men	53.00	159.00	370.00
2	17.00	51.00	120.00
3–5	11.00	34.00	80.00
6–10	7.10	21.00	50.00
11–20: 12-Beatles cameo (12/65)	5.00	15.00	35.00
21-26, 28-30: 21-Batman, Robin, Flash x-over			
	3.60	11.00	25.00
27-Origin Metal Men retold	6.40	19.00	45.00
31-41: 38-Last 12¢ issue. 41 (12-1/69-70)	2.90	8.60	20.00
42-56: 42-44-All-r . 48, 49-Reintro Eclipso (42-44-1973; 45-1976)			
	1.60	4.70	11.00

Note: 3-year delay between #41 & #42.

METAL MEN
Oct, 1993-No. 4, Jan, 1994 (1.25, color, mini-series)
DC Comics

| 1-(2.50)-Foil cover | 0.50 | 1.00 | 2.50 |
| 2-4: 2-Origin | 0.30 | 0.50 | 1.25 |

METAMORPHO (See Brave & the Bold #57, 58)
July-Aug, 1965-No. 17, Mar-Apr, 1968

	Good	Fine	N-Mint
National Periodical Publications			
1-3rd app. Metamorpho	10.00	30.00	70.00
2, 3	5.70	17.00	40.00
4–6	3.60	10.70	25.00
7–9	2.90	8.60	20.00
10-Origin & 1st app. Element Girl	3.60	11.00	25.00
11–17	2.10	6.40	15.00

METAMORPHO
Aug, 1993-No. 4, Nov, 1993 (1.50, color, mini-series)
DC Comics

	Good	Fine	N-Mint
1–4	0.30	0.60	1.50

METAPHYSIQUE
Apr, 1995-Present (2.95, color, limited series)
Malibu Comics (Bravura)

	Good	Fine	N-Mint
1-Norm Breyfogle	0.60	1.20	3.00

METROPOLIS S.C.U
Nov, 1994-Feb, 1995 (1.50, color, limited series)
DC Comics

	Good	Fine	N-Mint
1-4: 1-Superman-c & app.	0.30	0.60	1.50

MEZZ: GALACTIC TOUR 2494
May, 1994 (2.50, color)
Dark Horse Comics

	Good	Fine	N-Mint
1	0.60	1.20	3.00

MICHAELANGELO, TEENAGE MUTANT NINJA TURTLE
1986 (1.50, B&W, one-shot)
Mirage Studios

	Good	Fine	N-Mint
1	0.90	3.00	6.00
1-2nd print; some new art	0.60	1.20	3.00

MICKEY AND DONALD (Becomes Walt Disney's Donald & Mickey)
Mar, 1988-No. 18, May, 1990 (Color)
Gladstone Publishing

	Good	Fine	N-Mint
1-Don Rosa art	0.80	1.60	4.00
2	0.50	1.00	2.50
3	0.40	0.80	2.00
4–8	0.20	0.50	1.20
9–15	0.20	0.40	1.00
16-(1.50, 52 pgs.)	0.30	0.60	1.50

17, 18-(1.95, 68 pgs.)	0.40	0.80	2.00

MICKEY MOUSE
No. 219-No. 256, April, 1990 (Color)
Gladstone Publ.

219	0.90	1.70	4.25
220, 221	0.60	1.20	3.00
222-225	0.50	1.00	2.50
226-230	0.30	0.60	1.50
231-243, 245-254	0.20	0.40	1.00
244-Squarebound, 60th birthday issue	0.60	1.20	3.00
255, 256-(1.95, 68 pgs.)	0.40	0.80	2.00

MICKEY SPILLANE'S MIKE DANGER
Sep 1995-Present (1.95, color)
Tekno•Comix

1,2; 1-Frank Miller-c	0.40	0.80	2.00

MIDNIGHT SONS UNLIMITED
Apr, 1993-Present (3.95, color, 68 pgs.)
Marvel Comics (Midnight Sons imprint #4 on)

1-9-Blaze, Darkhold (by Quesada #1), Ghost Rider, Morbius, & Night-stalkers. 3-Spiderman app. 4-Siege of Darkness Pt. 17; new Dr. Strange & new Ghost Rider app.; spot varnish-c	0.80	1.60	4.00

MIGHTY COMICS (...Presents) (Formerly Flyman)
No. 40, Nov, 1966-No. 50, Oct, 1967 (All 12¢ issues)
Radio Comics (Archie)

40-Web app.	1.90	6.00	13.00
41-50: Archie super-heroes app.	1.80	5.00	11.00

MIGHTY CRUSADERS, THE (Also see Advs. Of The Fly)
Nov, 1965-No. 7, Oct, 1966 (All 12¢ issues)
Mighty Comics Group (Radio Comics)

1-Origin The Shield	4.00	12.00	28.00
2-Origin Comet	2.10	6.40	15.00
3-Origin Fly-Man retold	1.90	5.60	13.00
4-1st S.A. app. Fireball, Inferno, Fox, plus Web app. (all-star cast); Jaguar x-over	2.40	7.30	17.00
5-7: 5-Intro Ultra-Men; 7-Origin Fly-Girl	1.90	5.60	13.00

MIGHTY CRUSADERS
Mar, 1983-No. 13, Sept, 1985 (1.00, Mando paper)

	Good	Fine	N-Mint

Red Circle Prod./Archie Enterprises #6 on

	Good	Fine	N-Mint
1-13: 1-Origin Black Hood, The Fly, Fly Girl, The Shield, The Wizard, The Jaguar, Pvt. Strong & The Web	0.20	0.40	1.00

MIGHTY HEROES (TV)
Mar, 1967-No. 4, July, 1967
Dell Publishing

	Good	Fine	N-Mint
1-Also has a 1957 Heckle & Jeckle-r; 1st app.	15.00	45.00	105.00
2-4: 4-Has two 1958 Mighty Mouse-r	13.30	40.00	80.00

MIGHTY MARVEL WESTERN, THE
Oct, 1968-No. 46, Sept, 1976 (1-14: 68 pgs.; 15, 16: 52 pgs.)
Marvel Comics Group

	Good	Fine	N-Mint
1-Begin Kid Colt, Rawhide Kid, Two-Gun Kid-r	1.20	2.90	7.00
2-10	0.60	1.20	3.00
11-20	0.40	0.80	2.00
21-46	0.20	0.50	1.20

MIGHTY MOUSE (TV)
No. 161, Oct, 1964-No. 172, Oct, 1968
Gold Key/Dell Publishing Co. No. 166 on

	Good	Fine	N-Mint
161 (10/64) - 165 (9/65)-Becomes Adventures of Mighty Mouse #166 on	4.30	12.90	30.00
166 (3/66), 167 (6/66) - 172	2.90	8.60	20.00

MIGHTY SAMSON
July, 1964-No. 20, Nov, 1969; No. 21, Aug, 1972;
No. 22, Dec, 1973-No. 31, Mar, 1976, No. 32, Aug, 1982
Gold Key

	Good	Fine	N-Mint
1-Origin/1st app.; Thorne-a begins	4.60	14.00	32.00
2-5	2.10	6.00	15.00
6-10	2.00	5.00	12.00
11-20	1.70	4.20	10.00
21-32: 21, 22, 32-Reprints	1.00	2.00	5.00

MILK AND CHEESE
1991-Present (2.50, B&W)
Slave Labor

	Good	Fine	N-Mint
1, Other #1, Third #1, Fourth #1, First Second Issue, #666-Evan Dorkin s/a	0.50	1.00	2.50

MIRACLEMAN
Aug, 1985-No. 15, Nov, 1988; No. 16, Dec, 1989-Present?
Eclipse Comics
1-r/British Marvelman series; Alan Moore scripts in #1-16

	0.60	1.20	3.00
1-Gold & Silver Editions	0.40	0.80	2.00
2-12: 8-Airboy preview. 9, 10-Origin Miracleman. 9-Shows graphic scenes of childbirth	0.30	0.50	1.25
13-15-(1.75)	0.40	0.70	1.75
16-18-(1.95): 17-Dave McKean-c begin, end #22; Neil Gaiman scripts in #17-24	0.40	0.80	2.00
19-24-(2.50): 23, 24-B. Smith-c	0.50	1.00	2.50
3-D 1 (12/85)	0.50	1.00	2.50

MISSION IMPOSSIBLE (TV)
May, 1967-No. 4, Oct, 1967; No. 5, Oct, 1969
Dell Publishing Co.

1-All have photo-c	8.00	24.00	55.00
2-5: 5-Reprints #1	5.00	15.00	35.00

MR. & MRS. J. EVIL SCIENTIST (TV) (See The Flintstones)
Nov, 1963-No. 4, Sept, 1966 (Hanna-Barbera) (All 12¢ issues)
Gold Key

1-From The Flintstones	5.40	16.00	38.00
2–4	3.00	9.40	22.00

MISTER E
Jun 1991-Sep 1991 (1.75, color, limited series)
DC Comics
1–4 John K. Snyder-a; follow-up to Books of Magic

	0.40	0.80	2.00

MISTER MIRACLE
Mar, 1971-No. 18, Feb, 1974; No. 19, Sept, 1977-No. 25, Aug, 1978
DC Comics

1-1st app.; Jack Kirby-a in all	3.90	11.60	27.00
2, 3	1.70	5.10	12.00
4-8: 25¢ giants	1.80	4.60	11.00
9, 10: 9-Origin Mr. Miracle; Darkseid cameo	1.50	3.80	9.00
11-18 (1974): 18-Darkseid cameo	1.30	3.00	8.00
19-25 (1977)	0.80	1.60	4.00
Special 1 (1987, 1.25)	0.60	1.20	3.00

	Good	Fine	N-Mint

MISTER MIRACLE
Jan, 1989-No. 28, June, 1991 (1.00, color)
DC Comics

1-28: 13, 14-Lobo app. 22-1st new Mr. Miracle w/new costume			
	0.20	0.40	1.00

MR. MONSTER (Doc Stearn No. 7 on)
Jan, 1985-No. 10, June, 1987 (color)
Eclipse Comics

1-1st story-r/Vanguard Illus. #7 (1st app.)	0.80	2.10	5.00
2-Dave Stevens-c	0.60	1.20	3.00
3-10: 10-6-D issue	0.40	0.80	2.00

MR. MONSTER
Feb, 1988-No. 8, July, 1991 (1.75, B&W)
Dark Horse Comics

1-7	0.40	0.70	1.75
8-(4.95, 60 pgs.)-Origins conclusion	1.00	2.00	5.00

MR. MONSTER'S SUPER DUPER SPECIAL
May, 1986-No. 8, July, 1987
Eclipse Comics

1-(5/86)... 3-D High Octane Horror #1	0.60	1.20	3.00
1-(5/86)... 2-D version, 100 copies	0.90	2.30	5.50
2-(8/86)...High Octane Horror #1	0.40	0.70	1.80
3-(9/86)...True Crime #1	0.40	0.70	1.80
4-(11/86)...True Crime #2	0.40	0.70	1.80
5-(1/87)...Hi-Voltage Super Science #1	0.40	0.70	1.80
6-(3/87)...High Shock Schlock #1	0.40	0.70	1.80
7-(5/87)...High Shock Schlock #2	0.40	0.70	1.80
8-(7/87)...Weird Tales Of The Future #1	0.40	0.70	1.80

MR. T AND THE T-FORCE
June, 1993-Present (1.95, color)
Now Comics

1-10-Newstand: 1-Neal Adams-a. 1-7-Polybagged w/photo trading card			
8-10-Not polybagged w/card	0.40	0.80	2.00
1-10-Direct market; polybagged w/trading card: 1-Gold foil card.			
1,2-Neal Adams-c(p). 3-Dorman-c	0.40	0.80	2.00

MISTER X
June, 1984-No. 14, Aug, 1988 (1.75, color, adult)
V2#1, Apr, 1989-No. 12, Mar, 1990

Mr. Publications/Vortex Comics

1	0.80	2.00	4.75
2	0.60	1.10	2.75
3-14: 11-McKean story & art (6 pgs.)	0.40	0.80	2.00
V2#1-11: (2.00) (Second Coming)	0.40	0.80	2.00
V2#12-(2.50)	0.50	1.00	2.50
Graphic Novel (11.95)	1.70	5.00	12.00
Hardcover Limited Edition (34.95)	5.00	15.00	35.00
Special (no date, 1990?)	0.40	0.80	2.00

MOBFIRE
Dec, 1994-May 1995 (2.50, color, limited series:6)
DC Comics

1-6	0.50	1.00	2.50

MODNIKS, THE
Aug, 1967-No. 2, Aug, 1970
Gold Key

10206-708 (#1), 2	1.30	3.30	8.00

MOD SQUAD (TV)
Jan, 1969-No. 8, Apr, 1971
Dell Publishing Co.

1-Photo-c	4.00	12.00	28.00
2-8: 2-4-Photo-c. 8-r/#2	2.30	6.90	16.00

MOD WHEELS
Mar, 1971-No. 19, Jan, 1976
Gold Key

1	1.70	4.00	10.00
2-19: 11, 15-Extra 16 pgs. of ads	1.00	2.00	5.00

MONKEES, THE (TV)
Mar, 1967-No. 17, Oct, 1969 (Photo-c: 1-4, 6, 7, 10)
Dell Publishing Co.

1-Photo-c	11.00	34.00	80.00
2-4, 6, 7, 10: Photo-c	6.40	19.00	45.00
5, 8, 9, 11-17: No photo-c	4.30	12.90	30.00

MONSTER HUNTERS
Aug, 1975-No. 9, Jan, 1977; No. 10, Oct, 1977-No. 18, Feb, 1979
Charlton Comics

1, 2: 1-Howard-a; Newton-c. 2-Ditko-a	1.00	2.00	5.00

	Good	Fine	N-Mint

Moon Knight #33 © MEG

Moonshadow #1 © DC

	Good	Fine	N-Mint
3-13, 15-18	0.40	0.80	2.00
14-Special all Ditko issue	0.70	1.40	3.50
1, 2-Modern Comics reprints, 1977	0.20	0.40	1.00

MONSTER MENACE
Dec, 1993-No. 4, Mar, 1994 (1.25, color, mini-series)
Marvel Comics

1-4-Kirby/Ditko pre-code Atlas reprints	0.30	0.50	1.25

MONSTERS ON THE PROWL (Formerly Chamber of Darkness)
No. 9, Feb, 1971-No. 27, Nov, 1973; No. 28, June, 1974-No. 30, Oct, 1974
Marvel Comics Group

9-Barry Smith-i	0.70	1.40	3.50

10-30: 13, 14-(52 pgs.). 16-King Kull app. (4/72, 2nd app. after Creatures

on the Loose)	0.40	0.80	2.00

MONSTERS UNLEASHED
July, 1973-No. 11, Apr, 1975; Summer, 1975 (B&W magazine)
Marvel Comics Group

1	1.00	2.10	5.00

2-11: 2-The Frankenstein Monster begins. 3-The Man-Thing begins
  (origin-r). 4-Intro Satana. 9-Wendigo app.

10-Origin Tigra	0.60	1.20	3.00
Annual 1 (Summer, 1975)-Kane-a	0.40	0.80	2.00

MOON KNIGHT (See Marc Spector:... & Werewolf By Night #32)
Nov, 1980-No. 38, July, 1984
Marvel Comics Group

1-Sienkiewicz-c/a begins	0.80	1.60	4.00
2-34, 36-38: 25-Double size	0.30	0.60	1.50

35-(1.00, 52 pgs.)-X-Men app.	0.40	0.80	2.00

MOON KNIGHT (Also see Marvel Spotlight #28, 29)
June, 1985-No. 6, Dec, 1985
Marvel Comics Group

V2#1-6: 1-Double size; new costume	0.20	0.40	1.00

MOON KNIGHT SPECIAL EDITION
Nov, 1983-No. 3, Jan, 1984 (2.00, mini-series)
Marvel Comics Group

1-3: Hulk Mag-r	0.30	0.60	1.50

MOONSHADOW
May, 1985-No. 12, Feb, 1987 (1.50, adult)
Epic Comics (Marvel)

1	0.70	1.40	3.50
2–12	0.50	0.90	2.25
Trade Paperback (1987?)-Reprints	2.00	6.00	14.00

MOONSHADOW
Sept 1994-Aug 1995 (2.25, color, limited series:12)
DC Comics

1–11	0.50	0.90	2.25
12-(2.95)	0.60	1.20	3.00

MORBIUS: THE LIVING VAMPIRE
(See Amazing Spider-Man 101, Fear 20 & Vampire Tales)
Sept, 1992-Present (1.75/1.95, color)
Marvel Comics (Midnight Sons imprint #16 on)

1-(2.75, 52 pg.)-Polybagged w/full color poster; Ghost Rider,			
Johnny Blaze app.	1.00	1.70	4.00
2	0.50	1.00	2.50
3-5: 3,4-Vs. Spider-Man-c/story	0.40	0.80	2.00
6-11, 13-20: 15-Ghost Rider app. 16-Spot varnish-c. 16, 17-Siege of			
Darkness Pt. 5 & 13. 18-Deathlok app.	0.40	0.70	1.75
12-(2.25)-Outer-c is a Darkhold envelope made of black parchment			
w/gold ink; Midnight Massacre	0.50	0.90	2.25
21-24,26-32: 21-Begin 1.95-c; bound-in trading card sheet; Spider-Man app.			
	0.40	0.80	2.00
25-(2.50, 52 pgs.)-Gold foil logo	0.50	1.00	2.50

MORTAL KOMBAT
July, 1994-Present (2.95, color)

	Good	Fine	N-Mint
Malibu Comics			
1-6: 1-Two variant covers exist	0.60	1.20	3.00
1-Limited edition gold foil embossed -c	1.70	4.00	10.00
#0-(12/94)	0.60	1.20	3.00
...Special Edition 1 (11/94)	0.60	1.20	3.00
...Tournament Edition (12/94, 3.95)	0.80	1.60	4.00

MORTAL KOMBAT: BARAKA
June 1995-Present (2.95, color)
Malibu Comics

	Good	Fine	N-Mint
1	0.60	1.20	3.00

MORTAL KOMBAT: BATTLEWAVE
Feb 1995-Present (2.95, color)
Malibu Comics

	Good	Fine	N-Mint
1–5	0.60	1.20	3.00

MORTAL KOMBAT: GORO, PRINCE OF PAIN
Sept, 1994-Present (2.95, color)
Malibu Comics

	Good	Fine	N-Mint
1–3	0.60	1.20	3.00

MORTAL KOMBAT: RAYDON &KANO
Mar 1995-May 1995 (2.95, color, limited series:3)
Malibu Comics

	Good	Fine	N-Mint
1–3	0.60	1.20	3.00

MORTAL KOMBAT U.S. SPECIAL FORCES
Jan 1995- Feb 1995 (3.50, color, limited series)
Malibu Comics

	Good	Fine	N-Mint
1–2	0.70	1.40	3.50

MOTORHEAD SPECIAL (Also see Comic's Greatest World)
Mar, 1994 (3.95, color, one-shot, 52 pgs.)
Dark Horse Comics

	Good	Fine	N-Mint
1-Barb Wire, The Machine & Wolf Gang app.; Jae Lee-c	0.80	1.60	4.00

MS. CYANIDE & ICE
June, 1995-Present (2.95, B&W)
Blackout Comics

	Good	Fine	N-Mint
0-	0.70	1.20	3.00

MS. MARVEL
Jan, 1977-No. 23, Apr, 1979
Marvel Comics Group

1-1st app. Ms. Marvel	0.80	1.60	4.00
2-Origin	0.50	1.00	2.50
3-10: 10-Last 30¢ issue	0.40	0.70	1.80
11-23: 20-New costume	0.30	0.60	1.50
16–17 Mystique cameo	1.20	2.40	6.00
18-1st full Mystique	2.40	4.80	12.00

MUNSTERS, THE (TV)
Jan, 1965-No. 16, Jan, 1968
Gold Key

1 (#10134-501)-All have photo-c	21.00	64.00	150.00
2	11.00	32.00	75.00
3–5	7.90	24.00	55.00
6–16	6.90	21.00	48.00

MUSHMOUSE AND PUNKIN PUSS (TV)
Sept, 1965 (Hanna-Barbera)
Gold Key

10153-509 (#1)	8.00	24.00	48.00

MY FAVORITE MARTIAN (TV)
Jan, 1964, No. 2, July, 1964-No. 9, Oct, 1966
Gold Key (1, 3-9 have photo covers)

1-Russ Manning-a	15.00	50.00	105.00
2-No photo cover	7.10	21.00	50.00
3–9	6.00	18.00	42.00

MY GREATEST ADVENTURE (Becomes Doom Patrol No. 86 on)
Jan-Feb, 1955-No. 85, Feb, 1964
National Periodical Publications

1-Before CCA	94.00	282.00	845.00
2	45.00	135.00	405.00
3–5	28.00	85.00	255.00
6–10	23.00	68.00	205.00
11-15, 19	18.00	53.00	160.00
16-18, 20, 21, 28: Kirby art	16.00	47.00	140.00
22-27, 29, 30	11.00	32.00	95.00
31-40	8.00	25.00	75.00
41-57, 59	6.00	18.00	55.00
58, 60, 61: Toth art, 61-Last 10¢ issue	6.00	18.00	55.00

	Good	Fine	N-Mint
62-79: 77-Toth art	3.00	8.00	25.00
80-Intro/origin Doom Patrol (6/63). Doom Patrol series begins, ends #85			
	36.00	95.00	325.00
81-85: Doom Patrol. 81, 85-Toth art	13.00	36.00	120.00

MY NAME IS HOLOCAUST
May, 1995-Present (2.50, color)
DC Comics

1-4	0.50	1.00	2.50

MYSTERIES OF UNEXPLORED WORLDS (Becomes Son of Vulcan)
Aug, 1956; No. 2, Jan, 1957-No. 48, Sept, 1965
Charlton Comics

1	23.00	69.00	160.00
2-No Ditko-a	8.00	24.00	55.00
3, 4, 8, 9-Ditko-a	14.00	41.00	95.00
5, 6-Ditko-c/a (all)	16.00	47.00	110.00
7-(2/58, 68 pgs.)-Ditko-a(4 stories)	16.00	47.00	110.00
10-Ditko-c/a(4 stories)	16.00	47.00	110.00
11-Ditko-c/a(3); signed J. Kotdi	16.00	47.00	110.00
12, 19, 21-24, 26-Ditko-a	10.70	32.00	75.00
13-18, 20	3.00	9.40	22.00
25, 27-30	2.30	6.90	16.00
31-45	1.70	4.00	10.00
46-Son of Vulcan begins (origin & 1st app.)			
	2.40	7.30	17.00
47, 48	1.70	4.00	10.00

Note: Ditko c-3-6, 10, 11, 19, 21-24.

MYSTERIOUS SUSPENSE
October, 1968 (12¢)
Charlton Comics
1-Return of The Question by Steve Ditko-c/a

	4.00	12.00	28.00

MYSTERY IN SPACE
No. 53, 8/59-No. 110, 9/66, No. 11, 9/80-No. 117, 3/81
National Periodical Publications/DC Comics
53-Adam Strange begins (4th app., 8/59); see Showcase #17 for 1st app.

	93.00	279.00	1115.00
54	38.00	114.00	305.00
55-Grey-tone-c	24.00	71.00	190.00
56-60	18.00	53.00	140.00

61-71: 71-Last 10¢ issue	13.00	39.00	105.00
72-74, 76-80	9.00	26.00	68.00
75-JLA x-over (5/62)	23.00	68.00	180.00
81-86	5.00	16.00	42.00
87-Hawkman app. (11/63) (begin 3rd Hawkman tryout series)			
	19.00	57.00	152.00
88-Hawkman app.	15.00	46.00	122.00
89-Hawkman app.	14.00	42.00	112.00
90-(3/64)-Pre-dates Hawkman #1 by 1 month; 1st Adam Strange			
& Hawkman teamup	17.00	51.00	137.00
91-103: 92-101, 103: Space Ranger	2.40	7.30	17.00
104-110: 110-(9/66)-Last 12¢ issue	0.80	2.10	5.00
111-117: 111-(9/80)	0.60	1.20	3.00

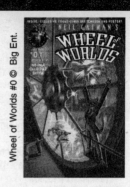

The Nam #79 © MEG

Wheel of Worlds #0 © Big Ent.

'NAM, THE	Good	Fine	N-Mint
Dec, 1986-No. 84, Sept, 1993			
Marvel Comics Group			
1	0.60	1.20	3.00
1-2nd printing	0.20	0.40	1.00
2	0.50	1.00	2.50
3–7	0.40	0.80	2.00
8-51, 54-64	0.30	0.60	1.50
52-Punisher app.	0.60	1.20	3.00
53-Punisher app.	0.40	0.80	2.00
52, 53-2nd printings	0.30	0.50	1.25
65-74, 76-84: 67-69: Punisher 3 part story		0.70	1.75
75-(2.25, 52 pgs.)	0.50	0.90	2.25
Trade Paperback 1-Reprints #1-4	0.90	1.80	4.50
Trade Paperback 2-Reprints #5-8	1.10	2.70	6.50

NAMOR, THE SUB-MARINER			
Apr, 1990-Present (1.00/1.25/1.50, color)			
Marvel Comics			
1-Byrne c/a-1-25; scripts 1-32	0.70	1.30	3.25
2–5	0.40	0.70	1.75
6-11: 8, 10-Re-intro Iron Fist (#8-cameo only)		0.30	0.60
1.50			
12-(1.50, 52 pgs.)-Re-intro The Invaders	0.40	0.80	2.00
13-22: 22-Last 1.00-c	0.20	0.40	1.00
23-25: 24-Namor vs Wolverine	0.30	0.50	1.25
26-Jae Lee-c/a begins (5/92), ends #40; 1st new costume & new look			
for Namor	1.00	2.50	6.00

27	0.90	1.80	4.50
28	0.80	1.60	4.00
29, 30: 28-Iron Fist app.	0.50	1.00	2.50
31-36, 38-49: 35-New Tiger Shark-c/story	0.30	0.50	1.25
37-(2.00)-Aqua holo-grafx foil-c	0.40	0.80	2.00
50-(2.95, 52 pgs.)-Collectors Edition w/foil-c; has bound-in Spider-Man			
trading card sheet (in both versions)	0.60	1.20	3.00
50-(1.75, 52 pgs.)-Newsstand Edition w/o foil			
	0.30	0.60	1.50
51-62: 51-Begin 1.50-c	0.30	0.60	1.50
Annual 1 ('91, 2.00)-3 pg. origin recap	0.40	0.80	2.00
Annual 2 ('92, 2.25)-New Defenders pt. 2	0.50	0.90	2.25
Annual 3 ('93, 2.95)-Polybagged w/card	0.60	1.20	3.00
Annual 4 ('94, 2.95, 68 pgs.)-Painted-c	0.60	1.20	3.00

NATURE BOY (Formerly Danny Blaze)
No. 3, March, 1956-No. 5, Feb, 1957
Charlton Comics

3-Origin Nature Boy; Blue Beetle story	16.00	49.00	115.00
4, 5: 4-Powell-a; Buscema-c/a in all	13.00	39.00	90.00

NAZA (Stone Age Warrior)
Nov-Jan, 1963-64-No. 9, March, 1966
Dell Publishing Co.

12-555-401 (#1)-Painted-c	2.10	6.40	15.00
2-9: 2-4-Painted-c	1.70	4.20	10.00

NEIL GAIMAN'S LADY JUSTICE
Sep 1995-Present (1.95/2.25, color)
Tekno•Comix

1-(2.25)-Sienkiewicz-c, pin-ups	0.40	0.90	2.25
1-(1.95)-Brereton-c	0.30	0.80	2.00

NEIL GAIMAN'S MR. HERO-THE NEWMATIC MAN
Mar, 1995-Present (1.95, color)
Tekno•Comixs
1-4:1-Intro Teknophage; bound-in game piece and trading card
4-w/Steel edition Teknophage #1 coupon; 5-7

	0.40	0.80	2.00

NEIL GAIMAN'S TEKNOPHAGE
Aug, 1995-Present (1.95, color)
Tekno•Comix

	Good	Fine	N-Mint
1–3	0.40	0.80	2.00
1–Steel Edition	1.00	2.00	5.00

NEIL GAIMAN'S WHEEL OF WORLDS
Apr, 1995-Present (2.95, color, 48 pgs.)
Tekno•Comix

| 0- 48 pgs., bound-in poster | 0.60 | 1.20 | 3.00 |
| 0–Regular edition | 0.40 | 0.80 | 2.00 |

NEUTRO
Jan, 1967
Dell Publishing Co.

| 1-Jack Sparling-c/a (super hero) | 2.40 | 7.30 | 17.00 |

NEW ADVENTURES OF CHARLIE CHAN, THE (TV)
May-June, 1958-No. 6, Mar-Apr, 1959
National Periodical Publ.

1-(Scarce)-Gil Kane/Sid Greene-a	47.00	141.00	375.00
2-(Scarce)	44.00	131.00	350.00
3-6-(Scarce)-Greene/Giella-a	26.00	77.00	205.00

NEW ADVENTURES OF HUCK FINN, THE (TV)
Dec, 1968 (Hanna-Barbera)
Gold Key

| 1-"The Curse of Thut"; part photo-c | 3.40 | 8.50 | 17.00 |

NEW ADVENTURES OF SPEED RACER
Dec, 1993-Present (1.95, color)
Now Comics

| 1–7 | 0.40 | 0.80 | 2.00 |
| 0-(Premiere)-3-D cover | 0.80 | 1.60 | 4.00 |

NEW GODS (See 1st Issue Special #13)
2-3/71-V2#11, 10/72; V3#12, 7/77-V3#19, 7-8/78
DC Comics

1-Darkseid cameo (3rd app., ties with Forever People #1); intro/1st app.

Orion; Kirby-c/a in #s 1-11	6.00	18.00	42.00
2-Darkseid-c/story; 2nd full app.	3.10	9.40	22.00
3-Last 15¢ issue	2.30	7.00	16.00

4-9: 52 pg. giants. 7-Darkseid app. (2-3/72); origin Orion

| | 1.70 | 5.10 | 12.00 |
| 10, 11 | 1.70 | 4.20 | 10.00 |

12-19: Darkseid storyline w/minor apps. 19-Story cont'd in Adventure

Comics #459, 460 one month later	1.00	2.00	5.00

NEW GODS
May, 1984-No. 6, Nov, 1984 (2.00, Baxter paper)
DC Comics

1-New Kirby-c; r/New Gods 1&2	0.40	0.80	2.00
2-6: 6-New art by Kirby	0.40	0.80	2.00

NEW GODS
Feb, 1989-No. 28, Aug, 1991 (1.50, color)
DC Comics

1–28	0.30	0.60	1.50

NEWMEN
Apr, 1994-Present (1.95, color)
Image Comics

1-5-Matsuda-c/a: 1-Liefeld/Matsuda plot	0.40	0.80	2.00
6-14-(2.50, 9/94) 10-Polybagged w/trading card			
11-Polybagged	0.50	1.00	2.50

NEW MUTANTS, THE
March, 1983-No. 100, April, 1991
Marvel Comics Group

1	1.10	2.70	6.50
2, 3: 3,4-Ties into X-Men #167	0.80	1.50	3.75
4–10	0.60	1.20	3.00
11-17, 19, 20: 16-1st app. Warpath (w/o costume)			
	0.50	1.00	2.50
18-Intro new Warlock	1.30	3.00	7.50
21-Double size; origin new Warlock	0.90	2.30	5.50
22-24, 28-30	0.50	1.00	2.50
25-Legion app. (cameo)	1.60	3.20	8.00
26-Legion app. (1st full)	2.00	4.00	10.00
27, 28-Legion app.	1.00	2.00	5.00
31-58: 43-Portacio-i. 44-Legion 50-(52 pgs.)			
	0.40	0.80	2.00
59-Fall Of The Mutants begins, ends #61	0.70	1.40	3.50
60-(1.25, double size)	0.50	1.00	2.50
61-Fall Of The Mutants ends	0.40	0.80	2.00
62, 64-72, 74-85: 85-Liefeld-c	0.30	0.50	1.25
63-X-Men, Wolverine app.	0.70	1.40	3.50
73-(1.50, double size)	0.40	0.80	2.00
86-Liefeld-c/a begins; Cable cameo	1.70	5.00	12.00

	Good	Fine	N-Mint
87-Intro/1st full app. of Cable (3/90)	6.00	17.00	40.00
87-2nd printing; metallic ink-c	0.30	0.60	1.50
88-2nd Cable	2.10	6.40	15.00
89-3rd Cable	1.70	5.00	12.00
90, 91-Sabretooth app.	1.60	4.70	11.00
92-Liefeld-c only	0.90	1.80	4.50
93, 94: Wolverine vs. Cable	1.70	5.00	12.00
95-97: X-Tinction Agenda	1.60	4.70	11.00
95-Gold 2nd printing	0.50	1.00	2.50
98-1st app. Deadpool, Gideon, & Domino	1.90	5.60	13.00
99-1st app. Feral of X-Force	1.20	3.00	7.00
100-(1.50, 52 pgs.)-1st app. X-Force	1.10	2.70	6.50
100-Gold 2nd printing (1.50)	0.60	1.20	3.00
100-Silver ink 3rd printing (1.50)	0.30	0.60	1.50
Annual 1 ('84)	0.60	1.20	3.00
Annual 2 ('86)-1st Psylocke	0.60	1.20	3.00
Annual 3 ('87, 1.25)	0.40	0.70	1.80
Annual 4 ('88, 1.75)-Evolutionary War	0.40	0.80	2.00
Annual 5 ('89)-1st Liefeld-c/a on New Mutants			
	2.00	6.00	14.00
Annual 6 ('90, 2.00)-1st app. (cameo) of Shatterstar of X-Force; 1st			
app. new costumes by Liefeld (3 pgs.)	0.40	0.80	2.00
Annual 7 ('91, 2.00)-No Liefeld-a; 2nd app. X-Force cont'd in New			
Warriors Annual #1	0.40	0.80	2.00
...nn ('82, 5.95, TPB)	1.00	2.50	6.00
Special 1 (1985)-Art Adams/Austin-a	1.00	2.00	5.00
Summer Special 1-('90, 2.95)	0.60	1.20	3.00

NEW ORDER, THE
Nov, 1994 (2.95, color)
CFD Publishing

1	0.60	1.20	3.00

NEW SHADOWHAWK, THE
June, 1995 (2.50, color)
Image Comics

1-Busiek scripts	0.50	1.00	2.50

NEW TEEN TITANS, THE (Becomes Tales of the Teen Titans 41 on)
Nov, 1980-No. 40, Mar, 1984
DC Comics

1-Partial origin; Perez-c/a begins	1.70	4.00	10.00
2-1st app. Deathstroke The Terminator (c/sty)			

	2.00	6.00	14.00
3-9: 4-Origin Starfire. 6-Raven origin	0.90	1.70	4.25
10-2nd full app. Deathstroke The Terminator; see Marvel & DC Present			
for 3rd app.	1.40	3.50	8.50
11–20	0.30	0.60	1.50
21-30: 23-1st app. Vigilante (not in costume)			
	0.20	0.50	1.20
31-33, 35-38, 40	0.20	0.40	1.00
34-4th app. Deathstroke (c/story)	0.80	1.50	3.75
39-Last Dick Grayson as Robin	0.40	0.80	2.00
Annual 1 (11/82)-Omega Men app.	0.30	0.60	1.40
Annual 2 (9/83)-1st Vigilante in costume	0.40	0.70	1.75

NEW TEEN TITANS, THE (Becomes The New Titans No. 50)
Aug, 1984-No. 49, Nov, 1988
DC Comics

1-Perez-c/a begins	0.80	1.60	4.00
2, 3	0.50	1.00	2.50
4–10	0.40	0.70	1.80
11–19	0.20	0.50	1.20
20-Robin (Jason Todd) joins	0.40	0.80	2.00
21-39: 37-Begin 1.75-c	0.30	0.60	1.40
40-49: 47-Origin each Titan member	0.30	0.60	1.40
Annual 1 (9/85)	0.40	0.80	2.00
Annual 2 (8/86, 2.50)-Byrne-c/a	0.50	1.00	2.50
Annual 3 (11/87, 2.25)	0.40	0.80	2.00
Annual 4 ('88, 2.50)	0.50	0.90	2.25

NEW TITANS, THE (Formerly New Teen Titans)
No. 50, Dec, 1988-Present (1.75/1.95, color)

New Teen Titans #38 © DC

Nexus #16 © M. Baron and S. Rude

	Good	Fine	N-Mint
DC Comics			
50-Perez-c/a begins	0.80	1.60	4.00
51-59	0.50	0.90	2.25
60-New Robin tie-in	0.90	2.30	5.50
61	0.80	1.50	3.75
62-65: Deathstroke-s	1.00	1.90	4.75
66-69, 71: 71-Deathstroke (cameo)	0.60	1.10	2.75
70-1st Deathstroke solo-c/story	0.60	1.20	3.00
72-79: Deathstroke-s in all. 74-Intro Pantha. 79-1st app. Team Titans			
in 1 panel cameo	0.60	1.20	3.00
80-99, 101-111: 80-2nd app. Team Titans	0.40	0.70	1.75
100-(3.50, 52 pgs.)-Holo-grafx foil-c	0.70	1.40	3.50
112-114: 112-Begin 1.95-c. 114-(9/94)	0.40	0.80	2.00
0,115-121: 0-(10/94). 115-(11/94)	0.40	0.80	2.00
122-begin 2.25-c; 123–124	0.50	0.90	2.25
Annual 5-9 ('89-'93, 3.50, 68 pgs.): 7-1st full app. new team Teen			
Titans. 8-Deathstroke app.	0.70	1.40	3.50
Annual 10 ('94, 3.50)-Elseworlds story	0.70	1.40	3.50

NEW TWO-FISTED TALES, THE
1993 (4.95, color, 52 pgs.)
Dark Horse Comics/Byron Preiss

1-Kurtzman-r & new-a	1.00	2.00	5.00

NEW WARRIORS, THE (See Thor #411, 412)
July, 1990-Present (1.00/1.25/1.50, color)
Marvel Comics

1	1.10	3.40	8.00
1-Gold 2nd printing (7/91)	0.60	1.10	2.75
2	0.70	2.10	5.00
3–5	0.70	2.00	4.00
6, 7, 10: 7-Punisher cameo (last page)	0.60	1.20	3.00
8, 9-Punisher app.	0.70	1.70	4.00
11-14: 14-Darkhawk x-over	0.50	0.90	2.25
15-19: 19-Last 1.00-c	0.30	0.50	1.25
20-24, 26-46: 31-Cannonball & Warpath app.			
	0.30	0.50	1.25
25-(2.50, 52 pgs.)-Die-cut-c	0.50	1.00	2.50
40-(2.25)-Gold foil collector's ed.	0.50	0.90	2.25
47-49,51-59, 61–: 47-Begin 1.50-c; bound-in trading card sheet.			
52-32 pgs. plus 12 pg. ad insert	0.30	0.60	1.50
50-(2.95, 52 pgs.)-Glow in the dark-c	0.60	1.20	3.00
60-(2.50)	0.50	1.00	2.50

Annual 1 ('91, 2.00, 68 pgs.)-3rd app. X-Force, cont'd from New
   Mutants Annual #7; origins of all members

	0.90	1.80	4.50
Annual 2 ('92, 2.25)	0.50	0.90	2.25
Annual 3 ('93, 2.95)-Polybagged w/card	0.60	1.20	3.00
Annual 4 ('94, 2.95)	0.60	1.20	3.00

NEXUS
June, 1981-No. 80, May, 1991
Capital Comics/First Comics

1-Magazine size	1.60	5.00	11.00
1-Limited edition	2.30	6.90	16.00
2-Magazine size	1.10	3.00	6.50
3-Magazine size	0.80	1.50	3.75
V2#1	0.60	1.20	3.00
2-80: 50-(3.50, squarebound)	0.40	0.80	2.00

NEXUS: ALIEN JUSTICE
Dec, 1992-No. 3, Feb, 1993 (3.95, color, mini-series)
Dark Horse Comics

1-3: Rude-c/a	0.80	1.60	4.00

NEXUS: THE WAGES OF SIN
Mar, 1995-Present (2.95, color, limited series:4)
Dark Horse Comics

1–3	0.60	1.20	3.00

NICK FURY, AGENT OF SHIELD (See Fury, S.H.I.E.L.D. & Strange Tales #135)
June, 1968-No. 15, Nov, 1969; No. 16, Nov, 1970-No. 18, Mar, 1971
Marvel Comics Group

1-Steranko covers 1-7, interiors 1-3, 5	6.40	19.00	45.00
2-4: 4-Origin retold	3.10	9.40	22.00
5-Classic cover	4.00	12.00	28.00
6, 7	2.10	6.40	15.00
8-11, 13: 13-Last 12¢ issue	1.20	2.90	7.00
12-Smith c/a	1.50	3.80	9.00
14	0.90	1.80	4.50
15-Last new story; death of Bullseye (11/69)	3.90	12.00	27.00
16-18: All-r/Strange Tales #135-143	0.50	1.00	2.50

NICK FURY, AGENT OF SHIELD
Dec, 1983-No. 2, Jan, 1984
Marvel Comics Group

	Good	Fine	N-Mint

Ninjak #2 © Acclaim

Nick Fury #6 © MEG

	Good	Fine	N-Mint
1, 2-Reprints; Steranko-c/a	0.40	0.80	2.00

NICK FURY, AGENT OF SHIELD
V2#1, Sept., 1989-No. 47, May, 1993 (1.50/1.75, color)
Marvel Comics

V2#1-26: 20-Guice-c/a begins	0.30	0.60	1.50
27-29: Wolverine-c/story	0.40	0.80	2.00
30-47: 30, 31-Deathlok-c/story. 32-Begin 1.75-c. 46-Gideon (of X-Force) app.	0.40	0.70	1.75

NICK FURY VS. S.H.I.E.L.D.
June, 1988-No. 6, Nov, 1988 (3.50, color, deluxe format)
Marvel Comics Group

1	1.10	2.70	6.50
2	1.30	3.00	7.50
3–6	0.70	1.30	3.25

NIGHT BEFORE CHRISTMASK, THE
Nov 1994 (9.95, color, one shot)
Dark Horse Comics

NN-Hardcover book Rick Geary/a	1.70	4.20	10.00

NIGHTCRAWLER (See X-Men)
Nov, 1985-No. 4, Feb, 1986 (Mini-series)
Marvel Comics Group

1	0.50	1.00	2.50
2–4	0.40	0.70	1.75

NIGHT GLIDER
April, 1993 (2.95, color, one-shot)

Topps Comics
1-Polybagged w/Kirbychrome trading card 0.60   1.20   3.00

NIGHT MAN, THE (See Sludge #1)
Oct, 1993-Present (1.95, color)
Malibu Comics (Ultraverse)
1-(2.50, 48 pgs)-Rune Flip-c/sty by B. Smith

	0.50	1.00	2.50
1-Ultra Limited silver foil-c	2.00	6.00	14.00

2-15, 17: 3-Break-Thru x-over; Freex app. 4-Origin Firearm by Chaykin
(2 pgs). 6-TNTNT app. 8-1st app. Teknight

	0.40	0.80	2.00
16-(3.50)-Flip book Ultraverse Premiere #11			
	0.70	1.40	3.50
....:The Pilgrim Conundrum Saga (1/95,3.95, 68 pgs) Strangers app.			
	0.80	1.60	4.00
18-21	0.50	1.00	2.50

NIGHTMARE
Dec 1994- Mar 1995 (1.95, color, limited series)
Marvel Comics
1-4   0.40   0.80   2.00

NIGHT RIDER
Oct, 1974- No. 6, Aug, 1975
Marvel Comics Group
1: 1-6-r/Ghost Rider 1-6 from '67   0.40   0.80   2.00
2–6   0.30   0.50   1.25

NIGHTSTALKERS (See Midnight Sons Unlimited)
Nov, 1992-Present (1.75, color)
Marvel Comics (Midnight Sons imprint #14 on)
1-(2.75, 52 pgs.)-Polybagged w/poster; Hannibal King, Blade & Frank Drake
begin (see Tomb of Dracula & Dr. Strange)0.60   1.10   2.75
2-9, 11-18: 7-Ghost Rider. 8, 9-Morbius. 14-Spot varnish-c. 14, 15-"Siege
of Darkness" Pt. 1 & 9   0.40   0.70   1.75
10-(2.25)-Outer-c is a Darkhold envelope made of black parchment
w/gold ink; Midnight Massacre part 1   0.50   0.90   2.25

NIGHT THRASHER
Aug, 1993-Apr 1995 (1.75/1.95, color)
Marvel Comics
1-(2.95, 52 pgs.)-Red Holo-grafx-c; origin 0.60   1.20   3.00

	Good	Fine	N-Mint
2-9-(1.75): 2-Intro Tantrum. 3-Gideon app.	0.40	0.70	1.75
10-21: 10-Begin 1.95-c; bound-in card sheet. 15-Hulk-c & app.			
21-Final issue	0.40	0.80	2.00

NIGHT THRASHER: FOUR CONTROL
Oct, 1992-No. 4, Jan, 1993 (2.00, color, mini-series)
Marvel Comics

1-New Warriors character	0.50	1.00	2.50
2–4	0.40	0.80	2.00

NIGHTWATCH
Apr, 1994 - Mar 1995 (1.50, color)
Marvel Comics

1-(2.95)-Collectors ed.; foil-c; Ron Lim-c/a begins; Spider-Man app.

	Good	Fine	N-Mint
	0.60	1.20	3.00
1-(1.50)-Regular ed.; Spider-Man app.	0.30	0.60	1.50

2-6: 2-Bound-in Spider-Man trading card sheet. 5,6-Venom-c & app.

	0.30	0.60	1.50
7-12: 7,11-Cardiac app.	0.30	0.60	1.50

NIGHTWING: ALFRED'S RETURN
July 1995-Present (3.50, color)
DC Comics

1–	0.70	1.40	3.50

1963
Apr, 1993-No. 6, Oct, 1993 (1.95, color, mini-series)
Image Comics

1-6-Alan Moore scripts, Veitch-p	0.40	0.80	2.00
1-Gold ed.	2.00	4.00	10.00

NINJAK (See Bloodshot #6, 7 & Deathmate)
Feb, 1994-Present (2.25, color)
Valiant

1-(3.50)-Chromium wraparound-c by Quesada

	Good	Fine	N-Mint
	0.70	1.40	3.50
1–Gold	2.00	4.00	10.00

2-14: Quesada c/a(p)1-3. 3-Batman, Spawn & Random (from X-Factor)
   app. as costumes at party (cameo). 4-w/bound-in trading card.
    12-Sneak peek card 5,6-X-O app. 13-Chromium Bloodshot card

	Good	Fine	N-Mint
	0.50	0.90	2.25
15-24-(2.50)	0.50	1.00	2.50
#0-(6/95)	0.50	1.00	2.50

#00-(2.50, 6/95)	0.50	1.00	2.50
Yearbook 1 ('94, 3.95)	0.80	1.60	4.00

NIRA X: CYBERANGEL
Dec 1994 (2.95, color)
Entity Comics

1-Foil logo	0.60	1.20	3.00
2–4-(2.50)	0.50	1.00	2.50
4-(6.95)-bagged with PC Game	1.40	2.80	7.00

NOCTURNALS, THE
Jan 1995-Present (2.95, color, limited series:6)
Bravura/Malibu

1-4-D.Brereton s/a	0.60	1.20	3.00
1-Glow-In-The-Dark -Premium Edition	1.40	4.30	10.00

NOCTURNE
Jun 1995-Present (1.50, color)
Marvel Comics

1	0.20	0.60	1.50

NOMAD (See Capt. America #180)
Nov, 1990-No. 4, Feb, 1991 (1.50, color, limited series)
Marvel Comics

1–4	0.30	0.60	1.50

NOMAD
V2#1, May, 1992-No. 25, May, 1994 (1.75, color)
Marvel Comics

V2#1-(2.00)-Gatefold-c w/map/poster	0.60	1.20	3.00
2-5: 4-Deadpool x-over. 5-Punisher battles Nomad			
	0.40	0.80	2.00
6-25: 7-Gambit-c/story. 10-Red Wolf app. 21-Man-Thing-c/story.			
25-Bound-in trading card sheet	0.40	0.70	1.75

NOMAN (See Thunder Agents)
Nov, 1966-No. 2, March, 1967 (25¢, 68 pgs.)
Tower Comics

1-Wood/Williamson-c	6.00	17.00	40.00
2-Wood-c	4.30	12.90	30.00

NORMALMAN
Jan, 1984-No. 12, Dec, 1985 (1.70/2.00, color)

	Good	Fine	N-Mint

Aardvark-Vanaheim/Renegade Press #6 on

1-5-(1.70)-Jim Valentino-c/a in all	0.30	0.70	1.70

6-12-(2.00, B&W): 10-Cerebus cameo; Dave Sim-a (2 pgs.)

	0.40	0.80	2.00

NORMALMAN-MEGATON MAN SPECIAL
Aug, 1994 (2.50, color, one-shot)
Image Comics

1	0.50	1.00	2.50

NORTHSTAR
Apr, 1994-No. 4, July 1994 (1.75, color, mini-series)
Marvel Comics

1-4-Character from Alpha Flight	0.40	0.70	1.75

NOT BRAND ECHH
Aug, 1967-No. 13, May, 1969
Marvel Comics Group

1	3.90	12.00	27.00
2-8: 8-Last 12¢ issue	2.00	6.00	14.00
9-13: 25¢ giants	2.10	6.00	15.00

NOVA
Sept, 1976-No. 25, May, 1979
Marvel Comics Group

1-Origin/1st app. Nova	0.80	2.10	5.00
2-11: 4-Thor x-over	0.50	1.00	2.50
12-Spider-Man x-over	0.80	1.60	4.00

13-25: 14-Last 30¢ issue. 19-Wally West (Kid Flash) cameo

	0.30	0.60	1.60

NOVA
Jan, 1994-June, 1995 (1.75, color)
Marvel Comics

1-(2.95, 52 pgs.)-Collectors Edition Foil-c	0.60	1.20	3.00
1-(2.25, 52 pgs.)-Newsstand Edition	0.50	0.90	2.25
2-4: 3-Spider-Man-c/story	0.40	0.70	1.75

5-18: 5-Begin 1.95-c; bound-in card sheet. 13-Firestar & Night Thrasher app.

14-Darkhawk & New Warriors app.	0.40	0.80	2.00

NTH MAN (See Marvel Comics Presents #25)
Aug, 1989-No. 16, Sept, 1990 (1.00, color)
Marvel Comics

1-7, 9-16	0.20	0.40	1.00
8-1st Keown-a at Marvel (1/90)	0.90	1.80	4.50

NUCLEUS (Also see Cerebus)
May, 1979 (1.50, B&W, adult fanzine)
Hero-Graphic Publications

1-Contains Demonhorn by Dave Sim; early app. of Cerebus the Aardvark, 4-pg. story	4.00	12.00	28.00

NUKLA
Oct-Dec, 1965-No. 4, Sept, 1966
Dell Publishing

1-Origin & 1st app. Nukla (super hero)	3.00	9.40	22.00
2, 3	1.70	5.10	12.00
4-Ditko-c(p)/a	3.10	9.00	22.00

Nocturnals #2 © Danial Brereton

Omac #3 © DC

	Good	Fine	N-Mint
OCCULT FILES OF DR. SPECKTOR, THE			
Apr, 1973-No. 24, Feb, 1977; No. 25, May, 1982			
Gold Key/Whitman No. 25			
1-1st app. Lakota; Baron Tibor begins	1.50	3.80	9.00
2–5	0.90	1.80	4.50
6-10: 8-Dracula app.	0.60	1.20	3.00
11-13, 15-25: 11-1st app. Spektor as Werewolf. 25-Reprints			
	0.50	1.00	2.50
14-Dr. Solar app.	1.00	2.50	6.00
9-Modern Comics reprint ('77)	0.30	0.60	1.50
OH MY GODDESS!			
Aug, 1994- Jan 1995 (2.50, B&W, limited series)			
Dark Horse Comics			
1–6	0.50	1.00	2.50
OH MY GODDESS! PART II			
Feb 1995-Present (2.50, B&W, limited series:8)			
Dark Horse Comics			
1-5	0.50	1.00	2.50
OMAC (One Man Army...Corps. #4 on)			
Sept-Oct, 1974-No. 8, Nov-Dec, 1975			
National Periodical Publications			
1-Origin; Kirby art in all	1.70	4.20	10.00
2–8	1.00	2.00	5.00
OMEGA MEN, THE (See Green Lantern #141)			
Dec, 1982-No. 38, May, 1986			
DC Comics			
1	0.30	0.60	1.50
2, 4, 6-8, 11-18	0.20	0.40	1.00
3-(6/83)-1st app. Lobo (5 pgs. + cover)	1.30	3.30	8.00
5, 9-Lobo cameo (2 pgs. each)	0.60	1.20	3.00
10-1st full Lobo story	1.30	3.30	8.00
19-Lobo app. (cameo)	0.30	0.60	1.50
20-2nd full Lobo story	1.00	1.90	4.75
21-36, 38	0.20	0.40	1.00
37-1st solo Lobo story (8 pgs.)	0.60	1.10	2.75
Annual 1, 2 (11/84, 11/85)	0.30	0.60	1.50

OMEGA THE UNKNOWN
Mar, 1976-No. 10, Oct, 1977
Marvel Comics Group

1-1st app.	0.60	1.20	3.00
2-7, 10: 2-Hulk-c/story. 3-Electro-c/story	0.40	0.70	1.80
8-Foolkiller cameo (Greg Salinger)	0.60	1.20	3.00
9-1st full app. 2nd Foolkiller	0.80	1.60	4.00

OMEN
1989-No. 3? (2.00, B&W, adult)
Northstar Publ.

1-Tim Vigil-c/a	1.30	3.00	7.50
1-2nd printing	0.50	0.90	2.25
2, 3	0.60	1.10	2.75

OMNI COMIX
Mar 1995-Present (2.95, color)
Omni Publications

1-Luis Royo-c	0.60	1.20	3.00

ONYX OVERLORD
Oct, 1992-No. 4, Jan, 1993 (2.75, color, mini-series)
Epic Comics (Marvel)

1-4: Moebius scripts	0.60	1.10	2.75

OPERATION: KNIGHTSTRIKE
May 1995-Present (2.50, color)
Image Comics

1	0.50	1.00	2.50

ORIGINAL SHIELD, THE
Apr, 1984-No. 4, Oct, 1984
Archie Enterprises, Inc.

1-4: 1, 2-Origin Shield; Ayers-a(p) in all	0.20	0.40	1.00

OTHERS, THE
Mar, 1995 (2.50, color)
Image Comics

#0-(1.00)-16 page preview	0.20	0.40	1.00
1-2	0.50	1.00	2.50

OUR ARMY AT WAR
No. 81, Apr, 1959-No. 301, Feb, 1977

	Good	Fine	N-Mint
National Periodical Publ./DC Comics			
81-1st app. Sgt. Rock	125.00	374.00	1245.00
82-Sgt. Rock cameo (6 panels)	39.00	118.00	315.00
83-1st Kubert Sgt. Rock	51.00	153.00	510.00
84, 86-90: 84 Kubert-c	18.00	53.00	140.00
85-Origin Ice Cream Soldier	19.00	58.00	155.00
91-All Sgt Rock iss;Grandenetti-c Kubert-a	39.00	118.00	355.00
92-100: 95-1st app. Bulldozer	10.00	30.00	90.00
101-120: 111-1st app. Sunny. 115-Rock revealed as orphan; 1st x-over			
Mlle Marie	6.00	17.00	45.00
121-127, 129-150: 140-All Sgt. Rock issue	3.00	9.00	25.00
128-Training & origin Sgt. Rock	16.00	47.00	125.00
151-Intro Enemy Ace by Kubert (2/65)	19.40	58.00	155.00
152, 154, 156, 157, 159-163, 165-170	3.00	8.00	22.00
153-2nd app. Enemy Ace	8.00	25.00	67.00
155-3rd app. Enemy Ace (see Showcase)	4.00	11.00	29.00
158-1st app. & intro Iron Major	3.00	9.00	25.00
164-Giant G-19	5.00	14.00	37.00
171-176, 178-181	1.90	5.60	13.00
177-Giant G-32	3.90	12.00	27.00
182, 183, 186-Adams art	2.10	6.00	15.00
184, 185, 187-189, 191-199: 186-Origin	1.50	3.80	9.00
190-Giant G-44	2.80	7.00	17.00
200-12 pg. Rock story told in verse	1.70	5.00	12.00
201-Krigstein-r/#14	1.30	3.00	7.50
202, 204-215: 204, 205-All-r	0.90	2.00	5.50
203-Giant G-56; all-r; no Sgt. Rock	1.50	4.00	9.00
216, 229-Giants G-68 & G-80	1.20	2.90	7.00
217-228, 230-239, 241	1.00	1.90	4.75
240-Adams art	1.00	2.50	6.00
242 (DC-9)	1.00	2.50	6.00
243-301: 280-200th app. Sgt. Rock (r/#81, 83)			
	0.90	1.80	4.50

OUR FIGHTING FORCES
Oct-Nov, 1954 -No. 181, Sept-Oct, 1978
National Periodical Publ./DC Comics

1	49.00	146.00	485.00
2	27.00	82.00	245.00
3-Kubert-c	25.00	75.00	225.00
4, 5	18.00	53.00	160.00
6–9	15.00	44.00	132.00
10-Wood-a	16.00	47.00	140.00

11-20: 20-Grey-tone-c (4/57)	11.00	33.00	100.00
21-30: 26-30 Kubert-c	8.00	24.00	65.00
31-40	9.00	26.00	60.00
41-Unknown Soldier tryout story	10.00	30.00	70.00
42-44	7.10	21.00	50.00
45-Gunner & Sarge begin	24.00	73.00	170.00
46	11.00	32.00	75.00
47	7.00	22.00	52.00
48,50	5.10	15.00	36.00
49-1st Pooch	9.00	26.00	60.00
51-64: 51-Grey-tone-c. 64-Last 10¢ issue	4.30	12.90	30.00
65-70	3.00	9.00	21.00
71-80: 71-Grey-tone-c	1.90	5.60	13.00
81-90	2.00	5.00	12.00
91-100: 99-Capt. Hunter begins, ends #106			
	1.30	3.30	8.00
101-181: 123-Losers series begins. 151-162 Kirby art			
	1.20	2.40	6.00

OUTBREED 999
May, 1994-Present (2.95, color)
Blackout Comics

1-6: 4-Ist app. Extreme Violet in 7 pg. backup story			
	0.60	1.20	3.00

OUTER LIMITS, THE (TV)
Jan-Mar, 1964-No. 18, Oct, 1969 (All painted-c)
Dell Publishing Co.

1	6.60	20.00	46.00
2	3.60	10.70	25.00
3-10	2.40	7.30	17.00
11-18: 17-Reprints #1. 18-r/#2	2.00	6.00	14.00

OUTLAW KID, THE
Aug, 1970-No. 30, Oct, 1975
Marvel Comics Group

1, 2-Reprints. 1-Wildey-r(3)	0.80	1.60	4.00
3, 9-Williamson-r	0.40	0.80	2.00
4-8: 8-Crandall-r	0.40	0.80	2.00
10-30: 10-Origin; new-a in #10-16	0.40	0.70	1.80

OUT OF THE VORTEX(Comics' Greatest World:... #1-4)
Oct, 1993-No. 12, Oct, 1994 (2.00, color)

	Good	Fine	N-Mint
Dark Horse Comics			
1-11: Foil logo. 6-Hero Zero x-over	0.40	0.80	2.00
12-(2.50)	0.50	1.00	2.50

OUTSIDERS
Nov, 1993-Present (1.75/1.95, color)
DC Comics

	Good	Fine	N-Mint
1-Alpha; Travis Charest-c(p)	0.40	0.70	1.75
1-Omega; Travis Charest-c(p)	0.40	0.70	1.75
2-9: 5-Atomic Knight app. 8-New Batman-c/s			
	0.40	0.70	1.75
10,11: 10-Begin 1.95-c. 11-(9/94)-Zero Hour			
	0.40	0.80	2.00
0,12-18: 0-(10/94). 12-(11/94). 13-Superman-c & app.			
	0.40	0.80	2.00
19-begin 2.25-c; 20–21; 21-Darkseid cameo			
	0.50	0.90	2.25

OWL, THE
April, 1967; No. 2, April, 1968 ('40s hero revived from Crackajack & Popular)
Gold Key

	Good	Fine	N-Mint
1, 2-Super hero; written by Jerry Siegel	3.00	9.00	21.00

OZ
1994-Present (2.95, B&W)
Caliber Press

	Good	Fine	N-Mint
1–7	0.60	1.20	3.00
1-(5.95) Limited edition double-c	1.00	2.50	6.00

OZ SQUAD
Dec, 1995 (2.95, B&W, 52 pgs.)
Patchwork Press

	Good	Fine	N-Mint
1-(3.95)	0.70	1.70	4.00
2–6	0.50	1.30	3.00

OZ SQUAD
1992-No. 3, 1992 (2.50, B&W)
Brave New Words
No. 4, 1994 (2.75, B&W)
Patchwork Press

	Good	Fine	N-Mint
1–3	0.50	1.00	2.50
4	0.60	1.10	2.75

Pacific Comics Presents #1 © Dave Stevens

Penthouse Comix #3 © Gen. Media

PACIFIC PRESENTS
Oct, 1982-No. 4, June, 1984 (Color)
Pacific Comics
1-Rocketeer by Dave Stevens (Ch. 3); Ditko-a

| | 0.80 | 2.10 | 5.00 |

2-Rocketeer by Dave Stevens (Ch. 4); Ditko-a

| | 0.80 | 1.60 | 4.00 |
| 3, 4: 3-Ditko-a | 0.40 | 0.80 | 2.00 |

PACT, THE
Feb, 1994-No. 3, June, 1994 (1.95, color, limited series)
Image Comics
1-3-Super group; Valentino co-scripts & layouts

| | 0.40 | 0.80 | 2.00 |

PARADOX
June, 1994-Present (2.95, B&W, mature)
Dark Visions Publishing

| 1-Linsner-c | 1.00 | 2.00 | 5.00 |
| 2-Boris-c | 1.00 | 2.00 | 5.00 |

PARTRIDGE FAMILY, THE (TV)
Mar, 1971-No. 21, Dec, 1973
Charlton Comics

1	2.40	7.00	17.00
2-4, 6-21	1.20	3.00	7.00
5-(52 pgs.)-Summer Special; Shadow, Lone Ranger, Charlie McCarthy,			
Flash Gordon, Hopalong Cassidy, others	2.40	7.30	17.00

	Good	Fine	N-Mint

PAUL THE SAMURAI (See The Tick #4)
July, 1992-No. 6, July, 1993 (2.75, B&W)
New England Comics

	Good	Fine	N-Mint
1-(7/92)	0.60	1.20	3.00
2–6	0.60	1.10	2.75

PEACEMAKER, THE (Also see Fightin' Five)
V3#1, Mar, 1967-No. 5, Nov, 1967 (All 12¢ issues)
Charlton Comics

	Good	Fine	N-Mint
1-Fightin' Five begins	2.30	6.90	16.00
2, 3, 5	1.50	3.80	9.00
4-Origin The Peacemaker	2.30	6.90	16.00
Modern Comics Reprints 1, 2 (1978)	0.20	0.40	1.00

PEANUTS (Charlie Brown)
May, 1963-No. 4, Feb, 1964
Gold Key

	Good	Fine	N-Mint
1	10.80	33.00	65.00
2–4	7.50	22.50	45.00

PEBBLES & BAMM BAMM (TV)
Jan, 1972-No. 36, Dec, 1976 (Hanna-Barbera)
Charlton Comics

	Good	Fine	N-Mint
1-From The Flintstones	4.30	12.90	30.00
2–10	2.10	6.00	15.00
11–36	1.50	3.80	9.00

PEBBLES AND BAMM-BAMM
Oct, 1993 (2.25, color)
Harvey Comics

	Good	Fine	N-Mint
1-Giant Size	0.50	1.00	2.50

PEBBLES FLıNTSTONE (TV)
Sept, 1963 (Hanna-Barbera)
Gold Key

	Good	Fine	N-Mint
1 (10088-309)	8.00	24.00	55.00

PENTHOUSE COMIX
1994-Present (4.95, color, bimonthly, magazine size, adult)
General Media International

	Good	Fine	N-Mint
1	2.50	6.30	15.00
2,3	1.70	4.20	10.00
4–8	1.00	2.00	5.00

PENTHOUSE MEN'S ADVENTURE COMIX
1995-Present (4.95, color, adult)
General Media International

1–Boris-c (Magazine size)	1.00	2.00	5.00
1–Boris-c (Comic Size)	1.00	2.00	5.00

PERG
Oct, 1993-Present (2.95, color)
Lightning Comics

1-(3.50)-Flip-c glow-in-the-dark	0.70	1.40	3.50
1-Platinum Edition	1.40	4.00	8.50
2–8: 4-1st app. Hellina. 6-Hellina-c & app. 8-1st app. Claire Voyance			
	0.60	1.20	3.00
2, 3-Platinum Edition	1.00	1.90	4.75
4-Platinum Edition	0.70	1.40	3.50
7-Blue & Pink cover versions	0.60	1.20	3.00

PETER PARKER, THE SPECTACULAR SPIDER-MAN
(See Spectacular Spider-Man, The)

PETER POTAMUS (TV)
Jan, 1965 (Hanna-Barbera)
Gold Key

1	7.50	23.00	45.00

PHANTOM, THE (No. 29 published overseas only)
Nov, 1962-No. 17, July, 1966; No. 18, Sept, 1966-No. 28,
Dec, 1967; No. 30, Feb, 1969-No. 74, Jan, 1977
Gold Key #1-17/King Comics #18-28/Charlton #30-74

1-Manning-a; painted c-1-17	9.00	28.00	65.00
2-King, Queen & Jack begins, ends #11	4.90	15.00	34.00
3–10	3.90	12.00	27.00
11-17: 12-Track Hunter begins	3.10	9.00	22.00
18-Flash Gordon begins, ends #20; Wood-a	3.40	10.00	24.00
19, 20-Flash Gordon by Gil Kane	2.40	7.30	17.00
21-24, 26, 27: 21-Mandrake begins	2.40	7.30	17.00
25-Jeff Jones-a(4 pgs.)	2.40	7.30	17.00
28-(nn)-Brick Bradford app.	2.00	6.00	14.00
30-40: 36, 39-Ditko-a	1.70	5.10	12.00
41-66: 46-Intro The Piranha	1.50	3.80	9.00
67-71, 73-Newton-c/a. 67-Origin retold	1.00	2.50	6.00
72, 74: 74-Newton flag-c & a	1.00	2.50	6.00

	Good	Fine	N-Mint

PHANTOM BLOT, THE (#1 titled New Adventures of...)
Oct, 1964-No. 7, Nov, 1966 (Disney)
Gold Key

	Good	Fine	N-Mint
1 (Meets the Beagle Boys)	5.00	15.00	35.00
2-1st app. Super Goof	2.90	8.60	20.00
3–7	2.10	6.40	15.00

PHANTOM FORCE
Dec, 1993-No. 2, Apr, 1994 (color)
Image Comics
1-(2.50)-Bagged w/card; Kirby plot/pencils; inks by Liefeld, McFarlane, Lee,
    Larsen, Silvestri, Ordway, Williams, Miki; Kirby/Liefeld-c

	Good	Fine	N-Mint
	0.50	1.00	2.50
2-(3.50)-Jack Kirby-a(p); Kirby/Larsen-c	0.70	1.40	3.50

PHANTOM FORCE
No. 0, Mar, 1994-Present (2.50, color)
Genesis West

	Good	Fine	N-Mint
0-Kirby/Jim Lee-c; Kirby-p pgs. 1,5,24-29	0.50	1.00	2.50
3-8: 3-(5/94)-Kirby/McFarlane-c. 4-(5/94)-Kirby-c(p). 5-(6/94)			
	0.50	1.00	2.50

PHANTOM STRANGER, THE (See Showcase)
May-June, 1969-No. 41, Feb-Mar, 1976
National Periodical Publications

	Good	Fine	N-Mint
1-Only 12¢ issue; 1st S.A. app.	6.90	21.00	48.00
2, 3	2.40	7.30	17.00
4-N. Adams-a; 1st new look Phantom Stranger			
	2.90	8.60	20.00
5–7	1.70	5.10	12.00
8-14: 14-Last 15¢ issue	1.50	3.80	9.00
15-19: (25¢, 52 pgs.)	1.10	2.20	5.50
20-41: 23-30: Spawn Of Frankenstein series by Kaluta. 31-Black Orchid			
begins. 39-41-Deadman app.	0.90	1.80	4.50

PHANTOM STRANGER
Oct, 1987-No. 4, Jan, 1988 (75¢, color, mini-series)
DC Comics

	Good	Fine	N-Mint
1-Eclipso app. in all	0.30	0.60	1.50
2–4	0.20	0.40	1.00

PHANTOM: THE GHOST WHO WALKS
Feb 1995- Apr 1995 (2.95, color, limited series)

Marvel Comics

1–3	0.60	1.20	3.00

PHANTOM 2040
May 1995-Present (1.50, color)
Marvel Comics

1-based on TV series; 2-4	0.30	0.60	1.50

PHOENIX (The Untold Story)
April, 1984 (2.00, one-shot)
Marvel Comics Group

1-Byrne/Austin-r/X-Men 137	1.40	2.80	7.00

PINHEAD
Dec 1993-Jun 1994 (2.50, color)
Epic Comics (Marvel)

1-(2.95)-Embossed foil-c; Intro Pinhead & Disciples (Snakeoil, Hangman, Fan Dancer & Dixie); Kelley Jones-c	0.60	1.20	3.00
2–6	0.50	1.00	2.50

PINHEAD VS. MARSHALL LAW (...Law in Hell)
Nov 1993-Dec 1993 (2.95, color, mini-series)
Epic Comics (Marvel)

1, 2-Embossed foil-c	0.60	1.20	3.00

PINK PANTHER, THE (TV)
April, 1971-No. 87, 1984
Gold Key

1-The Inspector begins	2.40	7.30	17.00
2–10	1.40	3.50	8.50
11-30: 16-Warren Tufts-a begins	1.10	2.70	6.50
31-60	0.80	1.50	3.75
61-87: 87-Last Tufts-a	0.60	1.20	3.00

PITT (See Youngblood #4)
Jan, 1993-Present (1.95, color)
Image Comics

1-1st app. Pitt by Dale Keown	1.20	2.40	6.00
2-4-Dale Keown-c/a	0.80	1.60	4.00
5-8-Dale Keown-c/a	0.40	0.80	2.00

PIXIE & DIXIE & MR. JINKS (TV)
July-Sept, 1960-No. 1, Feb, 1963 (Hanna-Barbera)

	Good	Fine	N-Mint
Dell Publishing Co./Gold Key			
Four Color 1112	7.50	23.00	45.00
Four Color 1196, 1264	5.80	18.00	35.00
01-631-207 (Dell, 7/62), 1 (G.K., 2/63)	5.80	18.00	35.00

PLANET OF THE APES (Magazine) (Also see Adventures On The...)
Aug, 1974-No. 29, Feb, 1977 (B&W) (Movie)
Marvel Comics Group

	Good	Fine	N-Mint
1-Ploog a-1-8,11,13,14,19	0.90	2.30	5.50
2	0.60	1.10	2.75
3–10	0.40	0.80	2.00
11–20	0.30	0.60	1.50
21-29	0.20	0.40	1.00

PLANET OF THE APES
Apr, 1990-No. 24, 1992 (2.50, B&W)
Adventure Comics

	Good	Fine	N-Mint
1-Movie tie-in; has outer-c	1.00	2.30	5.50
1-Limited serially #'d (5.00-c)	0.80	2.10	5.00
1-2nd print (2.50-c)	0.50	1.00	2.50
2–24	0.50	1.00	2.50
Annual 1 (3.50)	0.70	1.40	3.50
...Urchak's Folly 1-4 (2.50, mini-series)	0.50	1.00	2.50

PLASTIC MAN (See Brave & The Bold, DC Special #15 & House of Mystery #160)
Nov-Dec, 1966-No. 10, May-June, 1968;
No. 11, Feb-Mar, 1976-No. 20, Oct-Nov, 1977
National Periodical Publ./DC Comics

	Good	Fine	N-Mint
1-1st real app. SA Plastic Man;Gil Kane-c/a	7.10	21.00	50.00
2-5 ('67)	3.30	10.00	23.00
6-10 ('68): 7-Origin; GA Plastic Man app.	1.70	5.10	12.00
11-20 ('76-'77)	0.70	1.40	3.50

PLOP!
Sept, 1973-No. 24, Nov, 1976
National Periodical Publications

	Good	Fine	N-Mint
1-20: Early Sergio Aragones-a	1.00	2.00	5.00
21, 22, 24-(52 pg. giants)	0.80	1.60	4.00
23-No Aragones art (52 pg. giant)	0.40	0.70	1.80

POISON ELVES
Jun 1995-Present (2.50, B&W)

Sirius

1,2; 1–Linsner-c; Drew Hayes-s/a	0.50	1.00	2.50

POWER & GLORY
Feb, 1994-No. 4, May, 1994 (2.50, color, mini-series, mature)
Malibu Comics (Bravura imprint)

1A, 1B-By Howard Chaykin, w/Bravura stamp			
	0.50	1.00	2.50
1-(2.95)-Newsstand edition polybagged w/children's warning on bag;			
Howard Chaykin-c/a begin	0.60	1.20	3.00
Gold Edition	4.00	8.00	20.00
Silver Foil	3.00	6.00	15.00
Blue Foil (5,000)	2.00	4.00	10.00
Serigraph (2,000)	2.00	4.00	10.00
2-4-Contains Bravura stamp	0.50	1.00	2.50
Holiday Special	0.60	1.20	3.00

POWER COMICS
1977-No. 5, Dec, 1977 (B&W)
Power Comics Co.

1-Contains A Boy And His Aardvark by Dave Sim; 1st Dave Sim aardvark			
(not Cerebus)	1.30	3.00	7.50
1-Reprint (3/77, black cover)	0.90	1.70	4.25
2-5: 2-Cobalt. 3-Nightwitch. 4-Northern Light			
	0.50	0.90	2.25

POWER MAN (And Iron Fist #68 on) (Formerly Hero for Hire)
No. 17, Feb, 1974-No. 125, Sept, 1986
Marvel Comics Group

17-Power Man begins; Iron Man app.	1.60	4.70	11.00
18-20: 18-Last 20¢ issue	0.90	2.30	5.50
21-31	0.70	1.40	3.50
32-47: 34-Last 25¢ issue. 45-Starlin-c	0.50	1.00	2.50
48-50: Byrne-a. 48-1st meeting w/Iron Fist	0.50	1.00	2.50
51-56, 58-60	0.30	0.60	1.50
57-New X-Men app. (6/79)	0.80	1.50	3.75
61-65,67-77,79-83,85-124: 75,100-(52 pgs.)			
	0.20	0.40	1.00
66-2nd app. Sabretooth (see Iron Fist #14)	3.00	8.60	20.00
78-3rd app. Sabretooth(cameo under cloak)	1.70	4.20	10.00
84-4th app. Sabretooth	1.70	4.20	10.00
125-Double size; death of Iron Fist	0.40	0.80	2.00
Giant Size 1 - See Giant-Size listing			

	Good	Fine	N-Mint
Annual 1 (11/76)-Punisher cameo flashback			
	0.60	1.20	3.00

POWER OF SHAZAM, THE
Mar 1995 - Present (1.50, color)
DC Comics

	Good	Fine	N-Mint
1-4-Jerry Ordway/s	0.30	0.60	1.50
5–begin 1.75-c, 6-Re-intro of Capt. Nazi	0.40	0.70	1.75

POWER PACK
Aug, 1984-No. 62, Feb, 1991
Marvel Comics Group

	Good	Fine	N-Mint
1-(1.00, 52 pgs)-Origin & 1st. app.	0.40	0.80	2.00
2-18, 20-26, 28, 30-45, 47-62	0.20	0.40	1.00
19-Double size; Wolverine app.	0.90	2.30	5.50
27-Wolverine & Sabretooth app.	1.00	2.50	6.00
29-Spider-Man/Hobgoblin app.	0.40	0.80	1.90
46-Punisher app.	0.60	1.20	3.00
...Holiday Special 1 ('92, 2.25)	0.20	0.40	1.00

PREACHER
Apr 1995-Present (2.50, color, Mature readers)
DC Comics

	Good	Fine	N-Mint
1-(2.95)-Fabry-c	0.80	1.60	4.00
2–5-(2.50)-Fabry-c	0.50	1.00	2.50

PREDATOR (Also see Aliens vs... & Dark Horse Presents)
June, 1989-No. 4, Mar, 1990 (2.25, color, mini-series)
Dark Horse Comics

	Good	Fine	N-Mint
1	2.90	8.60	20.00
1-2nd printing	0.80	2.10	5.00
2	1.40	4.00	10.00
3-4	1.00	2.50	6.00

PREDATOR: BAD BLOOD
Dec, 1993-No. 4, June, 1994 (2.50, color, mini-series)
Dark Horse Comics

	Good	Fine	N-Mint
1–4	0.50	1.00	2.50

PREDATOR: BIG GAME
Mar, 1991-No. 4, June, 1991 (2.50, color, mini-series)
Dark Horse Comics

	Good	Fine	N-Mint
1-Contains 2 Dark Horse trading cards	0.80	1.50	3.75

2-4: 2, 3-Contain trading cards	0.60	1.20	3.00

PREDATOR BLOODY SANDS OF TIME
Feb, 1992-No. 2, Feb, 1992 (2.50, color)
Dark Horse Comics

1, 2	0.50	1.00	2.50

PREDATOR: COLD WAR
Sept, 1991-No. 4, Dec, 1991 (2.50, color, mini-series)
Dark Horse Comics

1–4	0.50	1.00	2.50

PREDATOR: INVADERS FROM THE FOURTH DIMENSION
July, 1994 (3.95, color, one-shot, 52 pgs.)
Dark Horse Comics

1	0.80	1.60	4.00

PREDATOR: JUNGLE TALES
Mar, 1995 (2.95, color,)
Dark Horse Comics

1-reprints Dark Horse Comics	0.60	1.20	3.00

PREDATOR: RACE WAR (See Dark Horse Presents #67)
Feb, 1993-No. 4, Oct, 1993 (2.50, color, mini-series)
Dark Horse Comics

1-4-Dorman painted-c	0.50	1.00	2.50
0-(4/93)	0.50	1.00	2.50

Predator: Invader from the Fourth Dimension © 20th Century Fox

Prime #10 © Malibu

	Good	Fine	N-Mint

PREDATOR 2
Feb, 1991-No. 2, June, 1991 (2.50, color, mini-series)
Dark Horse Comics

1-Contains 2 trading cards	0.50	1.00	2.50
2-Contains 2 trading cards			
	0.50	1.00	2.50

PREDATOR VS. MAGNUS ROBOT FIGHTER
Oct, 1992-No. 2, 1993 (2.95, color)
Dark Horse/Valiant

1-(Regular ed.)-B. Smith-c	1.20	2.90	7.00
1-(Platinum edition, 11/92)	4.00	11.00	25.00
2-Two bound-in trading cards	0.90	2.30	5.50

PRIMAL FORCE
No. 0, Oct, 1994-Present (1.95, color)
DC Comics
0-8: Red Tornado, Golem, Jack O'Lantern, Meridian & Silver Dragon

	0.40	0.80	2.00
9-begin 2.25-c; 10–	0.50	0.90	2.25

PRIME (Also see Flood Relief)
June, 1993-Present (1.95, color)
Malibu Comics (Ultraverse)
1-1st app. Prime; has coupon for Ultraverse Premiere #0

	0.80	2.10	5.00
1-With coupon missing	0.30	0.60	1.50

1-Full cover holographic edition, 1st of kind w/Hardcase #1 & Strangers #1

	4.30	13.00	30.00
1-Ultra 5,000 edition w/silver ink-c	3.60	11.00	25.00
2-Bagged w/card & coupon for U. Premiere #0			
	0.80	2.10	5.00
3,4-Prototype app.: 4-Direct sale ed. w/o card			
	0.60	1.10	2.75
4-(2.50)-Newsstand ed. bagged w/card	0.50	1.00	2.50

5-(2.50, 48 pgs)-Rune flip-c/story part B by Barry Smith; see Sludge #1
   for 1st app. Rune; 3 pg. Night Man preview

	0.50	1.00	2.50

6-11,14-19: 7-Break-Thru x-over. 8-Mantra app.; 2 pg. origin Freex by
   Simonson. 10-Firearm app. 14-1st app. Papa Verite. 16- Intro Turbo Charge

17-brief recap of different Prime identities	0.40	0.80	2.00

12-(3.50, 68 pgs.)-flip-c w/Ultraverse Premiere #3; silver foil logo

	0.70	1.40	3.50
13-(2.95, 52 pgs.); Variant-c exists	0.60	1.20	3.00

20-23-(2.50)	0.50	1.00	2.50
...: Gross and Disgusting 1 (10/94, 3.95)-B. Vallejo-c; "ANNUAL" on-c,			
"Published monthly" in indicia	0.80	1.60	4.00
...Month "Ashcan" (8/94, 75¢)-Vallejo-c	0.20	0.30	0.75
...Time: A Prime Collection ('94, 9.95)-r/1-4			
	1.70	4.20	10.00

PRIMER
Oct, 1982-No. 6, Feb, 1984 (B&W)
Comico

1-(52 pgs.)	0.80	1.60	4.00
2-1st app. Grendel	4.30	12.90	30.00
3, 4	0.60	1.20	3.00
5-1st app. The Maxx & 1st Sam Kieth-a (1983)			
	1.70	4.20	10.00
6-1st app. Evangeline	0.80	1.60	4.00

PRINCE VALIANT
Dec 1994-Mar 1995 (3.95, color, limited series)
Marvel Comics

1-4	0.80	1.60	4.00

PRINCE VANDAL
Nov, 1993-Present (2.50, color)
Triumphant Comics

1-6: 1, 2-Triumphant Unleashed x-over	0.50	1.00	2.50

PROJECT A-KO
Mar, 1994-Present (2.95, color)
Malibu Comics

1-4-Based on anime film	0.60	1.20	3.00

PROJECT A-KO 2
May 1995-Present (2.95, color, limited series)
CPM Comics

1,2	0.60	1.20	3.00

PROPELLERMAN
Jan, 1993-No. 8, Mar, 1993 (2.95, color, limited series)
Dark Horse Comics

1-8: 2, 4, 8-Contain 2 trading cards	0.60	1.20	3.00

	Good	Fine	N-Mint

PROPHET (See Youngblood #2)
Oct, 1993-Present (1.95, color)
Image Comics

	Good	Fine	N-Mint
1-(2.50)-Liefeld/Panosian-c/a; 1-3 contain coupons for #0; Liefeld scripts in #1-4; 1st app. Mary McCormick	0.60	1.20	3.00
1-Gold foil embossed-c ed. rationed to dealers	1.00	2.00	5.00
2-4: 2-Liefeld-c(p). 3-1st app. Judas. 4-1st app. Omen. Black and White part 3 by Thibert	0.40	0.80	2.00
4-Alternate cover by Stephen Platt	2.60	5.20	13.00
5,6-Platt-c/a	0.40	0.80	2.00
0-(7/94, 2.50)-San Diego Comic Con edition	0.20	0.40	1.00
7-10: 7-(9/94, 2.50)-Platt-c/a 8-Bloodstrike app.	0.50	1.00	2.50
10-Polybagged w/trading card Platt-c			

PROTECTORS
Sept, 1992-No. 20, May, 1994 (1.95-2.50/2.25/2.50, color)
Malibu Comics

	Good	Fine	N-Mint
1-12-(2.50)-Coll. Ed. w/poster & diff.-c: 1-Has 3/4 outer-c; origin	0.50	1.00	2.50
1-12-(1.95)-Newsstand Ed. w/o poster	0.40	0.80	2.00
13-16-(2.25): 13-Polybagged w/Skycap	0.50	0.90	2.25
17-20: 17-Begin 2.50-c	0.50	1.00	2.50

PROTOTYPE (Also see Flood Relief)
Aug, 1993-Present (1.95, color)
Malibu Comics

	Good	Fine	N-Mint
1, 2	0.40	0.80	2.00
1-Ultra Limited silver foil-c	2.00	6.90	16.00
1–Hologram-c	3.00	8.60	20.00
3-(2.50, 48 pgs.)-Rune flip-c/sty by B. Smith	0.50	1.00	2.50
4-12: 4-Intro Wrath. 5-Strangers app. 6-Arena cameo. 7, 8-Arena-c/story. 12-(7/94)	0.40	0.80	2.00
0-(8/94, 2.50, 44 pgs.)	0.50	1.00	2.50
13-(8/94, 3.50)-Ultraverse Premiere #6 flip book	0.70	1.40	3.50
14-17: 14-(10/94)	0.40	0.80	2.00
18-(2.50)	0.50	1.00	2.50
Giant Size… 1 (10/94, 2.50, 44 pgs.)	0.50	1.00	2.50

PROWLER, THE
Nov, 1994-Present (1.75, color)
Marvel Comics

1-4: 1-Spider-Man app.	0.40	0.70	1.75

PSI-LORDS
Sept, 1994-Present (2.25, color)
Valiant

1-(3.50)-Chromium wraparound-c	0.70	1.40	3.50
2-10: 3-Chaos Effect Epsilon Pt. 2			
	0.50	0.90	2.25

PSYBA-RATS
Apr 1995-June, 1995 (2.50, color, limited series:3)
DC Comics

1-3	0.50	1.00	2.50

PUMPKINHEAD: THE RITES OF EXORCISM
1993-No. 2, 1993 (2.50, color, mini-series)
Dark Horse Comics

1, 2-Based on movie; painted-c by McManus	0.50	1.00	2.50

PUNISHER (See Amazing Spider-Man #129 & Marvel Preview)
Jan, 1986-No. 5, May, 1986 (Mini-series)
Marvel Comics Group

1-Double size	3.60	11.00	25.00
2	2.00	6.40	15.00
3-(75¢ & 95¢ versions exist); 4–5	0.90	3.00	6.00

PUNISHER
V2#1, July 1987-July 1995
Marvel Comics Group

V2#1	2.00	6.40	15.00
2	1.40	4.00	10.00
3–7	0.80	2.00	5.00
8-Portacio/Williams-c/a begins, ends #18	1.00	2.50	6.00
9-Scarcer, lower distribution	1.00	2.50	6.00
10-Daredevil app.; tie-in D.D. 257	2.10	6.00	15.00
11–15	0.80	2.10	5.00
16-20	0.80	1.60	4.00
21-24, 26-30: 24-1st app. Shadowmasters	0.40	0.80	2.00
25-(1.50, 52 pgs.)	0.60	1.20	3.00
31-40	0.30	0.60	1.60

	Good	Fine	N-Mint

Psi-Lords #2 © Voyager

The Punisher #94 © MEG

	Good	Fine	N-Mint
41-49: (1.25-c)	0.20	0.40	1.00
50-(1.50, 52 pgs.)	0.30	0.60	1.50
51-59: 57-Direct sale has outer-c (newsstand does not). 59-Punisher has			
skin grafts	0.20	0.40	1.00
60-74,76-85,87-89: 60-62-Cage app. 76-Stroman-p (9 pgs.). 85-Suicide			
Run pt 0. 87,88-Suicide Run pts 6 & 9	0.20	0.40	1.00
75-(2.75, 52 pgs.)-Embossed silver foil-c	0.60	1.10	2.75
86-(2.95, 52 pgs.)-Embossed foil-c; Suicide Run Pt. 3			
	0.60	1.20	3.00
90-99, 101-104: 90-Begin 1.50-c; bound-in card sheet 99-Cringe app.			
102-Bullseye 104-Final issue	0.30	0.60	1.50
100-(2.95, 68 pgs)	0.60	1.20	3.00
100-(3.95, 68 pgs)-Foil cover	0.80	1.60	4.00
"Ashcan" Edition-(75¢)-Joe Kubert-c	0.20	0.30	0.75
Annual 1 ('88, 1.75)-Evolutionary War	1.00	3.00	7.00
Annual 2 ('89, 2.00)-Jim Lee back-up story	0.80	2.10	5.00
Annual 3, 4 ('90, '91, 2.00, 68 pgs.)	0.40	0.80	2.00
Annual 5 ('92, 2.25)	0.50	0.90	2.25
Annual 6 ('93 ,2.95)-Polybagged w/card; intro Eradikator 6			
	0.60	1.20	3.00
Annual 7 ('94, 2.95, 68 pgs.)-Rapido app.	0.60	1.20	3.00
...: A Man Named Frank ('94, 6.95, TPB)	1.20	2.90	7.00
...And Wolverine in African Saga nn ('89, 52 pgs.)-Reprints Punisher War			
Journal #6, 7 by Jim Lee	1.00	2.50	6.00
...Back To School Special 1 (11/92, 2.95)	0.60	1.20	3.00
...Back To School Special 2 (10/93, 2.95)	0.60	1.20	3.00
...Back To School Special 3 (10/94, 2.95)	0.60	1.20	3.00
.../Batman: Deadly Knights (10/94, 4.95)	1.00	2.00	5.00
...Bloodlines nn ('91, 5.95, 68 pgs.)	1.00	2.50	6.00
...Die Hard in the Big Easy nn ('92, 4.95)	1.00	2.00	5.00

...G-Force ('92, 4.95)	1.00	2.00	5.00
...Holiday Special 1 (1/93, 2.95)-Red foil-c	0.60	1.20	3.00
...Holiday Special 2 (1/94, 2.95, 68 pgs.)	0.60	1.20	3.00
...Holiday Special 3 (1/95, 2.95, 68 pgs)	0.60	1.20	3.00

...Invades the 'Nam: Final Invasion nn (2/94, 6.95)-J. Kubert-c & chapter
  break art; reprints The 'Nam #52, 53, 67-69

	1.20	2.90	7.00

...Meets Archie (8/94, 3.95, 52 pgs.)-Die-cut-c; no ads; same contents

as Archie Meets The Punisher	0.80	1.60	4.00
Movie Special 1 (6/90, 5.95)	1.00	2.50	6.00
...No Escape ('90, 5.95)	1.00	2.50	6.00
...The Prize ('90, 4.95)	1.00	2.00	5.00
...Summer Special 1 (8/91, 2.95, 52 pgs.)	0.60	1.20	3.00
...Summer Special 2 (8/92, 2.50, 52 pgs.)	0.50	1.00	2.50
...Summer Special 3 (8/93, 2.50, 52 pgs.)	0.50	1.00	2.50
...Summer Special 4 (7/94, 2.95, 52 pgs.)	0.60	1.20	3.00

PUNISHER ARMORY, THE
July, 1990-Present (2.00, color)
Marvel Comics

1-(1.50)-Jim Lee-c	0.60	1.20	3.00
2-(1.75)-Jim Lee-c	0.40	0.80	2.00
3-10-All new material	0.40	0.80	2.00

PUNISHER: ORIGIN MICRO CHIP, THE
July, 1993-No. 2, Aug, 1993 (1.75, color, mini-series)
Marvel Comics

1, 2	0.40	0.70	1.75

PUNISHER: P.O.V.
1991-No. 4, 1991 (4.95, color, mini-series)
Marvel Comics

1-4-Starlin scripts; Wrightson painted-c/a	1.00	2.00	5.00

PUNISHER: THE GHOSTS OF INNOCENTS
Jan, 1993-No. 2, Jan, 1993 (5.95, color)
Marvel Comics

1, 2-Starlin scripts	1.00	2.50	6.00

PUNISHER 2099 (See Punisher War Journal #50)
Feb, 1993-Present (1.25/1.50, color)
Marvel Comics

1-(1.75)-Foil stamped-c	0.50	1.00	2.50

	Good	Fine	N-Mint
1-2nd printing (1.75)	0.40	0.70	1.75
2-15: 13-Ron Lim-c(p); Spider-Man 2099 app.			
	0.30	0.50	1.25
16-24, 26-27: 16-Begin 1.50-c; bound-in card sheet			
	0.30	0.60	1.50
25-(2.95, 52 pgs)-Deluxe edition Embossed foil-c			
	0.60	1.20	2.95
25-(2.25, 52 pgs)	0.50	0.90	2.25
28-begin 1.95-c; 29-30	0.40	0.80	2.00

PUNISHER WAR JOURNAL
Nov 1988-July 1995 (1.50/1.75/1.95, color)
Marvel Comics

	Good	Fine	N-Mint
1-Origin retold; Jim Lee-c/a begin	1.40	4.30	10.00
2–5	1.00	3.00	7.00
6-Two part Wolverine story begins	1.30	3.90	9.00
7-Wolverine cover & story	0.80	2.10	5.00
8–10	0.60	1.20	3.00
11, 12, 17-19: 19-Last Jim Lee-a	0.60	1.20	3.00
13-16, 20-22: No Jim Lee-a. 13-Lee-c only	0.40	0.80	2.00
23-28, 31-49, 51-60, 62-63, 65: 23-Begin 1/75-c. 57,58-Ghost Rider, Daredevil x-over. 62, 63-Suicide Run Pt. 4 & 7			
	0.40	0.70	1.75
29, 30-Ghost Rider app.	0.40	0.80	2.00
50-(2.95, 52 pgs.)-Embossed-c; Punisher 2099 preview (1st app.)			
	0.60	1.20	3.00
61-(2.95, 52 pgs.)-Embossed foil-c; Suicide Run Pt. 1			
	0.60	1.20	3.00
64-(2.25, 52 pgs.)-Newsstand Ed.; Suicide Run Pt. 10			
	0.50	0.90	2.25
64-(2.95, 52 pgs.)-Collectors Ed.; die-cut-c	0.60	1.20	3.00
66-74, 76-80: 66-Begin 1.95-c; bound-in card sheet, 80-Last issue			
	0.40	0.80	2.00
75-(2.50, 52 pgs)	0.50	1.00	2.50

PUNISHER: WAR ZONE, THE
Mar, 1992-Present (1.75/1.95, color)
Marvel Comics

	Good	Fine	N-Mint
1-(2.25, 40 pgs.)-Die-cut-c	0.60	1.20	3.00
2	0.40	0.80	2.00
3-22, 24, 26: 19-Wolverine app. 24-Suicide Run Pt. 5			
	0.40	0.70	1.75
23-(2.95, 52 pgs)-Embossed foil-c; Suicide Run Pt. 2			

	0.60	1.20	3.00
25-(2.25, 52 pgs.)-Suicide Run Pt. 8; painted-c			
	0.50	0.90	2.25
27-40: 27-Begin 1.95-c; bound-in card sheet			
	0.40	0.80	2.00
Annual 1 ('93, 2.95)-Polybagged w/card	0.60	1.20	3.00
Annual 2 ('94, 2.95, 68 pgs.)	0.60	1.20	3.00

PUNISHER: YEAR ONE
Dec, 1994-Present (2.50, color, limited series:4)
Marvel Comics

1-4	0.50	1.00	2.50

	Good	Fine	N-Mint
QUACK!			
July, 1976-No. 6, 1977? (1.25, B&W)			
Star Reach Productions			
1-Brunner-c/a (Duckaneer)	0.90	1.70	4.25
1-2nd printing (10/76)	0.30	0.60	1.50
2, 4-6: 2-Aragones-a	0.40	0.80	2.00
3-The Beavers by Dave Sim in #3-5	0.80	1.60	4.00
QUASAR (See Avengers 302 & Inc. Hulk 234)			
Oct, 1989-No. 60, July, 1994 (1.00/1.25, color)			
Marvel Comics			
1-Origin retold (formerly Marvel Boy)	0.40	0.80	2.00
2–5	0.30	0.60	1.50
6-Venom cameo (2 pgs.)	0.40	0.80	2.00
7-Cosmic Spidey app.	0.50	1.00	2.50
8-15, 18-24: 11-Excalibur x-over. 14-McFarlane-c. 23-Ghost Rider app.			
	0.20	0.50	1.20
16-(1.50, 52 pgs.)	0.30	0.60	1.50
17-Flash parody (Buried Alien)	0.40	0.80	2.00
25-(1.50, 52 pgs.)	0.30	0.60	1.50
26-Infinity Gauntlet x-over; Thanos-c/story	0.40	0.80	2.00
27-Infinity Gauntlet	0.30	0.60	1.50
28-30: 30-Last 1.00-c	0.20	0.40	1.00
31-49, 51-60: 38-Vs. Warlock. 40-Thanos app. 42-Punisher-c/story.			
53-Warlock & Moondragon app. 58-Bound-in card sheet			
	0.30	0.50	1.25
50-(2.95, 52 pgs.)-Holo-grafx foil-c; Silver Surfer, Man-Thing,			
Ren & Stimpy app.	0.60	1.20	3.00
Special 1-3 (1.25)-Newsstand; same as 32-34			
	0.30	0.50	1.25
QUESTION, THE (Also see Blue Beetle & Mysterious Suspense)			
Feb, 1987-No. 36, Mar, 1990 (1.50, color)			
DC Comics			
1–36	0.30	0.60	1.50
Annual 1 ('88, 2.50)	0.50	1.00	2.50
Annual 2 ('89, 3.50)	0.70	1.40	3.50
QUICK-DRAW MCGRAW (TV) (Hanna-Barbera)			
No. 1040, 12-2/59-60-No. 14, 4/63; No. 15, 6/69			
Dell Publishing Co./Gold Key #12 on			

Four Color 1040 (#1)	12.50	38.00	75.00
2-6: 2, 4-Augie Doggie, Snooper & Blabber in each (early apps.). 5-Early			
Snagglepuss app.; last 10¢ issue	8.30	25.00	50.00
7–11	6.70	20.00	40.00
12, 13-(…Fun-Type Roundup, 84 pgs.)	8.00	24.00	65.00
14, 15	5.80	17.50	35.00

QUICK-DRAW MCGRAW (TV)
Nov, 1970-No. 8, Jan, 1972 (Hanna-Barbera)
Charlton Comics

1	4.40	13.00	31.00
2–8	2.30	6.90	16.00

Q-UNIT
Dec, 1993 (2.95, color)
Harris Comics

1-Bagged w/trading card version 1.2	0.60	1.20	3.00

R

	Good	Fine	N-Mint

RACK & PAIN
Mar, 1994-No. 4, June 1994
(2.50, color, limited series)
Dark Horse Comics

	Good	Fine	N-Mint
1-4-Greg Capullo-c	0.50	1.00	2.50

RADICAL DREAMER
No. 0, May, 1994-July 1994 (1.75?, color)
Blackball Comics

	Good	Fine	N-Mint
0,1-(1.99)-Poster format	0.40	0.80	2.00

RADICAL DREAMER
June 1995-Present (2.95, B&W)
Mark's Giant Economy Size Comics

	Good	Fine	N-Mint
1	0.60	1.20	3.00

RADIOACTIVE MAN
1993-No. 6 Nov. 1994 (1.95/2.25, color, limited series)
Bongo Comics Group

	Good	Fine	N-Mint
1-(2.95)-Origin; pull out poster; glow-in-the-dark-c; has cover date of Nov, 1952	0.70	1.30	3.25
2-(1.95)-Cover "dated" May 1962 #88	0.40	0.80	2.00
3-(1.95)-Cover "dated" Aug 1972 #216	0.40	0.80	2.00
4-(2.25)-Cover "dated" Oct 1980 #412 w/trading card	0.50	0.90	2.25
5-(2.25)-Cover "dated" Jan 1986 #679 w/trading card	0.50	0.90	2.25
6-(2.25)-Cover dated" Jan 1995 #1000	0.50	0.90	2.25

RAGMAN
Aug-Sept, 1976-No. 5, June-July, 1977
National Periodical Publications

	Good	Fine	N-Mint
1-Origin & 1st app. Ragman	0.60	1.20	3.00
2-5: 2-Origin ends. 4,5-Kubert-a; c-1-5	0.30	0.60	1.50

RAGMAN
Oct, 1991-No. 8, May, 1992 (1.50, color, mini-series)
DC Comics

	Good	Fine	N-Mint
1	0.50	1.00	2.50
2-8: 3-Origin. 8-Batman-c/story	0.30	0.60	1.50

Rai #26 © Voyager

The Ray #5 © DC

RAGMAN: CRY OF THE DEAD
Aug, 1993-No. 6, Jan, 1994 (1.75, color, mini-series)
DC Comics

1-6-Joe Kubert-c	0.40	0.70	1.75

RAI (... and The Future Force #9- on)(See Magnus #5-8)
(Valiant's first original character)
3/92-No. 0, 11/92: No. 9, 5/93-Present (1.95/2.25, color)
Valiant

1	1.00	4.30	10.00
2	1.10	3.40	8.00
3	2.10	6.00	15.00
4-Low print run	2.60	8.00	18.00
5-8: 7-Death of Rai	0.70	2.10	5.00
0-(11/92)-1st full app. & partial origin Bloodshot; origin & 1st app.			
new Rai (Rising Spirit)	1.30	3.00	8.00
9-(2.50)-Gatefold-c	0.50	1.00	2.50
10-33: 15-Manowar armor app. 17-19-Magnus x-over. 21-w/bound-in			
trading card; 1st app. Starwatchers (cameo). 22-Death of Rai.			
26-Chaos Effect Epsilon Pt. 3	0.50	0.90	2.25

RAMM
May, 1987-No. 2, Sept, 1987 (1.50, B&W)
Megaton Comics

1, 2-Both have 1-pg. Youngblood ad by Liefeld			
	0.30	0.60	1.50

RAMPAGING HULK (Becomes The Hulk #11 on)
Jan, 1977-No. 10, Aug, 1978 (1.00, B&W, magazine)
Marvel Comics Group

	Good	Fine	N-Mint
1-Bloodstone featured	1.00	2.00	5.00
2-Origin old & new X-Men in text	1.30	3.30	8.00
3-10: 9-Thor vs. Hulk battle. 10-Color issue			
	0.50	0.90	2.25

RAPHAEL (See Teenage Mutant Ninja Turtles)
1985 (1.50, B&W, one-shot)
Mirage Studios

	Good	Fine	N-Mint
1-Magazine size	1.00	3.00	6.00
1-2nd print (11/87); new 8 pg. story	0.80	1.60	4.00

RASCALS IN PARADISE
Aug, 1994 (3.95, color, limited series:3)
Dark Horse Comics

	Good	Fine	N-Mint
1-3-Jim Silke-a/3-part story	0.80	1.60	4.00

RAT PATROL (TV)
March, 1967-No. 5, Nov, 1967; No. 6, Oct, 1969
Dell Publishing Co.

	Good	Fine	N-Mint
1-Christopher George photo-c	6.70	20.00	40.00
2-No photo-c	4.30	13.00	26.00
3-6-Photo-c	3.20	10.00	19.00

RAVAGE 2099 (See Marvel Comics Presents #117)
Dec, 1992-Present (1.25/1.50, color)
Marvel Comics

	Good	Fine	N-Mint
1-(1.75)-Gold foil stamped-c; by Stan Lee	0.50	1.00	2.50
1-2nd printing (1.75)	0.40	0.70	1.75
2, 3	0.40	0.80	2.00
4-17: 14-Punisher 2099 x-over. 15-Lim-c(p)	0.30	0.50	1.25
18-24,26-30: 18-Begin 1.50-c; bound-in card sheet			
	0.30	0.60	1.50
25-(2.25, 52 pgs)	0.50	0.90	2.25
25-(2.95, 52 pgs)-Silver foil embossed-c	0.60	1.20	3.00
31-33, 31-begin 1.95-c	0.40	0.80	2.00

RAY, THE
Feb, 1992-No. 6, July, 1992 (1.00, mini-series)
DC Comics

	Good	Fine	N-Mint
1-Joe Quesada-a(p) in 1-5; c-3-6p	1.00	2.50	6.00
2	0.70	1.30	3.25
3	0.60	1.10	2.75
4-6: 6-Quesada layouts only	0.40	0.70	1.80
In a Blaze of Power ('94, 12.95)-r/1-6 with new Quesada-c			

	1.90	5.60	13.00

RAY, THE
May, 1994-Present (1.75/1.95, color)
DC Comics

1-3: 1,2-Quesada-c(p); Superboy app.	0.40	0.70	1.75
1-(2.95)-Collectors Edition w/different Quesada-c; embossed foil-c			
	0.60	1.20	3.00
4,5: 4-Begin 1.95-c. 5-(9/94)	0.40	0.80	2.00
0,6-12: 0-(10/94). 6-(11/94)	0.40	0.80	2.00
13-begin 2.25-c;14, 15–	0.50	0.90	2.25
Annual 1-Superman app (3.95, 68 pgs.)	0.80	1.60	4.00

RAY BRADBURY COMICS
Feb, 1993-Present (2.95, color)
Topps Comics

1-5-Polybagged w/3 trading cards	0.60	1.20	3.00
…Special Edition 1 ('94, 2.95)-The Illustrated Man			
	0.60	1.20	3.00
…Trilogy of Terror, V3#1 (5/94, 2.50)	0.50	1.00	2.50
…Martian Chronicles V4 #1 (6/94, 2.50)-Steranko-c			
	0.50	1.00	2.50

RAZOR
May, 1992-Present (3.95, B&W, mature)
London Night Studios

0-(5/92, 3.95)-Direct market	2.00	5.00	12.00
0-(4/95, 3.00)-London Night Edition	0.50	1.30	3.00
1/2-(Apr, 1995)1st Poizon; Linsner-c	1.20	2.90	7.00
1-(8/92, 2.50)-Fathom Press	2.00	4.00	10.00
1-2nd printing	0.60	1.20	3.00
2-(2.95)-J. O'Barr-c	1.60	3.20	8.00
2-Limited editions in red and blue	1.70	4.20	10.00
2-Platinum-no price on cover	1.70	4.20	10.00
3-(3.95)-Jim Balent-c	1.00	2.00	5.00
3-w/poster insert	1.00	2.00	5.00
4-Vigil-c	1.00	2.00	5.00
4-w/poster insert	1.00	2.00	5.00
5-Linsner-c	1.30	3.30	8.00
5-Platinum	1.70	4.20	10.00
6–10	0.80	1.60	4.00
11,12-(3.00)-Rituals Pt. 1 & 2	0.60	1.20	3.00
13, 14-Uncut	0.60	1.20	3.00

	Good	Fine	N-Mint
Annual 1 (1993, 2.95)-1st app. Shi	4.30	12.90	30.00
Annual 1-Gold (1,200 printed)	3.60	10.70	25.00
Annual 2 (Late 1994, 3.00)	0.60	1.20	3.00
...: The Suffering 1 (2.95)	0.60	1.20	3.00
...: The Suffering 1 Director's Cut (3.00)	0.60	1.20	3.00
...: The Suffering 1-Platinum	1.70	4.20	10.00
...: The Suffering 2 (9/94, 3.00)	0.60	1.20	3.00
.../Shi Special 1 (7/94, 3.00)	1.00	2.00	5.00
...: Burn 1-3 (3.00)	0.60	1.20	3.00
...Swimsuit Special-painted-c	0.60	1.20	3.00

RAZOR/DARK ANGEL: THE FINAL NAIL
June, 1994-No. 2, June, 1994 (2.95, B&W, mature)
Boneyard Press #1/London Night Studios #2

	Good	Fine	N-Mint
1,2	0.60	1.20	3.00

REALM, THE
Feb, 1986-No. 20? (B&W, 1.50/1.95/2.50)
Arrow Comics/Wee Bee Comics #13/ Caliber #14 on

	Good	Fine	N-Mint
1	0.80	1.60	4.00
2	0.40	0.80	2.00
3, 5-16	0.30	0.50	1.25
4-1st app. Deadworld (9/86)	1.40	4.30	10.00
17-20: 17-Begin 2.50-c	0.50	1.00	2.50
Book 1 (4.95)	1.00	2.00	5.00

REBELS, THE
Nov 1994 - Present (2.25, color)
Warp Graphics

	Good	Fine	N-Mint
1	0.50	0.90	2.25

R.E.B.E.L.S. '94
No. 0, Oct, 1994-Present (1.95, color)
DC Comics

	Good	Fine	N-Mint
0-7: 3-(R.E.B.E.L.S. '95 begins)	0.40	0.80	2.00
8-begin 2.25-c; 9–10	0.50	0.90	2.25

REBEL SWORD
Oct, 1994-Present (2.50, B&W)
Dark Horse

	Good	Fine	N-Mint
1–6	0.50	1.00	2.50

RED SONJA
Jan, 1977-V3#13, May, 1986
Marvel Comics Group

1	0.60	1.20	3.00
2–5	0.40	0.80	2.00
6–15	0.20	0.40	1.00
V1#1, V2#2 (1983)	0.20	0.40	1.00
V3 #1-4 (1.00-c)	0.20	0.50	1.20
5-13	0.20	0.40	1.00

RED WOLF (See Avengers #80, Marvel Spotlight #1)
May, 1972-No. 9, Sept, 1973
Marvel Comics Group

1-Western hero begins, ends #6	0.80	1.60	4.00
2-9: 7-Begin Red Wolf as super hero	0.40	0.80	2.00

REGULATORS
June 1995-Present (2.50, color)
Image Comics

1-Busiek-s	0.50	1.00	2.50

REN & STIMPY SHOW, THE (TV)
Dec, 1992-Present (1.75/1.95, color) (Nickelodeon cartoon characters)
Marvel Comics

1-(2.25)-Polybagged; premiums enclosed (scratch & sniff Ren or Stimpy air fowlers); Tank & Brenner story	2.10	6.40	15.00
1-2nd printing	0.50	0.90	2.25
2	1.70	5.10	12.00
3	0.80	2.10	5.00
4-6: 4-Muddy Mudskipper back-up. 6-Spider-Man vs. Powdered Toast Man	0.80	1.60	4.00
7-17: 12-1st solo back-up w/Tank & Brenner	0.40	0.70	1.75
18-33: 18-Begin 1.95-c; Powdered Toast Man app.	0.40	0.80	2.00
25-(2.95)-Deluxe edition w/die cut-c.	0.60	1.20	3.00
...Don't Try This at Home (3/94, 12.95)-r/#9-12	1.90	5.60	13.00
...Holiday Special 1994 (2/95, 2.95, 52 pgs)		1.20	3.00
...Pick of the Litter ('93, 12.95)-r/#1-4	1.90	5.60	13.00
...Powdered Toast an Cereal Serial (4/95, 2.95)	0.60	1.20	3.00
...Seeck Leetle Monkeys (1/95,12.95) r/#17-20	1.90	5.60	13.00

	Good	Fine	N-Mint
...Special: Powdered Toast Man 1 (4/94, 2.95, 52 pgs.)			
	0.60	1.20	3.00
...Special 2-(7/94, 2.95, 52 pgs.)	0.60	1.20	3.00
...Special 3-(10/94, 2.95, 52 pgs.)-Choose your own adventure book			
	0.60	1.20	3.00
...Special: Fours Werks (1/95, 2.95, 52 pgs) FF #1 c-swipe			
Cover reads Four Swerks w/5 page "coloring book"			
	0.60	1.20	3.00
...Special:Powdered Toastman's Cereal Serial (4/95, 2.95)			
	0.60	1.20	3.00
...Tastes Like Chicken (11/93, 12.95)-r/#5-8			
	1.90	5.60	13.00
...Your Pals (8/94, 12.95) r/#13-16	1.90	5.60	13.00
...Eenteractive Special ('95, 2.95)	0.40	1.30	3.00

RENFIELD
1994-Present (2.95, B&W, limited series:5)
Caliber Press

1–3	0.60	1.20	3.00

REPTILICUS (Reptisaurus #3 on)
Aug, 1961-No. 2, Oct, 1961
Charlton Comics

1 (Movie)	11.00	33.00	78.00
2	7.00	22.00	52.00

REPTISAURUS (Formerly Reptilicus)
Jan, 1962-No. 8, Dec, 1962
Charlton Comics

V2#3-8	4.30	13.00	30.00
Special Edition 1 (Summer, 1963)	3.90	11.60	27.00

RESTAURANT AT THE END OF THE UNIVERSE, THE
1994 (6.95, color, limited series:3)
DC Comics

1-3	1.20	2.90	7.00

RETURN OF GORGO, THE (Formerly Gorgo's Revenge)
No. 2, Aug, 1963; No. 3, Fall, 1964 (#2: last 10¢ issue, 3 is 15¢)
Charlton Comics

2,3-Ditko-c/a; based on M.G.M. movie	6.30	19.00	44.00

RETURN OF KONGA, THE (Becomes Konga's Revenge)

1962
Charlton Comics
nn   6.30   19.00   44.00

RETURN TO JURASSIC PARK
Apr, 1995-Present (2.50, color)
Topps Comics

1-2	0.40	1.00	2.50
3-begin 2.95	0.60	1.20	3.00

RICHARD DRAGON, KUNG-FU FIGHTER
Apr-May, 1975-No. 18
Nov-Dec, 1977 (1-4 based on novel)
National Periodical Publ.

1, 2: 2-Starlin-a(p)	0.30	0.60	1.50
3-18: 3-Kirby-a(p). 4-8-Wood-i	0.20	0.40	1.00

RIMA, THE JUNGLE GIRL
Apr-May, 1974-No. 7, Apr-May, 1975
National Periodical Publ. (#1-5: 20¢; 6, 7-25¢)

1-Origin, part 1	0.40	0.80	2.00
2-4: Origin parts 2-4	0.20	0.40	1.00
5-7: 7-Origin & only app. Space Marshal	0.20	0.40	1.00

RINGO KID, THE
Jan, 1970-No. 23, Nov, 1973; No. 24, Nov, 1975-No. 30, Nov, 1976
Marvel Comics Group

1-Williamson-r from #10 (1956)	0.80	1.60	4.00
2-30: 13-Wildey-r. 20-Williamson-r/#1	0.40	0.80	2.00

RIOT GEAR
Sept, 1993-Present (2.50, color, serially numbered)
Triumphant Comics
1-8: 1- 2nd app. Riot Gear;2-1st app. Rabin; 3-1st app. Surzar.
  3,4-Triumphant Unleashed x-over. 4-Death of Captn. Tich

	0.50	1.00	2.50
...Violent Past 1, 2: 1-(2/94, 2.50)	0.50	1.00	2.50

RIPCLAW
Apr 1995-Present (2.50, color)
Image Comics

1-3-B. Peterson-a(p)	0.50	1.00	2.50

	Good	Fine	N-Mint

RIPFIRE
Jan 1995 - Present (2.50, color)
Malibu Comics

| #0 | 0.50 | 1.00 | 2.50 |

RIP HUNTER TIME MASTER(See Showcase #20, 21, 25, 26)
Mar-Apr, 1961-No. 29, Nov-Dec, 1965
National Periodical Publications

1	51.00	152.00	355.00
2	24.00	71.00	165.00
3-5: 5-Last 10¢ issue	14.00	40.00	100.00
6, 7-Toth art	11.00	33.00	78.00
8–15	8.00	24.00	56.00
16-20	6.40	19.00	45.00
21-29	5.10	15.00	36.00

ROACHMILL
May, 1988-No. 10, Dec, 1990 (1.75, B&W)
Dark Horse Comics

| 1-10: 10-Contains trading cards | 0.40 | 0.70 | 1.75 |

ROARIN' RICK'S RARE BIT FIENDS
July, 1994 (2.95, B&W, mature)
King Hell Press

| 1-11-R. Veitch | 0.60 | 1.20 | 3.00 |

ROBIN
Jan, 1991-No. 5, May, 1991 (1.00, color, mini-series)
DC Comics

1-Includes poster by Neal Adams	0.90	2.30	5.50
1-2nd & 3rd printing w/o poster	0.30	0.60	1.50
2	0.30	0.50	1.25
2-2nd print	0.20	0.40	1.00
3–5	0.30	0.60	1.50
Annual 1 (1992, 2.50)-Sam Kieth -c	0.50	1.00	2.50
Annual 2 (1993, 2.50)-Intro Razorsharp	0.50	1.00	2.50

ROBIN
Nov, 1993-Present (1.50, color)
DC Comics

1-(2.95) Collectors edition w/foil embossed-c; Azrael as Batman app.;			
1st app. Redbird (Robin's car)	0.60	1.20	3.00
1-(1.50) Newsstand Edition	0.30	0.60	1.50

2-10: 6-The Huntress-c/sty. 7-Knightquest the Conclusion w/new Batman vs.
     Bruce Wayne. 8-KnightsEnd Pt. 5. 9-KnightsEnd Aftermath; Batman-c &
     app. 10-(9/94)-Zero Hour   0.30   0.60   1.50
0,11-16: 0-(10/94). 11-(11/94)   0.30   0.60   1.50
14-(2.50) Embossed-c, Troika Pt.4   0.50   1.00   2.50
17-begin 1.95-c; 18–19   0.40   0.80   2.00
Annual 3 ('94, 2.95)-Elseworlds story   0.60   1.20   3.00

ROBIN II
Oct, 1991-No. 4, Dec, 1991 (Color, mini-series)
DC Comics
1-Direct (4 diff-c, hologram, 1.50)   0.30   0.60   1.50
1-4-Newsstand (1.00)   0.20   0.40   1.00
2-Direct (3 diff-c, hologram, 1.50)   0.30   0.60   1.50
3-Direct (2 diff-c, hologram, 1.50)   0.30   0.60   1.50
4-Direct (only 1 cover, hologram, 1.50)   0.30   0.60   1.50
Collector's Set 1 (1 of each #1, bagged, w/card)
                                                   1.70   4.20   10.00
Collector's Set 2 (1 of each #2, bagged, w/card)
                                                   1.30   3.30   8.00
Collector's Set 3 (1 of each #3, bagged, w/card)
                                                   1.00   2.50   6.00
Collector's Set 4 (1 of each #4, bagged, w/card)
                                                   0.80   1.60   4.00
Multi-pack (all 4 issues w/hologram sticker)0.80   1.60   4.00

ROBIN III: CRY OF THE HUNTRESS
Dec, 1992-No. 6, Mar, 1993 (Color, mini-series)
DC Comics
1-6: (2.50)-Deluxe; polybagged w/mini-poster & movement enhanced-c
                                                   0.50   1.00   2.50
1-6: (1.25)-Newsstand   0.30   0.50   1.25

ROBIN 3000
Nov, 1992-No. 2, 1992 (4.95, color, mini-series)
DC Comics
1,2-Foil logo; Russell-c/a   1.00   2.00   5.00

ROBOCOP
Mar, 1990-No. 23, Jan, 1992 (1.50, color)
Marvel Comics
1-Movie tie-in   0.30   0.80   2.00
2–23   0.40   0.70   1.75

	Good	Fine	N-Mint

Robin #8 © DC

Robocop #2 © MEG

	Good	Fine	N-Mint
nn-(1990, 4.95)-Movie adapt.	1.00	2.00	5.00

ROBOCOP: MORTAL COILS
Sept, 1993-No. 4, Dec, 1993 (2.50, color, mini-series)
Dark Horse Comics

1-4: 1, 2-Cago painted-c	0.50	1.00	2.50

ROBOCOP: PRIME SUSPECT
Oct, 1992-No. 4, Jan, 1993 (2.50, color, mini-series)
Dark Horse Comics

1-4: Nelson painted-c	0.50	1.00	2.50

ROBOCOP: ROULETTE
Dec, 1993-No. 4, Mar, 1994 (2.50, color, limited series, painted-c)
Dark Horse Comics

1-4: 1, 3-Nelson-c. 2, 4-Bolton-c	0.50	1.00	2.50

ROBOCOP 2
Aug, 1990-No. 3, Sept, 1990 (1.00, color)
Marvel Comics

nn-(8/90, 4.95, 68 pgs.)	1.00	2.00	5.00
1: 1-3-r/68 pg. issue	0.60	1.20	3.00
2, 3	0.30	0.60	1.50

ROBOCOP 3
July, 1993-No. 3, Nov, 1993 (2.50, color, limited series)
Dark Horse Comics

1-3-Nelson painted-c; Nguyen-a	0.50	1.00	2.50

ROBOCOP VERSUS THE TERMINATOR

Sept, 1992-No. 4, Dec, 1992 (2.50, color, mini-series)
Dark Horse Comics

1-4: All contain cardboard cut-out standup	0.50	1.00	2.50
1-Platinum Edition	2.10	6.40	15.00

ROBOTECH DEFENDERS
Mar, 1985-No. 2, Apr, 1985 (2 issue mini-series)
DC Comics

1, 2	0.20	0.40	1.00

ROBOTECH MASTERS
July, 1985-No. 23, Apr, 1988 (Color)
Comico

1	0.50	1.00	2.50
2–23	0.30	0.60	1.60

ROBOTECH: THE MACROSS SAGA (Formerly Macross)
Feb, 1985-No. 36, Feb, 1989 (Color)
Comico

2	0.60	1.20	3.00
3–10	0.40	0.80	2.00
11-36: 26-34-(1.75). 35, 36-(1.95)	0.40	0.70	1.75

ROBOTECH: THE NEW GENERATION
July, 1985-No. 25, July, 1988 (Color)
Comico

1–25	0.30	0.60	1.50

ROBOTECH WARRIORS
Feb 1995-Present (2.95, B&W)
Academy Comics, Ltd.

1	0.60	1.20	3.00

ROCKETEER ADVENTURE MAGAZINE, THE
July, 1988-No. 2, July, 1989 (Color, annual)
Comico

1-(2.00)-Dave Stevens & Kaluta-a in each	1.00	2.00	5.00
2-(2.75)-Stevens/Dorman painted-c	0.60	1.20	3.00

ROCKETEER SPECIAL EDITION
Nov, 1984 (One-shot)
Eclipse Comics

1-Dave Stevens-c/a (Chap. 5)	1.70	4.00	10.00

	Good	Fine	N-Mint

ROCKETEER: THE OFFICIAL MOVIE ADAPTATION
1991
W.D. Publications (Disney)

	Good	Fine	N-Mint
nn-(5.95, 68 pgs.)-Squarebound deluxe ed.	1.00	2.50	6.00
nn-(2.95, 68 pgs.)-Stapled regular edition	0.60	1.20	3.00
...3-D Comic Book ('91, 7.98, 52 pgs.)	1.30	3.30	8.00

ROCK FANTASY COMICS
Dec, 1989-No. 16? 1991 (2.25/3.00, B&W, 36 pgs.)
Rock Fantasy Comics

	Good	Fine	N-Mint
1-Pink Floyd part I	0.80	1.60	4.00
1-Pink Floyd, 2nd print (3.00-c)	0.60	1.20	3.00
2, 3: 2-Rolling Stones #1. 3-Led Zeppelin #1	0.60	1.20	3.00
2, 3-2nd printings (3.00-c, 1/90 & 2/90)	0.60	1.20	3.00
4-Stevie Nicks (not published)			
5-Monstrosities Of Rock #1	0.50	1.00	2.50
5-2nd printing (3.00, 3/90)	0.60	1.20	3.00
6, 7, 9-15,17,18: 10-Kiss #1; photo back-c	0.60	1.20	3.00
8-Alice Cooper; not published			
16-(5.00, 68 pgs.)	1.00	2.00	5.00

ROCK N' ROLL COMICS
June, 1989-Present? (1.50, B&W)
Revolutionary Comics

	Good	Fine	N-Mint
1-Guns 'N Roses	1.70	4.00	10.00
1-2nd through 6th printings	0.30	0.60	1.50
1-7th print (full color w/new art)	0.40	0.80	2.00
2-Metalica	1.00	2.00	5.00
2-2nd through 6th printings	0.30	0.60	1.50
3-Bon Jovi (no reprints)	0.50	1.00	2.50
4-8,10-64	0.50	1.00	2.50
9-Kiss	0.80	1.60	4.00
9-2nd & 3rd printings	0.40	0.80	2.00

ROCKO'S MODERN LIFE (TV)
June, 1994-Present (1.95, color) (Nickelodeon cartoon)
Marvel Comics

	Good	Fine	N-Mint
1–7	0.40	0.80	2.00

ROCKY AND HIS FIENDISH FRIENDS (TV)(Bullwinkle)
Oct, 1962-No. 5, Sept, 1963 (Jay Ward)

Gold Key
1-(25¢, 84 pgs.)	20.00	69.00	185.00
2, 3-(25¢, 84 pgs.)	16.00	41.00	125.00
4, 5-Regular size, 12¢ issues	11.00	28.00	85.00

ROGAN GOSH
1994 (6.95, color)
DC Comics (Vertigo)
nn-Peter Milligan scripts	1.20	2.90	7.00

ROGER RABBIT
June, 1990-No. 18, Nov, 1991 (1.50, color)
Disney Comics
1	0.80	1.60	4.00
2,3	0.40	0.80	2.00
4–18	0.30	0.60	1.50

ROGUE
Jan 1995-Apr 1995 (2.95, color, limited series)
Marvel Comics
1-4: 1-Gold foil logo	0.60	1.20	3.00

ROMAN HOLIDAYS, THE (TV)
Feb, 1973-No. 4, Nov, 1973 (Hanna-Barbera)
Gold Key
1	1.90	6.00	13.00
2–4	1.70	4.20	10.00

RONIN
July, 1983-No. 6, Aug, 1984 (Mini-series)

Roarin Ricks Rare Bit Fiends #1
© King Hell Press

Rune #5 © BWS

	Good	Fine	N-Mint
DC Comics			
1-Frank Miller-c/a & scripts in all	0.80	1.60	4.00
2–5	0.60	1.20	3.00
6-Scarcer; fold-out poster	1.00	2.50	6.00
Trade Paperback (12.95, 1987)	1.90	5.60	13.00

ROOK
June 1995-Present (2.95, color)

0–3 short stories w/preview	.60	1.20	3.00

ROOM 222 (TV)
Jan, 1970; No. 2, May, 1970-No. 4, Jan, 1971
Dell Publishing Co.

1	5.10	15.00	36.00
2-4: 2, 4-Photo-c	3.00	9.00	21.00

ROSE N' GUNN
Jan 1995-Present (2.95, B&W, Mature readers)
Bishop Press

1–2	0.60	1.20	3.00

RUFF AND REDDY (TV)
No. 937, Sept, 1958-No. 12, Jan-Mar, 1962 (Hanna-Barbera)
Dell Publishing Co.
4 Color 937 (#1)-1st Hanna-Barbera comic

	13.00	39.00	90.00
4 Color 981, 1038 (#2, 3)	10.00	30.00	60.00
4 (1-3/60) - 12: 8-Last 10¢ issue	6.00	18.00	42.00

RUNE (See Sludge #1 & all other Ultraverse titles for preview)
Jan, 1994-Present (1.95, color)
Malibu Comics (Ultraverse)
1,2,4-9-Windsor-Smith-c/a/sty begin: 2-(2/94). 5-1st app. Gemini

6-Prime & Mantra app.	0.40	0.80	2.00
1-Ultra 5000 Limited silver foil ed.	3.00	9.00	20.00

0-Obtained by sending coupons from 11 comics; came w/Solution #0,

poster, temp. tattoo, card	1.70	4.20	10.00

3-(3/94, 3.50, 68 pgs.)-Flip-book w/Ultraverse Premiere #1

	0.70	1.40	3.50

1-(1/94)-"Ashcan" edition flip book w/Wrath #1

	0.20	0.40	1.00
Giant Size 1-(2.50, 44 pgs)	0.50	1.00	2.50

RUNE/SILVER SURFER
Apr, 1995 (5.95/2.95, color)
Marvel/Malibu

1-Direct Market-BWS-c	1.20	2.40	6.00
1-Newstand-BWS-c	0.60	1.20	3.00
1-Collector's Limited Edition	2.00	4.00	10.00

RUST
July, 1987-No. 15, 1988; V2#1, Feb, 1989-No. 7, 1989
Now Comics

1-3 (1.50)	0.30	0.60	1.50
4-11, 13-15 (1.75)	0.40	0.70	1.75
12-(8/88)-5 pg. preview of The Terminator (1st app.)			
	0.80	2.10	5.00
V2#1-7 (1.75)	0.40	0.70	1.75

Savage Dragon #15 © Erik Larsen

Sav Sword of Conan #15 © Conan Properties

	Good	Fine	N-Mint

SABAN'S MIGHTY MORPHIN POWER RANGERS
Dec, 1994 (1.95, color, limited series: 6)
Hamilton Comics

	Good	Fine	N-Mint
1-6:1-w/bound in Power Ranger Barcode Card	0.40	0.80	2.00

SABRETOOTH (See Iron Fist, Power Man, X-Factor #10, & X-Men)
Aug, 1993-No. 4, Nov, 1993 (2.95, color, mini-series)
Marvel Comics

	Good	Fine	N-Mint
1-4: 1-Die-cut-c. 3-Wolverine app.	0.80	1.60	4.00
TPB (12/94, 12.95) r/#1-4	2.00	5.60	13.00

SABRETOOTH CLASSIC
May, 1994-Present (1.50, color)
Marvel Comics

1-15: 1-3-r/Power Man & Iron Fist #66,78,84. 4-r/Spec. S-M #116
9-r/Uncanny X-Men #212, 10-r/Uncanny X-Men #213
11- r/Daredevil #238, 12-r/Classic X-Men #10

	Good	Fine	N-Mint
	0.30	0.60	1.50

SACHS AND VIOLENS
Nov, 1993-No. 4, July, 1994 (2.25, color, mini-series, adult)
Epic Comics (Marvel)

	Good	Fine	N-Mint
1-(2.75)-Embossed-c w/bound-in trading card	0.60	1.10	2.75
1-(3.50)-Platinum edition	1.40	4.00	8.50
2-4-Perez-c/a; w/bound-in trading card: 2-(5/94)	0.50	0.90	2.25

SADE
May 1995-Present (2.95, B&W, Mature readers)
Bishop Press

1-Razor app.	0.60	1.20	3.00
1-(4.95)-Limited Edition, Razor app.	1.00	2.00	5.00

SAFEST PLACE IN THE WORLD, THE
1993 (2.50, color, one-shot)
Dark Horse Comics

1-By Steve Ditko (c/a/scripts)	0.50	1.00	2.50

SAGA OF SWAMP THING (See Swamp Thing)

SAGA OF THE ORIGINAL HUMAN TORCH
Apr, 1990-No. 4, July, 1990 (1.50, limited series)
Marvel Comics

1-4: 1-Origin; Buckler-c/a(p). 3-Hitler-c	0.30	0.60	1.50

SAGA OF THE SUB-MARINER, THE
Nov, 1988-No. 12, Oct, 1989 (1.25/1.50 #5 on, color)
Marvel Comics

1-12: 9-Original X-Men app.	0.30	0.60	1.50

SAINT SINNER (See Razorline)
Oct, 1993-Present (1.75, color)
Marvel Comics

1-(2.50)-Foil embossed cover	0.50	1.00	2.50
2-7: 5-Ectokid x-over	0.40	0.70	1.75

SAMSON
1995 (2.50, color)
Samson Comics

1-Tucci-c	0.50	1.00	2.50

SAMURAI
1985-No. 22, 1988? (1.70, B&W)
Aircel

1	0.80	1.50	3.75
1-2nd & 3rd printings	0.30	0.70	1.70
2–12	0.30	0.70	1.70
2-2nd printing	0.30	0.70	1.70
13-1st Dale Keown-a (1987)	1.10	2.70	6.50

	Good	Fine	N-Mint
14-16: Keown-a	0.90	1.80	4.50
17-22	0.30	0.70	1.70

SAMUREE
May, 1993-Present (2.50, color)
Continuity Comics

	Good	Fine	N-Mint
V2#1-4-Embossed cover	0.50	1.00	2.50

SANDMAN, THE
Winter, 1974; No. 2, Apr-May, 1975-No. 6, Dec-Jan, 1975-76
National Periodical Publications

	Good	Fine	N-Mint
1-1st app. Sandman; Kirby-a	1.30	3.30	8.00
2-6: 6-Kirby/Wood-c/a	0.90	1.70	4.25

SANDMAN (See Books of Magic & Vertigo Preview)
Jan, 1989-Present (1.50-1.95, color, mature)
DC Comics (Vertigo imprint #47 on)

	Good	Fine	N-Mint
1-(2.00, 52 pgs.)-1st app. modern day Sandman; Neil Gaiman scripts begin; Sam Kieth-a(p)	10.00	31.00	72.00
2-Sam Kieth-a(p); Cain & Abel app.	5.30	16.00	37.00
3-5: Sam Kieth-a(p). 3-Constantine app.	4.70	14.00	33.00
6, 7	3.00	9.90	23.00
8-Regular edition has Jeanette Kahn Publishorial & American Cancer Society ad (with no indicia) on inside front cover; Death-c/story (1st app.)	7.10	21.00	50.00
8-Limited edition (only 600+/- copies) has Karen Berger editorial & next issue teaser on inside covers	25.00	80.00	175.00
9-13: 10-Explains #8 mix-up; has bound-in Shocker movie poster	2.00	5.00	12.00
14-(2.50, 52 pgs.)-Nightbreed fold-out	2.00	6.00	14.00
15-20: 17, 18-Kelley Jones-a	1.30	3.10	7.50
18-Error version with 1st three panels on pg. 1 in blue ink	1.30	3.10	7.50
19-Error version w/switched pgs. (no 2 pg. spread)	1.20	2.90	7.00
21, 23-27: Seasons of Mist storyline	1.20	2.90	7.00
22-Daniel app.	1.70	4.20	10.00
28-30	0.80	1.60	4.00
31-35, 37-48: 41,44-50,57-Metallic ink	0.60	1.20	3.00
36-(2.50, 52 pgs.)	0.90	1.70	4.25
49, 51-53, 55: 49-Begin 1.95-c	0.50	1.00	2.50
50-(2.95, 52 pgs.)-Black-c w/metallic ink by McKean; Russell-a; McFarlane pin-up	0.70	1.40	3.50

50–Platinum ed.	10.00	20.00	50.00
50-(2.95)-Signed & Limited (5,000)-Treasury Edition with sketch of			
Neil Gaiman	1.70	4.00	10.00
54-Re-intro Prez; Death app.	0.70	1.40	3.50
56-68: 65-w/bound-in trading card	0.40	0.80	2.00
69-begin 2.50-c; 70-Zulli-a	0.50	1.00	2.50
Annual 1 (10/94, 3.95)	0.80	1.60	4.00
Special 1 ('91, 3.50, 68 pgs.)-Glow-in-dark	1.10	2.70	6.50
...: A Gallery of Dreams (2.95)-Intro by Gaiman			
	0.60	1.20	3.00
...: (The) Brief Lives (19.95) r/#41-49	3.00	8.60	20.00

SANDMAN MYSTERY THEATRE
Apr, 1993-Present (1.95, color, mature)
DC Comics (Vertigo)

1-27: 1-Matt Wagner scripts begin	0.40	0.80	2.00
28-begin 2.25-c; 29-Hourman app.	0.50	0.90	2.25
… Annual 1 (10/94, 3.95, 68 pgs.)	1.00	2.00	5.00

SARGE STEEL (Becomes Secret Agent #9 on; see Judomaster)
Dec, 1964-No. 8, Mar-Apr, 1966 (All 12¢ issues)
Charlton Comics

1-Origin & 1st app.	1.70	5.10	12.00
2-5, 7, 8	1.00	2.50	6.00
6-2nd app. Judomaster	1.40	3.50	8.50

SATAN'S SIX
Apr, 1993-No. 4, July, 1993 (2.95, color, limited series)

1-Polybagged w/Kirbychrome card; Kirby/McFarlane-c; Kirby-p (8 pgs.)			
	0.60	1.20	3.00
2-4-Polybagged w/3 trading cards. 4-Teenagents Preview			
	0.60	1.20	3.00

SATAN'S SIX: HELLSPAWN
June, 1994-No. 3, July, 1994 (2.50, color, limited series)
Topps Comics

1-3: 1-(6/94)-Indicia incorrectly shows "Vol. 1 #2". 2-(6/94)			
	0.50	1.00	2.50

SAVAGE DRAGON, THE (See Megaton)
July, 1992-No. 3, Dec, 1992 (1.95, color, mini-series)
Image Comics
1-Erik Larsen-c/a; has bound-in poster in all; 4 cover color variations

	Good	Fine	N-Mint
w/4 diff. posters	1.10	2.70	6.50
2-Intro Super Patriot-c/story (10/92)	0.80	1.60	4.00
3-Has Image #0 coupon	0.70	1.30	3.25
3-With coupon missing	0.40	0.80	2.00
...Vs. Savage Megaton Man 1 (3/93, 1.95, color, one-shot)-Larsen			
& Simpson-c/a	0.40	0.80	2.00
TPB ('93, 9.95) r/#1-3	1.70	4.20	10.00

SAVAGE DRAGON, THE
June, 1993-Present (1.95, color)
Image Comics

	Good	Fine	N-Mint
1-Erik Larsen-c/a & scripts begin	0.60	1.20	3.00
2-(2.95, 52 pgs.)-Teenage Mutant Ninja Turtles app.; flip book features			
Vanguard #0 (see Megaton for 1st app.)	0.70	1.30	3.25
3-7: 3-Mighty Man back up story w/Austin-i. 4-Flip book w/Ricochet.			
5-Mighty Man flip-c, 7 pg. story & poster. 6-Jae Lee poster. 7-Vanguard			
poster	0.50	0.90	2.25
8-12,14-15: 8-Deadly Duo poster by Larsen. 13-Larsen version			
15-S.Dragon poster by Larson	0.40	0.80	2.00
13, 16-19: (2.50)-13: Jim Lee-c(p)	0.50	1.00	2.50

SAVAGE DRAGON/TEENAGE MUTANT NINJA TURTLES CROSSOVER
Sept, 1993 (2.75, color)
Mirage Publishing

	Good	Fine	N-Mint
1-Larsen-c(i) only	0.60	1.10	2.75

SAVAGE SHE-HULK, THE (Also see Sensational She-Hulk)
Feb, 1980-No. 25, Feb, 1982
Marvel Comics Group

	Good	Fine	N-Mint
1-Origin & 1st app. She-Hulk	1.00	2.50	6.00
2-10	0.60	1.10	2.75
11-25: 25-(52 pgs)	0.50	0.90	2.25

SAVAGE SWORD OF CONAN
Aug, 1974-July 1995 (B&W, magazine)
Marvel Comics Group

	Good	Fine	N-Mint
1-3rd app. Red Sonja; Boris painted-c	11.00	33.00	78.00
2-Neal Adams-c/a	5.00	15.00	35.00
3-Adams-a; Severin/Smith-a	2.90	8.60	20.00
4-N. Adams/Kane-r; Boris painted-c	2.10	6.40	15.00
5-10: 5,7,9,10,12,15-Boris painted-c	1.70	5.10	12.00
11-20: 14-N. Adams-a(p)	1.50	3.80	9.00
21-50: 45-Red Sonja returns	1.30	3.00	8.00

51-100: 83-Red Sonja-r by N. Adams	1.00	2.00	5.00
101-176: 163-Begin 2.25-c	0.60	1.20	3.00
177-235: 211-Rafael Kayanan's 1st Conan-a, also 211-213,215,217;			
235-final issue	0.50	0.90	2.25
Special 1 (1975)-Smith-r/Conan #10, 13	1.30	3.30	8.00

SAVAGE TALES (Magazine, B&W)
May, 1971; No. 2, Oct, 1973; No. 3, Feb, 1974-No. 12, Summer, 1975
Marvel Comics Group

1-Origin & 1st app. The Man Thing; Conan The Barbarian by Barry Smith			
begins; Ka-Zar by Buscema	19.00	58.00	135.00
2-Wrightson King Kull-r/Creatures On The Loose #10; Brunner,			
Williamson-a	6.00	19.00	45.00
3-Smith, Brunner, Steranko, Williamson-a	4.30	12.90	30.00
4, 5: 5-Last Conan; Adams-c	2.90	8.60	20.00
6-KaZar begins; Adams-c	1.10	2.70	6.50
7-Adams inks; Boris-c (also #10)	0.90	1.80	4.50
8-Shanna The She Devil begins, ends #10	0.80	1.60	4.00
9, 11	0.60	1.20	3.00
10-Adams-a(inks)	0.80	1.60	4.00
...Featuring Ka-Zar Annual 1 (#12 inside, Sum/75)-Ka-Zar origin by Gil			
Kane; Smith-r	1.00	2.00	5.00

SAVAGE TALES (Magazine)
Nov, 1985-No. 9, Mar, 1987

1-1st app. The Nam	0.60	1.20	3.00
2-9: 4-2nd Nam story	0.30	0.60	1.50

SCARAB
Nov, 1993-No. 8, June, 1994 (1.95, color, limited series)
DC Comics (Vertigo)

1-8-Fabry-c: 2-Phantom Stranger app.	0.40	0.80	2.00

SCARLETT
Jan, 1993-No. 14, Feb, 1994 (1.75, color)
DC Comics

1-(2.95, 52 pgs.)	0.60	1.20	3.00
2–14	0.40	0.70	1.75

SCARLET WITCH (See X-Men #4)
Jan, 1994-No. 4, Apr, 1994 (1.75, color, mini-series)
Marvel Comics

1–4	0.40	0.70	1.75

	Good	Fine	N-Mint

SCAVENGERS
1993 (July)-Present (2.50, color, serially numbered)
Triumphant Comics
1-9: 5, 6-Triumphant Unleashed x-over. 9-(3/94)

	Good	Fine	N-Mint
	0.50	1.00	2.50
0-Retail Edition (3/94, 2.50, 36 pgs.)	0.50	1.00	2.50
0-Giveaway Edition (3/94, 20 pgs.)	0.30	0.60	1.50
0-Coupon redemption edition	0.50	1.00	2.50
10,11: 10-(4/94)	0.50	1.00	2.50

SCOOBY DOO (TV) (…Where Are You? #1-16, 26; …Mystery Comics #17 on)
Mar, 1970-No. 30, Feb, 1975 (Hanna-Barbera)
Gold Key

	Good	Fine	N-Mint
1	4.60	14.00	32.00
2–5	2.90	8.60	20.00
6–10	2.30	7.00	16.00
11-20: 11-Tufts-a	1.70	4.20	10.00
21-30	1.20	2.40	6.00

SCOOBY DOO (TV)
Apr, 1975-No. 11, Dec, 1976 (Hanna-Barbera)
Charlton Comics

	Good	Fine	N-Mint
1	2.30	6.90	16.00
2–5	1.10	2.70	6.50
6–11	1.10	2.20	5.50

SCOOBY DOO (TV)
Oct, 1977-No. 9, Feb, 1979 (Hanna-Barbera)

	Good	Fine	N-Mint
Marvel Comics Group	0.60	1.20	3.00
1	0.30	0.60	1.50
2–9			

SCUD: THE DISPOSABLE ASSASSIN
Feb, 1994-Present (2.95, B&W)
Fireman Press

	Good	Fine	N-Mint
1–7	0.60	1.20	3.00

SEA DEVILS (See Showcase #27-29)
Sept-Oct, 1961-No. 35, May-June, 1967
National Periodical Publications

	Good	Fine	N-Mint
1-Grey-tone-c	40.00	130.00	355.00
2-Last 10¢ issue; grey-tone-c	20.00	60.00	160.00

Sec Life of Dr. Mirage #12 © Voyager

Secret Origins Special #1 © DC

3-Grey-tone-c	16.00	50.00	110.00
4, 5-Grey-tone-c	15.00	45.00	105.00
6-10: 10-Last Russ Heath-a	8.00	24.00	55.00
11, 12, 14-20: 14-16-Heath-c	5.70	17.00	40.00
13-Kubert, Colan art	6.00	18.00	42.00
21-35	3.90	12.00	27.00

SEAQUEST (TV)
Mar, 1994 (2.25, color)
Nemesis Comics
1-Has 2 different-c stocks (slick & cardboard)

	0.50	0.90	2.25

SEBASTION O
May, 1993-No. 3, July, 1993 (1.95, color, mini-series)
DC Comics (Vertigo)

1-3-Grant Morrison scripts	0.40	0.80	2.00

SECOND LIFE OF DOCTOR MIRAGE, THE(See Shadowman #16)
Nov, 1993-Present (2.50, color)
Valiant
1-18: 1-With bound-in poster. 5-Shadowman app. 7-w/bound-in
trading card. 13-Soap opera's Walt Willey app.

	0.50	1.00	2.50
1-Gold ink logo edition; no price on-c	1.30	3.10	7.50

SECRET AGENT (Formerly Sarge Steel)
V2#9, Oct, 1966; V2#10, Oct, 1967
Charlton Comics

V2#9-Sarge Steel part-r begins	1.40	3.50	8.50

	Good	Fine	N-Mint
10-Tiffany Sinn, CIA app.	0.90	1.70	4.25

SECRET AGENT (TV)
Nov, 1966; No. 2, Jan, 1968
Gold Key

1-Photo-c	11.00	34.00	80.00
2-Photo-c	7.00	21.00	50.00

SECRET CITY SAGA (See Jack Kirby's...)

SECRET DEFENDERS(See Fantastic Four #374)
Mar, 1993-Present (1.75/1.95, color)
Marvel Comics

1-(2.50)-Red foil-c; Dr. Strange, Wolverine, Nomad, Darkhawk,			
& Spider-Woman begin	0.60	1.10	2.75
2-11,13,14: 9-New team begins w/Silver Surfer			
	0.40	0.70	1.75
12-(2.50)-Prismatic cover; Thanos app.	0.50	1.00	2.50
15-24: 15-Begin 1.95-c; bound-in card sheet. 18-Giant Man & Iron Fist app.			
	0.40	0.80	2.00
25-(2.50, 52 pgs)	0.50	1.00	2.50

SECRET ORIGINS (See 80 Page Giant #8)
Aug-Oct, 1961 (Annual)
National Periodical Publications

1-Reprints origins Adam Strange (Showcase 17), Green Lantern (G.L. 1),			
Challengers (Showcase 6), J'onn J'onzz (Det. 225), The Flash			
(Showcase 4), Superman-Batman team (World's Finest 94), Wonder			
Woman (W.W. 105)	28.00	83.00	330.00

SECRET ORIGINS
Feb-Mar, 1973-No. 6, Jan-Feb, 1974; No. 7, Oct-Nov, 1974
National Periodical Publications (All origin reprints) (All 20¢)

1-r/1 pg. origin/Action #1 & Showcase #4	2.00	5.00	12.00
2-4: 2-New Green Lantern; new Atom	1.10	2.20	5.50
5-7: 6-Legion. 7-Origin Robin	0.90	1.70	4.25

SECRET ORIGINS
April, 1986-No. 50, Aug, 1990
DC Comics

1-Origin Superman retold	0.60	1.20	3.00
2	0.40	0.80	2.00
3-5: 3-Shazam. 4-Firestorm	0.40	0.80	2.00

6-Golden Age Batman app.	0.80	1.60	4.00
7-10, 11, 12, 14-26	0.40	0.80	2.00
13-Origin Nightwing	0.80	1.60	4.00
27-38, 40-44: 27-Begin 1.50-c	0.30	0.60	1.50
39-Animal Man-c/story	0.60	1.20	3.00
45-49	0.30	0.60	1.50
50-(3.95, 100 pgs.)-Flash of Two Worlds	0.80	1.60	4.00
Annual 1 ('87, 2.00). Annual 2 ('88, 2.00)	0.40	0.80	2.00
Annual 3 ('89, 2.95, 80 pgs.)	0.60	1.20	3.00
Special 1-(10/89, 2.00)-Batman Villains; Penguin (w/Kieth-a), Riddler,			
Two-Face; Gaiman scripts (2 stories)	1.00	2.00	5.00

SECRET ORIGINS OF THE WORLD'S GREATEST SUPER-HEROES
1989 (4.95, 148 pgs.)
DC Comics

nn-r/origin Batman, Superman, JLA	1.00	2.00	5.00

SECRET SIX
Apr-May, 1968-No. 7, Apr-May, 1969
National Periodical Publications

1-Origin/1st app.	5.00	15.00	35.00
2–7	2.90	9.00	20.00

SECRET SOCIETY OF SUPER-VILLAINS
May-June, 1976-No. 15, June-July, 1978
National Periodical Publications

1-Origin; JLA cameo & Capt. Cold app.	0.50	1.00	2.50
2-5: 2-Re-intro/origin Capt. Comet;	0.40	0.80	2.00
6-15: 9, 10-Creeper x-over	0.30	0.60	1.50

SECRETS OF HAUNTED HOUSE
Apr-May, 1975-No. 46, Mar., 1982
National Periodical Publications/DC Comics

1	0.70	1.30	3.25
2–10	0.50	0.90	2.25
11-46: 31-Mr. E begins, ends 41	0.30	0.60	1.50

SECRETS OF SINISTER HOUSE (Sinister House of Secret Love #1-4)
No. 5, June-July, 1972-No. 18, June-July, 1974
National Periodical Publications

5-9: 7-Redondo-a	0.50	1.00	2.50
10-Neal Adams-a(i)	1.00	2.50	6.00
11-18: 17-Early Chaykin-a(1 pg.)	0.40	0.70	1.80

	Good	Fine	N-Mint

SECRET SQUIRREL (TV)
October, 1966 (Hanna-Barbera, 12¢)
Gold Key

| 1 | 10.00 | 28.00 | 75.00 |

SECRET WEAPONS
Sept, 1993-Present (2.25, color)
Valiant

1-10,12-21: 3-Reese-i. 5-Ninjak app. 9-w/bound-in trading card.			
12-Bloodshot app.	0.50	0.90	2.25
11-(2.50)-Enclosed in manilla envelope; Sep on envelope, Aug on-c;			
Bloodshot app.	0.50	1.00	2.50

SELF-LOATHING COMICS
Feb, 1995 (2.95, B&W)
Fantagraphics Books

| 1-Robert Crumb | 0.60 | 1.20 | 3.00 |

SENSATIONAL SHE-HULK (Also see Savage She-Hulk)
May, 1989-No. 60, Feb, 1994 (1.50, color)
Marvel Comics

V2#1-John Byrne-a begins, ends #8	0.70	1.30	3.25
2–8	0.40	0.90	2.20
9-49, 51-60: 29-Wolverine app. 56-War Zone app.; Hulk cameo. 57-Vs.			
Hulk-c/sty. 58-Electro-c/s. 59-Jack O'Lantern			
	0.40	0.70	1.75
50-(2.95, 52 pgs.)-Embossed green foil-c	0.60	1.20	3.00

Note: Dale Keown c(p)-13, 15-22.

Shadow Cabinet #1 © Milestone

Shadowhawk III #1 © Jim Valentino

SGT. FURY (& His Howling Commandos; also see Fury)
May, 1963-No. 167, Dec, 1981
Marvel Comics Group

1-1st app. Sgt. Fury; Kirby a-1-7, 13p	70.00	210.00	685.00
2	28.00	84.00	225.00
3-5: 3-Reed Richards x-over	15.00	45.00	120.00
6-10: 10-1st app. Capt. Savage (9/64)	10.00	30.00	80.00
11, 12, 14-20: 15-Ditko art(i)	7.10	21.00	50.00
13-Early Capt. America & Bucky app. (12/64); 2nd solo Capt. America			
x-over outside the Avengers	24.00	71.00	190.00
21-30: 25-Red Skull app.	5.00	15.00	35.00
31-50: 34-Origin Howling Commandos	2.90	8.60	20.00
51-60	2.30	7.00	16.00
61-80: 64-Capt Savage x-over	2.30	5.80	14.00
81-100: 98-Deadly dozen x-over	1.70	4.20	10.00
101-120: 101-Origin retold	1.00	2.50	6.00
121-130	1.00	2.00	5.00
131-150	0.80	1.60	4.00
151-167	0.80	1.60	4.00
Annual 1 ('65)-One new story plus r/#4, 5	13.00	39.00	90.00
Special 2 ('66)	5.70	17.00	40.00
Special 3 ('67)	4.00	10.70	25.00
Special 4 ('68)-Severin-a	2.50	6.30	15.00
Special 5-7 ('69-'71): 6-Severin-a	1.40	4.00	8.50

SGT. ROCK (Formerly Our Army at War)(See Brave & the Bold 52)
No. 302, March, 1977-No. 422, July, 1988
National Periodical Publications/DC Comics

302	1.70	4.20	10.00
303-310	1.30	3.30	8.00
311-320	1.00	2.00	5.00
321-350	0.80	1.60	4.00
351-422	0.50	0.90	2.25
Annual 2-4: Formerly Sgt. Rock's Prize...	0.60	1.20	3.00

SGT. ROCK SPECIAL (Sgt. Rock #14 on)
Oct, 1988-No. 21, Feb, 1992 (2.00, color, 52 pgs.)
DC Comics

1	0.50	1.00	2.50
2-8, 10-21: 13-Dinosaur story	0.40	0.80	2.00
9-Enemy Ace reprint	0.50	1.00	2.50
1 ('92, 2.95, 68 pgs.)-Unpublished Kubert	0.60	1.20	3.00
2 ('94, 2.95, 68 pgs.)-Heath, Chaykin-a; Brereton-c			

	Good	Fine	N-Mint
	0.60	1.20	3.00

SGT. ROCK'S PRIZE BATTLE TALES (Becomes Sgt. Rock Annual #2 on)
Winter, 1964 (One-shot, 80 pg. giant)
National Periodical Publications

| 1-Kubert, Heath-r; new Kubert-c | 23.00 | 69.00 | 160.00 |

SHADE, THE CHANGING MAN
June-July, 1977-No. 8, Aug-Sept, 1978
National Periodical Pub./DC Comics

| 1-1st app.; Ditko-c/a in all | 1.00 | 2.00 | 5.00 |
| 2-8 | 0.60 | 1.10 | 2.75 |

SHADE, THE CHANGING MAN
July, 1990-Present (1.50/1.75/1.95, color, mature)
DC Comics (Vertigo imprint #33 on)

1-(2.50, 52 pgs.)-Milligan scripts in all	0.80	1.60	4.00
2-40: 16-Last 1.50-c.	0.40	0.80	2.00
41-49,51-59-(1.95): 42-44-J. Constantine app. 55-w/bound in trading card			
	0.40	0.80	2.00
50-(2.95, 52 pgs.)	0.70	1.40	3.50
60-begin 2.25-c; 61–62	0.50	0.90	2.25

SHADOW, THE
Aug, 1964-No. 8, Sept, 1965 (All 12¢ issues)
Archie Comics (Radio Comics)

1	4.00	12.00	28.00
2-8: 3, 4, 6, 7-The Fly 1-pg. strips in each. 7-The Shield app.			
	2.60	7.70	18.00

SHADOW, THE
Oct-Nov, 1973-No. 12, Aug-Sept, 1975
National Periodical Publications

1-Kaluta art #s 1-6	3.60	11.00	25.00
2	2.10	6.00	15.00
3-Kaluta/Wrightson art	2.40	7.30	17.00
4, 6-Kaluta art ends	2.00	5.00	12.00
5, 7-12	0.80	2.10	5.00

SHADOW, THE
May, 1986-No. 4, Aug, 1986 (Mini-series)
DC Comics

| 1-4: Howard Chaykin art in all | 0.40 | 0.80 | 2.00 |

Blood & Judgement (12.95)-r/1-4	1.90	6.00	13.00

SHADOW, THE
Aug, 1987-No. 19, Jan, 1989 (1.50, color)
DC Comics

1–19	0.30	0.60	1.50
Annual 1 (12/87, 2.25), Annual 2 (1988)	0.50	0.90	2.25

SHADOW, THE
June, 1994-No. 2, July, 1994 (2.50, color)
Dark Horse Comics

1,2-Adaptation from Universal Pictures	0.50	0.90	2.25

SHADOW: HELL'S HEAT WAVE, THE
Apr, 1995- June, 1995 (2.95, color, limited series)
Dark Horse Comics

1–3, Kaluta-s	0.60	1.20	3.00

SHADOW AND THE MYSTERIOUS 3, THE
Sept, 1994 (2.95, color, one-shot)
Dark Horse Comics

1	0.60	1.20	3.00

SHADOW CABINET
Jan, 1994-Present (1.75, color)
DC Comics (Milestone)

0-(2.50, 52 pgs.)-Silver ink-c; Simonson-c	0.50	1.00	2.50
1-13: 1-Byrne-c	0.40	0.70	1.75
14-(2.50, 36 pgs.) 15-(2.50)	0.50	1.00	2.50

SHADOW EMPIRES: FAITH CONQUERS
Aug, 1994-Present (2.95, color, limited series:4)
Dark Horse Comics

1–3	0.60	1.20	3.00

SHADOWHAWK (See Images of... & Youngblood #2)
Aug, 1992-No. 4, Mar,1993 (1.95/2.50, color)
Image Comics

1-Embossed & silver foil stamped-c; has Image #0 coupon			
	1.30	3.00	8.00
1-With coupon missing	0.70	1.40	3.50
1-(1.95)-Newsstand version w/o foil-c	0.50	1.00	2.50
2-Shadowhawk poster w/McFarlane-i; brief Spawn app.; wraparound-c			

	Good	Fine	N-Mint
w/silver ink highlights; Intro Arson	0.60	1.20	3.00
3-(2.50)-Glow-in-the-dark-c;	0.50	1.00	2.50
4-(1.95)-Savage Dragon-c/story	0.40	0.80	2.00

SHADOWHAWK(Continues from ShadowHawk III)
No. 12, Aug, 1994-Present (1.95, color)
Image Comics

12,13: 12-Pull-out poster by Texeira. 13-w/ShadowBone poster; WildC.A.T.s app.	0.40	0.80	2.00
0-(10/94)-Liefeld-c/a/story; ShadowBart poster	0.40	0.80	2.00
14-16:14-(10/94, 2.50) 14-The Others app. 16-18:16-Supreme app. 17-Shadowbean poster by L.Marder	0.50	1.00	2.50
Special 1 (12/94, 3.50,52 pgs) Silver-Age Shadowhawk flip book	0.70	1.40	3.50
...:Out of the Shadows (19.95) r/Youngblood #2, Shadowhawk #1-4, ...Image Comics #0, Operation:Urban Storm	2.90	8.60	20.00

SHADOWHAWK II
May, 1993-No. 3, Aug, 1993 (Color, mini-series)
Image Comics

1-(3.50)-Die-cut mirricard-c	0.70	1.40	3.50
2-(1.95)-Foil embossed logo; reveals ident.	0.40	0.80	2.00
3-(2.95)-Pop-up-c w/Pact "ashcan" insert	0.60	1.20	3.00

SHADOWHAWK III
Nov, 1993-No. 4, Mar, 1994 (1.95, color, limited series)
Image Comics

V3 #1-Red foil & gold foil editions exist; intro Valentine	0.40	0.80	2.00
2-4: 2-(52 pgs.)-Shadowhawk contracts HIV virus; has free extra 16 pg. insert of U.S. Male by Murphy Anderson; silver foil-c	0.40	0.80	2.00

SHAWDOWHAWK GALLERY
Apr, 1994 (1.95, color)
Image Comics

1	0.40	0.80	2.00

SHADOW: IN THE COILS OF LEVIATHON, THE
Oct, 1993-No. 4, Apr, 1994 (2.95, color, mini-series)
Dark Horse Comics

1-4-Kaluta-c & part scripts	0.60	1.20	3.00
TPB (10/94, 13.95) r/1-4	2.00	6.00	14.00

SHADOWHAWK-VAMPIRELLA
Feb 1995 (4.95, color, limited series)
Image Comics

2-See Vampirella-Shawdowhawk for Pt 1			
	0.80	2.10	5.00

SHADOWMAN (See X-O Manowar #4)
May, 1992-Present (2.50, color)
Valiant Comics

1-Partial origin	1.40	4.30	10.00
2-5: 3-1st Sousa the Soul Eater	0.90	3.00	6.00
6,7	0.50	1.00	2.50
8-1st app. Master Darque	0.90	2.30	5.50
9, 10	0.50	1.00	2.50
11-15, 17-41: 15-Minor Turok app. 17, 18-Archer & Armstrong x-over. 19-Aerosmith-c/story. 23-Doctor Mirage app. 24-(4/94). 25-w/bound-in trading card. 29-Chaos Effect	0.50	1.00	2.50
16-1st app. Dr. Mirage (8/93)	0.70	1.80	4.25
0-(2.50, 4/94)-Regular edition	0.50	1.00	2.50
0-(3.50, 4/94)-Chromium cover edition	0.70	1.40	3.50
Yearbook 1 (12/94, 3.95)	0.80	1.60	4.00

SHADOW OF THE BATMAN
Dec, 1985-No. 5, April, 1986 (1.75, mini-series)
DC Comics

1-Reprints from Detective Comics	0.90	2.30	5.50
2, 3, 5	0.70	1.40	3.50
4-Joker cover/story	1.00	1.90	4.75

SHADOWS FALL
Nov, 1994- Apr, 1995 (2.95, color, limited series)
DC Comics

1–6	0.60	1.20	3.00

SHAMAN'S TEARS
May, 1993-No. 2, Aug, 1993 (2.50, color)
Image Comics

1,-3: 1-Embossed & red foil stamped-c; Mike Grell-c/a/scripts. 2-Cover unfolds into poster; 8/93-c, 7/93 inside. 3-(11/94)			
	0.50	1.00	2.50

	Good	Fine	N-Mint
4-8-(1.95); Jon Sable app.	0.40	0.80	2.00
9	0.40	0.80	2.00

SHANNA, THE SHE-DEVIL
Dec, 1972-No. 5, Aug, 1973 (All 20¢ issues)
Marvel Comics Group

1-1st app. Shanna; Steranko-c	1.00	2.00	5.00
2-Steranko-c	0.50	1.00	2.50
3–5	0.40	0.70	1.80

SHAZAM!
Feb, 1973-No. 35, May-June, 1978
National Periodical Pub./DC Comics
1-1st revival Capt. Marvel since G.A.; origin

	0.60	1.20	3.00
2-35: 8, 12-17: 100 pg. issues	0.30	0.60	1.50

SHAZAM: THE NEW BEGINNING
Apr, 1987-No. 4, July, 1987 (mini-series)
DC Comics

1-4: 1-New origin	0.20	0.40	1.00

SHE-BAT (See Murcielaga, She-Bat & Valeria the She Bat)

S.H.I.E.L.D. (Also see Nick Fury)
Feb, 1973-No. 5, Oct, 1973
Marvel Comics Group

1: 1-5-r/Strange Tales 146-155	0.80	1.60	4.00
2–5	0.40	0.80	2.00

SHI: THE WAY OF THE WARRIOR (See Razor Annual #1 for 1st app.)
Mar, 1994-Present (2.50, color)
Crusade Comics

1	3.30	8.30	20.00
1-Commemorative ed., B&W, new-c; given out at 1994 San Diego Comic Con			
	7.00	14.00	35.00
1-Fan Appreciation -reprint #1	0.40	0.80	2.00
1–Fan Appreciation-variant	1.60	3.20	8.00
2	2.00	4.00	10.00
3	1.00	2.00	5.00
4–5; 4-Silvestri poster	0.60	1.20	3.00
5-variant-c-Silvestri	1.00	2.00	5.00
TPB ('95, 12.95) r/#1-4	1.90	5.60	13.00

Showcase #48 © DC

Showcase #98 © DC

SHOGUN WARRIORS
Feb, 1979-No. 20, Sept, 1980
Marvel Comics Group

1-Early Japanese animation adaptation	0.40	0.80	2.00
2–10	0.30	0.60	1.50
11–20	0.30	0.60	1.50

SHOWCASE
Mar-Apr, 1956-No. 104, Sept, 1978
National Periodical Publications/DC Comics

1-Fire Fighters	220.00	660.00	2200.00
2-King Of The Wild; Kubert-a	75.00	225.00	600.00
3-The Frogmen by Heath; early grey-tone	69.00	206.00	550.00
4-Origin & 1st app. Silver Age Flash; 1st Silver Age super-hero (9-10/56); Infantino/Kubert-c	1402.00	4205.00	22000.00
5-Manhunters	89.00	268.00	715.00
6-Origin & 1st app. The Challengers by Kirby (1-2/57)(1st DC Silver Age Super-Hero team)	167.00	500.00	2500.00
7-Challengers by Kirby (2nd app.)	109.00	326.00	1305.00
8-Flash (2nd app.); origin/1st app. Capt. Cold	656.00	1967.00	5900.00
9-(7-8/57)-Lois Lane (pre-No. 1)	333.00	1000.00	2900.00
10-Lois Lane	146.00	438.00	1750.00
11-Challengers by Kirby (3rd app.)	117.00	351.00	1170.00
12-Challengers by Kirby (4th app.)	101.00	303.00	1210.00
13-The Flash (3rd app.)	271.00	813.00	2710.00
14-The Flash (4th app.)	293.00	878.00	3510.00
15-Space Ranger; 1st app. (7-8/58)	77.00	230.00	1150.00
16-Space Ranger; 2nd app. (9-10/58)	65.00	195.00	650.00

	Good	Fine	N-Mint
17-Adventures on Other Worlds; origin & 1st app. Adam Strange (11-12/58)			
	121.00	363.00	1450.00
18-Adam Strange (2nd app.)	103.00	309.00	825.00
19-Adam Strange (3rd app.)	95.00	285.00	950.00
20-Origin & 1st app. Rip Hunter	61.00	180.00	550.00
21-Rip Hunter; 2nd app.	36.00	108.00	325.00
22-Origin & 1st app. Silver Age Green Lantern (9-10/59)			
	329.00	988.00	3950.00
23-Green Lantern (11-12/60)-2nd app.	146.00	437.00	1310.00
24-Green Lantern (1-2/60)-3rd app.	148.00	443.00	1330.00
25, 26-Rip Hunter by Kubert (3rd/4th app.). 25-Grey-tone-c			
	26.00	79.00	210.00
27-Sea Devils (1st app., 7-8/60)-Grey-tone-c; Russ Heath-c/a begins,			
ends #29	68.00	204.00	545.00
28-Sea Devils (2nd app.)-Grey-tone-c	39.00	118.00	315.00
29-Sea Devils (3rd app.)-Grey-tone-c	40.00	120.00	320.00
30-Origin Aquaman retold (see Adv. 260)	55.00	164.00	545.00
31, 32-Aquaman (3-4/61 & 7-8/61)	31.00	92.00	305.00
33-Aquaman (7-8/61)	37.00	110.00	365.00
34-Origin & 1st app. Silver Age Atom by Kane & Anderson (9-10/61);			
reprinted in Secret Origins #2	122.00	367.00	1100.00
35-The Atom (2nd app.); last 10¢ issue	97.00	291.00	680.00
36-The Atom(3rd app.;pre-dates Atom #1)	72.00	216.00	505.00
37-1st app. Metal Men (3-4/62)	59.00	178.00	475.00
38-Metal Men (5-6/62, 2nd app.)	45.00	135.00	360.00
39-Metal Men (7-8/62, 3rd app.)	34.00	103.00	275.00
40-Metal Men (9-10/62, 4th app.)	32.00	96.00	255.00
41, 42-Tommy Tomorrow	16.00	47.00	125.00
43-Dr. No; 1st DC Silver Age movie adapt.	41.00	122.00	325.00
44-Tommy Tomorrow	10.00	30.00	80.00
45-Sgt. Rock; origin retold	20.00	60.00	160.00
46, 47-Tommy Tomorrow	8.00	24.00	65.00
48, 49-Cave Carson (3rd tryout series; see Brave & the Bold)			
	5.00	15.00	45.00
50, 51-I Spy (#50 is not a reprint)	4.00	13.00	40.00
52-Cave Carson	4.00	12.00	35.00
53, 54-G. I. Joe; Heath-a	5.00	15.00	45.00
55-Dr. Fate & Hourman; 1st solo G.A. Green Lantern app. in S.A. (3-4/65)			
(pre-dates Green Lantern 40); 1st Silver Age app. Solomon Grundy			
	21.00	62.00	185.00
56-Dr. Fate & Hourman	6.00	19.00	58.00
57-Enemy Ace by Kubert (4th app. after Our Army at War 155)			
	13.00	40.00	90.00

58-Enemy Ace by Kubert (5th app.)	10.90	25.00	85.00
59-Teen Titans (3rd app., 11-12/65)	8.00	25.00	75.00
60-1st SA app. Spectre (1-2/66); text origin	26.00	77.00	180.00
61-The Spectre by Anderson (2nd app.)	15.00	45.00	105.00
62-Origin/1st app. Inferior Five (5-6/66)	6.00	18.00	55.00
63, 65-Inferior Five. 65-X-Men parody	4.00	10.50	28.00
64-The Spectre (3rd app.)	13.00	40.00	93.00
66, 67-B'Wana Beast	2.00	6.00	14.00
68, 69, 71-Maniaks	2.00	6.00	14.00
70-Binky (9-10/67)-Tryout issue	2.00	6.00	14.00
72-Top Gun (Johnny Thunder-r); Toth-a	2.00	6.00	14.00
73-Origin & 1st app. Creeper; Ditko-c/a	10.00	30.00	90.00
74-1st app. Anthro (5/68)	6.00	18.30	55.00
75-1st app. Hawk & Dove by Ditko (6/68)	8.00	23.00	75.00
76-1st app. Batlash (8/68)	4.00	11.00	35.00
77-1st app. Angel and the Ape (9/68)	4.00	11.00	35.00
78-1st app. Jonny Double (11/68)	2.30	7.00	16.00
79-1st app. Dolphin; origin Aqualad (12/68)	3.00	9.00	30.00
80-Phantom Stranger-r; Neal Adams-c	1.90	6.00	13.00
81-Windy & Willy	1.70	5.00	12.00
82-1st app. Nightmaster (5/69); Kubert-c	4.00	13.00	42.00
83, 84-Nightmaster by Wrightson/Jones/Kaluta with Kubert-c. 83-Last 12¢			
issue. 84-Origin retold; 15¢ issues begin	4.00	11.00	38.00
85-87: Firehair by Kubert	1.80	5.00	11.00
88-90: Jason's Quest	1.00	2.50	6.00
91-93 (9/70)-Manhunter 2070. 92-Origin	1.00	2.50	6.00
94-Intro/origin New Doom Patrol (8-9/77)	1.30	3.00	7.50
95,96-The Doom Patrol	1.00	2.00	5.00
97-99: Power Girl. 97, 98-Origin	1.00	2.00	5.00
100-(52 pgs.)-Most Showcase characters app.			
	1.00	2.00	5.00
101-103-Hawkman; Adam Strange x-over	1.00	2.00	5.00
104-(52 pgs.)-O.S.S. Spies at War	1.00	2.00	5.00

SHOWCASE '93
Jan, 1993-No. 12, Dec, 1993 (1.95, color)
DC Comics

1-6,9-12: 1-Catwoman begins. 6-Azrael in Bat-costume (2 pgs.).			
10-Azrael as Batman app.	0.40	0.80	2.00
7,8-Knightfall Pts. 13 & 14	0.50	1.00	2.50

SHOWCASE '94
Jan, 1994-No. 12, Dec, 1994 (1.95, color, limited series)

	Good	Fine	N-Mint

DC Comics
1-12: 1, 2-Joker-c/story. 4-Riddler-story. 5, 6-Huntress-c/story w/new
  Batman in #5 & Robin in #6 (x-over w/Robin #6). 6-Atom-story.
  7-Penguin-c/story. 8,9-Scarface-c & origin, Pt. 1 & Pt. 2; Prelude To Zero

	Good	Fine	N-Mint
Hour. 10-Zero Hour. 11-Man-Bat	0.40	0.80	2.00

SHOWCASE '95
Jan 1995-Present (2.50, color, limited series: 12)
DC Comics
1-4-Supergirl c/story 3-Eradicator-c 4,5-Thorn c/story

	Good	Fine	N-Mint
	0.50	1.00	2.50
5-begin 2.95-c; 6,7–	0.60	1.20	3.00

SHROUD, THE (See Super-Villain Team-Up #5)
Mar, 1994-No. 4, June, 1994 (1.75, color, mini-series)
Marvel Comics

	Good	Fine	N-Mint
1-4: 1, 2, 4-Spider-Man & Scorpion app.	0.40	0.70	1.75

SILVER SABLE AND THE WILD PACK (See Amazing Spider-Man #265)
June, 1992-Present (Color)
Marvel Comics

	Good	Fine	N-Mint
1-(2.00)-Embossed foil-c; Spidey app.	0.60	1.20	3.00
2-4: 4, 5-Dr. Doom-c/story	0.40	0.70	1.75

5-23: 9-Origin. 10-Punisher. app. 13,14-Cage app. 16-Intruders.
  18-Venom. 19-Siege of Darkness x-over; Venom app. 23-Daredevil (in

	Good	Fine	N-Mint
new costume) & Deadpool app.	0.30	0.50	1.25

24,26-35: 24-Begin 1.50-c; bound-in card sheet 35-Li'l Silvie backup story

	Good	Fine	N-Mint
	0.30	0.60	1.50
25-(2.00, 52 pgs)-Li'l Sylvie backup story	0.40	0.80	2.00

SILVER STAR (Also see Jack Kirby's…)
Feb, 1983-No. 6, Jan, 1984 (1.00, color)
Pacific Comics
1-6: 1-1st app. Last of the Viking Heroes. 1-5-Kirby-c/a. 2-Ditko-a

	Good	Fine	N-Mint
	0.20	0.40	1.00

SILVER SURFER (See Fantastic Four #48 for 1st app.)
Aug, 1968-No. 18, Sept, 1970 (#1-7 are 25¢, 68 pg. giants)
Marvel Comics Group

	Good	Fine	N-Mint
1-1st detailed origin; Buscema a-1-17p	51.00	154.00	410.00
2	19.00	56.00	150.00
3-1st app. Mephisto	16.00	47.00	125.00
4-Scarcer; low dist.; Thor, Loki app.	47.00	141.00	375.00

5-7: 7-Last giant size	9.00	28.00	75.00
8-10: 8-Begin 15¢ issues	7.00	21.00	55.00

11-13, 15-18: 15-Silver Surfer vs. Human Torch; F.F. app. 17-Nick Fury
app. 18-Vs. The Inhumans — 5.00 — 16.00 — 42.00

14-Spider-Man x-over	8.00	24.00	64.00
V2#1 (June 1982, one shot)-Byrne art	1.50	3.80	9.00

SILVER SURFER
July, 1987-Present
Marvel Comics Group

V3#1-(1.25, double size)	1.20	2.90	7.00
2	0.60	1.20	3.00
3-10	0.40	0.80	2.00
11-14	0.40	0.80	2.00
15-Ron Lim-a begins (9/88)	0.70	1.70	4.00
16, 17	0.70	1.70	4.00
18-20	0.60	1.20	3.00
21-24, 26-30, 33, 40-43	0.40	0.80	2.00
25, 31-(1.50, 52 pgs.)	0.40	0.80	2.00
32, 39-No Ron Lim-c/a	0.30	0.60	1.50

34-Return of Thanos (c/cameo); Starlin scripts begin
— 0.90 — 2.60 — 6.00

35-1st full Thanos app. in S.S.; re-intro Drax the Destroyer on last page
— 1.10 — 3.40 — 8.00

36-Recaps history of Thanos	0.80	2.10	5.00
37-1st full app. Drax; Drax-c	1.00	2.00	5.00
38-Surfer battles Thanos	0.80	2.00	5.00
44, 45, 49-Thanos stories (c-44, 45)	0.50	1.00	2.50

46, 47-Return of Adam Warlock. 47-Warlock battles Drax
— 0.80 — 2.10 — 5.00

48-Last Starlin scripts (also #50)	0.40	0.80	1.90

50-(1.50)-Silver foil-stamped logo; Surfer Battles Thanos (briefly); story
cont'd in Infinity Gauntlet #1 — 0.80 — 2.00 — 5.00

50-2nd & 3rd printing (1.50)	0.50	1.00	2.50
51-53: Infinity Gauntlet x-over	0.60	1.10	2.75

54-57: 54-59: Infinity Gauntlet x-over. 55, 56-Thanos-c/stories
— 0.50 — 0.90 — 2.25

58, 59: Thanos joins. 59-Silver Surfer battles Thanos-c/story
— 0.80 — 1.50 — 3.75

60-66: 61-Last 1.00-c;	0.30	0.60	1.50
67-69: Infinity War x-over	0.40	0.80	2.00

70-74, 76-81, 83-91: 83, 84-Infinity Crusade x-over; Thanos cameo. 85-
Thor-c/story. 87-Warlock, Dr. Strange. 88-Thanos-c/story.

	Good	Fine	N-Mint
90-Legacy app.	0.30	0.50	1.25
75-(2.50, 52 pgs.)-Embossed foil stamped-0.70		1.40	3.50
82-(1.75, 52 pgs.)-Last Ron Lim-a	0.40	0.70	1.75

92-99, 101-106: 92-Begin 1.50-c; bound-in card sheet. 95-FF app. 96-Hulk & FF app. 97-Terrax and Nova app.; 106-Doc Doom app.

	Good	Fine	N-Mint
	0.30	0.60	1.50
100-(2.25, 52 pgs) Wraparound-c	0.50	0.90	2.25
100-(3.95, 52 pgs) Enhanced-c	0.80	1.60	4.00

Annual 1 ('88, 1.75)-Evolutionary War; 1st Ron Lim-a on Surfer

(20 pgs back-up stories & pin-ups)	0.80	2.10	5.00

Annual 2 ('89, 2.00)-Atlantis Attacks; Lim-c/a

	0.50	1.00	2.50
Annual 3 ('90, 2.00)	0.50	1.00	2.50

Annual 4 ('91, 2.00)-3 pg. origin; Surfer battles Guardians of the Galaxy

	0.50	1.00	2.50

Annual 5 ('92, 2.25)-Return Of The Defenders pt. 3; Ron Lim-c/a;

(3 pgs. of pin-ups)	0.50	1.00	2.50

Annual 6 ('93, 2.95)-Polybagged w/card; 1st app. Legacy (Captain Marvel's

son)	0.60	1.20	3.00
Annual 7 ('94, 2.95, 68 pgs.)	0.60	1.20	3.00
Graphic Novel (Hardcover, 14.95)	2.10	6.00	15.00
Graphic Novel (The Enslavers, 16.95)	2.40	7.00	17.00

..."The First Coming of Galactus" nn (11/92, 5.95)-r/F.F. 48-50 with new

Ron Lim-c	1.00	2.50	6.00

SILVER SURFER, THE
Dec, 1988-No. 2, Jan, 1989 (1.00, color, limited series)
Epic Comics

1,2-By Stan Lee & Moebius	0.50	1.00	2.50

SILVER SURFER/WARLOCK: RESURRECTION
Mar, 1993-No. 4, June, 1993 (2.50, color, mini-series)
Marvel Comics

1-4: Starlin-c/a & scripts	0.50	1.00	2.50

SIMPSONS COMICS
1993-Present (1.95, color)
Bongo Comics Group

1-(2.25)-FF#1-c swipe; pull out poster	0.60	1.20	3.00

2, 3-(1.95): 2-Patty & Selma on flip-side. 3-Krusty, Agent of K.L.O.W.N.

flip-c/story	0.40	0.80	2.00

4-(2.25)-Infinity-c; flip-c of Busman #1; w/trading card

	0.50	0.90	2.25

5-Wraparound-c w/ trading card	0.50	0.90	2.25
6-flip book w/Chief Wiggum's "Crime Comics"			
	0.50	0.90	2.25
7-Flip book w/"McBain Comics"	0.50	0.90	2.25
8-Flip book w/"Edna, Queen of the Congo"	0.50	0.90	2.25
9-Flip Book w/"Barney Gumble"	0.50	0.90	2.25
10-Flip Book w/"Apu"	0.50	0.90	2.25
Simpsons Comics Extravaganza ('94, 10.00) r/Issues #1-#4;			
infinity-c	1.70	4.00	10.00

SIMPSONS COMICS AND STORIES
1993 (2.95, color)
Welsh Publishing Group

1-(Direct sale)-Polybagged w/Bartman poster			
	0.60	1.20	3.00
1-(Newsstand)-w/o poster	0.60	1.20	3.00

SIN CITY: A DAME TO KILL FOR (See Dark Horse Presents)
Nov, 1993-No. 6, May, 1994 (2.95, B&W, limited series)
Dark Horse Comics (Legend imprint)

1-6-By Frank Miller, c/a/scripts	0.60	1.20	3.00
...A Dame to Kill For-TPB (11/94,15.00)	2.10	6.00	15.00

SIN CITY:THE BABE WORE RED AND OTHER STORIES
Nov, 1994 (2.95, B&W)
Dark Horse Comics

1-Frank Miller s/a	0.60	1.20	3.00

SIN CITY: THE BIG FAT KILL
Nov 1994 (2.95, B&W, limited series:5)
Dark Horse Comics

1-4-Frank Millers s/a/c	0.60	1.20	3.00
5-(3.50)	0.70	1.40	3.50

SINISTER HOUSE OF SECRET LOVE (Becomes Secrets of Sinister House)
Oct-Nov, 1971-No. 4, Apr-May, 1972
National Periodical Publications

1	1.40	2.80	7.00
2-4: 2-Jeff Jones-c. 3-Toth-a (36 pgs.)	0.50	1.00	2.50

SKELETON WARRIORS
Apr 1995-Present (1.50, color)
Marvel Comics

	Good	Fine	N-Mint
1-4 -Based on the animated series	0.30	0.60	1.50

SKIN GRAFT: THE ADVENTURES OF A TATTOED MAN
July, 1993-No. 4, Oct, 1993 (2.50, color, adult)
DC Comics (Vertigo)

| 1–4 | 0.50 | 1.00 | 2.50 |

SKULL, THE SLAYER
August, 1975-No. 8, Nov, 1976 (20¢/25¢ issues)
Marvel Comics Group

| 1-Origin & 1st app.; Gil Kane-c | 0.30 | 0.60 | 1.50 |
| 2-8: 2-G. Kane-c. 8-Kirby-c | 0.20 | 0.40 | 1.00 |

SLACKER COMICS
Aug, 1994-Present (2.95, B&W, quarterly, adult)
Slave Labor Graphics

| 1,2 | 0.60 | 1.20 | 3.00 |

SLUDGE
Oct, 1993-Present (1.95, color)
Malibu Comics (Ultraverse)

1-(2.50, 48 pgs.)-Intro/1st app. Sludge; flip-side has Rune-c/story (1st app., 3 pgs.)by B. Smith; 3 pg. preview The Night Man			
	0.50	1.00	2.50
1-Ultra 5000 Limited silver foil	2.10	6.40	15.00
2-11: 4-2 pg. Mantra origin. 8-Bloodstorm app.			
	0.40	0.80	2.00
12-(3.50)-Ultraverse Premiere #8 flip book	0.70	1.40	3.50
...:Red X-Mas (12/94, 2.50, 44 pgs)	0.50	1.00	2.50

SNAGGLEPUSS (TV)
Oct, 1962-No. 4, Sept, 1963 (Hanna-Barbera)
Gold Key

| 1 | 9.20 | 27.50 | 55.00 |
| 2–4 | 5.80 | 17.50 | 35.00 |

SNOOPER AND BLABBER DETECTIVES (TV)
Nov, 1962-No. 3, May, 1963 (Hanna-Barbera)
Gold Key

| 1 | 9.20 | 27.50 | 55.00 |
| 2, 3 | 6.70 | 20.00 | 40.00 |

Solar #33 © Voyager

Solitaire #5 © Malibu

SNOW WHITE
Jan, 1995 (1.95, color, one-shot)
Marvel Comics

1-r/1937 Sunday newspaper pages	0.40	0.80	2.00

SOLAR (Also see Dr. Solar)
Sept, 1991-Present (Color)
Valiant Comics

1-Layton-a(p); Smith a-1-10	2.10	6.40	15.00
2	1.60	5.00	11.00
3-1st Harada (11/91)	2.00	6.40	15.00
4	1.70	5.10	12.00
5-9: 7-Vs. X-O Armor; last 1.95-c	1.70	4.20	10.00
10-(3.95)-Black embossed-c; 1st app. Eternal Warrior (6/92); origin &			
1st app. Geoff McHenry (Geomancer)	4.00	11.00	25.00
10-2nd printing (3.95)	0.80	1.60	4.00
11-1st full Eternal Warrior (7/92); Ditko-a(p)	1.00	2.50	6.00
12, 13, 15: 12, 13-Unity x-over. 15-2nd Dr. Eclipse			
	1.00	1.90	4.75
14-1st app. Fred Bender who becomes Dr. Eclipse; Ditko-a(p)			
	1.40	4.00	10.00
16-45: 17-X-O Manowar app. 23-Solar splits. 29-1st Valiant Vision book			
(3-D); Quesada-c(p). 33-w/bound-in trading card. 33-35-Valiant Vision.			
36-Dr. Eclipse & Ravenus app. 38-Chaos Effect Epsilon Pt. 1			
	0.50	0.90	2.25
46-50 -(2.50)-Dan Jurgens s/a D. Giordano inks			
	0.50	1.00	2.50
0-(9.95)-TPB-Alpha and Omega r/origin story polybagged w/poster			
	1.70	4.00	10.00
...Second Death ('94, 9.95)-r/Issues #1-4	1.70	4.00	10.00

Note: #1-10 have free 8-pg. insert which is 10-chapter Solar origin story.

	Good	Fine	N-Mint

SOLITAIRE
Nov 1993- Dec 1994 (1.95, color, Limited series)
Malibu Comics (Ultraverse)

	Good	Fine	N-Mint
1-(2.50)-Black polybag w/playing card	0.50	1.00	2.50
1-12: 1-Regular ed. w/o card. 2-Break-Thru x-over. 3-2 pg. origin The			
Night Man	0.40	0.80	2.00

SOLO
Sept, 1994-No. 4, Dec, 1994 (1.75, limited series)
Marvel Comics

	Good	Fine	N-Mint
1-4-Spider-Man app.: 3-Spider-Man-c	0.40	0.70	1.75

SOLUTION,THE
Sept, 1993-Present (1.95, color)
Malibu Comics (Ultraverse)

	Good	Fine	N-Mint
1, 3-10: 1-Intro Meathook, Deathdance, Black Tiger & Tech. 4-Break-Thru			
x-over; gatefold-c. 5-2 pg. origin Strangers			
	0.40	0.80	2.00
1-(2.50)-Newsstand ed. bagged w/card	0.50	1.00	2.50
1-Ultra 5000 Limited silver foil	2.00	6.00	15.00
0-Obtained w/Rune #0 by sending coupon	1.00	3.00	9.00
2-(2.50, 48 pgs.)-Rune flip-c/s by Smith	0.50	1.00	2.50
11-15: 11-Brereton-c	0.40	0.80	2.00
16-(3.50)-Flip-c Ultraverse Premiere #10			
	0.70	1.40	3.50
17-(2.50)	0.50	1.00	2.50

SON OF SATAN (Also see Ghost Rider #1, Hellstorm & Marvel Spotlight #12)
Dec, 1975-No. 8, Feb, 1977
Marvel Comics Group

	Good	Fine	N-Mint
1	1.70	4.20	10.00
2-8: 2-Origin The Possessor	1.20	2.40	6.00

SON OF VULCAN (Formerly Mysteries of Unexplored Worlds; becomes
Thunderbolt V3#51 on)
V2#49, Nov, 1965-V2#50, Jan, 1966
Charlton Comics
V2#49, 50: 50-Roy Thomas scripts (1st pro work)

	Good	Fine	N-Mint
	2.00	5.00	10.00

SOULSEARCHERS AND COMPANY
Jun 1994-Present (2.50, B&W)

Claypool Comics
| 1–12-Peter David-s | 0.50 | 1.00 | 2.50 |

SOVEREIGN SEVEN
July 1995-Present (1.95, color)
DC Comics
| 1,2-Claremont-s | 0.40 | 1.00 | 2.00 |

SPACE ADVENTURES
No. 33, Mar, 1960-No. 59, Nov, 1964; V3#60, Oct, 1967; V1#2, July, 1968;
V1#8, July, 1969; No. 9, May, 1978-No. 13, Mar, 1979
Charlton Comics
33-Origin&1st app.Captain Atom by Ditko	28.00	84.00	225.00
34-40, 42: All Capt. Atom by Ditko	11.00	34.00	90.00
41, 43-59: 44, 45-Mercury Man app.	2.00	6.00	17.00
V3#60 (#1, 10/67)-Origin & 1st app. Paul Mann & The Saucers From			
The Future	3.00	9.40	22.00
2-8 ('68-69): 2, 5, 6, 8-Ditko art	1.60	4.00	9.50
9-13 (78-79)-Capt. Atom reprints	0.40	0.80	2.00

SPACED
1982-No. 13, 1988? (1.50, B&W)
Unbridled Ambition/Eclipse
1	3.00	8.60	20.00
2	2.00	5.60	13.00
3, 4	1.00	3.00	6.00
5, 6	0.60	1.20	3.00
7-13: 10-Eclipse issues begin	0.30	0.60	1.50
Special Edition (1983, printed on mimeo)	1.00	2.50	6.00

SPACE FAMILY ROBINSON (TV) (...Lost In Space #15-36, becomes
Lost In Space #37 on)
Dec, 1962-No. 36, Oct, 1969 (All have painted covers)
No. 37, 10/73-No. 54, 11/78; No. 55, 3/81-No. 59, 5/82
Gold Key
1-Low dist.; Spiegle-a in all	24.00	71.00	190.00
2 (3/63)	10.00	30.00	80.00
3-10: 6-Captain Venture begins	5.00	16.00	42.00
11–20	4.00	11.00	28.00
21-36: 28-Last 12¢ issue	2.00	7.00	18.00
37-48	0.80	1.50	3.75
49-59: 49,55-59-Reprints	0.40	0.90	2.20

	Good	Fine	N-Mint

SPACE GHOST (TV) (See Hanna-Barbera Super TV Heroes)
March, 1967 (Hanna-Barbera)
Gold Key

	Good	Fine	N-Mint
1 (10199-703)	50.00	100.00	250.00

SPACE 1999 (TV)
Nov, 1975-No. 7, Nov, 1976
Charlton Comics

	Good	Fine	N-Mint
1-Origin Moonbase Alpha; Staton-c/a	0.70	1.40	3.50
2, 7: 2-Staton-a	0.50	1.00	2.50
3-6: All Byrne-a; c-3, 5, 6	0.40	0.80	2.00

SPACE 1999 (TV)
Nov, 1975-No. 8, Nov, 1976 (B&W magazine)
Charlton Comics

	Good	Fine	N-Mint
1-Origin Moonbase Alpha; Morrow-c/a	0.70	1.30	3.25
2, 3-Morrow-c/a	0.50	0.90	2.25
4-8: 4-6-Morrow-c. 5, 8-Morrow-a	0.40	0.70	1.75

SPACE USAGI
June, 1992-No. 3, 1993 (2.00, B&W, mini-series)
Nov, 1993-Present (2.75, color)
Mirage Studios

	Good	Fine	N-Mint
1-3: Usagi Yojimbo by Stan Sakai	0.40	0.80	2.00
V2#1-3	0.60	1.10	2.75

SPACE WAR (Becomes Fightin' Five #28 on)
10/59-No. 27, 3/64; No. 28, 3/78-No. 34, 3/79
Charlton Comics

	Good	Fine	N-Mint
1-Giordano-c 1-3	12.00	36.00	85.00
2, 3	6.00	18.00	42.00
4-6, 8, 10-Ditko-c/a	12.00	36.00	85.00
7, 9, 11-15: 15-Last 10¢ issue	3.00	9.40	22.00
16-27	2.70	8.10	19.00
28, 29, 33, 34-Ditko-c/a(r)	4.70	14.00	33.00
30-Ditko-c/a(r); Staton, Sutton, Wood-a	5.00	15.00	35.00
31-Ditko-c/a(3); atom blast-c	5.30	16.00	37.00
32-r/Charlton Premiere V2#2	0.60	1.20	3.00

SPAWN (Also see Violator)
May, 1992-Present (1.95, color)
Image Comics

	Good	Fine	N-Mint
1-Todd McFarlane-c/a begins	2.20	5.00	13.00

2-1st app. Violator	1.70	4.00	10.00
3-Violator app. (also in #4)	1.70	4.20	10.00
4-Coupon for Image Comics #0	1.70	4.20	10.00
4-With coupon missing	0.40	0.80	2.00
4-Newsstand ed. without poster or coupon	1.00	2.00	5.00
5-Cerebus cameo (1 pg.) as stuffed animal	1.00	2.00	5.00
6-8,10; 7-Spawn Mobile Poster, 8-Miller poster, Moore-s, 10-Cerebus app.			
Dave Sim-s	0.80	1.60	4.00
9-1st Angela	1.00	2.00	5.00
11-30; 11-Miller-s, Darrow Poster, 12-Liefeld-Bloodwulf poster, 14,			
15-Violator app. 16-18 -Morrison-s, Capullo-a, 25-(10/94) 19,20;-			
19(10/94), 20(11/94)	0.60	1.20	3.00
31-New Costume cameo, 32-New Costume	0.40	0.80	2.00
Note: Issues 1-4, 7-9, 11, 12 have bound-in posters.			

SPAWN-BATMAN (See Batman/Spawn under Batman one-shots)
1994 (3.95, color, one-shot)
Image Comics

1-Miller scripts; McFarlane-a	0.80	1.60	4.00

SPAWN BLOOD FEUD
June 1995-Present (2.25, color)

1-Alan Moore-s, Tony Daniel-a	0.50	0.90	2.25

SPECIAL COLLECTORS' EDITION
Dec, 1975 (No month given) (10-1/4x13-1/2")
Marvel Comics Group

1-Kung-Fu, Iron Fist & Sons of the Tiger	0.70	1.30	3.25

SPECIAL EDITION X-MEN
Feb, 1983 (One-shot)
Marvel Comics Group

1-Reprints Giant-Size X-Men #1	1.90	5.60	13.00

SPECIAL MARVEL EDITION (Master Of Kung-Fu #17 on)
Jan, 1971-No. 16, Feb, 1974 (1-4 are 25¢ giants; 5-16 are 20¢)
Marvel Comics Group

1-(68 pgs.): 1-4 are Thor-r	1.10	2.70	6.50
2–4	1.00	1.90	4.75
5-14: Sgt. Fury-r. 11-r/Sgt. Fury 13	0.80	1.60	4.00
15-Master Of Kung-Fu begins (1st app.)	5.00	15.00	35.00
16-2nd Kung Fu; Starlin-a in #15, 16	3.10	9.40	22.00

	Good	Fine	N-Mint
SPECIAL WAR SERIES			
Aug, 1965-No. 4, Nov, 1965			
Charlton Comics			
V4#1-D-Day	1.50	3.80	9.00
2-Attack!	1.10	2.70	6.50
3-War & Attack	1.10	2.70	6.50
4-Judomaster (intro/1st app.)	3.60	10.70	25.00
SPECIES			
June 1995-Present (2.50, color, limited series)			
Dark Horse Comics			
1-adaptation of movie	0.50	1.00	2.50
SPECTACULAR SPIDER-MAN, THE (Magazine)			
July, 1968-No. 2, Nov, 1968 (35¢)			
Marvel Comics Group			
1-B&W mag.; updated origin	8.30	25.00	58.00
2-Color; Green Goblin-c & 58-pg. story	11.00	33.00	78.00
SPECTACULAR SPIDER-MAN, THE(Peter Parker... #54-132,134)			
Dec, 1976-Present			
Marvel Comics Group			
1-Origin recap in text	6.90	21.00	48.00
2-Kraven the Hunter app.	2.90	8.60	20.00
3-5: 3-Intro Lightmaster	1.90	6.00	13.00
6-8: Morbius app. 6-r/Marvel Team-Up #3	2.90	8.60	20.00
9-20: 11-Last 30¢ issue	1.10	2.70	6.50
21, 24-26	1.10	2.20	5.50
22, 23-Moon Knight app.	1.70	4.20	10.00
27-Miller's first Daredevil	2.10	6.40	15.00
28-Miller Daredevil	1.80	5.00	11.00
29-55, 57, 59: 38-Morbius app.	1.00	2.00	5.00
56-2nd app. Jack O' Lantern (Macendale); 1st Jack O'Lantern/Spider-Man			
battle (7/81)	1.50	3.80	9.00
58-Byrne-a	1.10	2.20	5.50
60-(52 pgs.)-Origin retold w/new facts revealed			
	1.00	2.00	5.00
61-63, 65-68, 71-74	0.70	1.40	3.50
64-1st app. Cloak & Dagger (3/82)	1.60	4.70	11.00
69, 70-Cloak & Dagger app.	1.70	4.00	10.00
75-Double size	1.00	2.00	5.00
76-80: 78, 79-Punisher cameo	0.70	1.40	3.50
81, 82-Punisher app.	1.40	4.00	10.00

83-Punisher origin retold	2.10	6.40	15.00
84, 86-99: 90-Spidey in new black costume			
	0.80	1.60	4.00
85-Hobgoblin (Ned Leeds) app. (12/83); gains powers of original			
Green Goblin	3.90	11.60	27.00
100-(3/85, 52 pgs.)	1.00	2.00	5.00
101-115, 117, 118, 120-129	0.70	1.40	3.50
116, 119-Sabretooth-c/story	1.10	2.70	6.50
130-Hobgoblin app.	1.00	2.00	5.00
131-Six part Kraven tie-in	1.20	2.90	7.00
132-Kraven tie-in	1.00	2.50	6.00
133-139: 139-Origin of Tombstone	0.50	0.90	2.25
140-Punisher cameo app.	0.70	1.30	3.25
141-Punisher app.	1.20	2.90	7.00
142,143-Punisher app.	0.90	1.80	4.50
144-146, 148-157	0.50	0.90	2.25
147-1st app. new demonic Hobgoblin (Macendale) in last pg. cameo			
(cont'd in Web of Spider-Man 48)	3.10	9.40	22.00
158-Spider-Man gets new powers	1.90	5.60	13.00
159-Cosmic Spider-Man app.	1.50	3.80	9.00
160-170: 161-163-Hobgoblin app.	0.40	0.80	2.00
171-184: 180, 181, 183, 184-Gr. Goblin app			
	0.30	0.60	1.50
185-188, 190-199, 201-211: 197-199-X-Men-c/sty. 207, 208-The Shroud			
app.	0.30	0.50	1.25
189-(2.95, 52 pgs.)-Silver hologram on-c; battles Green Goblin; origin Spidey			
S-M retold; Vess poster w/Spidey & Hobgoblin			
	1.40	3.50	8.50
189-2nd printing; gold Hologram on-c	0.50	1.00	2.50
195-Deluxe, polybagged w/audio cassette	0.50	1.00	2.50
200-(2.95, 52 pgs.)-Holo-grafx foil-c; Green Goblin-c/story			
	0.60	1.20	3.00
212-219, 221-222, 224, 226– : 212-Begin 1.50-c; bound-in card sheet.			
215,216-Scorpion app. 217-Power & Responsibility Pt. 4. 219-Daredevil			
app.	0.30	0.60	1.50
213-Collectors Ed. polybagged w/16 pg. preview & animation cel; foil-c;			
1st meeting Spidey & Typhoid Mary	0.60	1.20	3.00
213-Version polybagged w/Gamepro #7; no cover date, no cover price			
	0.30	0.60	1.50
217-(2.95)-Deluxe edition foil-c; flip book	0.60	1.20	3.00
220-(2.25, 52 pgs)-Flip book, Mary Jane reveals pregnancy			
	0.60	1.20	3.00
223-(2.50)	0.50	1.00	2.50

	Good	Fine	N-Mint
223-(2.95)-Die-cut-c	0.60	1.20	3.00
225-(3.95)-Direct Market-Holodisk-c-Green Goblin			
	0.80	1.60	4.00
225-(2.95)-Newstand-Green Goblin	0.60	1.20	3.00
Annual 1 ('79)-Doc Octopus-c/story	0.90	2.30	5.50
Annual 2 ('80)	0.90	1.70	4.25
Annual 3-7 ('81-'87)	0.70	1.30	3.25
Annual 8 ('88)-Evolutionary War; Daydreamer returns Gwen Stacy "clone"			
back to real self (not Gwen Stacy)	0.80	1.60	4.00
Annual 9 ('89, 2.00)-Atlantis Attacks	0.60	1.20	3.00
Annual 10 ('90, 2.00)-McFarlane backup story			
	0.50	1.00	2.50
Annual 11 ('91, 2.00)-Larsen/Austin-c	0.40	0.80	2.00
Annual 12 ('92, 2.25)-Venom solo story cont'd from Amazing			
Spider-Man Annual 26	0.50	0.90	2.25
Annual 13 ('93, 2.95)-Polybagged w/card	0.60	1.20	3.00
Annual 14 ('94, 2.95)	0.60	1.20	3.00

SPECTRE, THE (See Brave & the Bold #72 & Showcase #60, 61, 64)
Nov-Dec, 1967-No. 10, May-June, 1969
National Periodical Publications

1-Anderson-c/a	11.00	32.00	75.00
2-5: Adams-c/a	7.10	21.00	50.00
6-8, 10	3.60	10.70	25.00
9-Wrightson-a	4.00	10.70	25.00

SPECTRE, THE
Dec, 1992-Present (1.75/1.95, color)
DC Comics

1-(1.95)-Glow-in-the-dark-c	1.60	3.20	8.00
2,3	1.00	2.00	5.00
4-7, 9-12, 14-20: 10-Kaluta-c. 11-Greg Hildebrandt painted-c.			
16-Aparo/K. Jones-a. 19-John K Snyder III 20-Sienkiewicz-c			
	0.40	0.80	2.00
8, 13-(2.50)-Glow-in-the-dark-c	1.00	2.00	5.00
21,22: 21-Begin 1.95-c. 22-(9/94)-Superman-c & app.			
	0.40	0.80	2.00
0,23-29: 0-(10/94). 23-(11/94)	0.40	0.80	2.00
30-begin 2.25-c; 31–32	0.50	0.90	2.25

SPEED BUGGY (TV) (Also see Funn-In)
July, 1975-No. 9, Nov, 1976 (Hanna-Barbera)
Charlton Comics

1	0.60	1.20	3.00
2–9	0.40	0.70	1.75

SPEED RACER
July, 1987-No. 38, Nov, 1990 (1.75, color)
Now Comics

1–38	0.40	0.70	1.75
1-2nd print	0.30	0.60	1.50
Special 1 (1988, 2.00)	0.40	0.80	2.00
Special 2 (1988, 3.50)	0.70	1.40	3.50

SPEED RACER FEATURING NINJA HIGH SCHOOL
Aug, 1993-No. 2, 1993 (2.50, color, mini-series)
Now Comics

1,2: 1-Polybagged w/card. 2-Exists?	0.50	1.00	2.50

SPEED RACER: RETURN OF THE GRX
Mar, 1994-No. 2, Apr, 1994 (1.95, color, limited series)
Now Comics

1, 2	0.40	0.80	2.00

SPIDER, THE
1991-Book 3, 1991 (4.95, color, 52 pgs)
Eclipse Books

Book 1-3: Truman-c/a	1.00	2.00	5.00

SPIDER-MAN
Aug, 1990-Present (1.75/1.95, color)
Marvel Comics

Spider-Man #4 © MEG

Spider-Man #50 © MEG

	Good	Fine	N-Mint
1-Platinum ed.; only mailed to retailers; no ads, no cover price, 10,000 print run (1991)	30.00	100.00	225.00
1-Silver ed., direct sale, unbagged	1.00	2.50	6.00
1-Silver bagged edition	3.00	8.60	20.00
1-Regular edition w/Spidey face in UPC area (green, unbagged)	1.00	2.00	5.00
1-Regular bagged edition w/Spidey face in UPC area	1.70	5.00	12.00
1-Newsstand bagged edition w/UPC code	1.00	2.00	5.00
1-Gold edition, 2nd print; Direct sale w/Spidey face in UPC box (no bagged editions were printed by Marvel)	0.90	1.70	4.25
1-Gold 2nd print; newsstand version w/UPC code (not scarce)	0.70	1.30	3.25
2	0.80	1.90	4.50
3-5	0.60	1.10	2.75
6, 7: Hobgoblin/Ghost Rider app.	0.80	2.00	4.75
8-Wolverine app. (cameo)	0.60	1.10	2.75
9-12: Wolverine storyline	0.60	1.10	2.75
13-Black costume returns; Morbius app.	1.00	2.00	5.00
14, 15: 14-Morbius app. 15-Erik Larsen-c/a	0.40	0.80	2.00
16-X-Force c/s w/Liefeld-a; last McFarlane issue	0.50	1.00	2.50
17-Thanos-c/story	0.50	1.00	2.50
18-23, 25: 18-23-Larsen-c/a/script	0.40	0.70	1.75
24-Demogoblin dons new costume & battles Hobgoblin(Macendale)-c/story	0.40	0.80	2.00
26-(3.50, 52 pgs.)-Photographic silver hologram-c; 3-part gatefold poster by Lim; Spidey retells his origin	0.70	1.40	3.50
26-2nd printing; gold hologram-c	0.70	1.40	3.50
27-45: 32-34-Punisher-c/story. 41-43-Iron Fist-c/story with Jae Lee-c/a. 42-Intro Platoon. 44-Hobgoblin app.	0.30	0.60	1.60
46-49,52,53,56, 58-61: 46-Begin 1.95-c; bound-in card sheet. 52,53-Venom app. 60-Kaine revealed. 61-Origin Kaine	0.40	0.80	2.00
46-(2.95)-Polybagged; silver ink-c w/16 pg cartoon series preview; bound-in trading card sheet	0.60	1.20	3.00
50-(2.50)-Newsstand edition	0.50	1.00	2.50
50-(3.95)-Collectors edition w/holographic-c	0.80	1.60	4.00
51-Power & Responsibility Pt. 3	0.40	0.80	2.00
51-(2.95)-Deluxe edition foil-c; flip book	0.60	1.20	3.00
54-(2.75, 52 pgs)-Flip book	0.60	1.10	2.75
57-(2.50)	0.50	1.00	2.50
57-(2.95) Die-cut-c	0.60	1.20	3.00

...: Carnage Trade paperback nn (6/93, 6.95)-Reprints Amazing Spider-Man
   #344, 345, 359-363   1.20   3.00   7.00
.../Dr. Strange: "The Way to Dusty Death" nn (1992, 6.95, 68 pgs.)
                                         1.20   3.00   7.00
Special Edition 1 (12/92-c, 11/92 inside)-The Trial of Venom; ordered thru
   mail w/$5.00 donation or more to UNICEF; came polybagged w/poster;
   embossed metallic ink-c; Daredevil app. 1.70   4.00   10.00
...Vs. Venom Trade paperback nn (1990, 8.95)-r/Amaz. Spider-Man
                                         1.50   3.80   9.00

SPIDER-MAN ADVENTURES
Dec 1994 (1.50, color)
Marvel Comics
1-8-(1.50)- Based on animated series   0.30   0.60   1.50
1-(2.95)-Foil embosed cover   0.60   1.20   3.00

SPIDER-MAN AND DAREDEVIL
March, 1984 (2.00, one-shot)
Marvel Comics Group
1-Miller-r/Spect. S-M #26-28   0.60   1.20   3.00

SPIDER-MAN AND HIS AMAZING FRIENDS
Dec, 1981 (One-shot)
Marvel Comics Group
1-Adapted from TV cartoon; Green Goblin-c/sty
                                        0.60   1.20   3.00

SPIDER-MAN AND X-FACTOR
May, 1994-No. 3, July, 1994 (1.95, color, limited series)
Marvel Comics
1-3   0.40   0.80   2.00

SPIDER-MAN CLASSICS
Apr, 1993-Present (1.25, color)
Marvel Comics
1-16: 1-r/Amazing Fantasy #15 & Str. Tales #115. 2-16-r/Amaz. Spider-Man
   #1-15   0.30   0.50   1.25
15-(2.95)-Polybagged w/16 pg insert & animation style print; reprints
   Amazing Spider-Man #14 (1st Green Goblin)
                                        0.60   1.20   3.00

SPIDER-MAN COLLECTORS' PREVIEW
Dec, 1994 (1.50, color, 100 pgs.)

	Good	Fine	N-Mint

Marvel Comics
1-Wraparound-c; no comics   0.30   0.60   1.50

SPIDER-MAN: FRIENDS AND ENEMIES
Jan, 1995- Apr 1995 (1.95, color, limited series)
Marvel Comics
1-4-Darkhawk, Nova & Speedball app.   0.40   0.80   2.00

SPIDER-MAN: FUNERAL FOR AN OCTOPUS
Mar 1995 -May 1995 (1.50, color, limited series:3)
Marvel Comics
1-3   0.30   0.60   1.50

SPIDER-MAN MAGAZINE
Mar, 1994-Present (1.95, magazine)
Marvel Comics
1-Contains 4 Spidey promo cards & 4 X-Men Ultra Fleer cards; Spider-Man
  by Romita, Sr. & X-Men stories reprints begin

	0.40	0.80	2.00

2,3: 2-Doc Octopus & X-Men stories   0.40   0.80   2.00

SPIDER-MAN: MAXIMUM CLONAGE ALPHA
Aug 1995-Present (4.95, color)
Marvel Comics
1–acetate-c   1.00   2.00   5.00

SPIDER-MAN MEGAZINE
Oct, 1994-Present (2.95, 100 pgs.)
Marvel Comics
1-6: 1-r/ASM #16,224,225, Marvel Team-Up 1

	0.60	1.20	3.00

SPIDER-MAN: POWER OF TERROR
Jan, 1995 -Apr, 1995(1.95, color, limited series)
Marvel Comics
1-4-Silvermane and Deathlok app.   0.40   0.80   2.00

SPIDER-MAN SUPER SPECIAL
July 1995-Present (3.95, color)
Marvel Comics
1-"Planet of the Symbiotes"   0.80   1.60   4.00

SPIDER-MAN:THE ARACHNIS PROJECT

Aug, 1994-Jan, 1995 (1.75, color, limited series)
Marvel Comics

1-6-Venom, Styx, Stone and Jury app.	0.40	0.70	1.75

SPIDER-MAN: THE CLONE JOURNAL
Mar 1995 - Present (2.95, color)
Marvel Comics

1	0.60	1.20	3.00

SPIDER-MAN: THE LOST YEARS
Aug 1995-Present (2.95, color)

1-DeMaatteis-s Romita Jr.-a	0.60	1.20	3.00

SPIDER-MAN: THE MUTANT AGENDA
Feb, 1994-No. 3, May, 1994 (1.75, color)
Marvel Comics

0-(1.25, 52 pgs.)-Comic bk/newspaper x-over			
	0.30	0.50	1.25
1-3: Beast & Hobgoblin app. 1-X-Men app.	0.40	0.70	1.75

SPIDER-MAN 2099 (See Amazing Spider-Man #365)
Nov, 1992-Present (1.25, color)
Marvel Comics

1-(1.75-c)-Red foil-c; origin of 21st Century Spider-Man begins;			
Leonardi/Williamson-c/a begins	0.60	1.20	3.00
1-2nd printing (1.75)	0.40	0.70	1.75
2-Origin of 21st Century's Spider-Man Pt. 2	0.50	1.00	2.50
3, 4: 4-Doom 2099 app.	0.40	0.80	2.00
5-18: 13-Extra Midnight Sons insert; Ron Lim-c(p). 18-Ron Lim-c/a(p)			
	0.30	0.50	1.25
19-24,26-31: 19-Begin 1.50-c; bound-in card sheet.			
	0.30	0.60	1.50
25-(2.25, 52 pgs.)-Newsstand edition	0.50	0.90	2.25
25-(2.95)-Deluxe Edition embossed foil-c	0.60	1.20	3.00
32-begin 1.95-c; 33-34	0.40	0.80	2.00
Annual 1 ('94, 2.95, 68 pgs.)	0.60	1.20	3.00

SPIDER-MAN UNLIMITED
May, 1993-Present (3.95, color, quarterly, 68 pgs.)
Marvel Comics

1-9: 1,2-Maximum Carnage storyline; Ron Lim-c/a(p) begins.			
2-Venom-c/story	0.80	1.60	4.00

	Good	Fine	N-Mint

SPIDER-MAN VS. DRACULA
Jan, 1994 (1.75, color)
Marvel Comics

1-r/Giant-Size Spider-Man #1	0.40	0.70	1.75

SPIDER-MAN VS. WOLVERINE
Feb, 1987 (2.50, one-shot, 68 pgs.)
Marvel Comics Group

1-Death of Ned Leeds (old Hobgoblin)	2.00	6.00	15.00
V2#1 (1990, 4.95)-Reprints 2/87 issue	1.00	2.00	5.00

SPIDER-MAN: WEB OF DOOM
Aug, 1994-No. 3, Oct, 1994 (1.75, color, limited series)
Marvel Comics

1-3	0.40	0.70	1.75

SPIDER-WOMAN
April, 1978-No. 50, June, 1982
Marvel Comics Group

1-New complete origin	1.00	2.00	5.00
2-36, 39-49: 6-Werewolf-c/sty. 49-Tigra-c/sty			
	0.30	0.60	1.50
37, 38: New X-Men app. 37-1st app. of Syrin of X-Force & origin retold			
	0.60	1.20	3.00
50-Double size; death of Spider-Woman	0.60	1.20	3.00

SPIDER-WOMAN
Nov, 1993-No. 4, Feb, 1994 (1.75, color, mini-series)
Marvel Comics

V2#1-4-Origin; U.S. Agent app.	0.40	0.70	1.75

SPIDEY SUPER STORIES
Oct, 1974-No. 57, Mar, 1982 (35¢, no ads)
Marvel/Children's TV Workshop

1-Origin	0.40	0.80	2.00
2-12: 2-Kraven app. 6-Iceman	0.30	0.60	1.50
13-38, 40-44, 46-57: 31-Moondragon-c/sty. 56-(2/82)-Battles Jack O'Lantern-c/story (1 yr. after Machine Man #19)			
	0.30	0.60	1.50
39-Thanos-c/story	0.40	0.80	2.00
45-Silver Surfer app.	0.40	0.80	2.00

SPIRIT, THE
Oct, 1966-No. 2, Mar, 1967 (25¢, 68 pg. giants)
Harvey Publications

1-Eisner-r plus 9 new pgs.	5.00	15.00	35.00
2-Eisner-r plus 9 new pgs. (origin Octopus)			
	5.00	15.00	35.00

SPIRIT, THE
Oct, 1983-No. 87, Jan, 1992 (Baxter paper)
Kitchen Sink Enterprises

1-87: 1-Origin-r/section 12/23/45	0.40	0.80	2.00
... In 3-D (12/85)-Listed as Will Eisner's...3-D			
	0.40	0.80	2.00

SPLITTING IMAGE
March, 1993-No. 2, 1993 (1.95, color)
Image Comics

1, 2-Simpson-c/a; parody comics	0.40	0.80	2.00

SPOOF
Oct, 1970; No. 2, Nov, 1972-No. 5, May, 1973
Marvel Comics Group

1-Infinity-c; Dark Shadows-c & parody	0.80	1.60	4.00
2-5: 3-Beatles, Osmonds, Jackson 5, David Cassidy, Nixon/Agnew-c.			
5-Rod Serling, Woody Allen, Ted Kennedy-c			
	0.40	0.80	2.00

SPYMAN
Sept, 1966-No. 3, Feb, 1967 (12¢ issues)
Harvey Publications

1-Steranko art (p), his first pro work	4.30	12.90	30.00
2, 3: Simon-c. 2-Steranko art (p)	2.90	8.60	20.00

SQUADRON SUPREME
Aug, 1985-No. 12 Aug, 1986 (Maxi-series)
Marvel Comics Group

1-Double size	0.30	0.60	1.50
2–12	0.20	0.40	1.00

S.R. BISSETTE'S TYRANT
Sept, 1994 (2.95, B&W)
SpiderBaby Grafix & Publications

1-3: 1- (9/94) 2-(11/94)	0.60	1.20	3.00

	Good	Fine	N-Mint

The Spirit #1 © Will Eisner

Star #1 © Rob Liefeld

STAINLESS STEEL ARMADILLO
Feb 1995-Present (2.95, B&W, Mature readers)
Antarctic Press

	Good	Fine	N-Mint
1-3	0.60	1.20	3.00

STALKER
June-July, 1975-No. 4, Dec-Jan, 1975-76
National Periodical Publications
1-Origin & 1st app. Stalker; Ditko/Wood-c/a

	Good	Fine	N-Mint
	0.70	1.30	3.25
2-4: Ditko/Wood-c/a in all	0.50	0.90	2.25

STANLEY & HIS MONSTER
No. 109, Apr-May, 1968-No. 112, Oct-Nov, 1968
National Periodical Publ.

	Good	Fine	N-Mint
109-112	2.00	5.00	12.00

STAN SHAW'S BEAUTY & THE BEAST
Nov, 1993 (4.95, color, one-shot)
Dark Horse Comics

	Good	Fine	N-Mint
1	1.00	2.00	5.00

STAR
June 1995-Present (2.50, color)
Image Comics

	Good	Fine	N-Mint
1	0.50	1.00	2.50

STARCHILD
1992-Present (2.25/2.50, B&W)

Taliesin Press
1, 2-(1992)	0.50	0.90	2.25

0-(4/93)-Illus by Chadwick, Eisner, Sim, M. Wagner; 2.50-c begins

	0.50	1.00	2.50
3-12: 3-(7/93). 4-(11/93). 6-(2/94)	0.50	1.00	2.50

STARFIRE (See New Teen Titans #4)
Aug-Sept, 1976-No. 8, Oct-Nov, 1977
National Periodical Publications
1-Origin	0.30	0.60	1.60
2–8	0.20	0.50	1.20

STAR HUNTERS
Oct-Nov, 1977-No. 7, Oct-Nov, 1978
National Periodical Publications/DC Comics
1-7: 1-Newton-a(p). 7-Giant	0.20	0.40	1.00

STARLORD, THE SPECIAL EDITION
Feb, 1982 (One-shot, direct sales only)
Marvel Comics Group
1-Byrne-a; 1st deluxe format comic	1.00	2.00	5.00

STARMAN
Oct, 1988-No. 45, Apr, 1992 (1.00, color)
DC Comics
1-27, 29-45	0.20	0.40	1.00
28-Starman disguised as Superman	0.40	0.80	2.00

STARMAN
No. 0, Oct, 1994-Present (1.95, color)
DC Comics
0,1-Robinson-s/Harris-a(p)	0.80	1.60	4.00
2-8-Robinson-s/Harris-a(p)	0.40	0.80	2.00
9,10; 9-begin 2.25-c	0.50	0.90	2.25

STAR SLAMMERS
May, 1994-Present (2.50, color, mini-series:5, mature)
Malibu Comics
1-4-W. Simonson-a/story begin	0.50	1.00	2.50

STARSLAYER
Feb, 1982-No. 34, Nov, 1985
Pacific Comics/First Comics (No. 7 on)

	Good	Fine	N-Mint
1-Rocketeer 1 pg. cameo leads into #2	0.60	1.20	3.00
2-Intro/origin Rocketeer by Stevens (Chap. 1)			
	1.40	4.00	10.00
3-2nd app. Rocketeer (Chap. 2) by Stevens	1.20	3.00	7.00
4	0.40	0.80	2.00
5-2nd app. Groo (1st app. in Destroyer Duck)			
	1.00	2.50	6.00
6, 7: 7-Last Mike Grell art	0.40	0.80	2.00
8-34: 10-1st app. Grimjack (11/83)	0.20	0.40	1.00

STARSLAYER
Jun 1993-Present (2.50, color)
Windjammer

1-7-Mike Grell s/a	0.50	1.00	2.50

STAR SPANGLED WAR STORIES (Unknown Soldier #205 on)(See Showcase)
#131, Aug, 1952-#133, Oct, 1952; #3, Nov, 1952-#204, Feb-Mar, 1977
National Periodical Publications

	Good	Fine	N-Mint
131 (#1)	72.00	216.00	575.00
132	53.00	159.00	425.00
133-Used in POP, pg. 94	50.00	150.00	400.00
3-6: 4-Devil Dog Dugan app.; 6-Evans-a	25.00	75.00	200.00
7–10	19.00	58.00	155.00
11–20	17.00	51.00	135.00
21-30: Last precode (2/55)	14.00	43.00	115.00
31-33, 35-40	10.00	31.00	72.00
34-Krigstein art	11.00	33.00	78.00
41-50: 45-1st DC grey-tone-c (5/56)	9.00	28.00	65.00
51-83: 67-Easy Co. story w/o Sgt. Rock	7.00	20.00	46.00
84-Origin Mlle. Marie	14.00	41.00	95.00
85-89: Mlle. Marie in all	7.40	22.00	52.00
90-1st Dinosaur issue; begin series	27.00	80.00	240.00
91, 93-No Dinosaur stories	5.10	15.00	36.00
92, 94-99: All Dinosaur-c/stories. 94-(12/60)-Ghost Ace story; Baron Von Richter as the Enemy Ace (see Our Army #151)			
	14.00	41.00	95.00
100-Dinosaur issue	16.00	49.00	115.00
101-115	9.00	28.00 ·	65.00
116-125, 127-133, 135-137: Last Dinosaur issues			
	8.00	24.00	55.00
126-No dinosaur story	4.00	13.00	30.00
134-Dinosaur issue; Adams-a	4.00	30.00	70.00
138-(4-5/68)-New Enemy Ace stories begin by Kubert, ends 150;			

also see Our Army At War & Showcase	9.00	26.00	60.00
139-Origin Enemy Ace (7/68)	7.10	21.00	50.00
140-143, 145: 145-Last 12¢ issue (6-7/69)	5.00	14.10	33.00
144-Adams/Kubert-a	4.00	12.00	28.00
146-Enemy Ace-c only	2.40	7.30	17.00
147, 148: New Enemy Ace stories	3.60	10.70	25.00
149, 150-Last new Enemy Ace by Kubert	2.90	8.60	20.00
151-(6-7/70)-1st Unknown Soldier; Enemy Ace reprints begin, end #161			
	4.70	14.10	33.00
152, 153, 155-Enemy Ace reprints	1.70	5.10	12.00
154-Origin Unknown Soldier	3.60	11.00	25.00
156-1st Battle Album	1.70	4.20	10.00
157-161: 157-Sgt. Rock x-over in Unknown Soldier story. 161-Last Enemy			
Ace (reprint)	1.20	2.90	7.00
162-204: 181-183, 200-Enemy Ace app.	0.80	1.60	4.00

STAR TREK (TV)
July, 1967; No. 2, June, 1968; No. 3, Dec, 1968;
No. 4, June, 1969-No. 61, Mar, 1979
Gold Key

1: 1-9 have photo covers	56.00	167.00	390.00
2	29.00	86.00	200.00
3–5	24.00	71.00	165.00
6-9-Last photo-c	19.00	56.00	130.00
10–20	10.00	30.00	70.00
21-30	7.10	21.00	50.00
31-40	5.00	15.00	35.00
41-61	3.10	9.00	22.00

Star Spangled War Stories #73 © DC

Star Trek DS 9 #2 © Paramount

	Good	Fine	N-Mint

STAR TREK
April, 1980-No. 18, Feb, 1982
Marvel Comics Group

	Good	Fine	N-Mint
1-r/Marvel Super Special	1.00	2.00	5.00
2-18: 5-Miller-c	0.70	1.40	3.50

STAR TREK
Feb, 1984-No. 56, Nov, 1988
DC Comics

	Good	Fine	N-Mint
1	1.80	5.00	11.00
2–5	1.20	2.90	7.00
6–10	1.10	2.20	5.50
11–20	0.80	1.50	3.75
21–32	0.60	1.10	2.75
33-Double size 20th ann.	0.80	1.60	4.00
34-49	0.40	0.80	2.00
50-(1.50, 52 pgs.)	0.60	1.20	3.00
51-56	0.30	0.60	1.50
Annual 1, 2, 3 (1985, '86, '88)	0.60	1.20	3.00

STAR TREK
Oct, 1989-Present (1.50/1.75/1.95, color)
DC Comics

	Good	Fine	N-Mint
1-Capt. Kirk & crew	1.30	3.00	7.50
2, 3	0.70	1.40	3.50
4-23, 25-30: 20-Last 1.50-c	0.50	1.00	2.50
24-(2.95, 68 pgs.)	0.70	1.30	3.25
31-49, 51-60	0.40	0.70	1.75
50-(3.50, 68 pgs.)-Painted-c	0.70	1.40	3.50
61-70: 61-Begin 1.95-c	0.40	0.80	2.00
71-74, 71-begin 2.50-c	0.50	1.00	2.50
Annual 1 ('90, 2.95); Annual 2 ('91, 2.95)	0.60	1.20	3.00
Annual 3, 4 ('92, '93, 3.50)	0.70	1.40	3.50
Annual 5 ('94, 3.95)	0.80	1.60	4.00
Special 1 ('94, 3.50, 68 pgs.)	0.70	1.40	3.50
Special 2 ('95, 3.50, 68 pgs)	0.70	1.40	3.50

STAR TREK: DEEP SPACE NINE
Aug, 1993-Present (2.50, color)
Malibu Comics

	Good	Fine	N-Mint
1-(2.50)-Direct Sale ed.; line drawn-c	0.50	1.00	2.50
1-(2.50)-Newsstand ed.; photo-c	0.50	1.00	2.50
2-23: 2-Polybagged w/trading card. 9-4 pg. prelude to Hearts & Minds			

	0.50	1.00	2.50
Annual 1 (1/95, 3.95, 68 pgs)	0.80	1.60	4.00
...Lightstorm (12/94, 3.50)	0.70	1.40	3.50
#0-(1/95, 2.95) "Terok Nor"	0.60	1.20	3.00

STAR TREK: DEEP SPACE NINE, THE CELBRITY SERIES;
BLOOD AND HONOR
May 1995-Present (2.95, color)
Malibu Comics

1–Mark Lenard-s	0.60	1.20	3.00

STAR TREK: DEEP SPACE NINE HEARTS AND MINDS
June, 1994-No. 4, Sept, 1994 (2.50, color, limited series)
Malibu Comics

1–4	0.50	1.00	2.50
1-Holographic cover	1.20	3.00	7.00

STAR TREK: DEEP SPACE NINE, THE MAQUIS
Feb 1995- Apr 1995 (2.50, color, limited series:3)
Malibu Comics

1-newsstand cover	0.50	1.00	2.50
1-photo cover	0.50	1.00	2.50
2-3	0.50	1.00	2.50

STAR TREK: DEEP SPACE NINE/THE NEXT GENERATION
Oct, 1994-Present (2.50, color)
Malibu Comics

1-2-Pt 2 & 4 of "Prophet and Losses"	0.50	1.00	2.50

STAR TREK GENERATIONS
1994 One shot
DC Comics

nn-(3.95, 68 pgs)-Movie adaptation	0.80	1.60	4.00
nn-(5.95, 68 pgs, square bound)	1.00	3.00	6.00

STAR TREK: THE ASHES OF EDEN
1995 One Shot
DC Comics

nn-(14.95, 100 pgs.) Shatner-s	2.50	6.00	15.00

STAR TREK: THE MODALA IMPERATIVE
Late July, 1991-No. 4, Early Sept, 1991 (1.75, mini-series)
DC Comics

	Good	Fine	N-Mint
1	0.50	1.00	2.50
2–4	0.40	0.80	2.00

STAR TREK: THE NEXT GENERATION (TV)
Feb, 1988-No. 6, July, 1988 (1.00, color, mini-series)
DC Comics

1-(1.50, 52 pgs.)	1.70	5.10	12.00
2–6	1.20	2.90	7.00

STAR TREK: THE NEXT GENERATION (TV)
Oct, 1989-Present (1.50/1.75/1.95, color)
DC Comics

1-Capt. Picard & crew	1.80	4.60	11.00
2, 3	1.30	3.00	7.50
4, 5	1.00	2.00	5.00
6–10	0.70	1.40	3.50
11-23, 25-30: 20-Last 1.50-c	0.50	0.90	2.25
24-(2.50, 52 pgs.)	0.50	1.00	2.50
31-49, 51-60	0.40	0.70	1.75
50-(3.50, 68 pgs.)-Painted-c	0.70	1.40	3.50
61-70: 61-Begin 1.95-c	0.40	0.80	2.00
71-begin 2.50-c; 72-74	0.50	1.00	2.50
Annual 1 ('90, 2.95, 68 pgs.)	0.70	1.40	3.50
Annual 2, 3 ('91, '92, 3.50, 68 pgs.)	0.80	1.60	4.00
Annual 4 ('93, 3.50, 68 pgs.)	0.70	1.40	3.50
Annual 5 ('94, 3.95, 68 pgs)	0.80	1.60	4.00
Special 1 ('93, 3.50 , 68 pgs.)	0.70	1.40	3.50
...Special 2 (Sum/94, 3.95, 68 pgs)	0.80	1.60	4.00
...The Series Finale-('94, 3.95, 68 pgs.)	0.80	1.60	4.00

STAR TREK: THE NEXT GENERATION - THE MODALA IMPERATIVE
Early Sept, 1991-No. 4, Late Oct, 1991 (1.75, mini-series)
DC Comics

1	0.50	1.00	2.50
2–4	0.40	0.80	2.00

STAR TREK: THE NEXT GENERATION-SHADOWHEART
Dec 1994 - Mar 1995 (1.95, color, limited series)
DC Comics

1-4	0.40	0.80	2.00

STAR TREK: THE NEXT GENERATION/STAR TREK: DEEP SPACE NINE
Dec, 1994-Present (2.50, color)

DC Comics			
1-2-Pt 1 & 4 of "Prophets and Losses"	0.50	1.00	2.50

STAR WARS
July, 1977-No. 107, Sept, 1986
Marvel Comics Group

1-Regular 30¢ edition; 1-6 adapt 1st movie	5.00	13.70	32.00
1-35¢ with UPC code; limited distribution	54.00	161.00	375.00
2-6: 2-4-30¢ issues. 6-D. Stevens-i	1.70	4.20	10.00
2-4-35¢ with UPC code; not reprints	1.70	4.20	10.00
7-38	1.00	2.00	5.00
39-44: Empire Strikes Back-r series	1.00	2.00	5.00
45-106: 92, 100-(52 pgs.).	1.00	2.00	5.00
107-Portacio-1	3.00	6.00	15.00
1-9 (Reprints, 35¢-c w/o UPC code)	0.40	0.80	2.00
Annual 1 (12/79)-Simonson-c	0.40	0.80	2.00
Annual 2, 3 (11/82, 12/83)	0.40	0.80	2.00

Note: The scarcer 35¢ edition has the cover price in a square box & the UPC box in the lower left hand corner has the UPC Code lines running through it.

STAR WARS: DARK EMPIRE
Dec, 1991-No. 6, Oct, 1992 (2.95, color, mini-series)
Dark Horse Comics

1-Dave Dorman painted-c on all	3.60	10.70	25.00
1-2nd printing	0.60	1.20	3.00
2-Low print run	4.00	12.00	28.00
2, 3-2nd printings	0.60	1.20	3.00
3	1.70	4.20	10.00
4	1.20	2.40	6.00
5, 6	1.00	2.00	5.00
Gold Embossed Set (1-6)-With gold embossed foil logo			
(price is for set)	11.00	32.00	75.00
Platinum Embossed Set (1-6)	21.00	64.00	150.00
TPB (4/93, 16.95)	2.40	7.00	17.00

STAR WARS: DARK EMPIRE II
Dec 1994- May 1995 (2.95, color, limited series:6)
Dark Horse Comics

1-Dave Dorman painted-c	0.80	1.60	4.00
2-6-Dorman-c	0.60	1.20	3.00

STAR WARS: DROIDS (See Dark Horse Comics #17-19)
Apr, 1994-No. 6, Sept, 1994 (2.50, color, limited series)

	Good	Fine	N-Mint
Dark Horse Comics			
1-(2.95)-Embossed-c	0.60	1.20	3.00
2-(2.25)	0.50	0.90	2.25
3–6	0.50	1.00	2.50
Special 1-(1/95, 2.50)	0.50	1.00	2.50
Volume 2; 1–3	0.50	1.00	2.50

STAR WARS: JABBA THE HUTT
Apr, 1995 (2.50, color, one-shot)
Dark Horse Comics

	Good	Fine	N-Mint
nn	0.50	1.00	2.50
...The Hunger of Princess Nampi-(2.50)	0.50	1.00	2.50

STAR WARS: RETURN OF THE JEDI
Oct, 1983-No. 4, Jan, 1984 (Mini-series)
Marvel Comics Group

	Good	Fine	N-Mint
1-4: Movie adaptation	0.20	0.40	1.00

STAR WARS: RIVER OF CHAOS
June 1995-Present (2.50, color, limited series)
Dark Horse Comics

	Good	Fine	N-Mint
1–L. Simonson-s	0.50	1.00	2.50

STAR WARS: TALES OF THE JEDI (See Dark Horse Comics #7)
Oct, 1993-No. 5, Feb, 1994 (2.50, color, limited series)
Dark Horse Comics

	Good	Fine	N-Mint
1-5-Dorman painted-c. 3-r/Dark Horse Comics #7-9 w/new coloring & some panels redrawn	0.60	1.20	3.00
1-5-Gold foil embossed logo; print run of 7500	4.00	10.70	25.00

STAR WARS: TALES OF THE JEDI-DARK LORDS OF THE SITH
Oct, 1994- Mar, 1995 (2.50, color, limited series)
Dark Horse Comics

	Good	Fine	N-Mint
1-6: 1-Polybagged w/trading card	0.60	1.20	3.00

STAR WARS: TALES OF THE JEDI-THE FREEDOM NADD UPRISING
Aug, 1994-No. 2, Sept, 1994 (2.50, color, limited series)
Dark Horse Comics

	Good	Fine	N-Mint
1,2	0.60	1.20	3.00

STATIC
June, 1993-Present (1.50/1.75, color)

Steel #7 © DC

Stormwatch #25 © Aegis Ent.

DC Comics (Milestone)

1-(2.95)-Collector's Edition; polybagged w/poster & trading card			
& backing board (direct sale only)	0.60	1.20	3.00
1-13: 2-Origin. 8-Shadow War; Simonson-c.0.30		0.60	1.50
14-(2.50, 52 pgs.)-Worlds Collide Pt. 14	0.50	1.00	2.50
15-24: 15-Begin 1.75-c 21-Blood Syndicate app.		0.40	0.70
1.75			
25-(3.95)	0.80	1.60	4.00
26- Long Hot Summer (2.50)	0.50	1.00	2.50

STEEL
Feb, 1994-Present (1.50, color)
DC Comics

1-8: 6,7-Worlds Collide Pt. 5 &12. 8	0.30	0.60	1.50
0,9-15: 0-(10/94). 9-(11/94)	0.30	0.60	1.50
16-begin 1.95-c; 17,18–	0.40	0.80	2.00
Annual 1 (1994, 2.95)-Elseworlds story	0.60	1.20	3.00

STEEL, THE INDESTRUCTIBLE MAN
March, 1978-No. 5, Oct-Nov, 1978
DC Comics

1	0.20	0.50	1.20
2-5: 5-Giant	0.20	0.40	1.00

STEVE ZODIAC & THE FIRE BALL XL-5 (TV)
Jan, 1964
Gold Key

10108-401 (#1)	7.10	21.00	50.00

	Good	Fine	N-Mint
STORMQUEST			
Nov, 1994-Present (1.95, color)			
Caliber Press (Sky Universe)			
1,2	0.40	0.80	2.00

STORMWATCH
Mar, 1993-Present (1.95, color)
Image Comics

1-8: 1-Jim Lee-c & part scripts (Lee plots in all). 1-3 contain coupon for			
limited edition Stormwatch trading card #00 by Lee. 3-1st app. Backlash			
(cameo)	0.40	0.80	2.00
0-(2.50)-Bagged w/card; 1st full app. Backlash			
	0.50	1.00	2.50
9-(4/94, 2.50)-Intro Defile	0.50	1.00	2.50
25-(5/94, June 1995 on-c; 2.50)	0.50	1.00	2.50
10-17: 10-(6/94). 11,12-(8/94). 13,14-(9/94). 15-(10/94)			
	0.40	0.80	2.00
10-Alternate Portacio-c, see Deathblow #5	0.40	0.80	2.00
18-20-(2.50); 21-(#1 on cover)	0.50	1.00	2.50
22-(1.95)-Newstand, WildStorm Rising pt.	0.40	0.80	2.00
22-(2.50)-Direct Market, WilStorm Rising pt. 9, Bound-in card, 23-Spartan			
joins	0.50	1.00	2.50
Special 1 (1/94, 3.50, 52 pgs.)	0.70	1.40	3.50
Special 2 (5/95, 3.50, 52 pgs.)	0.70	1.40	3.50
...:Sourcebook 1-(1/94, 2.50)	0.50	1.00	2.50

STRANGE ADVENTURES
No. 54, 1955-No. 244, Oct-Nov, 1973
National Periodical Publications

54-70: 54-1st code approved issue	13.00	39.00	105.00
71-99	9.00	26.00	70.00
100	12.10	36.00	85.00
101-110: 104-Space Museum begins	8.00	24.00	55.00
111-116, 118, 119: 114-Star Hawkins begins, ends No. 185			
	7.10	21.00	50.00
117-Origin/1st app. Atomic Knights (6/60)			
	38.00	114.00	380.00
120-2nd app. Atomic Knights	17.00	51.00	170.00
121, 122, 124, 125, 127, 128, 130, 131, 133, 134: 134-Last 10¢ issue			
	5.70	17.10	40.00
123, 126: 3rd & 4th app. Atomic Knights	10.00	29.00	95.00
129, 132, 135, 138, 141, 144, 147: Atomic Knights app. 144-Only Atomic			
Knights cover	6.00	18.00	55.00

136, 137, 139, 140, 142, 143, 145, 146, 148, 149, 151, 152, 154, 155,			
157-159	4.30	12.90	30.00
150, 153, 156, 160: Atomic Knights in each; 160-Last Atomic Knights			
	5.70	17.10	40.00
161-179: 161-Last Space Museum	2.90	9.00	20.00
180-Origin & 1st app. Animal Man	27.00	81.00	180.00
181-183, 185-189	1.30	3.30	8.00
184-2nd app. Animal Man	16.00	47.00	110.00
190-1st Animal Man in costume	19.00	58.00	135.00
191-194, 196-200, 202-204	1.00	2.50	6.00
195-1st full Animal Man app.	11.00	32.00	75.00
201-2nd full Animal Man app.	5.70	17.00	40.00
205-Intro & origin Deadman (10/67)	7.10	21.00	50.00
206-Deadman begins; Adams-a only	5.00	15.00	35.00
207-210: Adams-c/a	3.60	10.70	25.00
211-216: 216-Last Deadman; Adams-c/a (1-2/69); Deadman storyline			
concludes in Brave and the Bold #86 by Adams (10-11/69)			
	2.90	8.60	20.00
217-221, 223-231: 217-Adam Strange & Atomic Knights-r begin. 226-New			
Adam Strange text story w/illos by Anderson. 228-Adams-c. 231-Last			
Atomic Knights-r	1.10	2.20	5.50
222-New A. Strange story by Kane/Anderson			
	1.70	4.20	10.00
232-244: 235-Neal Adams-c	0.70	1.40	3.50

STRANGERS, THE
June, 1993-Present (1.95, color)
Malibu Comics (Ultraverse)

1-4,6-12,14-20: 1-1st app. The Strangers; 1st app. the Night Man (not in			
costume); has coupon for Ultraverse Premiere #0. 2-Polybagged			
w/card. 7-Break-thru x-over. 8-2 pg. origin Solution. 12-Silver foil logo;			
wraparound-c. 17-Rafferty app.	0.40	0.80	2.00
1-With coupon missing	0.30	0.60	1.50
1-Full cover holographic edition; 1st of kind w/Hardcase #1 & Prime #1			
	3.60	11.00	25.00
1-Ultra 5000 Limited silver foil	2.10	6.00	15.00
4-(2.50)-Newsstand ed. bagged w/card	0.50	1.00	2.50
5-(2.50, 52 pgs.)-Rune flip-c/story by B. Smith; 3-pg. Night Man preview			
	0.50	1.00	2.50
13-(3.50, 68 pgs.)-Mantra app.; flip book w/Ultraverse Premiere #4			
	0.70	1.40	3.50
21-24 (2.50)	0.50	1.00	2.50
...:The Pilgrim Conundrum Saga (1/95, 3.95, 68 pgs)			

	Good	Fine	N-Mint
	0.80	1.60	4.00

STRANGERS IN PARADISE
Nov 1993-Feb 1994- (2.75, B&W)
Antarctic Press

	Good	Fine	N-Mint
1–3	1.00	2.00	5.00

STRANGERS IN PARADISE
Sep 1994-Present (2.75, B&W)

	Good	Fine	N-Mint
1	0.80	1.60	4.00
2–5	0.60	1.10	2.75

STRANGE SPORTS STORIES (See Brave & the Bold #45-49)
Sept-Oct, 1973-No. 6, July-Aug, 1974
National Periodical Publications

	Good	Fine	N-Mint
1	1.30	3.00	8.00
2-6: 3-Swan/Anderson-a	1.00	2.00	5.00

STRANGE SUSPENSE STORIES(Becomes Captain Atom #78 on)
No. 75, 6/65-No. 77, 10/65; V3#1, 10/67-V1#2-9, 9/69
Charlton Comics (All are 12¢ issues)

	Good	Fine	N-Mint
75-r/origin/1st app. Captain Atom by Ditko	12.00	40.00	85.00
76, 77: Captain Atom-r by Ditko	5.00	15.00	35.00
V3#1(10/67)-4	1.70	4.20	10.00
V1#2-9: 2-Ditko-c/a; atom bomb cover	1.10	2.20	5.50

STRANGE TALES (Becomes Dr. Strange No. 169 (June, 1968))
June, 1951-No. 168, May, 1968
No. 169, Sept, 1973-No. 188, Nov, 1976
Atlas/ Marvel Comics #86 (7/61) on

	Good	Fine	N-Mint
1	175.00	525.00	1750.00
2	72.00	216.00	575.00
3, 5: 3-Atom Bomb panels	51.00	154.00	410.00
4-The Evil Eye cosmic eyeball story	56.00	169.00	450.00
6–9	39.00	120.00	310.00
10-Krigstein art	41.00	124.00	330.00
11-14, 16-20	23.00	69.00	185.00
15-Krigstein art	24.00	71.00	190.00
21, 23-27, 29-34: 34-Last pre-code (2/55)	19.00	56.00	150.00
22-Krigstein-a	19.00	58.00	155.00
28-J. Katz story used in Senate investigation	20.00	60.00	160.00
35-41, 43, 44: 37-Vampire story by Colan	14.00	43.00	115.00

42, 45, 59, 61-Krigstein art (61 is 2/58)	15.00	45.00	120.00
46-57, 60 (60 is 8/57)	12.00	36.00	95.00
58, 64-Williamson-a	13.00	38.00	100.00
62, 63, 65, 66: 62-Torres-a. 66-Crandall-a	10.00	30.00	90.00
67-Quicksilver prototype (3/58)	14.00	43.00	130.00
68, 71, 72, 74, 77, 80: Ditko/Kirby a-67-80	12.00	35.00	105.00

69,70,73,75,76,78,79: 69-Professor X prototype. 70-Giant-Man prototype.
 73-Ant-Man prototype. 75-Iron Man prototype. 76-Human Torch prototype. 78-Ant-Man prototype. 79-Dr. Strange prototype story (12/60)

	18.00	53.00	160.00
81-83, 85-88, 90-91: Ditko/Kirby-a in 81-92	10.00	30.00	90.00
84-Magneto prototype (5/61)	16.00	50.00	145.00
89-1st Fin Fang Foom by Kirby	31.00	93.00	280.00
92-Ancient One prototype; last 10¢ issue	12.00	37.00	110.00
93, 95, 96, 98-100: Kirby art	9.00	28.00	85.00
94-The Thing prototype; Kirby-a	11.00	33.00	100.00

97-Aunt May & Uncle Ben prototype by Ditko; 3 months before Amazing

Fantasy #15	26.00	78.00	235.00

101-Human Torch begins by Kirby (10/62); recaps origin of Fantastic

Four	72.00	215.00	645.00
102-1st app. Wizard	31.00	94.00	250.00
103-105	23.00	69.00	185.00
106, 108, 109: 106-F.F. app.	16.00	49.00	130.00

107-Human Torch/Sub-Mariner battle; 4th S.A. Sub-Mariner app. & 1st

x-over outside of Fantastic Four (4/63)	19.00	56.00	150.00

110-1st app. Dr. Strange, Ancient One & Wong by Ditko (7/63)

	83.00	248.00	745.00
111-2nd app. Dr. Strange	31.00	94.00	250.00
112, 113	10.00	30.00	80.00

114-Acrobat disguised as Capt. America (1st app. since the Golden Age);
 Dr. Strange series begins (11/63, 3rd app.)

	29.00	88.00	265.00

115-Origin Dr. Strange; Human Torch vs. Sandman (2nd app. & brief origin of

Sandman); early Spider-Man x-over	41.00	123.00	370.00

116-Human Torch vs. Thing; 1st Thing x-over

	10.00	30.00	80.00
117, 118, 120: 120-1st Iceman x-over	7.00	21.00	55.00
119-Spider-Man (cameo)	10.00	30.00	80.00

121, 122, 124, 126-134: 130-Beatles cameo. 134-Last Human Torch;

Watcher-c/story	6.40	19.00	45.00

123-1st app. The Beetle (see Amazing Spider-Man #21); 1st Thor x-over

app. (8/64)	7.00	21.00	50.00

125-Torch & Thing battle Sub-Mariner (10/64)

	Good	Fine	N-Mint
	6.40	19.00	45.00

135-Origin/1st app. Nick Fury & begin (8/65)

	10.00	30.00	90.00

136-147, 149, 150: 145-Alternating-c features begin w/Nick Fury (odd #'s) &
   Dr. Strange (even #'s). 146-Only Ditko Dr. Strange-c this title. 150-John

Buscema's 1st Marvel work (10/66)	4.30	12.90	30.00
148-Origin Ancient One	7.00	17.00	55.00
151-1st Marvel work by Steranko	5.70	17.00	40.00
152-158: Steranko-a	4.30	12.90	30.00

159-Capt. America-c/story; origin Nick Fury retold; Steranko-a in 151-168

	4.90	15.00	34.00

160-166, 168: 168-Last Nick Fury & Dr. Strange; (both get own title next

month; becomes Doctor Strange w/#169	4.00	12.00	28.00
167- Steranko classic-c plus-a	5.40	16.00	38.00

169-177, 182-188: 169, 170-1st app. Brother Voodoo; origin in each.

174-Origin Golem	0.70	1.40	3.50

178-Warlock begins by Starlin (2/75); origin Warlock & Him retold;

1st app. Magus	2.90	8.60	20.00

179-181: Warlock by Starlin cont'd. 181-(8/75)-Story cont'd in Warlock #9

	1.50	3.80	9.00

Annual 1 (1962)-Pre-hero-r/JIM, Strange Tales, TOS, TTA

(1st Marvel annual?)	40.00	120.00	360.00

Annual 2 (1963)-1st Spidey x-over, battles Human Torch; tied for 6th app.

w/Amazing Spider-Man #5; Kirby-c	47.00	142.00	425.00

STRANGE TALES
Apr, 1987-No. 19, Oct, 1988
Marvel Comics Group

V2#1-19	0.20	0.40	1.00

STRANGE TALES
Nov, 1994 (6.95, color)
Marvel Comics

V3 #1-(6.95)-Acetate -c.	1.20	2.90	7.00

STRANGE WORLDS
Dec, 1958-No. 5, July-Aug, 1959
Marvel Comics Group
1-Kirby-a; Ditko-a in 1-5; Flying Saucer issue

	34.00	102.00	340.00
2-Ditko-c/a; Don Heck-a	21.00	63.00	210.00
3-Ditko & Kirby-a	17.00	51.00	170.00
4-Ditko & Williamson art	16.00	48.00	160.00

5-Ditko art	14.00	42.00	140.00

STRAY BULLETS
1995 (2.95, B&W, Adult readers)
El Capitan Books

1-4 David Lapham	0.60	1.20	3.00

STREET FIGHTER: THE BATTLE FOR SHADALOO
1995 (3.95, color, One-shot)
DC Comics/CAP CO. LTD.

1-Polybagged w/trading card & Tattoo	0.80	1.60	4.00

STREET FIGHTER II
Apr, 1994-No. 8 (2.95, color, limited series)
Tokuma Comics (Viz)

1–7	0.60	1.20	3.00

STRIKEBACK!
Oct, 1994-Present (2.95, color, limited series:6)
Malibu (Bravura)

1-3	0.60	1.20	3.00
1-Gold foil embossed cover	1.70	4.20	10.00

STRYFE'S STRIKE FILE
Jan, 1993 (1.75, color, one-shot, no ads)
Marvel Comics

1-Stroman, Capullo, Peterson, Andy Kubert-a; wraparound-c w/silver metallic ink-c; X-Cutioner's Song tie-in	0.40	0.70	1.75
1-2nd printing w/gold metallic ink	0.40	0.70	1.75

STRYKE
1995 (3.00, color)
London Night Studios

#0	0.60	1.20	3.00
#0-Alternate-c	1.00	2.00	5.00

STYGMATA
No. 0, Early 1994 (2.95, color);
July, 1994-No. 3, Oct, 1994 (2.95, B&W, limited series)
Entity Comics

0-Foil-c	0.60	1.20	3.00
1-3: 1-Foil logo. 3-Silver foil logo	0.60	1.20	3.00
...Yearbook 1 ('95, 2.95)	0.60	1.20	3.00

	Good	Fine	N-Mint

Strikeback #3 © Peterson

Stygmata #2 © Raff Lenco

SUB-MARINER, THE
No. 33, Apr, 1954-No. 42, Oct, 1955
Atlas Comics

	Good	Fine	N-Mint
33-Origin Sub-Mariner; Human Torch app.; Namora x-over in 33-42	71.00	214.00	500.00
34, 35-Human Torch in each	54.00	160.00	380.00
36, 37, 39-41: 36, 39-41-Namora app.	54.00	160.00	380.00
38-Origin Sub-Mariner's wings; Namora app.; last pre-code issue (2/55)	65.00	195.00	455.00
42-Last issue	66.00	197.00	460.00

SUB-MARINER, THE (Also see Namor, ... & Tales To Astonish)
May, 1968 - No. 72, Sept, 1974
Marvel Comics Group

	Good	Fine	N-Mint
1-Origin Sub-Mariner; story cont'd from Iron Man & Sub-Mariner #1	19.00	56.00	130.00
2-Triton app.	7.00	21.00	50.00
3-10: 5-1st app. Tiger Shark. 6-2nd app. Tiger Shark cont'd from #5. 8-Sub-Mariner vs. Thing	4.30	13.00	30.00
11-13, 15: 15-Last 12¢ issue	3.00	8.60	20.00
14-Sub-Mariner vs. Golden Age Human Torch; death of Toro (1st modern app. & only app. Toro)	5.00	15.00	35.00
16-20: 19-1st Sting Ray	1.70	5.00	12.00
21-33, 36-40: 22-Dr. Strange x-over. 30-Capt. Marvel x-over. 38-Origin retold. 40-Spider-Man x-over	1.30	3.00	7.50
34, 35-Both tie in with 1st Defenders. 34-Hulk & Silver Surfer x-over. 35-Namor/Hulk/Silver Surfer team-up to battle Avengers-c/story (3/71)	2.40	7.30	17.00

41-49, 51-72: 42-Last 15¢ issue. 44, 45-Vs. Human Torch. 49-Cosmic
Cube story. 59-1st battle with Thor. 61-Last Everett-a. 67-New costume

	1.00	2.00	5.00
50-1st app. Nita from New Warriors	1.20	2.90	7.00
Special 1 (1971)-r/TTA 70-73	1.20	2.90	7.00
Special 2 (1972)-r/TTA 74-75	1.20	2.90	7.00

SUGAR & SPIKE (See DC Silver Age Classics)
Apr-May, 1956-No. 98, Oct-Nov, 1971
National Periodical Publications

1 (Scarce)	83.00	248.00	825.00
2	43.00	128.00	385.00
3-5: 3-Letter column begins	37.00	112.00	335.00
6–10	22.00	67.00	200.00
11–20	19.00	58.00	175.00
21-29, 31-40: 26-Christmas-c	13.00	39.00	90.00
30-Scribbly x-over	14.00	40.00	100.00
41-60	8.00	24.00	55.00
61-80	5.00	15.00	35.00
81-98: 85, 96-(68 pgs.). 97, 98-(52 pgs.)	3.60	10.70	25.00

SUPERBOY (...& the Legion of Super Heroes starting with No. 231)
(Becomes The Legion of Super Heroes No. 259 on)
No. 39, Mar, 1955-No. 258, Dec, 1979
National Periodical Publications/DC Comics

39-48, 50: 39-1st code issue	13.00	40.00	120.00
49-1st app. Metallo (6/56)	16.00	48.00	145.00
51-60	11.00	32.00	95.00
61-67	9.00	27.00	80.00
68-Origin/1st app. original Bizarro (10-11/58)			
	45.00	135.00	405.00
69-77, 79: 76-1st Supermonkey	7.00	20.00	60.00
78-Origin Mr. Mxyzptlk retold	12.00	37.00	110.00
80-1st meeting of Superboy & Supergirl (4/60)			
	11.00	32.00	95.00
81, 83-85, 87, 88	6.00	17.00	50.00
82-1st Bizarro Krypto	5.00	16.00	48.00
86-4th Legion app. (1/61)	11.00	32.00	95.00
89-1st app. Mon-el (6/61)	21.00	62.00	185.00
90-92: 92-Last 10¢ issue	6.00	17.00	50.00
93-10th Legion app. (12/61)	4.50	17.00	40.00
94-97, 99	4.00	10.70	25.00
98-Origin/1st. app. Ultra Boy	5.00	15.00	35.00
100-Origin Superboy retold (10/62)	21.00	62.00	145.00
101-120: 104-Origin Phantom Zone. 117-Legion app.			

	Good	Fine	N-Mint
	2.10	6.40	15.00
121-128: 126-Origin Krypton w/new facts	1.70	4.00	10.00
129, 138-Giants G-22 & G-35	2.30	5.80	14.00
130-137, 139, 140: 133-Superboy meets Robin			
	1.00	2.00	5.00
141-146, 148-155, 157-164, 166-173, 175, 176: 176-Partial photo-c			
	0.80	1.50	3.75
147 (G-47)-Origin Saturn Girl, Lightning Lad & Cosmic Boy (6/68)			
	1.60	4.00	9.50
156, 165, 174-Giants G-59, G-71, G-83	1.50	3.80	9.00
177-184, 186, 187: All 52 pgs.	0.70	1.40	3.50
185-100 pg. Super Spec. #12	1.00	2.00	5.00
188-196: 191-Origin Sunboy retold	0.50	0.90	2.25
197-Legion series begins	1.00	2.50	6.00
198, 199	0.50	1.00	2.50
200-Bouncing Boy, Duo Damsel marry	1.00	2.00	5.00
201, 204, 206, 207, 209: 204-Supergirl quits			
	0.60	1.10	2.75
202, 205-(100 pgs.)	0.70	1.30	3.25
203-Invisible Kid dies	0.80	1.50	3.75
208, 210: 208-(68 pgs.)	0.70	1.30	3.25
211-220	0.50	1.00	2.50
221-249	0.40	0.80	1.90
250-258	0.40	0.80	1.90
Annual 1 (Sum/64)-Origin Krypto-r	10.00	40.00	110.00
Spectacular 1 (1980, Giant)-Mostly-r	0.40	0.80	1.90

SUPERBOY
Feb, 1994-Present (1.50, color)
DC Comics

1-5-Metropolis Kid from Reign/Supermen	0.30	0.60	1.50
6-8: 6,7-Worlds Collide Pt. 3 & 8. 8-(9/94)-Zero Hour			
	0.30	0.60	1.50
0,9-15: 0-(10/94). 9-(11/94)-King Shark app.			
	0.30	0.60	1.50
16-18, 16-begin 1.95-c	0.40	0.80	2.00
Annual 1 ('94, 2.95, 68 pgs.)-Elseworlds sty, part 2 of The Super Seven (see Advs. Of Superman Annual 6)	0.60	1.20	3.00

SUPERCAR (TV)
Nov, 1962-No. 4, Aug, 1963 (All have painted-c)
Gold Key

1	•	25.00	75.00	175.00

2, 3	14.00	41.00	95.00
4	19.00	58.00	135.00

SUPER DC GIANT
No. 13, 9-10/70-No. 26, 7-8/71; V3#27, Summer, 1976
National Periodical Publications

S-13: Binky	0.80	1.60	4.00
S-14: Top Guns Of The West	0.80	1.60	4.00
S-15: Western Comics	1.00	2.00	5.00
S-16: Best Of The Brave And The Bold	1.00	2.00	5.00
S-17: Love 1970	0.70	1.40	3.50
S-18: Three Mouseketeers	0.80	1.60	4.00
S-19: Jerry Lewis	0.80	1.60	4.00
S-20: House Of Mystery	1.00	2.00	5.00
S-21: Love 1971	0.60	1.20	3.00
S-22: Top Guns Of The West	0.70	1.40	3.50
S-23: The Unexpected	1.00	2.00	5.00
S-24: Supergirl	0.60	1.20	3.00
S-25: Challengers Of The Unknown	0.80	1.60	4.00
S-26: Aquaman (1971)	0.80	1.60	4.00
27-Strange Flying Saucers Adventures	0.60	1.20	3.00

SUPER FRIENDS (TV)
Nov, 1976-No. 47, Aug, 1981
National Periodical Pub./ DC Comics

1-Superman, Batman, Atom, et al app.	0.50	1.00	2.50
2-47: 2-Penguin-c/story. 7-Batgirl x-over. 28-Bizarro app.			
	0.40	0.80	2.00
Special 1 ('81)-Giveaway	0.40	0.70	1.80

SUPERGIRL
Nov, 1972-No. 9, Dec-Jan, 1973-74; No. 10, Sept-Oct, 1974
National Periodical Publications (All 20¢ issues?)

1-1st solo title	1.00	2.00	5.00
2-10: 8-JLA x-over	0.60	1.20	3.00

SUPERGIRL
Feb, 1994-No. 4, May, 1994 (1.50, color, mini-series)
DC Comics

1-4: 1-Guice-i	0.30	0.60	1.50

SUPERGIRL/LEX LUTHOR SPECIAL (Supergirl and Team Luthor on-c)
1993 (2.50, color, 68 pgs.)

	Good	Fine	N-Mint
DC Comics			
1-Pin-ups by Byrne, Thibert	0.50	1.00	2.50

SUPER GREEN BERET (Tod Holton...)
Apr, 1967-No. 2, June, 1967 (25¢, 68 pgs.)
Lightning Comics

	Good	Fine	N-Mint
1, 2	3.60	9.00	18.00

SUPER HEROES
Jan, 1967-No. 4, June, 1967
Dell Publishing Co.

	Good	Fine	N-Mint
1-Origin & 1st app. The Fab. 4	2.90	9.00	20.00
2–4	1.70	5.10	12.00

SUPER-HEROES BATTLE SUPER-GORILLAS
Winter, 1976 (One-shot, 52 pgs.)
National Periodical Publications

	Good	Fine	N-Mint
1-Superman, Batman, Flash reprint stories	0.30	0.50	1.25

SUPER HEROES PUZZLES AND GAMES
1979 (32 pgs., regular size)
General Mills (Marvel Comics Group)

	Good	Fine	N-Mint
nn-Four 2-pg. origin stories of Spider-Man, Captain America, The Hulk & Spider-Woman	0.90	1.80	4.50

SUPER HEROES VERSUS SUPER VILLAINS
July, 1966 (68 pgs.)
Archie Publications

	Good	Fine	N-Mint
1-Flyman, Black Hood, The Web, Shield-r	5.00	15.00	35.00

SUPERMAN (Becomes Adventures Of Superman #424 on)
No. 96, Mar, 1955-No. 423, Sept, 1986
National Periodical Publications/DC Comics

	Good	Fine	N-Mint
96-99: 96-1st code approved issue	25.00	75.00	225.00
100 (9-10/55)	127.00	380.00	1265.00
101-110	24.00	73.00	195.00
111-120	21.00	64.00	170.00
121-130: 123-Pre-Supergirl tryout. 127-Origin/1st app. Titano	18.00	54.00	145.00
131-139	14.00	41.00	110.00
140-1st Blue Kryptonite, 1st Bizarro Supergirl; origin Bizarro Jr.	16.00	47.00	125.00
141-145, 148: 142-2nd Batman x-over	11.00	32.00	85.00

146-Superman's life story	13.00	39.00	105.00
147-1st app. Legion of Super Villains; 7th Legion app.			
	12.00	36.00	95.00
149-Last 10¢ issue; 9th Legion app.; "The Death of Superman"			
imaginary story	11.00	32.00	85.00
150-162: 158-1st app. Flamebird & Nightwing			
	6.00	17.00	40.00
161-2nd printing (1987, 1.25)-New DC logo; sold thru So Much Fun			
Toy Stores (Superman Classic on-c)	0.50	0.90	2.25
163-166, 168-180: 170-JFK tribute issue. 169-The Bizarro Invasion of			
Earth-c/story	4.30	13.00	30.00
167-New origin Braniac	9.00	26.00	60.00
181, 182, 184-186, 188-192	3.10	9.40	22.00
183,187,193,197-Giants G-18,G-23,G-31,G-36			
	3.90	11.60	27.00
194-196, 198, 200	3.10	9.40	22.00
199-1st Superman/Flash race (8/67)	24.00	71.00	165.00
201, 203-206, 208-211, 213-216	2.20	5.00	13.00
202, 207, 212, 217-Giants G-42, G-48, G-54, G-60. 202-All Bizarro issue.			
207-30th ann. Superman; Legion app.	2.60	7.70	18.00
218-221, 223-226, 228-231	1.80	5.00	11.00
222, 227, 232-Giants G-66, G-72, G-78	2.60	7.70	18.00
233-238	1.80	5.00	11.00
239-Giant G-84	2.60	7.70	18.00
240-Kaluta art	1.00	2.50	6.00
241-244: All 52 pgs.	1.10	2.20	5.50
245-DC 100 pg. Super Spec. No.7	2.00	3.80	9.00
246-248, 250, 251, 253 (All 52 pgs.)	1.00	1.90	4.75
249, 254-Adams art	1.40	4.00	8.50
252-DC 100 pg. Super Spec. No. 13	1.30	3.30	8.00
255-271, 273-277, 279-283: 263-Photo-c. 264-1st app. Steve Lombard			
279-Batman & Batgirl guest star	0.50	1.00	2.50
272, 278, 284-All 100 pgs.; G.A.-r	1.00	2.00	5.00
285-299: 292-Origin Lex Luthor retold	0.50	1.00	2.50
300-Retells origin (6/76)	1.00	2.70	6.50
301-399: 366-Fan letter by Todd McFarlane			
	0.50	0.90	2.25
400-(10/84, 68 pgs.)	1.00	2.00	5.00
401-422	0.50	0.90	2.25
423-Alan Moore scripts; Perez inks	1.70	4.00	10.00
Annual 1 (10/60, 84 pgs.)-1st S.A. DC Annual; r/Lois Lane #1 & Action 252			
(1st Supergirl)	58.00	174.00	580.00
Annual 2 ('60)-Bizarro origin-r	31.00	93.00	280.00

	Good	Fine	N-Mint

Superman #90 © DC

Superman #400 © DC

	Good	Fine	N-Mint
Annual 3 ('61)	26.00	77.00	205.00
Annual 4 ('61)-1st Legion origins	22.00	66.00	175.00
Annual 5 (Sum/62)-All Krypton issue	20.00	60.00	140.00
Annual 6 (Win/62-63)-r/Adv. 247	18.00	54.00	125.00
Annual 7 (Sum/63)-Origin-r/Superman/Batman team from Adv. 275			
	14.00	41.00	95.00
Annual 8 (Win/63-64)-All origins issue	11.00	34.00	80.00
Annual 9 ('83)-Toth/Austin-a	1.20	2.40	6.00
Annual 10-12: 11-Moore scripts	1.00	2.00	5.00
Special 1-3 ('83-'85). 1-Gil Kane-c/a	1.00	2.00	5.00

SUPERMAN (2nd series)(Also see Man of Steel)
Jan, 1987-Present
DC Comics

	Good	Fine	N-Mint
1-Byrne-c/a; intro new Metallo	0.60	1.20	3.00
2-8, 10	0.40	0.80	2.00
9-Joker cover	0.70	1.40	3.50
11-49, 51, 52, 54-56, 58-67: 41-Lobo app.	0.40	0.70	1.80
50-Clark Kent proposes (1.50-c)	0.90	1.70	4.25
50-2nd printing	0.40	0.70	1.75
53-Clark reveals identity to Lois Lane	0.60	1.20	3.00
53-2nd printing (1.00-c)	0.30	0.60	1.50
57-(1.75, 52 pgs.)	0.40	0.70	1.75
68-72: 65, 66, 68-Deathstroke-c/story. 70-Superman/Robin team-up			
	0.30	0.60	1.50
73-Doomsday cameo	0.80	1.60	4.00
74-Doomsday battle with Superman	1.00	2.10	5.00
73,74-2nd printings	0.40	0.70	1.80
75-(2.50)-Collector's Ed.; death of Superman; polybagged w/premiums			

	2.10	6.00	15.00
75-Direct sale/no upc (1st print, 1.25)	0.80	1.50	3.75
75-Direct sale/no upc (2nd print, 1.25)	0.30	0.50	1.25
75-Direct sale/no upc (3rd & 4th prints)	0.30	0.50	1.25
75-Newsstand copy w/upc	0.70	1.40	3.50
75-Platinum Edition-Giveaway to retailers	13.00	39.00	90.00
76, 77-Funeral For A Friend issues	0.50	0.90	2.25
78-(1.95)-Collector's Ed. w/die-cut outer-c & bound-in mini-poster;			
Doomsday cameo	0.50	0.90	2.25
78-(1.50)-Newsstand ed. w/poster & different-c; Doomsday-c & cameo			
	0.40	0.70	1.80
79-81, 83-89: 83-Funeral for a Friend epilogue; new Batman cameo.			
87,88-Bizarro-c/story	0.40	0.70	1.80
82-(3.50)-Collector's Ed. w/all foil-c; real Superman revealed; Green			
Lantern x-over from G.L. #46; no ads	0.70	1.40	3.50
82-(2.00, 44 pgs.)-Regular ed. w/different-c			
	0.40	0.80	2.00
90-93: 93-(9/94)-Zero Hour	0.30	0.60	1.50
0,94-99: 0-(10/94). 94-(11/94). 95-Atom app. 96-Return of Brainiac			
	0.30	0.60	1.50
100-Death of Clark Kent-foil-c	0.80	1.60	4.00
100-Newsstand	0.60	1.20	3.00
102-begin 1.95-c, Black Adam app. 103–	0.40	0.80	2.00
Annual 1, 2 ('87, '88)	0.30	0.60	1.50
Annual 3 ('91, 2.00)-Armegeddon 2001	0.40	0.80	2.00
Annual 3-2nd, 3rd printings (2.00)	0.40	0.80	2.00
Annual 4 ('92, 2.50)-Eclipso app.; Quesada-c			
	0.50	1.00	2.50
Annual 5 ('93, 2.50, 68 pgs.)	0.50	1.00	2.50
Annual 6 ('94, 2.95, 68 pgs.)-Elseworlds story			
	0.60	1.20	3.00
Annual 7 ('95, 3.95, 69 pgs.)-Year One	0.80	1.60	4.00
Special 1 ('92, 3.50)-Walt Simonson-c/a	0.70	1.40	3.50
The Death of Superman (TPB, 4.95)-Reprints all Death of Superman			
issues (2nd, 3rd printings exist)	1.00	2.00	5.00
The Death of Superman Platinum Edition	2.10	6.00	15.00
The Superman Gallery 1 ('93, 2.95)-Poster art			
	0.60	1.20	3.00
...:Kal ('95, 5.95) Elseworlds story	1.20	2.40	6.00
...: The Legacy of Superman 1-(3/93, 2.50, one-shot, 68 pgs.)-Art			
Adams-c; Simonson-a	0.50	1.00	2.50
...: Under a Yellow Sun nn-(1994, 5.95, 68 pgs.)-Embossed-c; a novel by			
Clark Kent	1.20	2.40	6.00

	Good	Fine	N-Mint
...: Time and Time Again ('94, 7.50)-Reprints			
	1.30	3.10	7.50

SUPERMAN/DOOMSDAY: HUNTER/PREY
1994-No. 3, 1994 (4.95, color, limited series, 52 pgs.)
DC Comics

	Good	Fine	N-Mint
1-3	1.00	2.00	5.00

SUPERMAN FAMILY, THE (Formerly Superman's Pal, Jimmy Olsen)
No. 164, Apr, 1974-No. 222, Sept, 1982
National Periodical Publications

	Good	Fine	N-Mint
164	0.40	0.80	2.00
165-176 (100-68 pgs.)	0.30	0.60	1.50
177-181 (52 pgs.)	0.30	0.60	1.50
182-Marshall Rogers-a;1.00-c issues begin			
	0.50	0.90	2.25
183-193, 195-222	0.30	0.50	1.25
194-Rogers-a	0.50	0.90	2.25

SUPERMAN: KAL
1995 (5.95, Color, 68pgs.)

	Good	Fine	N-Mint
nn-Elseworlds	1.20	2.40	6.00

SUPERMAN RECORD COMIC
1966 (Golden Records)
National Periodical Publications
(With record)-Record reads origin of Superman from comic; came w/iron-on
 patch, decoder, membership card & button; comic-r/Superman #125,146

	Good	Fine	N-Mint
	13.00	39.00	90.00
Comic only	5.00	15.00	35.00

SUPERMAN'S GIRLFRIEND LOIS LANE (See 80 Page Giant &
Showcase #9, 10)
Mar-Apr, 1958-No. 137, Sept-Oct, 1974
National Periodical Publications

	Good	Fine	N-Mint
1	160.00	480.00	1600.00
2	64.00	191.00	510.00
3	44.00	133.00	355.00
4, 5	31.00	94.00	250.00
6-10: 9-Pat Boone-c/story	21.00	64.00	170.00
11-20: 14-Supergirl x-over	12.00	36.00	85.00
21-29: 27-Bizarro-c/story. 29-Last 10¢ iss.	9.00	27.00	62.00
30-32, 34-46,48,49	4.30	12.90	30.00

47-Legion app.	4.60	13.70	32.00
33-Mon-el app.	5.00	15.00	35.00
50-(7/64)-Triplicate Girl, Phantom Girl, & Shrinking Violet app.			
	4.00	11.10	26.00
51-55, 57-67, 69: 59-Batman back-up story			
	2.60	8.00	18.00
56-Saturn Girl app.	2.60	7.70	18.00
68-Giant G-26	5.00	13.70	32.00
70-1st S.A. Catwoman app. (11/66); Penguin app.; Batman & Robin cameo			
	19.00	56.00	130.00
71-2nd S.A. Catwoman app. (story cont'd from #70); see Detective 369			
	12.00	36.00	85.00
for 3rd app.	11.00	34.00	80.00
72, 73, 75, 76, 78	1.70	4.20	10.00
74-1st Bizarro Flash (5/67)	2.90	8.60	20.00
77-Giant G-39	2.40	7.30	17.00
79-Adams covers begin, end 95, 108	1.00	2.50	6.00
80-85, 87-94: 89-Batman x-over	1.00	2.00	5.00
86, 95-Giants G-51 & G-63	2.20	5.40	13.00
96-103, 105-111: 105-Origin & 1st app. The Rose & the Thorn			
	0.90	1.80	4.50
104, 113-Giants G-75 & G-87	2.20	5.40	13.00
112, 114-123: 52 pg. issues. 123-G.A. Batman-r/Batman #35 w/Catwoman			
	1.00	2.00	5.00
124-137	0.60	1.20	3.00
Annual 1 (Sum/62)-Aquaman app.	13.00	39.00	130.00
Annual 2 (Sum/63)	7.00	22.00	72.00

SUPERMAN'S PAL, JIMMY OLSEN (Superman Family No. 164 on)
Sept-Oct, 1954-No. 163, Feb-Mar, 1974
National Periodical Publications

1	220.00	660.00	2200.00
2	93.00	280.00	840.00
3-Last pre-code issue	56.00	167.00	500.00
4, 5	36.00	108.00	325.00
6–10	26.00	77.00	230.00
11–20	17.00	52.00	155.00
21-30: 29-Krypto app.	13.00	39.00	90.00
31-40: 31-Origin Elastic Lad	10.00	29.00	67.00
41-50	7.00	20.00	52.00
51-56: 56-Last 10¢ issue	5.00	16.00	42.00
57-62, 64-70	1.65	4.70	14.00
63-Legion Of Super Villains app.	1.90	6.00	13.00

	Good	Fine	N-Mint
71, 74, 75, 78, 80-84, 86, 89, 90	2.50	6.30	15.00
72-(10/63)-Legion app.	2.50	6.00	15.00
73-Ultra Boy app.	1.80	5.00	11.00
76, 85-Legion app.	2.50	6.00	15.00
77, 79: 77-Origin Titano retold	1.50	3.80	9.00
87-Legion of Super Villians app.	1.80	5.00	11.00
88-Star Boy app.	1.50	3.80	9.00
91-94, 96-99	1.20	2.90	7.00
95, 104-Giants G-25 & G-38	2.60	8.00	18.00
100-Legion app. (cameo)	1.30	3.00	8.00
101-103, 105-112, 114-121, 123-130, 132	0.80	1.60	4.00
113, 122, 131, 140-Giants G-50, G-62, G-74, G-86			
	1.80	3.60	9.00
133-Newsboy Legion by Kirby begins (10/70)			
	2.20	5.40	13.00
134-1st app. Darkseid (cameo) (12/70)	3.00	7.50	18.00
135-2nd app. Darkseid (1pg. cameo; 1/71)	2.20	5.40	13.00
136-139, 141-163: 138-Partial photo-c. 139-Last 15¢ issue. 141-150-(25¢,			
52 pgs.). 148-Kirby-a ends	1.00	2.00	5.00

SUPERMAN: SPEEDING BULLETS
1993 (4.95, color, one-shot, 52 pgs.)
DC Comics

	Good	Fine	N-Mint
1-Elseworlds storyline	1.00	2.00	5.00

SUPERMAN: THE EARTH STEALERS
1988 (2.95, color, deluxe format, one-shot)
DC Comics

	Good	Fine	N-Mint
1-Byrne scripts	0.70	1.40	3.50
1-2nd printing	0.60	1.20	3.00

SUPERMAN: THE MAN OF STEEL
July, 1991-Present (1.00/1.25/1.50, color)
DC Comics

	Good	Fine	N-Mint
1-(1.75, 52 pgs.)-Painted-c	0.60	1.20	3.00
2-10: 10-Last 1.00-c	0.20	0.40	1.00
11-16: 14-Superman/Robin team-up	0.30	0.50	1.25
17-1st app. Doomsday (cameo)	0.70	1.40	3.50
17-2nd printing	0.30	0.50	1.25
18-First full app. Doomsday	1.30	3.00	8.00
18-2nd & 3rd printings	0.30	0.50	1.25
19-Doomsday battle w/Superman	0.50	1.00	2.50
20, 21-Funeral For A Friend issues	0.40	0.80	2.00

Superman: Man of Steel Ann. #3
© DC

Superpatriot #1 © Rob Liefeld

22-(1.95)-Collector's Ed. w/die-cut outer-c & bound-in mini-poster;			
Steel-c/story	0.40	0.80	2.00
22-(1.50)-Reg. Ed. w/poster & different-c	0.30	0.60	1.50
23-37: 23-Begin 1.50-c. 32-Bizarro-c/story. 35,36-Worlds Collide Pt.			
1 & 10. 37-(9/94)-Zero Hour	0.30	0.60	1.50
30-(2.50)-Collector's Ed. polybagged w/Superman & Lobo vinyl clings			
that stick to wraparound-c; Lobo-c/story	0.50	1.00	2.50
0,38-45: 0-(10/94). 38-(11/94)	0.30	0.60	1.50
46-begin 1.95-c; 47–	0.40	0.60	2.00
Annual 1 ('92, 2.50)-Eclipso app.	0.50	1.00	2.50
Annual 2 ('93, 2.50)-Intro Edge	0.50	1.00	2.50
Annual 3 ('94, 2.95)-Elseworlds story; Batman app.			
	0.60	1.20	3.00
Annual 4 ('95,2.95)-Year One	0.60	1.20	3.00

SUPERMAN: THE MAN OF TOMORROW
1995 (1.95, Color, Quarterly)

1–Lex Luthor app.	0.40	0.80	2.00

SUPERMAN: THE SECRET YEARS
Feb, 1985-No. 4, May, 1985 (Mini-series)
DC Comics

1	0.30	0.60	1.50
2–4	0.20	0.40	1.00

SUPERMAN VS. ALIENS
July 1995-Present (4.95, color, limited series)
DC Comics/Dark Horse Comics

1,2– Jurgens-p	1.00	2.00	5.00

	Good	Fine	N-Mint

SUPERMAN VS. THE AMAZING SPIDER-MAN
1976 (2.00, over-sized, 100 pgs.)
National Periodical Publications/Marvel Comics

1-Andru/Giordano-a	0.50	1.30	3.00
1-2nd printing; 5000 numbered copies signed by Stan Lee & Carmine			
Infantino on front-c & sold thru mail	2.30	6.90	16.00

SUPERNATURAL THRILLERS
Dec, 1972-No. 6, Nov, 1973; No. 7, July, 1974-No. 15, Oct, 1975
Marvel Comics Group (Issues 1-6 are 20¢)

1-3: 1-It!. 2-The Invisible Man	0.60	1.10	2.75
4-15: 5-1st app. The Living Mummy	0.50	1.00	2.50

SUPERPATRIOT (See Freak Force & Savage Dragon #2)
July, 1993-No. 4, Dec, 1993 (1.95, color, mini-series)
Image Comics

1-4-Dave Johnson-c/a; Larsen scripts	0.40	0.80	2.00
...:Liberty & Justice 1–	0.50	1.00	2.50

SUPER POWERS
July, 1984-No. 5, Nov, 1984 (First series)
DC Comics

1-Joker/Penguin-c/story; Batman app.	0.40	0.80	2.00
2-5: 5-Kirby-c/a	0.40	0.80	2.00
Sept, 1985-No. 6, Feb, 1986 (Second series)			
1-6: Kirby-c/a in all; Darkseid storyline	0.40	0.80	2.00
Sept, 1986-No. 4, Dec, 1986 (Third series)			
1-4-Darkseid storyline	0.40	0.80	2.00

SUPER-TEAM FAMILY
10-11/75-No. 15, 3-4/78 (#1-4: 68 pgs.; #5 on: 52 pgs.)
National Periodical Publications/DC Comics

1-Reprints by Neal Adams & Kane/Wood	0.40	0.80	2.00
2, 3-New stories	0.30	0.60	1.50
4-7-Reprints; 4-G.A. JSA-r	0.20	0.40	1.00
8-10-New Challengers of the Unknown stories		0.50	0.90
2.25			
11-15-New stories	0.30	0.50	1.30

SUPER-VILLAIN CLASSICS
May, 1983 (One-shot)
Marvel Comics Group

1-Galactus - The Origin	0.20	0.40	1.00

SUPER-VILLAIN TEAM-UP (Also see Giant-Size...)
Aug, 1975-No. 17, June, 1980
Marvel Comics Group

1-Sub-Mariner & Dr. Doom begin, end #10	1.00	2.00	5.00
2-17: 5-1st app. The Shroud. 11-15-Dr. Doom & Red Skull			
	0.50	1.00	2.50

SUPREME (See Youngblood #3)
Nov, 1992-Present (1.95, color, created by Liefeld)
Image Comics

V2#1-Embossed silver foil logo: Liefeld part scripts, inks			
	0.70	1.40	3.50
V2#1-Gold Edition	1.40	4.00	10.00
V2#2-(3/93)-Liefeld co-plots/inks; 1st app. Grizlock			
	0.40	0.80	2.00

V2#3-12,25: Liefeld co-plots in 2-4, story in 5, 6. 3-1st app.
Bloodstrike & Khrome. 5-1st app. Thor. 6-1st app. (cameo) The Starguard.
7-1st full app. Starguard. 7-9-Thibert-c(i). 10-Black and White Pt. 1 (1st
app., 2 pgs.) by Art Thibert. 11-Coupon #4 for Extreme Prejudice #0; Black
and White Pt. 7 by Thibert. 12-(4/94)-S. Platt-c. 25-(5/94)-Platt-c.

	0.40	0.80	2.00
13-24, : 13-Begin 2.50-c. 13,14-(6/94). 15,16-(7/94)			
25-27; 23-Polybagged w/trading card:	0.50	1.00	2.50
Annual 1-(2.95)	0.60	1.20	3.00

SUPREME: GLORY DAYS
Oct 1994 (2.95, color, limited series:2)
Image Comics

1-2	0.60	1.20	3.00

SWAMP THING (Also see House Of Secrets #92 & Saga of...)
Oct-Nov, 1972-No. 24, Aug-Sept, 1976
National Periodical Publications/DC Comics

1-Classic Wrightson art, issues #1-10	9.00	28.00	65.00
2	4.30	13.00	30.00
3-Intro Patchworkman	2.30	6.90	16.00
4-6, 8-10: 10-Last Wrightson issue	2.00	6.00	14.00
7-Batman-c/story	3.30	9.90	23.00
11-24: Nestor Redondo-a	0.60	1.20	3.00

SWAMP THING(Saga Of The... #1-38, 42-45)
May, 1982-Present

	Good	Fine	N-Mint
DC Comics (Vertigo imprint #129 on, mature)			
1-Origin retold, movie adapt.	0.40	0.70	1.80
2-15: 2-Photo cover from movie	0.30	0.50	1.25
16-19: Bissette art	0.50	0.90	2.25
20-1st Alan Moore issue	2.70	8.00	19.00
21-New origin by Moore	2.30	6.90	16.00
22-25	1.10	2.70	6.50
26-30	0.90	1.70	4.25
31-33: 33-Reprints H.O.S. #92	0.60	1.10	2.75
34	1.50	3.80	9.00
35, 36	0.50	0.90	2.25
37-1st app. John Constantine (6/85)	2.50	6.00	15.00
38-40: Early John Constantine apps.	1.00	2.00	5.00
41-45: 44, 45-John Constantine app.	0.40	0.80	2.00
46-51: John Constantine in all. 50-Double size			
	0.40	0.80	2.00
52-Arkham Asylum	0.70	1.40	3.50
53-Double size; Arkham Asylum	0.90	1.80	4.50
54-64: 64-Last Alan Moore iss.	0.30	0.60	1.50
65-83, 85-99, 101-124, 126-130	0.40	0.70	1.75
84-Sandman app.	1.40	2.80	7.00
100-(2.50, 52 pgs.)	0.50	1.00	2.50
125-(2.95, 52 pgs.)-Anniversary iss.	0.60	1.20	3.00
131-149, 151-154: 131-Begin 1.95-c. 140-New direction &			
Grant Morrison scripts begin	0.40	0.80	2.00
150-(2.95, 52 pgs)-Anniversary iss.	0.60	1.20	3.00
155-begin 2.25-c; 156–157	0.50	0.90	2.25
Annual 1-(1982)-Movie adaptation	0.20	0.40	1.00
Annual 2-(1985)-Alan Moore	0.60	1.20	3.00
Annual 3-('87, 2.00)	0.40	0.80	2.00
Annual 4-6: 4-('88)-Batman-c/story. 5-('89, 2.95)-Batman cameo.			
6-('91, 2.95)	0.60	1.20	3.00
Annual 7-('93, 3.95)-Children's Crusade	0.80	1.60	4.00

SWORD OF SORCERY
Feb-Mar, 1973-No. 5, Nov-Dec, 1973 (All 20¢ issues)
National Periodical Publications

	Good	Fine	N-Mint
1-Fafhrd & the Grey Mouser; Chaykin/Neal Adams (Crusty Bunkers) art;			
Kaluta-c	0.60	1.20	3.00
2-Wrightson-c(i); Adams-a(i)	0.40	0.80	2.00
3-5: 3-Wrightson-i (5 pgs.). 5-Starlin-a; Conan cameo			
	0.30	0.60	1.50

SYPHONS
May, 1994-No. 3, 1994 (2.50, color, limited series)
Now Comics
V2#1, 2: 1-Stardancer, Knightfire, Raze & Brigade begin

| | 0.50 | 1.00 | 2.50 |

SYPHONS: THE SYGATE STRATAGEM
Dec 1994-Present (2.95, color, limited series:3)
Now Comics

| 1 | 0.60 | 1.20 | 3.00 |

Tales Of Suspense #1 © MEG

Tales Of Suspense V2 #1 © MEG

	Good	Fine	N-Mint
TALE OF ONE BAD RAT, THE Oct, 1994- Jan 1995 (2.95, color, limited series) Dark Horse Comics			
1-4-Neil Gaiman intro.	0.60	1.20	3.00

TALES CALCULATED TO DRIVE YOU BATS
Nov, 1961-No. 7, Nov, 1962; 1966 (Satire)
Archie Publications

1-Only 10¢ issue; has cut-out Werewolf mask (price includes mask)			
	8.00	25.00	58.00
2-Begin 12¢ issues	4.90	15.00	34.00
3–6	3.00	9.40	22.00
7-Storyline change	2.60	7.70	18.00
1 (1966, 25¢)	3.30	9.90	23.00

TALES FROM THE CRYPT
July, 1990-No. 6, May, 1991 (1.95, color)
Gladstone Publ.

1-6-Reprints in all	0.40	0.80	2.00

TALES OF ASGARD (See Journey Into Mystery)
Oct, 1968 (68 pgs., one-shot); Feb, 1984 (1.25, 52 pgs.)
Marvel Comics Group

1-Thor-r from J.I.M. #97-106 by Kirby	3.60	10.70	25.00
V2#1-(2/84)-Simonson cover	0.20	0.40	1.00

TALES OF SUSPENSE (Becomes Captain America No. 100 on)
Jan, 1959-No. 99, Mar, 1968

Marvel Comics Group

1-Williamson-a (5 pgs.); 1-4-Sci/fi-c	115.00	345.00	1150.00
2, 3: 2-Ditko-c. 3-Flying saucer-c/story	44.00	133.00	400.00
4-Williamson, Kirby, Everett art	41.00	122.00	365.00
5, 6, 8, 10: 5-Kirby monster-c begin	26.00	78.00	235.00
7-Lava Man prototype	34.00	103.00	275.00
9-Iron Man prototype	38.00	113.00	300.00
11-15, 17-20: 12-Crandall art	21.00	64.00	170.00
16-1st Metallo (7/61); Iron Man prototype	29.00	86.00	230.00
21-25: 25-Last 10¢ issue	16.00	47.00	125.00
26, 27, 29, 30, 33, 34, 36-38: 32-1st Sazzik The Sorcerer			
	15.00	45.00	120.00
28-Stone Men prototype	16.00	49.00	130.00
31-Dr. Doom prototype	18.00	53.00	140.00
32-Dr. Strange prototype	18.00	53.00	140.00
35-The Watcher prototype	16.00	49.00	130.00
39-Origin & 1st Iron Man (3/63) begins	333.00	1000.00	3000.00
40-Iron Man in new gold armor	119.00	358.00	1075.00
41-3rd app. Iron Man	78.00	234.00	545.00
42-45	34.00	103.00	240.00
46, 47: 46-1st app. Crimson Dynamo	21.00	64.00	150.00
48-New armor for Iron Man by Ditko	26.00	77.00	180.00
49-1st X-Men x-over (1/64); same date as X-Men #3; 1st Tales of the Watcher (2nd app.) back-up story; 1st Avengers x-over (without Captain America)	19.00	58.00	135.00
50-1st app. Mandarin	13.00	39.00	90.00
51-1st app. Scarecrow	11.00	33.00	78.00
52-1st app. The Black Widow (4/64)	15.00	45.00	105.00
53-Origin The Watcher (5/64)	13.00	39.00	90.00
54-56: 56-4th Avengers x-over app. (8/64)	8.00	25.00	58.00
57-Origin & 1st app. Hawkeye (9/64)	18.00	54.00	125.00
58-Capt. America battles Iron Man (10/64); classic-c; 1st app. Cap in this title; 2nd Craven Hunter app.	32.00	96.00	225.00
59-Iron Man & Capt. America double feature series begins. 1st S.A. solo Capt. America story	32.00	96.00	225.00
60-2nd app. Hawkeye	14.00	40.00	100.00
61, 62, 64: 62-Origin Mandarin	8.00	25.00	58.00
63-1st S.A. origin Capt. America (3/65)	24.00	71.00	165.00
65, 66-1st S. A. Red Skull(origin #66)	14.00	40.00	100.00
67-78, 81-98: 70-Alternating-c features begin with Iron Man (odd #'s) & Captain America (even #'s)	6.40	19.00	45.00
79-Sub-Mariner-c & cameo; begin 3 part Iron Man/Sub-Mariner battle story; 1st Cosmic Cube	7.10	21.00	50.00

	Good	Fine	N-Mint
80-Ironman/Sub-Mariner battle story; continues into TTA 82	8.00	24.00	55.00
99-Iron Man story cont'd into Iron Man & Sub-Mariner #1. Capt. America			
story cont. into Captain America #100	9.00	26.00	60.00

TALES OF SUSPENSE
Jan, 1995 (6.95, color)
Marvel Comics

V2#1-Acetate-c; Capt. America & Iron Man-c & story; Robinson-s			
	1.20	2.90	7.00

TALES OF THE BEANWORLD
Feb, 1985-No. 19, 1991; No. 20, 1993-Present (1.50/2.00, B&W)
Beanworld Press/Eclipse

1	0.80	1.60	4.00
2–19	0.40	0.80	2.00
20-(2.50)	0.50	1.00	2.50
21-(2.95)	0.60	1.20	3.00

TALES OF THE GREEN HORNET
Sept, 1990-No. 2, 1990 (1.75, color)
V3#1, Sept, 1992-No. 3, Nov, 1992
Now Comics

1, 2	0.40	0.70	1.75
V3#1-(9/92, 2.75)-Polybagged w/hologram trading card			
	0.60	1.10	2.75
V3#2, 3-(2.50)	0.50	1.00	2.50

TALES OF THE GREEN LANTERN CORPS
May, 1981-No. 3, July, 1981 (Mini-series)
DC Comics

1-3: 1-Origin of G. L. & the Guardians	0.30	0.50	1.25
Annual 1 (1/85)-Gil Kane-c/a	0.30	0.60	1.40

TALES OF THE LEGION (Formerly Legion of Super-Heroes)
No. 314, Aug, 1984-No. 354, Dec, 1987
DC Comics

314-354: 321-Reprints begin	0.30	0.50	1.25
Annual 4, 5 (1986-87)-Formerly LSH Annual	0.30	0.60	1.40

TALES OF THE MARVELS: BLOCKBUSTER
Apr, 1995 (5.95, color, one-shot)
Marvel Comics

1-Acetate-c-painted	1.20	2.40	6.00

TALES OF THE MYSTERIOUS TRAVELER
8/56-No. 13, 6/59; V2#14, 10/85-No. 15, 12/85
Charlton Comics

1-No Ditko-a	29.00	88.00	205.00
2-Ditko-a (1 story)	29.00	90.00	200.00
3-Ditko-c/a(1)	25.00	75.00	175.00
4-6-Ditko-c/a(3-4 each)	31.00	90.00	215.00
7-9-Ditko-a(1-2 each)	25.00	75.00	175.00
10, 11-Ditko-c/a(3-4 each)	28.00	84.00	195.00
12, 13	10.00	31.00	72.00
V2#14, 15-Ditko-c/a (1985)	0.20	0.40	1.00

TALES OF THE NEW TEEN TITANS
June, 1982-No. 4, Sept, 1982 (Mini-series)
DC Comics

1-4	0.20	0.40	1.00

TALES OF THE TEENAGE MUTANT NINJA TURTLES
May, 1987-No. 7, Aug, 1989 (1.50, B&W)
Mirage Studios

1	1.00	1.90	4.75
2-7	0.60	1.10	2.75

TALES OF THE TEEN TITANS (Formerly The New Teen Titans)
No. 41, April, 1984-No. 91, July 1988
DC Comics

41, 45-91: 52-1st app. Azrael (cameo); not same as later character. 53-1st full app. Azrael; Deathstroke cameo. 54, 55-Deathstroke-c/story. 59-Begin-r	0.20	0.40	1.00
42-44: Deathstroke app. (Judas Contract). 44-Dick Grayson becomes Nightwing; origin of Deathstroke	1.00	2.50	6.00
Annual 3 (1984)-Deathstroke-c/story (Judas)	0.60	1.20	3.00
Annual 4, 5 (1986-87, 1.25)	0.30	0.50	1.25

TALES OF THE UNEXPECTED (The Unexpected No. 105 on)
Feb-Mar, 1956-No. 104, Dec-Jan, 1968 (15, 17-Grey-tone-c)
National Periodical Publications

1	80.00	240.00	800.00
2	46.00	137.00	365.00
3-5	32.00	96.00	255.00

	Good	Fine	N-Mint
6–10	24.00	71.00	190.00
11, 14, 19, 20	14.00	41.00	110.00
12, 13, 15-18, 21-24: Kirby-a	18.00	53.00	140.00
25-30	13.00	39.00	105.00
31-39	11.00	32.00	85.00
40-Space Ranger begins (3rd app., 8/59); see Showcase #15 for 1st app.			
	71.00	212.00	705.00
41, 42-Space Ranger stories	28.00	84.00	225.00
43-1st Space Ranger-c this title	55.00	164.00	545.00
44-46	23.00	69.00	160.00
47-50	16.00	47.00	110.00
51-60: 54-Dinosaur-c/story	14.00	41.00	95.00
61-67: 67-Last 10¢ issue	11.00	32.00	75.00
68-82: 82-Last Space Ranger	5.00	16.00	37.00
83-100: 91-1st Automan (also in 94, 97)	4.00	11.60	27.00
101-104	3.10	9.40	22.00

TALES TO ASTONISH (The Incredible Hulk No. 102 on)
January, 1959-No. 101, March, 1968
Marvel Comics Group

	Good	Fine	N-Mint
1-Jack Davis-a	111.00	333.00	1110.00
2-Flying saucer-c by Ditko	51.00	152.00	455.00
3, 4	35.00	105.00	315.00
5-Stone Men prototype; Williamson-a (4 pgs.)			
	37.00	112.00	335.00
6, 8-10	27.00	82.00	245.00
7-Toad Men prototype	28.00	85.00	255.00
11-14, 17-20	22.00	66.00	175.00
15-Electro prototype	26.00	77.00	205.00
16-Stone Men prototype	25.00	75.00	200.00
21-26, 28-34	16.00	49.00	130.00
27-1st app. The Antman (1/62) (not in costume); last 10¢ issue			
	217.00	650.00	2600.00
35-2nd Antman, 1st time in costume (9/62); series begins			
	125.00	375.00	1250.00
36-3rd Antman	51.00	152.00	455.00
37-40: 38-1st app. Egghead	32.00	96.00	225.00
41-43	21.00	64.00	150.00
44-Origin/1st app. The Wasp (6/63)	26.00	77.00	180.00
45-48	16.00	49.00	115.00
49-Antman becomes Giant Man	20.00	60.00	140.00
50-56, 58: 52-Origin/1st app Black Knight	11.00	34.00	80.00
57-Early Spider-Man app. (7/64)	15.00	50.00	105.00

59-Giant Man battles The Hulk; 1st app. Hulk in this title

	16.00	49.00	115.00

60-Giant Man & Incredible Hulk double feature begins (10/64);
   Giant Man series ends #69   19.00   58.00   135.00
61-69: 61-All Ditko issue   8.00   24.00   55.00
70-Sub-Mariner & Incredible Hulk double feature begins
                        11.00   32.00   75.00
71-81, 83-91, 94-99: 72-Alternating-c features begin w/Hulk (odd #'s)
   & Sub-Mariner (even #'s). 79-Hulk vs. Hercules-c/story. 81-1st app.
   Boomerang. 90-1st Abomination   5.70   17.00   40.00
82-Iron Man battles Sub-Mariner; story cont'd from TOS 79, 80; 1st Iron
   Man x-over outside Avengers & TOS   8.00   24.00   55.00
92-1st Silver Surfer x-over outside F.F. (cameo)
                        7.10   21.00   50.00
93-Hulk battles Silver Surfer-c/s (1st full x-over)
                        8.00   24.00   55.00
100-Hulk battles Sub-Mariner   7.10   21.00   50.00
101-Hulk story cont'd in Incredible Hulk #102; Sub-Mariner story cont'd
   in Iron Man And Sub-Mariner #1   9.00   28.00   65.00

TALES TO ASTONISH (2nd series)
Dec, 1979-No. 14, Jan, 1981
Marvel Comics Group

V1#1-r/Sub-Mariner #1 by Buscema	0.30	0.60	1.50
2-14: r/Sub-Mariner 2-14	0.30	0.50	1.30

TALES TO ASTONISH
Oct, 1994 (6.95, color, graphic novel)
Marvel Comics

V3#1-Acetate-c; P. David-story	1.20	3.00	7.00

TANK GIRL
May, 1991-Aug, 1991 (2.25, B&W, limited series)
Dark Horse Comics

1-4	0.50	1.00	3.00

TANK GIRL 2
Feb 1995 (17.95, color, One-shot, Adult readers)
Dark Horse Comics

1	3.00	9.00	18.00

TANK GIRL MOVIE ADAPTATION
1995 (5.95, Color, 68pgs.)

	Good	Fine	N-Mint
DC Comics			
nn-Movie Adaptation-Peter Milligan-s	1.00	3.00	6.00

TANK GIRL: THE ODYSSEY
May 1995-Present (2.25, color, limited series)
DC Comics

	Good	Fine	N-Mint
1,2-Milligan-s, Hewlett-a	0.40	1.10	2.25

TARZAN (...of the Apes #138 on)
No. 132, Nov, 1962-No. 206, Feb, 1972
Gold Key

	Good	Fine	N-Mint
133-154	1.60	4.70	11.00
132-1st Gold Key issue	2.10	6.40	15.00
155-Origin Tarzan	3.00	8.00	16.00
156-161: 169-Leopard Girl app.	1.30	3.00	7.50
162, 165, 168, 171 (TV): Ron Ely photo-c	1.90	6.00	13.00
163, 164, 166, 167, 169, 170	1.20	2.90	7.00
172-199, 201-206: 178-Tarzan-r/#155	1.20	2.40	6.00
200 (Scarce)	1.20	2.90	7.00
Story Digest 1 (6/70, Gold Key)	1.20	2.90	7.00

TARZAN (Continuation of Gold Key series)
No. 207, April, 1972-No. 258, Feb, 1977
National Periodical Publications

	Good	Fine	N-Mint
207-Origin Tarzan by Joe Kubert	1.70	3.40	8.50
208, 209: Last 52 pg. giant	1.10	2.20	5.50
210-229, 231-258: 231-235,238-(100 pgs.)	0.80	1.60	4.00
230-DC 100 pg. Super Spectacular	0.90	1.80	4.50
Comic Digest 1 (Fall, 1972, 50¢, 160 pgs.)-Digest size; Manning-a; Kubert-c	0.90	1.80	4.50

Tarzan #28 © Edgar Rice Burroughs

Team 7:Objective Hell © Aegis Ent.

TARZAN
June, 1977-No. 29, Oct, 1979
Marvel Comics Group
1-Buscema-a begins, ends 18	0.40	0.80	2.00
2-29: 2-Origin by Buscema	0.30	0.60	1.50
Annual 1-3: (1977-79)	0.30	0.60	1.50

TARZAN, LORD OF THE JUNGLE
Sept, 1965 (25¢ giant, soft paper-c)
Gold Key
1-Marsh-r	6.00	18.00	42.00

TASMANIAN DEVIL & HIS TASTY FRIENDS
Nov, 1962 (12¢)
Gold Key
1-Bugs Bunny & Elmer Fudd x-over	6.00	18.00	75.00

TEAM AMERICA
June, 1982-No. 12, May, 1983
Marvel Comics Group
1-Origin, Ideal motorcycle toy characters	0.20	0.50	1.20
2–10	0.20	0.40	1.00
11-Ghost Rider app.	1.00	2.00	5.00
12-Double size; classic cover	0.40	0.80	2.00

TEAM 7
Oct 1994 - Feb 1995(2.50, color)
Image Comics, Inc.
1-4:1-Two variant-c, one by Whilce Portacio	0.50	1.00	2.50
1A-Variant-c	1.00	2.00	5.00

TEAM 7-OBJECTIVE: HELL
May 1995-Present (1.95/2,50, color)
1-Newstand: BWS-c (1.95)	0.40	0.80	2.00
1-Direct Market; BWS-c, Bound-in card (2.50)			
	0.50	1.00	2.50
2-(2.50)	0.50	1.00	2.50

TEAM TITANS
Sept, 1992-Present (1.75, color)
DC Comics
1-Five versions (Kilowat, Mirage, Nightrider, Redwing, Terra); origins of

	Good	Fine	N-Mint
each member	0.50	0.90	2.25
2	0.40	0.80	2.00
3-21: 11-Metallik app.	0.40	0.70	1.75
22-24: 22-Begin 1.95-c. 24-Zero Hour	0.40	0.80	2.00
Annual 1 (1993, 3.50, 68 pgs.)	0.70	1.40	3.50
Annual 2 (1994, 3.50)-Elseworlds story	0.70	1.40	3.50

TEAM YOUNGBLOOD (Also see Youngblood)
Sept, 1993-Present (1.95/2.50, color, on-going series)
Image Comics (Extreme Studios)

	Good	Fine	N-Mint
1-9-Liefeld stories. 1,2,4-6,8-Thibert-c(i). 1-1st app. Dutch & Masada. 3-Spawn cameo. 5-1st app. Lynx. 7, 8-Black and White part 4 & 8 by Thibert; has coupon #1 & 5 for Extreme Prejudice #0. 9-Liefeld-c(p)/a(p) on Pt. 1; wraparound-c	0.40	0.80	2.00
10-17: 10-Begin 2.50-c; Liefeld-c(p) 16-polybagged w/trading card			
17-Polybagged w/trading card	0.50	1.00	2.50
18-Extreme 3000 prelude	0.50	1.00	2.50

TEENAGE MUTANT NINJA TURTLES
1984-No. 62, Aug, 1993 (1.50/1.75, B&W)
Mirage Studios

	Good	Fine	N-Mint
1-1st printing (3,000 printed)	32.00	96.00	225.00
1-2nd printing (6/84)	4.30	13.00	30.00
1-3rd printing (2/85)	1.40	4.00	10.00
1-4th printing, new cover	1.30	3.00	7.50
1-5th printing (11/88)	0.40	0.80	2.00
1-Counterfeit!! Note: most counterfeit copies have a 1/2" wide white streak or scratch marks across the center of back cover. Black part of cover is a bluish black instead of a deep black. Inside paper is very white, inside cover is bright white.		no value	
2-1st printing ('84)	10.00	30.00	70.00
2-2nd printing	1.50	3.80	9.00
2-3rd printing; new Corben-c/a (2/85)	0.60	1.10	2.75
2-Counterfeit!! Glossy cover stock		no value	
3-1st printing ('85, 44 pgs.)	3.90	11.60	27.00
3-Variant; 500 copies, given away in NYC. Has Laird's photo in white rather than light blue	11.00	34.00	80.00
3-2nd print; contains new backup story	0.60	1.10	2.75
4-1st print (1985, 44 pgs.)	1.90	5.60	13.00
4-2nd print (5/87)	0.40	0.70	1.75
5-1st print; 1st full color-c	1.70	4.00	10.00
5-2nd print (11/87)	0.40	0.70	1.75
6-1st print (1986)	1.30	3.00	7.50

6-2nd print (5/88)	0.40	0.70	1.75
7-4 page color insert; 1st colorTMNT(1.75)	1.30	3.00	7.50
7-2nd print (1.50, 1/89)	0.40	0.70	1.75
8-Cerebus x-over w/Sim-a	1.00	2.50	6.00
9, 10: 9-Rip in Time by Corben	1.00	1.90	4.75
11–15	0.70	1.30	3.25
16-18	0.60	1.10	2.75
18-2nd printing; 1st time in color	0.40	0.70	1.80
19-49, 51: 34-Last 1.75-c	0.40	0.70	1.80
32-2nd printing (Full color, 2.75-c)	0.50	1.00	2.50
50-(2.00)-Pin-ups by McFarlane, Simonson, & others; Eastman & Laird			
story & art	0.40	0.70	1.80
52-62: 52-Begin 2.25-c	0.50	0.90	2.25
… nn (1990, 5.95)-Movie adapt.	1.00	2.50	6.00
...Christmas Special (12/90, 1.75)	0.40	0.70	1.75
...Special (The Maltese Turtle) nn (1/93, 2.95, color, 44 pgs.)			
	0.60	1.20	3.00
...Special: Times Pipeline nn (9/92, 2.95, color)			
	0.60	1.20	3.00

TEENAGE MUTANT NINJA TURTLES
V2#1, Oct, 1993-Present (2.75, color)
Mirage Studios

V2#1-8	0.60	1.10	2.75

TEENAGE MUTANT NINJA TURTLES ADVENTURES
Aug, 1988-No. 3, Dec, 1988 (1.00, color, mini-series)
Mar, 1989-Present (1.00/1.25/1.50, color, on-going series)
Archie Comics

1-Not by Eastman/Laird	0.60	1.20	3.00
2, 3	0.40	0.80	2.00
1-Second series begins (3/89)	0.50	1.00	2.50
2–5	0.40	0.80	2.00
6-49, 51-58: 20-Begin 1.25-c	0.30	0.50	1.25
50-(1.50)-Poster by Eastman/Laird	0.30	0.60	1.50
59-61,63-68 : 59-Begin 1.50-c	0.30	0.60	1.50
62-(1.75)-w/poster	0.40	0.70	1.75
1-11: 2nd printings	0.20	0.40	1.00
...Meet Archie (Spr, 1991, 2.50)	0.50	1.00	2.50
...Meet The Conservation Corps. 1 ('92, 2.50)			
	0.50	1.00	2.50
Movie II (Summer, '91, 2.50)	0.50	1.00	2.50
...III The Movie: The Turtles are back...In Time (1993, 2.50, 68 pgs.)			

	Good	Fine	N-Mint
	0.50	1.00	2.50
Special 1 (Summer, '92, 2.50)	0.50	1.00	2.50
Special 4 (Spr, 1993, 2.50)	0.50	1.00	2.50
Special 5 (Sum/93, 2.50, 52 pgs.)	0.50	1.00	2.50
Giant Size Special 6 (Fall/93, 1.95, 52 pgs.)	0.40	0.80	2.00
Special 7, 8 (Win/93. Spr/94, 1.95, 52 pgs.)	0.40	0.80	2.00
Special 9 (Sum/94, 1.95, 52 pgs.)-Jeff Smith-c			
	0.40	0.80	2.00
Special 10 (Fall/94, 2.00, 52 pgs.)	0.40	0.80	2.00

TEENAGE MUTANT NINJA TURTLES/FLAMING CARROT CROSSOVER
Nov, 1993-No. 4, Feb, 1994 (2.75, color, mini-series)
Mirage Publishing

1-4-Bob Burden story	0.60	1.10	2.75

TEENAGE MUTANT NINJA TURTLES PRESENTS...

...: April O'Neil 1-3 (3/93-6/93, 1.25, color)	0.30	0.50	1.25
...: Donatello and Leatherhead 1-3 (7/93-9/93, 1.25)			
	0.30	0.50	1.25
...: Merdude 1-3 (10/93-12/93, 1.25, color)	0.30	0.50	1.25

TEEN BEAM (Formerly Teen Beat #1)
No. 2, Jan-Feb, 1968
National Periodical Publications

2-Orlando, Drucker-a(r); Monkees photo-c	2.10	6.40	15.00

TEEN BEAT (Becomes Teen Beam #2)
Nov-Dec, 1967
National Periodical Publications

1-Photos & text only; Monkees photo-c	3.00	9.40	22.00

TEEN TITANS (See Brave & the Bold #54, 60, DC Super-Stars #1 & Showcase #59)
Jan-Feb, 1966-No. 53, Feb, 1978
National Periodical Publications/DC Comics

1	22.00	66.00	155.00
2	11.00	32.00	75.00
3-5	5.40	16.00	38.00
6-10: 6-Doom Patrol app.	4.30	12.90	30.00
11-19: 18-1st app. Starfire	2.90	8.60	20.00
20-22: Adams-a. 21-Last 12¢ issue	3.30	10.00	23.00
23-30	1.70	5.10	12.00
31-43: 36-39-(52 pgs.). 43-Dated 1-2/73	1.30	3.00	8.00

Tek World #24 © Wm Shatner

Terminator: The Enemy Within #3
© Cinema 84

44 (11/76), 45, 47, 49, 51, 52	0.90	1.80	4.50
46-Joker's daughter begins	1.70	4.20	10.00
48-Joker's daughter becomes Harlequin	1.70	4.20	10.00
50-1st revival original Bat-Girl	1.50	3.80	9.00
53-Origin retold	1.00	2.00	5.00

TEEN TITANS SPOTLIGHT
Aug, 1986-No. 21, Apr, 1988
DC Comics

1–21	0.20	0.40	1.00

TEKWORLD (WILLIAM SHATNER'S...)
Sept, 1992-Present (1.75, color)
Epic Comics (Marvel)

1	0.50	1.00	2.50
2–24	0.40	0.70	1.75

TERMINATOR, THE (See Rust #12)
Sept, 1988-No. 17, 1989 (1.75, color)
Now Comics

1-Based on movie	2.00	5.10	12.00
2–5	0.70	2.00	5.00
6–10	0.80	1.60	4.00
11, 13-17	0.40	0.80	2.00
12-(2.95, 52 pgs.)-Intro John Connor	0.60	1.20	3.00
Trade Paperback ('89, 9.95)	1.40	4.00	10.00

TERMINATOR, THE (Also see Robocop Vs. ...)
Aug, 1990-No. 4, Nov, 1990 (2.50, color, mini-series)

	Good	Fine	N-Mint
Dark Horse Comics			
1	0.80	1.60	4.00
2–4	0.50	1.00	2.50

TERMINATOR: ALL MY FUTURES PAST, THE
V3#1, Aug, 1990-V3#2, Sept, 1990 (1.75, color, mini-series)
Now Comics

	Good	Fine	N-Mint
V3 #1, 2	0.40	0.70	1.75

TERMINATOR: END GAME, THE
Sept, 1992-No. 3, Nov, 1992 (2.50, color, mini-series)
Dark Horse Comics

	Good	Fine	N-Mint
1-3: Guice-a(p); painted-c	0.50	1.00	2.50
TPB ('92, 9.95)	1.40	4.00	10.00

TERMINATOR: HUNTERS AND KILLERS, THE
Mar, 1992-No. 3, May, 1992 (2.50, color, mini-series)
Dark Horse Comics

	Good	Fine	N-Mint
1-3	0.50	1.00	2.50
TPB ('92, 9.95)	1.40	4.00	10.00

TERMINATOR: ONE SHOT, THE
July, 1991 (5.95, color, 56 pgs.)
Dark Horse Comics

	Good	Fine	N-Mint
nn-Matt Wagner-a; stiff pop-up	1.00	2.50	6.00

TERMINATOR: SECONDARY OBJECTIVES
July, 1991-No. 4, Oct, 1991 (2.50, color, mini-series)
Dark Horse Comics

	Good	Fine	N-Mint
1-Movie tie-in; Gulacy-c/a in all	0.50	1.00	2.50
2–4	0.50	1.00	2.50

TERMINATOR: THE BURNING EARTH
V2#1, Mar, 1990-V2#5, July, 1990 (1.75, color, mini-series)
Now Comics

	Good	Fine	N-Mint
V2#1-5	0.40	0.70	1.75

TERMINATOR: THE ENEMY WITHIN, THE
Nov, 1991-No. 4, Feb, 1992 (2.50, color, mini-series)
Dark Horse Comics

	Good	Fine	N-Mint
1-4: Bisley painted-c	0.50	1.00	2.50
TPB (11/92, 13.95)	2.00	6.00	14.00

TERMINATOR 2: JUDGEMENT DAY
Early Sept, 1991-No. 3, Early Oct, 1991 (1.00, color, mini-series)
Marvel Comics

1-Based on movie	0.20	0.40	1.00
2, 3	0.20	0.40	1.00
nn ('91, 4.95)-Photo-c	1.00	2.00	5.00
nn (2.25, B&W, magazine)	0.50	0.90	2.25

THANOS QUEST, THE (See Iron Man 55)
1990- No. 2, 1990 (4.95, color, squarebound)
Marvel Comics

1-Starlin scripts and covers	1.20	3.00	7.00
2	0.90	2.00	5.50
1, 2-2nd printings	1.00	2.00	5.00

THAT CHEMICAL REFLEX
1994 (2.50, B&W, adult)
CFD Productions

1-Dan Brereton-a	0.50	1.00	2.50

THB
Oct 1994-Present (2.95, B&W)
Horse Press

1-(5.50)	1.40	2.80	7.00
2-(2.50)	0.80	1.60	4.00
3–5	0.60	1.20	3.00

T.H.E. CAT (TV)
March, 1967-No. 4, Oct, 1967 (All have photo-c)
Dell Publishing Co.

1	4.30	13.00	30.00
2–4	2.90	8.60	20.00

THING, THE
July, 1983-No. 36, June, 1986
Marvel Comics Group

1-Byrne scripts begin	0.40	0.80	2.00
2-36: 5-Spider-Man app.	0.20	0.50	1.20

THING, THE (…From Another World)
1991-No. 2, 1992 (2.95, color, mini-series, stiff-c)
Dark Horse Comics

1, 2-Based on Universal movie; painted-c/a	0.60	1.20	3.00

	Good	Fine	N-Mint

THING FROM ANOTHER WORLD: CLIMATE OF FEAR, THE
July, 1992-No. 4, Dec, 1992 (2.50, color, mini-series)
Dark Horse Comics

1-4: Painted-c	0.50	1.00	2.50

THING FROM ANOTHER WORLD: ETERNAL VOWS, THE
Dec, 1993-No. 4, Mar, 1994 (2.50, color, limited series)
Dark Horse Comics

1-4-Gulacy-c/a	0.50	1.00	2.50

THOR (Formerly Journey Into Mystery; becomes The Mighty Thor #413 on)
March, 1966-Present
Marvel Comics Group

126-Cont'd from Journey Into Mystery	13.00	39.00	105.00
127-133, 135-140	5.00	16.00	42.00
134-Intro High Evolutionary	7.00	20.00	54.00
141-157, 159, 160: 146-Inhumans begins (11/67, early app.), ends #151			
(origin in #146, 147). 148, 149-Origin Black Bolt			
	4.00	11.00	28.00
158-Origin-r/J.I.M. 83	8.00	23.00	60.00
161, 167, 170-179: Kirby-a	2.00	7.00	18.00
162, 168, 169: Origin Galactus; Kirby-a	4.00	11.00	30.00
163,164-Brief cameo of Him in each;Kirby	3.00	8.00	20.00
165-1st full app. Warlock (Him) (6/69); see Fantastic Four #66, 67;			
Kirby-a; last 12¢ issue	6.00	17.00	44.00
166-2nd full app. Warlock (Him) (7/69); Kirby-a; Thor battles Him			
	5.00	15.00	39.00
180, 181-Neal Adams-a	2.00	5.00	12.00
182-192, 194-200	1.00	2.50	6.00
193-(52 pgs.)-Silver Surfer x-over	4.00	12.00	32.00
201-250	0.80	1.60	4.00
251-280: 271-Iron Man x-over	0.60	1.20	3.00
281-299: 294-Origin Asgard & Odin	0.50	1.00	2.50
300-(12/80)-End of Asgard; origin Odin	1.00	2.50	6.00
301-336	0.40	0.80	1.90
337-Thor by Simonson; New Thor	1.00	2.50	6.00
338-60 & 75 cent variants exist	0.70	1.40	3.50
339, 340	0.40	0.80	1.90
341-373, 375-381, 383: 341-Clark Kent & Lois Lane cameo			
	0.30	0.60	1.40
374-Mutant Massacre; X-Factor app.	1.50	3.80	9.00
382-(1.25, 52 pgs.)-Last Simonson Thor	0.50	1.00	2.50

384-Intro new Thor	0.50	0.90	2.25
385-399, 401-410, 413-428: 385-Hulk x-over. 391-1st Eric Masterson			
	0.30	0.50	1.25
400-(1.75, 68 pgs.)-Origin Loki	0.50	1.00	2.50
411-Intro New Warriors (cameo)	0.70	1.30	3.25
412-1st full app. New Warriors	1.70	5.00	12.00
429, 430-Ghost Rider app.	0.70	1.30	3.25
431, 434-449: 434-Capt. America x-over. 437-Thor vs. Quasar.			
443-Dr. Strange & Silver Surfer x-over	0.30	0.60	1.50
432-(1.50, 52 pgs.)-r/1st app. from Journey Into Mystery #83			
	0.70	1.30	3.25
433-Intro new Thor	0.90	2.30	5.50
450-(2.50, 68 pgs.)-Double gatefold-c	0.70	1.30	3.25
451-473: 457-Old Thor returns (3 pgs.). 459-Intro Thunderstrike. 460-			
Starlin scripts begin. 472-Intro the Godlings			
	0.30	0.60	1.50
474,476-481,483-488: 474-Begin 1.50-c; bound-in trading card sheet			
	0.30	0.60	1.50
475-(2.00, 52 pgs.)-Regular edition	0.40	0.80	2.00
475-(2.50, 52 pgs.)-Coll. Ed. w/foil embossed-c			
	0.50	1.00	2.50
482-(2.95, 84 pgs)-400th Issue	0.60	1.20	3.00
Giant Size 1 ('75) - See Giant-Size listing			
Special 2 (9/66)-See JIM for 1st annual	5.60	17.00	45.00
Special 3 (1/71)	1.50	3.80	9.00
Special 4 (12/71)-Reprints 131, 132, JIM 113			
	1.50	3.80	9.00
Annual 5-8 (11/76-1979): 6-Guardians Of The Galaxy app. 8-Thor Vs.			
Zeus-c/story	1.20	2.90	7.00
Annual 9-12 (1981-84)	0.70	1.40	3.50

Thor #366 © MEG

Thor #478 © MEG

	Good	Fine	N-Mint
Annual 13-16: 13 ('85). 14 ('89). 15 ('90, 2.00). 16 ('91, 2.00)-Guardians			
app.	0.40	0.80	2.00
Annual 17 ('92, 2.25)	0.50	0.90	2.25
Annual 18 ('93, 2.95)-Polybagged w/card	0.60	1.20	3.00
Annual 19 ('94, 2.95, 68 pgs.)	0.60	1.20	3.00
Thor Alone Against The Celestials nn (6/92, 5.95)-r/387-389			
	1.00	2.50	6.00

THOR CORPS
Sept, 1993-No. 4, Dec, 1993 (1.75, color, mini-series)
Marvel Comics

	Good	Fine	N-Mint
1-4: 1-Invaders cameo. 2-Invaders app. 3-Spider-Man 2099 app.			
	0.40	0.70	1.75

THRILL-O-RAMA
Oct, 1965-No. 3, Dec, 1966
Harvey Publications (Fun Films)

	Good	Fine	N-Mint
1-Fate (Man in Black) by Powell app.	1.70	4.20	10.00
2-Pirana begins; Fate (Man in Black) app.	1.70	4.20	10.00
3-Fate (Man in Black) app.	1.30	3.30	8.00

THUNDER AGENTS
Nov, 1965-No. 17, Dec, 1967; No. 18, Sept, 1968, No. 19,
Nov, 1968; No. 20, Nov, 1969 (1-16: 68 pgs.; No. 17 on: 52 pgs.)
Tower Comics

	Good	Fine	N-Mint
1-Origin & 1st app. Dynamo, Noman, Menthor & Thunder Squad			
	13.00	39.00	90.00
2-Death of Egghead	7.90	24.00	55.00
3-5: 4-Guy Gilbert becomes Lightning	5.00	15.00	35.00
6-10: 7-Death of Menthor. 8-Origin & 1st app. The Raven			
	3.10	9.40	22.00
11-15: 13-Undersea Agent app.	2.70	6.70	16.00
16-19	2.00	5.00	12.00
20-Collector's Ed.; all reprints	1.00	2.00	5.00

THUNDERBOLT
Jan, 1966; No. 51, Mar-Apr, 1966-No. 60, Nov, 1967
Charlton Comics

	Good	Fine	N-Mint
1-Origin	1.40	3.50	8.50
51-Formerly Son Of Vulcan #50	1.00	2.00	5.00
52-59: 54-Sentinels begin. 59-Last Thunderbolt & Sentinels			
	0.70	1.30	3.25
60-Prankster app.	1.00	2.00	5.00

57, 58-Modern Comics-r (1977)	0.20	0.40	1.00

THUNDERSTRIKE (See Thor #459)
June, 1993-Present (1.25, color)
Marvel Comics

1-(2.95, 52 pgs.)-Holo-grafx foil-c; Bloodaxe returns			
	0.60	1.20	3.00
2-7: 2-Juggernaut-c/sty. 4-6-Spider-Man app.			
	0.30	0.50	1.25
8-22: 8-Begin 1.50-c; bound-in trading card sheet 18-Bloodaxe app.			
	0.30	0.60	1.50
Marvel Double Feature...Thunderstrike/Code Blue #13-15 (2.50)-Same as Thunderstrike #13-16 w/Code Blue flip book			
	0.50	1.00	2.50

TICK, THE
June, 1988-No. 12, May, 1993 (1.75, B&W)
New England Comics Press

Special Edition 1-First comic book app.; serially numbered and limited to 5000 copies	5.70	17.00	40.00
Special Edition 2-Serially numbered & limited to 3000 copies			
	5.00	15.00	35.00
1-Reprints SE #1 with minor changes	5.00	15.00	35.00
1-2nd printing	0.70	1.40	3.50
1-3rd printing (1.95, 6/89)	0.40	0.80	2.00
1-4th printing (2.25)	0.50	0.90	2.25
1-5th printing (2.75)	0.60	1.10	2.75
2-Reprints SE #2 with minor changes	2.90	8.60	20.00
2-2nd printing (1.95)	0.60	1.20	3.00
2-3rd & 4th printings	0.50	0.90	2.25
2-5th printing (2.75)	0.60	1.10	2.75
3-5: (1.95): 4-1st app. Paul the Samurai	0.90	1.70	4.25
3-2nd & 3rd printings (2.25)	0.50	0.90	2.25
3-4th printing (2.75)	0.60	1.10	2.75
4-2nd printing (2.25)	0.50	0.90	2.25
4-3rd-5th printings (2.75)	0.60	1.10	2.75
6-8: (2.25)	0.50	0.90	2.25
5-8: 2nd printings (2.75)	0.60	1.10	2.75
6-3rd printing (2.75)	0.60	1.10	2.75
8-Variant with no logo error	1.70	4.00	10.00
9-12: (2.75)	0.60	1.10	2.75

	Good	Fine	N-Mint
TICK'S GIANT CIRCUS OF THE MIGHTY, THE			
Summer, 1992-No. 3, Fall, 1993 (2.75, B&W)			
New England Comics			
1-(A-O). 2-(P-Z). 3-1993 Update	0.60	1.10	2.75
TICK KARMA TORNADO, THE			
Oct, 1993-Present (2.75, color)			
New England Comics			
1-(3.25)	0.70	1.30	3.25
2–9	0.60	1.10	2.75
TIGER GIRL			
September, 1968 (15¢ cover)			
Gold Key			
1 (10227-809)-Jerry Siegel scripts	3.00	9.40	22.00
TIMECOP			
Sept, 1994-No. 2, Sept, 1994 (2.50, color, limited series)			
Dark Horse Comics			
1,2-Movie adaptation	0.50	1.00	2.50
TIME TUNNEL (TV)			
Feb, 1967-No. 2, July, 1967 (12¢)			
Gold Key			
1, 2-Photo back-c	4.60	14.00	32.00
TIMEWALKER			
Jan, 1994-Oct., 1995 (2.50, color)			
Valiant Comics			
1-15: 2-"JAN" on-c, "February, 1995" in indicia			
	0.50	1.00	2.50
Yearbook 1 (5/95, 2.95)	0.60	1.20	3.00
TITAN SPECIAL			
June, 1994 (3.95, color)			
Dark Horse Comics			
1-(3.95, 52 pgs)	0.80	1.60	4.00
TITANS SELL-OUT SPECIAL			
Nov, 1992 (3.50, color, 52 pgs.)			
DC Comics			
1-Fold-out Nightwing poster; 1st Teeny Titans			
	0.70	1.40	3.50

TOKA (Jungle King)
Aug-Oct, 1964-No. 10, Jan, 1967
Dell Publishing Co.

1-Painted-c	2.10	6.00	15.00
2-Painted-c	1.30	3.00	8.00
3–10	1.10	2.70	6.50

TOMB OF DARKNESS (Formerly Beware)
No. 9, July, 1974-No. 23, Nov., 1976
Marvel Comics Group

9-23: 15, 19-Ditko-r. 20-Everett Venus-r	0.30	0.50	1.25

TOMB OF DRACULA
Apr, 1972-No. 70, Aug, 1979
Marvel Comics Group

1-1st app. Dracula & Frank Drake; Colan-p in all			
	9.00	28.00	65.00
2	5.00	15.00	35.00
3–5	3.30	10.00	23.00
6-10: 10-1st app. Blade the Vampire Slayer	2.40	7.30	17.00
11-20: 13-Origin Blade	1.60	4.70	11.00
21-40: 25-Origin/1st app. Hannibal King	1.40	3.50	8.50
41-49, 51-60	0.90	2.30	5.50
50-Silver Surfer app.	1.40	3.50	8.50
61-70: 70-Double size	0.90	1.80	4.50

TOMB OF DRACULA (Also see Dracula)
Oct, 1979-No. 6, Aug, 1980 (B&W magazine)
Marvel Comics Group

1, 4-6	0.70	1.40	3.50
2, 3: 2-Ditko-a (36 pgs.). 3-Miller sketch	0.90	1.80	4.50

TOMB OF DRACULA
1991-No. 4, 1992 (4.95, color, mini-series)
Epic Comics (Marvel)

1-4: Colan/Williamson-a	1.00	2.00	5.00

TOMOE
July 1995-
Crusade

1-Commemorative Ed. (limited to 5000)	2.00	4.00	10.00

	Good	Fine	N-Mint

Tomb of Dracula #70 © MEG

Top Cat #2 © H-B

TOP CAT (TV)

12-2/61-62-No. 31, 9/70 (Hanna-Barbera)

Dell Publishing Co./Gold Key

	Good	Fine	N-Mint
1-TV show debuted 9/27/61	16.00	50.00	115.00
2-Augie Doggie back-ups in #1-4	9.20	27.50	55.00
3-5: 3-Last 15¢ issue. 4-Begin 12¢ issues; 1st app. Yakky Doodle in 1 pg.			
strip. 5-1st Touche' Turtle	6.20	18.50	37.00
6–10	4.00	12.50	25.00
11–20	3.00	10.00	20.00
21-31: 21, 24, 25, 29-Reprints	2.50	6.00	15.00

TOP CAT (TV)

Nov, 1970-No. 20, Nov, 1973 (Hanna-Barbera)

Charlton Comics

	Good	Fine	N-Mint
1	4.60	13.70	32.00
2–10	2.60	7.70	18.00
11–20	2.00	5.00	12.00

TOP COW PRODUCTIONS INC./BALLISTIC STUDIOS SWIMSUIT SPECIAL

May 1995-Present (2.95, color, one-shot)

Image Comics

	Good	Fine	N-Mint
1	0.50	1.00	3.00

TOPPS COMICS PRESENTS

1993 (Free, B&W)

Topps Comics

	Good	Fine	N-Mint
0-Dracula vs. Zorro, Teenagents, Silver Star	0.20	0.40	1.00

TORCH OF LIBERTY SPECIAL

Jan 1995 (2.50, color, one shot)

Dark Horse Comics
1-John Byrne/s	0.50	1.00	2.50

TOTAL WAR (M.A.R.S. Patrol #3 on)
July, 1965-No. 2, Oct, 1965 (Painted covers)
Gold Key
1, 2-Wood-a in each	4.60	13.70	32.00

TOWER OF SHADOWS (Creatures On The Loose #10 on)
Sept, 1969-No. 9, Jan, 1971
Marvel Comics Group
1-Steranko, Craig-a	3.00	9.00	21.00
2-Neal Adams-a	1.70	4.00	10.00
3-Smith, Tuska-a	1.70	4.00	10.00
4-Marie Severin-c	1.20	3.00	7.00
5, 7-Smith (p), Wood-a	1.50	3.80	9.00
6, 8-Wood art. 8-Wrightson-c	1.20	3.00	7.00
9-Wrightson-c	1.00	2.50	6.00
Special 1 (12/71)-Adams-a	1.00	2.50	6.00

TRANSFORMERS: GENERATION 2
Nov, 1993-No. 12, Oct, 1994 (1.75, color)
Marvel Comics
1-(2.95, 68 pgs.)-Coll. Ed. w/bi-fold metallic-c			
	0.60	1.20	3.00
1-(1.75, 68 pgs.)-Regular Edition	0.40	0.70	1.75
2–11	0.40	0.70	1.75
12-(2.25, 52 pgs.)	0.50	0.90	2.25

TRENCHER (See Blackball Comics)
May, 1993-No. 4, Oct, 1993 (1.95, color)
Image Comics
1-4-By Keith Giffen. 3-Supreme-c/story	0.40	0.80	2.00

TRIBE (See Wildcats #4)
April, 1993 (2.50, color)
Image Comics
1-Gold foil & embossed-c; by Johnson/Stroman			
	0.50	1.00	2.50
1-Ivory Edition (2.50)-Gold foil & embossed-c; available only through			
the creators (white-c)	1.00	1.90	4.75

	Good	Fine	N-Mint

TRIBE
V1#2, Sept, 1993-V1#3, 1994 (1.95, color)
Axis Comics

	Good	Fine	N-Mint
V1#2, 3-By Johnson & Stroman	0.40	0.80	2.00

TRINITY (See DC Universe: Trinity)

TRIPLE - X
Dec 1994 - Present (3.95, B&W, limited series:7)
Dark Horse Comics

	Good	Fine	N-Mint
1–6	0.80	1.60	4.00

TRIUMPH
June, 1995-Present (1.75, color, limited series)
DC Comics

	Good	Fine	N-Mint
1–3	0.40	0.70	1.75

TRIUMPHANT UNLEASHED
Nov, 1993-No. 1, Nov, 1993 (2.50, color, limited series)
Triumphant Comics

	Good	Fine	N-Mint
0-Serially numbered	0.50	1.00	2.50
0-Red logo	0.50	1.00	2.50
0-White logo, no price; giveaway	0.50	1.00	2.50
1-Cover is negative & reverse of #0-c	0.50	1.00	2.50

TROLL
Dec, 1993 (2.50, color, one-shot, 44 pgs.)
Image Comics (Extreme Studios)

	Good	Fine	N-Mint
1-Matsuda-c/a(p); Liefeld scripts	0.50	1.00	2.50
...Halloween Special ('94, 2.95) Maxx app.	0.60	1.20	3.00

TROLL II
July, 1994 (3.95, color, 52 pgs., one-shot)
Image Comics

	Good	Fine	N-Mint
1-Square-back binding	0.80	1.60	4.00

TROLL: ONCE A HERO
Aug, 1994 (2.50, color, one-shot)
Image Comics

	Good	Fine	N-Mint
1	0.50	1.00	2.50

TUROK, DINOSAUR HUNTER (See Magnus #12)
June, 1993-Present (2.50, color)

Valiant

1-(3.50)-Chromium & foil-c	0.70	1.40	3.50
1-Gold foil-c variant	2.10	6.40	15.00
2-32: 4-Andar app. 5-Death of Andar. 11-w/bound-in trading card.			
16-Chaos Effect	0.50	1.00	2.50
...Yearbook 1 ('94, 3.95, 52 pgs.)	0.80	1.60	4.00

TUROK, SON OF STONE
No. 596, 12/54-No. 29, 9/62; No. 30, 12/62-No. 91, 7/74;
No. 92, 9/74-No. 125, 1/80; No. 126, 3/81-No. 130, 4/82
Dell Publ. Co #1-29/Gold Key #30-85/Gold Key or Whitman
#86-125/Whitman #126 on

4-Color 596 (12/54)(#1)-1st app. Turok & Andar; dinosaur-c			
	75.00	225.00	525.00
4-Color 656 (10/55)(#2)-1st mention of Lanok			
	45.00	135.00	315.00
3 (3-5/56)-5	30.00	90.00	210.00
6–10	19.00	58.00	135.00
11-20: 17-Prehistoric pygmies	11.00	34.00	80.00
21-30	8.00	24.00	55.00
31-40: 31-Drug use story	6.40	19.00	45.00
41-50	5.00	15.00	35.00
51-60: 58-Flying saucer-c/story	4.30	12.90	30.00
61-70: 62-12 & 15 cent variants	4.00	10.70	25.00
71-84: 84-Origin & 1st app. Hutec	2.50	6.30	15.00
85-130: 114, 115-(52 pgs.)	1.40	3.50	8.50
Giant 1 (30031-611) (11/66)-Slick-c; r/#10-12 & 16 plus cover to #11			
	11.00	34.00	80.00
Giant 1-Same as above, but paper-c	13.00	39.00	90.00

TURTLE SOUP (See Teenage Mutant Ninja Turtles)
Sept, 1987 (2.00, B&W)
Mirage Studios

1	0.70	1.40	3.50

TV STARS
Aug, 1978-No. 4, Feb, 1979
Marvel Comics Group

1-Hanna-Barbera TV tie-in	0.90	2.30	5.50
2, 4	0.50	1.00	2.50
3-Toth-c/a	0.90	1.80	4.50

12 O'CLOCK HIGH (TV)
Jan-Mar, 1965-No. 2, Apr-June, 1965 (Photo-c)

	Good	Fine	N-Mint

2099 #6 © MEG

The Twilight Zone #01860-207 © CBS

Dell Publishing Co.

	Good	Fine	N-Mint
1, 2	4.30	13.00	30.00

2099 A.D.
May 1995 (3.95, color)
Marvel Comics

1- Acetate-c by Quesada/Palmiotti	0.80	1.60	4.00

2099 UNLIMITED
Sept, 1993-Present (3.95, color, 68 pgs.)
Marvel Comics
1-9: 1-1st app. Hulk 2099 & begins. 1-3: Spidey 2099 app.

9-Joe Kubert-c	0.80	1.60	4.00

2099 WORLD OF DOOM SPECIAL
May, 1995 (2.25, color, one-shot)
Marvel Comics

1-Doom's "Contract with America"	0.50	0.90	2.25

TWILIGHT ZONE, THE (TV)
No. 1173, 3-5/61-No. 91, 4/79; No. 92, 5/82
Dell Publishing/Gold Key/Whitman #92

4-Color 1173	19.00	58.00	135.00
4-Color 1288	11.00	34.00	80.00
01-860-207 (5-7/62, 15¢)	8.00	24.00	55.00
12-860-210 (8-10/62)-Evans-a(3)	8.00	24.00	55.00
1 (11/62, Gold Key)-Crandall-a	9.30	28.00	65.00
2	6.40	19.00	45.00
3-11: 3, 4, 9-Toth-a	4.30	13.00	30.00
12-Williamson-a	4.00	10.70	25.00

13, 15-Crandall-a	3.00	8.60	20.00
14-Orlando/Crandall/Torres-a	3.00	8.60	20.00
16-20	2.10	6.00	15.00
21-27: 26-Flying saucer-c/story	1.80	5.00	11.00
28-32	1.10	2.20	5.50
33-51: 43-Crandall-a. 51-Williamson-a	0.90	1.80	4.50
52-70	0.50	0.90	2.25
71-92: 83, 84-(52 pgs.)	0.30	0.60	1.60
Mini Comic #1 (1976; 3-1/4 x 6-1/2")	0.30	0.60	1.60

TWILIGHT ZONE, THE
Nov, 1990 (2.95/1.75, color)
Oct, 1991; V2#1, Nov, 1991-No. 14?, 1992 (1.95, color)
V3#1, 1993-No. 4, 1993 (2.50, color)
Now Comics

1-(11/90, 2.95, 52 pgs.)-N. Adams-a	0.80	2.10	5.00
1-(11/90, 1.75)-Newsstand ed.	0.40	0.80	2.00
1-(10/91, 4.95)-Prestige ed.; N. Adams-c/a	1.00	2.00	5.00
1-(10/91, 2.50)-Collector's edition, polybagged, gold logo;			
r/Nov, 1990 issue	0.80	2.10	5.00
1-Reprint (2.50)-r/direct sale 11/90 ed.	0.50	1.00	2.50
1-Reprint (2.50)-r/newsstand 11/90 ed.	0.50	1.00	2.50
V2#1-Direct sale & newsstand versions	0.40	0.80	2.00
2-8, 10-14	0.40	0.80	2.00
9-(2.95)-3-D Special; polybagged w/hologram on-c			
	0.60	1.20	3.00
9-(4.95)-Prestige edition; polybagged; two extra stories			
& different hologram on-c	1.00	2.00	5.00
V3#1-4	0.50	1.00	2.50
Anniversary Special ('92, 2.50)	0.50	1.00	2.50
Annual 1 (4/93, 2.50)-No ads	0.50	1.00	2.50

TWISTED TALES
Nov, 1982-No. 10, Dec, 1984
Pacific Comics/Independent Comics Group

1-10	0.30	0.60	1.50

	Good	Fine	N-Mint

ULTRAFORCE
Aug, 1994-Present (1.95, color)
Malibu Comics

	Good	Fine	N-Mint
1-(2.50, 44 pgs)-w/bound-in trading card; team consisting of Prime, Prototype, Hardcase, Pixx, Ghoul, Contrary & Topaz			
	0.50	1.00	2.50
1-Holographic-c, no price	2.90	8.60	20.00
0-(9/94, 2.50)	0.50	1.00	2.50
2-5-(10/94, 1.95)	0.40	0.80	2.00
2-(2.50)-Flourescent logo; limited edition stamp on-c			
	0.50	1.00	2.50
6-begin 2.50-c; 7-8, 8-Black Knight app.	0.50	1.00	2.50
Malibu "Ashcan": Ultraforce (6/94)	0.20	0.30	0.75

ULTRAMAN
Mar, 1994-Present (1.75/1.95, color)
Nemesis Comics, Inc.

	Good	Fine	N-Mint
-1,1-(1.75)-Newsstand ed.	0.40	0.70	1.75
-1,1-(2.25): Collectors editions. -1-w/foil-c. 1-Special 3/4 wraparound-c			
	0.50	0.90	2.25
2-4: 3-Begin 1.95-c	0.40	0.80	2.00

ULTRAVERSE DOUBLE FEATURE
Jan 1995-Present (3.95, color)
Malibu Comics

	Good	Fine	N-Mint
1-(68 pgs) Flip-c. featuring Prime and Solitaire			
	0.80	1.60	4.00

ULTRAVERSE ORIGINS
Jan, 1994 (99¢, color)
Malibu Comics

	Good	Fine	N-Mint
1-Gatefold-c; 2 pg. origins all characters	0.20	0.40	1.00
1-Newsstand ed.; diff-c; no gatefold	0.20	0.40	1.00

ULTRAVERSE PREMIERE
1994
Malibu Comics

	Good	Fine	N-Mint
0-Ordered thru mail w/coupons	0.80	2.10	5.00

ULTRAVERSE ZERO:THE DEATH OF THE SQUAD
Apr, 1995- (2.95, color)
Malibu Comics

1–3; 3-Codename: Firearm back story	0.50	1.30	3.00

UNCANNY TALES
Dec, 1973-No. 12, Oct, 1975
Marvel Comics Group

1-Crandall-r/Uncanny Tales #9 (1950s)	0.50	1.00	2.50
2–12	0.50	1.00	2.50

UNCANNY X-MEN, THE (The X-Men, Nos. 1-141; see Giant-Size X-Men)
Sept, 1963 - Present
Marvel Comics Group

142-Rachel app.	2.70	8.10	19.00
143-Last Byrne issue	1.50	3.80	9.00
144-150: 150-Double size	1.30	3.00	7.50
151-157, 159-161, 163, 164	1.00	2.00	5.00
158-1st app. Rogue in X-Men	1.00	3.30	8.00
162-Wolverine solo story	1.70	4.20	10.00
165-Paul Smith art begins, ends #175	1.50	4.00	9.00
166-Double size, Paul Smith art	1.20	2.90	7.00
167-170: 167-New Mutants/X-Men 1st meet; same date as New Mutants			
#1 (3/83); contains skin "Tattooz" decals	1.10	2.20	5.50
171-Rogue joins The X-Men; see Avengers Annual #10			
	1.70	4.20	10.00
172-174: 172, 173-Wolverine solo story	1.00	2.00	5.00
175-Double size	1.00	2.50	6.00
176-185: 182-Rogue solo story. 184-1st app. Forge			
	1.00	2.00	5.00
186-(52 pgs.)-B. Smith/Austin-a	1.00	2.00	5.00
187-192, 194-199	0.80	1.60	4.00
193-Double size; special 100th app. New X-Men; 1st app. Warpath			
	1.00	2.50	6.00
200-(12/85, 1.25, 52 pgs.)	1.70	4.20	10.00
201-1st app. Cable (as baby)? (1/86); 1st Portacio-c/a(i) in X-Men			
	3.60	10.70	25.00
202-204, 206-209: 204-2nd Portacio-i on X-Men			
	1.00	2.50	6.00
205-Wolverine solo story by Barry Smith	2.40	7.30	17.00
210, 211: 210-213: Mutant Massacre	2.90	9.00	20.00
212, 213-Wolverine Battles Sabretooth. 212-(12/86)-See X-Factor #10			
	5.00	15.00	35.00
214-221, 223, 224: 219-Havok joins (7/87)	1.00	2.00	5.00
222-Wolverine battles Sabretooth-c/story	2.40	7.30	17.00
225-227: Fall Of The Mutants. 226-(52 pgs.)	1.50	3.80	9.00

	Good	Fine	N-Mint
228-239, 241	1.00	2.00	5.00
240-Sabretooth app.	1.00	2.50	6.00
242-Double size; Inferno tie-in	1.00	2.00	5.00
243,245-247: 245-Liefeld(p)	0.80	1.60	4.00
244-1st app. Jubilee	2.50	6.30	15.00
248-1st Jim Lee art on X-Men	4.30	13.00	30.00
248-2nd printing ('92, 1.25)	0.30	0.50	1.25
249-252: 252-Jim Lee-c	0.50	1.00	2.50
253-255: 253-All new X-Men begin. 254-Jim Lee-c			
	0.90	1.80	4.50
256, 257-Jim Lee-a	1.70	5.10	12.00
258-Wolverine solo story; Lee-a	2.00	6.00	14.00
259-Silvestri-c/a (no Lee-a)	1.00	2.50	6.00
260-265: No Lee-a; 260, 261, 264-Lee-c	0.50	1.00	2.50
266-1st full app. Gambit (See Annual 14)	5.00	15.00	35.00
267-Lee-c/a series begins; 2nd full Gambit app.			
	2.00	6.00	14.00
268-Lee-a; Wolverine, Capt. America, Black Widow team-up			
	3.30	9.90	23.00
269-Lee-a	1.00	2.90	7.00
270-X-Tinction Agenda begins	1.70	5.10	12.00
270-Gold 2nd printing	0.80	1.60	4.00
271, 272: X-Tinction Agenda	1.30	3.00	8.00
273-New Mutants (Cable) & X-Factor app.	1.20	2.90	7.00
274	1.00	2.50	6.00
275-(1.50, 52 pgs.)-Tri-fold-c; Prof. X	1.20	2.90	7.00
275-Gold 2nd printing	0.50	1.00	2.50
276-280: 277-Last Jim Lee-c/a	0.40	0.80	2.00
281-New X-Men team/Byrne scripts & Whilce Portacio-c/a begin			
(white logo)	1.10	2.70	6.50
281-2nd printing (red logo)	0.30	0.50	1.25
282-1st app. Bishop (cover + 1 pg.)	1.30	3.30	8.00
282-Metallic ink 2nd printing (1.00-c)	0.20	0.40	1.00
283-1st full app. Bishop	1.70	4.20	10.00
284-293: 287-Bishop joins team. 290-Last Portacio-c/a. 294-Brandon			
Peterson-a begins, ends 299	0.30	0.50	1.25
294-296-(1.50)-Polybagged w/trading card	0.40	0.80	2.00
297-299, 301-303, 305-309, 311	0.30	0.50	1.25
310-(1.95) w/bound in trading card sheet	0.40	0.80	2.00
300-(3.95, 68 pgs.)-Holo-grafx foil-c; Romita, Jr.-c/a			
	0.80	1.60	4.00
304-(3.95, 68 pgs.)-Magneto hologram on-c; 30th anniversary issue;			
Jae Lee-a (4 pgs.)	0.80	1.60	4.00

312-321: 312-Begin 1.50-c; bound-in card sheet

	0.30	0.60	1.50

316,317-(2.95)-Foil enhanced editions 0.60 1.20 3.00
318-322-(1.95)-Deluxe edition 0.40 0.80 2.00
323-return from "Age of Apocalypse" 0.40 0.80 2.00
Special 1 (12/70)-Kirby-c/a 6.40 19.00 45.00
Special 2 (11/71) 5.70 17.00 40.00
Annual 3 ('79)-New art; Wolverine still in old yellow costume
    2.40 7.30 17.00
Annual 4 ('80)-Dr. Strange-c/story 1.30 3.00 7.50
Annual 5 ('81) 1.00 2.50 6.00
Annual 6-8 ('82-84, 52 pgs.): 6-Dracula app.1.00 2.00 5.00
Annual 9 (1985)-Art Adams-a; New Mutants x-over from New Mutants
  Special #1 1.90 5.60 13.00
Annual 10 (1986)-Art Adams-a 1.60 4.70 11.00
Annual 11 ('87) 0.60 1.20 3.00
Annual 12 ('88)-Evol. War; Art Adams-a(p) 0.80 1.60 4.00
Annual 13 ('89)-Atlantis Attacks 0.60 1.20 3.00
Annual 14 ('90, 2.00)-1st app. Gambit (minor app.); Art Adams-c/a
    1.30 3.30 8.00
Annual 15 ('91, 2.00)-4 pg. origin; Wolverine solo back-up story; 4th app.
  X-Force cont'd/New Mutants 0.80 1.60 4.00
Annual 16 ('92, 2.25)-Jae Lee-c/a(2 stories)0.50 0.90 2.25
Annual 17 ('93, 2.95)-Polybagged w/card 0.60 1.20 3.00
Annual 18 ('94, 2.95, 68 pgs.) 0.60 1.20 3.00
…-The Dark Phoenix Saga (1990, 12.95) 1.90 5.60 13.00

UNCANNY X-MEN AT THE STATE FAIR IN TEXAS, THE
1983 (One-shot)
Marvel Comics Group

Uncanny X-Men #317 © MEG

Union #3 © Aegis Ent.

	Good	Fine	N-Mint
nn-Supplement to The Dallas Times Herald 3.00		8.60	20.00

UNCANNY X-MEN IN DAYS OF FUTURE PAST, THE
1989 (3.95, color, 52 pages)
Marvel Comics Group

	Good	Fine	N-Mint
nn-Byrne/Austin-r	0.80	1.60	4.00

UNDERDOG (TV)
July, 1970-No. 10, Jan, 1972; Mar, 1975-No. 23, Feb, 1979
Charlton Comics/Gold Key

	Good	Fine	N-Mint
1 (1st series, Charlton)	7.10	21.00	50.00
2–10	4.30	12.90	30.00
1 (2nd series, Gold Key)	5.00	15.00	35.00
2–10	3.30	8.00	20.00
11-23: 13-1st app. Shack of Solitude	2.20	5.00	13.00

UNDERDOG SUMMER SPECIAL
Oct, 1993 (2.25, color)
Harvey Comics

	Good	Fine	N-Mint
1	0.50	0.90	2.25

UNEARTHLY SPECTACULARS
Oct, 1965-No. 3, Mar, 1967 (#1: 12¢; 2, 3: 25¢ giants)
Harvey Publications

	Good	Fine	N-Mint
1-Tiger Boy; Simon-c	1.90	5.60	13.00
2-Jack Q. Frost, Tiger Boy & Three Rocketeers app.; Williamson, Wood, Kane-a	3.00	9.40	22.00
3-Jack Q. Frost app.; Williamson/Crandall-a	3.00	9.40	22.00

UNEXPECTED, THE (Formerly Tales of the...)
No. 105, Feb-Mar, 1968-No. 222, May, 1982
National Periodical Publications/DC Comics

	Good	Fine	N-Mint
105-Begin 12¢ issues	2.00	6.00	14.00
106-113: 113-Last 12¢ issue	1.70	4.20	10.00
114, 115, 117, 118, 120, 122-127	1.00	2.50	6.00
116, 119, 121, 128-Wrightson-a	1.30	3.00	8.00
129-162: 132-136-(52 pgs.). 157-162-(100 pgs.)			
	0.60	1.20	3.00
163-188: 187, 188-(44 pgs.)	0.30	0.60	1.60
189, 190, 192-195-(1.00, 68 pgs)	0.40	0.80	2.00
191-Rogers-a(p) (1.00, 68 pgs)	0.60	1.20	3.00
196-221: 200-Return of Johnny Peril	0.30	0.60	1.40

UNION
June, 1993-No. 0, July, 1994 (1.95, color)
Image Comics

1-(2.50)-Embossed foil-c; Texeira-c/a in all	0.50	1.00	2.50
1-(1.95)-Newsstand ed. w/o foil-c	0.40	0.80	2.00
2–4: 4-(7/94)	0.40	0.80	2.00
0-(7/94, 2.50)	0.50	1.00	2.50
0-Alternate Portacio-c, see Deathblow #5	0.50	1.00	2.50

UNION
Feb 1995-Present (2.50, color)
Image Comics

1–3, 5–	0.50	1.00	2.50
4-(1.95)-Newstand, WildStorm Rising Part 3	0.40	0.80	2.00
4-(2.50)-Direct Market, WildStorm Rising Part 3, Bound in Card			
	0.50	1.00	2.50

UNITY
No. 0, Aug, 1992-No. 1, 1992 (Free, color)
Valiant

0-(Blue)-Smith-c/a; prequel to Unity x-overs in all Valiant titles; free to everyone that bought all 8 Unity titles that month			
	0.80	2.00	5.00
0-Red logo; scarcer (5,000 made)	4.00	11.00	25.00
0-Gold variant	2.00	6.00	15.00
1-Epilogue to Unity x-overs; 1 copy available for every 8 Unity books ordered			
	0.70	2.00	5.00
1-(Gold)-Promotional copy	4.00	11.00	25.00
1-(Platinum)-Promo copy; scarcer	5.00	15.00	35.00
…Yearbook 1 (2/95, 3.95)-"1994" in indicia	0.80	1.60	4.00

UNIVERSAL MONSTERS
1993-Present (3.95/4.95, color, 52 pgs.)
Dark Horse Comics

Frankenstein-nn-Original movie adaptation; painted-c			
	0.80	1.60	4.00
Dracula-nn-(4.95)-Original movie adaptation	1.00	2.00	5.00
Mummy-nn-(4.95)-Original movie adaptation			
	1.00	2.00	5.00
Creature from the Black Lagoon-(4.95)-A. Adams/Austin-c/a			
	1.00	2.00	5.00

	Good	Fine	N-Mint

UNKNOWN SOLDIER (Formerly Star-Spangled War Stories)
205, Apr.-May, 1977-No. 268, Oct, 1982
National Periodical Publications/DC Comics

	Good	Fine	N-Mint
205-268: 251-Enemy Ace begins	0.40	0.80	2.00

UNKNOWN WORLDS
Aug, 1960-No. 57, Aug, 1967
American Comics Group

	Good	Fine	N-Mint
1-Whitney-c/a most issues	13.00	38.00	115.00
2-5: 2-Dinosaur-c/story	7.00	20.00	60.00
6-11: 9-Dinosaur-c/story. 11-Last 10¢ issue	5.00	15.00	45.00
12-19: 12¢ issues thru #57	4.00	12.00	35.00
20-Herbie cameo (12-1/62-63)	4.00	13.00	40.00
21-35	2.00	7.00	22.00
36-"The People vs. Hendricks" by Craig; most popular ACG story ever			
	3.00	9.00	27.00
37-46	2.00	7.00	20.00
47-Williamson-r/Advs. into the Unknown #96, 3 pgs.; Craig-a			
	2.00	7.00	22.00
48-57: 49, 50, 54-Ditko-a. 53-Frankenstein app.			
	2.00	6.00	17.00

UNKNOWN WORLDS OF SCIENCE FICTION
Jan, 1975-No. 6, Nov, 1975 (1.00, B&W magazine)
Marvel Comics Group

	Good	Fine	N-Mint
1-Williamson/Krenkel/Torres/Frazetta-r/Witzend #1; N. Adams-r/Phase 1; Brunner & Kaluta-r	0.80	1.60	4.00
2-6: 2, 3-Perez-a	0.60	1.20	3.00
Special 1 ('76, 100 pgs.)-Newton painted-c	0.60	1.20	3.00

UNTOLD LEGEND OF THE BATMAN, THE
July, 1980-No. 3, Sept,1980 (Mini-series)
DC Comics

	Good	Fine	N-Mint
1-Origin; Joker-c; Byrne-a	0.80	1.60	4.00
2, 3	0.60	1.20	3.00
1-3: Batman Cereal premiums (1989, 28 pgs., 6x9")-1st & 2nd printings exist	0.40	0.80	2.00

UNUSUAL TALES (Blue Beetle #50 on)
Nov, 1955-No. 49, Mar-Apr, 1965
Charlton Comics

	Good	Fine	N-Mint
1	15.00	50.00	120.00
2	7.00	21.00	55.00

3–5	4.00	12.00	33.00
6-Ditko-c only	6.00	17.00	44.00
7, 8-Ditko-c/a	12.00	36.00	95.00
9-Ditko-c/a (20 pgs.)	13.00	38.00	100.00
10-Ditko-c/a(4)	15.00	43.00	120.00
11-(3/58, 68 pgs.)-Ditko-a(4)	14.00	41.00	110.00
12, 14-Ditko-a	9.00	28.00	75.00
13, 16-20	3.00	10.00	26.00
15-Ditko-c/a	9.00	27.00	72.00
21, 24, 28	2.00	7.00	18.00
22, 23, 25-27, 29-Ditko-a	6.00	18.00	48.00
30-49	2.00	6.00	16.00

U.S. AGENT (See Captain America #354)
June, 1993-No. 4, Sept, 1993 (1.75, color, mini-series)
Marvel Comics

1–4	0.40	0.70	1.75

USAGI YOJIMBO (See Albedo & Space Usagi)
July, 1987-No. 36? (2.00, B&W)
Fantagraphics Books

1	0.80	1.60	4.00
1, 8, 10-2nd printings (2.00)	0.40	0.80	2.00
2-9, 11-28	0.40	0.80	2.00
10-TMNT app.	0.80	1.60	4.00
29-36: (2.25-c)	0.50	0.90	2.25
Color Special 1 (11/89, 2.95)	0.60	1.20	3.00
Summer Special 1 (1986, 2.75, B&W)	1.30	3.30	8.00

USAGI YOJIMBO
Mar, 1993-Present (2.75, color)
Mirage Studios

V2#1-13: 1-TMNT app.	0.60	1.10	2.75

V

	Good	Fine	N-Mint

VALERIA THE SHE BAT
May, 1993-Present (Color)
Continuity Comics
(See Comics Debut #1, June 1993 for Valeria/Spawn x-over, 5 pages)
1-Premium given to retailers; glow-in-the-dark-c; N. Adams-a

	Good	Fine	N-Mint
	1.40	4.00	10.00
2-5 -(11/93) 5-Embossed-c; N. Adams-a & scripts			
	0.50	1.00	2.50

VALOR
Nov, 1992-No. 23, Sept, 1994 (1.25/1.50, color)
DC Comics

	Good	Fine	N-Mint
1-12: 2-Vs. Supergirl. 4-Vs. Lobo(cameo 12)	0.30	0.50	1.25
13-23: 13-Begin 1.50-c. 17-Death of Valor. 18-22-Build-up			
to Zero Hour. 23-Zero Hour	0.30	0.60	1.50

VAMPIE BITES
May 1995-Present (2.95, B&W)
Brainstorm Comics

	Good	Fine	N-Mint
1-color pin-up	0.60	1.20	3.00

VAMPIRE LESTAT, THE
Jan, 1990-No. 12, 1991 (2.50, mini-series)
Innovation

	Good	Fine	N-Mint
1	4.30	12.90	30.00
1-2nd printing	0.60	1.20	3.00
1-3rd & 4th printings	0.50	1.00	2.50
2	2.10	6.40	15.00
2-2nd & 3rd printings	0.50	1.00	2.50
3–5	1.30	3.30	8.00
6–12	1.00	2.00	5.00

Note: 2nd printings of most issues exist and are worth cover price.

VAMPIRELLA
Sept, 1969-No. 112, Feb, 1983, No. 113, Jan, 1988
Warren Publishing Co. (B&W, magazine size)

	Good	Fine	N-Mint
1-Intro Vampirella, Frazetta-c	31.00	94.00	220.00
2-Amazonia series begins, ends #12	13.60	41.00	95.00
3-Scarce, low distribution	32.00	96.00	225.00
4-7: 5, 7-Frazetta-c	6.00	19.00	45.00
8-Vampirella begins as serious series	5.70	17.00	40.00

9-Smith art; Boris cover	6.00	18.00	43.00
10-No Vampirella story	2.90	9.00	20.00
11-15: 11-Origin & 1st app. Pendragon	4.30	12.90	30.00
16-18, 20-25	2.90	8.60	20.00
19-(1973 Annual)	4.00	10.70	25.00
26, 28-36, 38-40: 31-Frazetta-c	1.70	4.20	10.00
27-(1974 Annual)	2.00	5.00	12.00
37-(1975 Annual)	1.70	4.20	10.00
41-45, 47-50	1.20	2.40	6.00
46-Origin of Vampirella retold (10/75)	1.20	2.40	6.00
51-99	1.00	2.00	5.00
100-(96 pgs.)-Reprint special, origin retold	1.00	2.00	5.00
101-110,112	1.00	2.00	5.00
111-Giant Collector's Edition (2.50)	1.00	2.00	5.00
113 (1988)	1.00	2.00	5.00
Annual 1 (1972)- New origin Vampirella	18.00	54.00	125.00
Special 1 (1977, large squarebound)	1.70	4.20	10.00

VAMPIRELLA (Also see Cain/… Flip Book, Vengeance of…)
Nov, 1992-No. 5, Nov, 1993 (2.95, color)
Harris Comics

0-	0.70	1.70	4.00
1-Jim Balent inks & A. Hughes-c in #1-3	4.60	13.70	32.00
1-2nd printing	1.00	2.00	5.00
2	3.60	7.20	18.00
3-5: 1-5 contain certificates for free Dave Stevens Vampi poster.			
5-D. Brereton-c	1.40	2.80	7.00
Vampirella TPB (10/93, 5.95)-r/1-4; Jusko-c	1.00	2.50	6.00

VAMPIRELLA CLASSIC
Feb 1995-Present (2.95, color)
Harris Comics

1-3- A. Goodwin/s-Gonzalez pinup	0.60	1.20	3.00

VAMPIRELLA: MORNING IN AMERICA
1991-No. 4, 1992 (3.95, B&W, mini-series)
Dark Horse/Harris

1-All have Kaluta painted-c	1.40	2.80	7.00
2–4	1.00	2.00	5.00

VAMPIRELLA/SHADOWHAWK: CREATURES OF THE NIGHT
1995 (4.95, color, limited series:2)
Harris Comics

1	1.00	2.00	5.00

	Good	Fine	N-Mint

VAMPIRE TALES
Aug, 1973-No. 11, June, 1975 (B&W magazine)
Marvel Comics Group

	Good	Fine	N-Mint
1-Morbius, the Living Vampire begins by Marcos (1st solo Morbius series & 5th Morbius app.)	3.00	9.90	23.00
2-Intro Satana; Steranko-r	1.70	4.00	10.00
3, 4, 7-11: 3-Satana app. 8-Blade app. (see Tomb of Dracula)			
	1.00	2.00	5.00
6-1st Lilith app.	1.00	2.00	5.00
5-Origin Morbius	1.30	3.00	7.50
Annual 1 (10/75)-Heath-r/#9	0.60	1.20	3.00

VAMPS
Aug, 1994- Jan, 1995 (1.95, color, limited series, mature)
DC Comics

	Good	Fine	N-Mint
1-Bolland-c	0.80	1.60	4.00
2–6 - Bolland-c	0.60	1.20	3.00

VANGUARD (OUTPOST: EARTH) (See Megaton & Savage Dragon)
1987 (1.50, color)
Megaton Comics

	Good	Fine	N-Mint
1-Erik Larsen-c(p)	0.70	1.40	3.50

VANGUARD
Oct, 1993-Present (1.95, color)
Image Comics

	Good	Fine	N-Mint
1-6: 1-Gatefold-c; Supreme x-over; Erik Larsen back-up. 3-(12/93)-Indicia December 1994. 4-Berzerker back-up. 5-Angel Medina-a(p)			
	0.40	0.80	2.00

VANGUARD ILLUSTRATED
Nov, 1983-No. 11, Oct, 1984
Pacific Comics

	Good	Fine	N-Mint
1-6, 8-11: 2-Dave Stevens-c	0.30	0.60	1.50
7-1st app. Mr. Monster	1.00	2.00	5.00

VAULT OF EVIL
Feb, 1973-No. 23, Nov, 1975
Marvel Comics Group

	Good	Fine	N-Mint
1-(1950s reprints begin)	0.60	1.20	3.00
2-23: 3,4-Brunner-c	0.40	0.70	1.75

VAULT OF HORROR, THE
Aug, 1990-No. 6, June, 1991 (1.95, color, 68 pgs.)
Gladstone Publ.

1	0.80	1.60	4.00
2-6: 4-Begins 2.00-c	0.40	0.80	2.00

VENGEANCE OF VAMPIRELLA
Apr, 1994-Present (2.95, color)
Harris Comics

1-(3.50)-Quesada/Palmiotti "bloodfoil" wraparound -c			
	3.30	8.30	20.00
1-(3.50)-2nd printing; blue foil-c	1.00	2.00	5.00
1-Gold	8.00	16.00	40.00
2	2.00	4.00	10.00
3,4	1.00	2.00	5.00
5–15: 8-Polybagged w/trading card ; 10-w/coupon for Hyde-25 poster			
11-Polybagged w/trading card	0.60	1.20	3.00
...:Bloodshed ('95, 6.95)	7.00	2.90	7.00

VENGEANCE SQUAD
July, 1975-No. 6, May, 1976 (#1-3 are 25¢ issues)
Charlton Comics

1-Mike Mauser, Private Eye begins by Staton	0.40	0.80	2.00
2-6: Morisi-a in all	0.30	0.60	1.60
5, 6-Modern Comics-r (1977)	0.30	0.60	1.40

VENOM: CARNAGE UNLEASHED
Apr 1995 - July 1995 (2.95, color, limited series:4)
Marvel Comics

1–4	0.60	1.20	3.00

VENOM: FUNERAL PYRE
Aug, 1993-No. 3, Oct, 1993 (2.95, color, limited series)
Marvel Comics

1-Holo-grafx foil-c; Punisher app. in all	0.60	1.20	3.00
2, 3	0.60	1.20	3.00

VENOM: LETHAL PROTECTOR (See Amazing Spider-Man #298)
Feb, 1993-No. 6, July, 1993 (2.95, limited series)
Marvel Comics

1-Red holo-grafx foil-c	1.00	2.00	5.00
1-Gold variant sold to retailers	2.60	8.00	18.00
1-Black-c variant	21.40	64.00	150.00

	Good	Fine	N-Mint
2-6: Spider-Man app. in all	0.60	1.20	3.00

VENOM: NIGHTS OF VENGEANCE
Aug, 1994-No. 4, Nov, 1994 (2.95, color, limited series)
Marvel Comics

1-4: 1-Red foil-c	0.60	1.20	3.00

VENOM: SEPARATION ANXIETY
Dec, 1994- Mar 1995 (2.95, color, limited series)
Marvel Comics

1-4: 1-Embossed-c	0.60	1.20	3.00

VENOM: THE ENEMY WITHIN
Feb, 1994-No. 3, Apr, 1994 (2.95, color, limited series)
Marvel Comics
1-3: Demogoblin & Morbius app. 1-Glow-in-the-dark-c

	0.60	1.20	3.00

VENOM: THE MACE
May, 1994-No. 3, July 1994 (2.95, color, limited series)
Marvel Comics

1-3: 1-Embossed cover	0.60	1.20	3.00

VENOM: THE MADNESS
Nov, 1993-No. 3, Jan, 1994 (2.95, color, limited series)
Marvel Comics

1-3: Kelley Jones-c/a. 1-Embosssed-c	0.60	1.20	3.00

VERTIGO JAM
Aug, 1993 (3.95, color, 68 pgs.)

Vengence of Vampirella #6
© Harris

Venom: Nights of Vengeance #2
© MEG

Violator 471

DC Comics
1-Sandman by Gaiman, Swamp Thing, etc. 0.80   1.60   4.00

VERTIGO PREVIEW
1992 (75¢, color, 36 pgs.)
DC Comics
1-Vertigo preview; Sandman story by Gaiman
0.40   0.80   2.00

VERTIGO VISIONS
June, 1993-Present (Color, 68 pgs.)
DC Comics (Vertigo)
The Geek 1 (3.95, 6/93)   0.80   1.60   4.00
The Phantom Stranger 1 (3.50, 10/93) 0.70   1.40   3.50
Dr. Occult 1 (3.95, 7/94)   0.80   1.60   4.00

VERY VICKY
1993?-Present (2.50, B&W)
Meet Danny Ocean
1–8   0.50   1.00   2.50

V FOR VENDETTA
Sept, 1988-No. 10, May, 1989 (2.00, color, maxi-series)
DC Comics
1-10: Alan Moore scripts in all   0.40   0.80   2.00
Trade paperback (1990, 14.95)   2.10   6.00   15.00

VICTORY
June, 1994-Dec 1994 (2.50, color, limited series:5)
Topps Comics
1-5   0.50   1.00   2.50

VINTAGE MAGNUS (Robot Fighter)
Jan, 1992-No. 4, Apr, 1992 (2.25, color)
Valiant
1-Layton-c; r/Magnus #22   1.00   2.00   5.00
2–4   0.60   1.20   3.00

VIOLATOR (See Spawn #2)
May, 1994-Present (1.95, color)
Image Comics
1-Alan Moore-s   0.60   1.60   4.00
2-3-Alan Moore scripts: 2,3-Bart Sears-c(p)/a(p)

	Good	Fine	N-Mint
	0.60	1.20	3.00

VIOLATOR VS. BADROCK
May 1995-Present (2.50, color, limited series)
Image Comics

	Good	Fine	N-Mint
1–Alan Moore-s; variant-c (3?)	0.50	1.00	2.50

VIRUS
1993-No. 4, 1993 (2.50, color)
Dark Horse Comics

1-4-Ploog-c	0.50	1.00	2.50

VISION, THE
Nov, 1994-Present (1.75, color)
Marvel Comics

1-4	0.40	0.70	1.75

VISIONS
No. 1, 1979-No. 5, 1983 (B&W, fanzine)
Vision Publications

1-Flaming Carrot stories	7.00	21.00	50.00
2-Flaming Carrot stories	3.60	11.00	25.00
3-Flaming Carrot stories	1.40	4.00	10.00
4-Flaming Carrot covers and info.	2.10	6.40	15.00
5-(1983)-1 page Flaming Carrot	1.20	2.90	7.00

Note: After No. 4, Visions became an annual publication of The Atlanta
Fantasy Fair.

VISITOR VS. THE VALIANT UNIVERSE, THE
Feb, 1995-Present (2.95, color, limited series:2)
Valiant

1-2: 1-X-O Manowar, Armorines & Dr. Solar app.			
	0.60	1.20	3.00

VORTEX
Nov, 1982-No. 15, 1988 (1.50/1.75, B&W)
Vortex Pubs.

1-Peter Hsu art, nudity	1.50	4.00	9.00
2-1st app. Mister X (on cover only)	0.80	1.60	4.00
3	0.60	1.20	3.00
4-15: 12-Sam Kieth-a	0.40	0.70	1.80

W

WALT DISNEY'S COMICS AND STORIES
No. 511, Nov, 1986-No. 547, April, 1990 (Color)
No. 548, May, 1990-Present
Gladstone Publ./Disney/Gladstone

511-Wuzzles app.	0.90	2.30	5.50
512	0.60	1.20	3.00
513-520: 518-Infinity-c	0.40	0.70	1.80
521-545: 541-545 are 52 pgs.	0.30	0.60	1.60
546, 547-(1.95, 68 pgs.)	0.50	0.90	2.25
548-(1.50, 6/90)-1st Disney issue	0.40	0.70	1.75
549, 551-570, 572, 573, 577-579, 581, 584	0.30	0.60	1.60
550-(2.25)-D. Duck by Barks	0.50	1.00	2.50
571-(2.95, 68 pgs.)-DD's Atom Bomb (r) by Barks from 1947 Cheerios			
Premium	0.80	1.50	3.75
574-576, 580, 582, 583: (2.95, 68 pgs.)	0.70	1.30	3.25
585-(2.50, 52 pgs.)-Reprints #140	0.70	1.30	3.25
586, 587-(1.50)-Gladstone begins again	0.40	0.70	1.75
588-596	0.30	0.60	1.50

WALT DISNEY'S DONALD AND MICKEY (Formerly Mickey and Donald)
No. 19, Sept, 1993-Present (1.50, color)
The Bruce Hamilton Company (Gladstone)
19, 21-24,26-30: 19-Barks, Murry-r. 22-Barks "Omelet" story r/WDC&S #146

	0.30	0.60	1.50
20-(2.95, 68 pgs.)-Barks-r	0.60	1.20	3.00
25-(2.95, 68 pgs)	0.60	1.20	3.00

WALT DISNEY'S DONALD DUCK
Oct, 1986-No. 279, May, 1990; No. 280, Sept, 1993-Present (Color)
Gladstone Publ.

246	1.70	4.00	10.00
247-249	0.80	1.60	4.00
250-(1.50, 68 pgs.)-Reprints FC #9	1.70	5.10	12.00
251-256	0.80	1.50	3.75
257-(1.50, 52 pgs.)-r/Vacation Parade #1	0.80	1.60	4.00
258-260	0.60	1.20	3.00
261-277	0.40	0.80	1.90
278, 279-(1.95, 68 pgs.)	0.50	1.00	2.50
280-285,287-291: 280-Begin 1.50-c. 283-Rosa-a/scripts & part-c			
	0.40	0.70	1.80
286-(2.95, 68 pgs.)-"Happy Birthday, Donald"-c			
	0.60	1.20	3.00

	Good	Fine	N-Mint
WALT DISNEY'S DONALD DUCK ADVENTURES			
Nov, 1987-No. 20, Apr, 1990 (95¢, color)			
No. 21, Aug, 1993-Present (1.50, color)			
Gladstone Publ./Disney Comics			
1	1.10	2.20	5.50
2-r/Four Color #308	0.50	0.90	2.25
3, 4, 6, 7, 9-11, 13, 15-18	0.40	0.80	2.00
5, 8-Rosa art	0.40	0.90	2.20
12-Rosa story/art w/ Barks poster	0.60	1.20	3.00
14-r/F.C. 29 - The Mummy's Ring (Barks)	0.50	1.00	2.50
19, 20-(1.95, 68 pgs.)	0.40	0.80	2.00
21-Rosa-c; r/Secret of Hondorica (D.D. #46)			
	0.40	0.70	1.80
22-r/FC 282-The Pixilated Parrot (Barks)	0.40	0.70	1.80
23-27,29,31: 21,23,29-Rosa-c. 31-P.Block-c0.30		0.60	1.50
28-(2.95, 68 pgs)-r/FC 199, Sheriff of Bullet Valley (Barks)			
	0.60	1.20	3.00
30-(2.95, 68 pgs)-r/FC 367 "Christmas for Shacktown" (Barks)			
	0.60	1.20	3.00
WALT DISNEY'S DONALD DUCK ADVENTURES			
June, 1990-No. 38, July, 1993 (1.50, color)			
Disney Comics			
1-Rosa story & art (1st Disney issue)	0.60	1.20	3.00
2–38	0.30	0.60	1.50
WALT DISNEY'S UNCLE SCROOGE			
Oct, 1986-No. 242, Apr, 1990 (Color)			
No. 243, June, 1990-Present			
Gladstone Publ./Disney Comics #243-280/Gladstone #281 on			
210-r/1st Beagle Boys	1.00	2.50	6.00
211-218	0.50	1.00	2.50
219-Son Of The Sun by Rosa	1.70	5.00	12.00
220-Don Rosa story	0.80	1.50	3.75
221-230: 224, 226, 227-Rosa-a	0.40	0.80	1.90
231-240: 235-Rosa story/art	0.30	0.60	1.50
241, 242-(1.95, 68 pgs.)	0.50	0.90	2.25
243-249, 251-284 (1.50): 283-r/WDCS #98	0.40	0.70	1.80
250-(2.25, 52 pgs.)-Barks-r	0.50	1.00	2.50
285-The Life and Times of Scrooge McDuck Pt.1; Rosa-c/a/scripts			
	0.80	1.60	4.00
286-291-The Life and Times of Scrooge McDuck Pt.2-7; Rosa-c/a/scripts			
	0.30	0.60	1.50

WALT DISNEY'S UNCLE SCROOGE ADVENTURES (Uncle Scrooge
Adventures #1-3)
Nov, 1987-No. 21, May, 1990 (95¢, color)
No. 22, Sept, 1993-Present (1.50, color)
Gladstone Publ.

1	1.00	2.50	6.00
2-5: 5-Rosa-c/a	0.40	0.70	1.80
6-19: 9, 14-Rosa art	0.30	0.50	1.30
20, 21-(1.95). 20-Rosa-c/a	0.50	0.90	2.25
22 (1.50); Rosa cover; r/US #26	0.40	0.80	1.90
23 (2.95, 68 pgs.)-Vs. Phantom Blot; Barks-r			
	0.70	1.40	3.50
24-26,29, 31-32: 24, 25, 29,31,32-Rosa-c. 25-r/US #21			
	0.30	0.60	1.50
27-Guardians of the Lost Library; Rosa-c/a/story; origin of the Junior			
Woodchuck Guidebook	0.40	0.70	1.75
28-(2.95, 68 pgs)-r/US #13 with restored missing panels; Rosa-c			
	0.60	1.20	3.00
30-(2.95, 68 pgs)-r/US #12; Rosa-c; 33-(2.95)			
	0.60	1.20	3.00

WALT KELLY'S ...
Dec, 1987-Apr, 1988
Eclipse Comics

... Christmas Classics 1 (1987, 1.75, color)	0.40	0.70	1.75
... Springtime Tales 1 (1988, 2.50)	0.50	1.00	2.50

WANTED: THE WORLD'S MOST DANGEROUS VILLAINS
July-Aug, 1972-No. 9, Aug-Sept, 1973 (All 20¢ issues)
DC Comics (All reprints)

1-Batman-c/story; Green Lantern-r/G.L. #1	1.00	2.00	5.00
2-Batman/Joker/Penguin-c/story reprinted from Batman #25			
	1.10	2.70	6.50
3-9: All GA reprints	0.60	1.20	3.00

WARBLADE : ENDANGERED SPECIES
Jan 1995 - Apr 1995 (2.50, color, limited series:4)
Image Comics

1-4:1-Gatefold wraparound-c	0.50	1.00	2.50

WARCHILD
Jan 1995 - Present (2.50, color)
Maximum Press

	Good	Fine	N-Mint
1-2:1-Liefeld-c/s	0.50	1.00	2.50

WARLOCK (The Power Of...) (See Fantastic Four 66, 67, Incred. Hulk 178, Infinity War, Marvel Premiere, Silver Surfer #46, Strange Tales, Thor 165)
Aug, 1972-No. 8, Oct, 1973; No. 9, Oct, 1975-No. 15, Nov, 1976
Marvel Comics Group

	Good	Fine	N-Mint
1-Origin retold by Kane	3.60	10.70	25.00
2, 3	1.60	5.00	11.00
4-8: 4-Death of Eddie Roberts	1.30	3.10	7.50
9-2nd Thanos saga begins; Thanos cameo; Starlin-c/a in #9-15			
	1.50	4.00	9.00
10-Origin recap Thanos & Gamora, Thanos-c/story; Thanos vs.			
Magus-c/story	4.30	13.00	30.00
11-Thanos app.; Warlock dies	3.60	11.00	25.00
12-14: Saga cont. 14-Last 25¢ issue	1.60	4.70	11.00
15-Thanos-c/story	3.30	10.00	23.00

WARLOCK (...Special Edition on cover)
Dec, 1982-No. 6, June, 1983 (2.00, Direct)
Marvel Comics Group

	Good	Fine	N-Mint
1-6: Thanos-r/Str. Tales 178-181, Warlock 9-15, Marv. Team-Up 55,			
Avengers Ann. 7, Marv. 2-in-1 Ann. 2	1.20	3.00	7.00
Special Edition #1 (12/83)	0.50	1.00	2.50

WARLOCK
May, 1992-No. 6, Oct, 1992 (2.50, color, mini-series)
Marvel Comics

	Good	Fine	N-Mint
V2#1-6-r/Warlock Special Edition series	0.50	1.00	2.50

WARLOCK AND THE INFINITY WATCH
Feb 1992-July 1995 (1.75/1.95 color)
Marvel Comics

	Good	Fine	N-Mint
1-Starlin scripts begin; Austin-c/a(i) in 1-4, 7; sequel to Infinity Gauntlet;			
brief origin recap Warlock	0.80	1.60	4.00
2-Reintro Moondragon	0.70	1.40	3.50
3	0.50	1.00	2.50
4-6	0.40	0.70	1.75
7-24,26,27: 7-Reintro The Magus; Moondragon app. 8, 9-Gamora battles			
Thanos-c/sty. 10-Thanos-c/sty. 13-Hulk	0.40	0.70	1.75
25-(2.95, 52 pgs.)-Die cut embossed double-c ; Thor & Thanos app.			
	0.60	1.20	3.00
28-42: 28-Begin 1.95-c; bound-in card sheet, 42-Final issue			
	0.40	0.80	2.00

WARLOCK CHRONICLES
June, 1993-No. 8, Feb, 1994 (2.00, color, mini-series)
Marvel Comics

1-(2.95)-Holo-grafx foil & embossed-c; origin retold; Starlin scripts begin; Keith Williams-i	0.60	1.20	3.00
2-8: 3-Thanos & Mephisto-c/story. 4-Vs. Magus-c/story	0.40	0.80	2.00

WARLORD, THE
Jan-Feb, 1976-No. 133, Winter 1988-89
National Periodical Publications/DC Comics
1-Cont'd from 1st Issue Special; Mike Grell-a

	2.10	6.40	15.00
2-Intro Machiste	1.30	3.30	8.00
3-5	0.90	2.30	5.50
6-10: 6-Intro Mariah. 9-New costume	0.90	1.70	4.25
11-20: 11-Origin-r	0.70	1.30	3.25
21-40: 37, 38-Origin Omac by Starlin	0.50	0.90	2.25
41-47, 49-52: 51-Reprints #1	0.30	0.60	1.40
48-(52 pgs.)-1st app. Arak	0.50	0.90	2.25
53-130, 132: 100-Double size	0.30	0.60	1.40
131-1st Liefeld-a at DC (9/88)	0.60	1.20	3.00
133-Last issue (52 pgs., 1.50)	0.30	0.60	1.50
Annual 1 (1982)	0.40	0.80	2.00
Annual 2-6 (1983-87)	0.20	0.40	1.00

WARLORD
Jan, 1992-No. 6, June, 1992 (1.75, color, mini-series)
DC Comics

1-6: Grell-c & scripts in all	0.40	0.70	1.75

WAR MACHINE (See Iron Man #281, 282 & Marvel Comics Presents #152)
Apr, 1994-Present (1.50, color)
Marvel Comics
"Ashcan" Edition (no date, 75¢, B&W, 16 pgs.)

	0.20	0.30	0.75
1-(2.95, 52 pgs.)-Collectors Ed.; embossed foil-c; Cable app.	0.60	1.20	3.00
1-(2.00, 52 pgs.)Newsstand Ed.;Cable app.	0.40	0.80	2.00
2-14, 16-17 : 2-Bound-in trading card sheet; Cable app. 2,3-Deathlok app. 8-Red logo	0.30	0.60	1.50
8-(2.95)-Polybagged w/16 pg. Marvel Action Hour preview and acetate			

	Good	Fine	N-Mint
print; yellow logo	0.60	1.20	3.00
15- (2.50)-Flip Book	0.50	1.00	2.50

WAR PARTY
Oct, 1994-Present (2.95, B&W)
Lightning Comics

1-1st app. Deathmark	0.60	1.20	3.00

WARRIOR NUN AREALA
Dec 1994 - Present (2.95, color)
Antarctic Press

1	1.00	2.00	5.00
2–3	1.00	1.20	3.00

WARSTRIKE
May, 1994-Present (1.95, color)
Malibu Comics (Ultraverse)

1–7: 1-Simonson-c	0.40	0.80	2.00
1-Ultra 5000 Limited silver foil	2.50	6.30	15.00
Giant Size 1-(12/94, 2.50, 44 pgs)-Prelude to Godwheel			
	0.50	1.00	2.50

WARZONE
1995 (2.95, B&W)
Entity Comics

1-3	0.60	1.20	3.00

WATCHMEN
Sept, 1986-No. 12, Oct, 1987 (maxi-series)
DC Comics

1–12	0.80	1.60	4.00

WEAPON X
Apr, 1994 (12.95, color, one-shot)
Marvel Comics

nn-r/Marvel Comics Presents 72-84	1.90	6.00	13.00

WEAPON X
Mar 1995 - Present (1.95, color)
Marvel Comics

1-Age of Apocalypse	1.20	2.40	6.00
2-4	0.60	1.20	3.00

Weapon X #3 © MEG

Web of Spider-Man #114 © MEG

WEAPON ZERO: T-MINUS-4
June 1995-Present (2.50, color)

1–	0.50	1.00	2.50

WEB OF SPIDER-MAN
April, 1985-Present
Marvel Comics Group

1-5th app. black costume	5.40	16.00	38.00
2, 3	1.40	3.50	8.50
4-8: 7-Hulk x-over	1.10	2.70	6.50
9-13: 10-Painted-c	1.10	2.20	5.50
14-28: 18-(9/86)-1st app. Venom (behind the scenes, not shown)			
19-Intro Himbug & Solo	1.00	2.00	5.00
29-New Hobgoblin (Macendale), Wolverine app.			
	2.30	6.90	16.00
30-Origin recap Rose & Hobgoblin (Leeds)	2.10	6.00	15.00
31, 32-Six part Kraven storyline begins	1.70	4.20	10.00
33-37, 39-47, 49	0.60	1.10	2.75
38-Hobgoblin app.	1.30	3.00	7.50
48-Origin & 1st full app. of demonic Hobgoblin (Demogoblin) cont'd			
from Spect. Spider-Man #147	3.60	11.00	25.00
50-(1.50, 52 pgs.)	0.50	1.00	2.50
51-58	0.40	0.80	2.00
59-Cosmic Spidey cont. from Sp. Spider-Man			
	1.70	4.00	10.00
60-65, 68-85, 87-89, 91-94: 84-Begin 6 part Rose & Hobgoblin II story.			
93, 94-Hobgoblin (Macendale) reborn-c/sty			
	0.40	0.80	2.00
66, 67-Green Goblin app. as a super-hero	0.60	1.20	3.00
86-Demon leaves Hobgoblin; 1st Demogoblin			

	Good	Fine	N-Mint
	0.60	1.20	3.00

90-(2.95, 52 pgs.)-Silver hologram-c, polybagged w/poster

	0.80	2.10	5.00

90-2nd print; gold hologram-c

	0.60	1.20	3.00

95-Begin 4-part x-over w/Spirits of Venom

	0.70	1.30	3.25

96-99, 101-106: 104-106-Nightwatch back-ups

	0.40	0.70	1.80

100-(2.95, 52 pgs.)-Holo-grafx foil-c; intro new Spider-Armor

	0.70	1.30	3.25

107-111: 107-Intro Sandstorm; Sand & Quicksand app.

	0.30	0.50	1.25

112-116,118,119,121-124, 126-127: 112-Begin 1.50-c; bound-in trading card sheet. 113-Gambit app. 118-1st solo clone, Venom app. 119-Intro Kaine, Scarlet Spider, Venom app. 127-Maximum Clonage pt. 2

	0.30	0.60	1.50

113-(2.95)-Collector's Ed. polybagged w/foil-c; 16 pg. preview of S-M cartoon & animation cel

	0.60	1.20	3.00

117-(1.50)-Flip book; Power & Responsibility Pt. 1

	0.30	0.60	1.50

117-(2.95)-Collectors edition; foil-c; flip book

	0.80	1.60	4.00

119-(6.45)-Direct ed. polybagged w/Marvel Milestone Amaz. S-M #150 & coupon for Amaz. S-M #396, S-M #53 & Spect. S-M #219

	1.10	2.70	6.50

120-(2.25)-Flip book w/preview of The Ultimate Spider-Man

	0.50	0.90	2.25

125-(3.95)-Holodisk-c-Gwen Stacy clone	0.80	1.60	4.00
125-(2.95)-Newstand	0.60	1.20	3.00
Annual 1-('85)	0.60	1.20	3.00
Annual 2-('86) Arthur Adams-a	1.30	3.00	7.50
Annual 3-('87)	0.60	1.20	3.00
Annual 4-('88)-Evolutionary War	0.70	1.40	3.50
Annual 5-('89, 2.00)-Atlantis Attacks	0.60	1.10	2.75
Annual 6-('90, 2.00)-Punisher story	0.60	1.10	2.75

Annual 7-('91, 2.00)-Origin recap of Hobgoblin I & II, Green Goblin I & II, Venom; Larsen/Austin-c

	0.60	1.10	2.75

Annual 8-('92, 2.25)-Venom story, pt. 3	0.60	1.10	2.75
Annual 9-('93, 2.95)-Polybagged w/card	0.70	1.30	3.25
Annual 10 ('94, 2.95, 68 pgs.)	0.60	1.20	3.00

WEIRD MYSTERY TALES (See DC 100 Page Super Spectacular #4)
July-Aug, 1972-No. 24, Nov, 1975
National Periodical Publications

1-Kirby-a; Wrightson splash pg.	1.20	2.40	6.00
2-24: 4-Starlin-a. 24-Wrightson-c	0.60	1.10	2.75

WEIRD SCIENCE
Sept, 1990-No. 4, Mar, 1991 (1.95, color, 68 pgs.)
Gladstone Publishing

1-4-Reprints. 3-Begin 2.00-c	0.40	0.80	2.00

WEIRD WAR TALES
Sept-Oct, 1971-No. 124, June, 1983
National Periodical Publications/DC Comics

1-Kubert-a in 1-4, 7; c-1-7	1.60	3.20	8.00
2, 3-Drucker-a. 2-Crandall-a. 3, 5-Heath-a	0.90	1.80	4.50
4-7, 9, 10: 5, 6, 10-Toth-a	0.70	1.40	3.50
8-Neal Adams-c/a(i)	1.10	2.20	5.50
11-50: 36-Crandall & Kubert-r/#2	0.50	0.90	2.25
51-63, 65-67, 69-124: 93-Intro/origin Creature Commandos.			
101-Intro/origin G.I. Robot	0.40	0.70	1.75
64, 68-Frank Miller-a	0.50	1.00	2.50

WEIRD WESTERN TALES (Formerly All-Star Western)
No. 12, June-July, 1972-No. 70, Aug, 1980
National Periodical Publications

12-(52 pgs.)-3rd app. Jonah Hex; Bat Lash & Pow Wow Smith-r;			
El Diablo by Neal Adams/Wrightson	2.60	8.00	18.00
13-4th app. Jonah Hex; Neal Adams-a	2.20	5.00	13.00
14, 29: 14-Toth-a. 29-Origin Jonah Hex	1.40	2.80	7.00
15-Neal Adams-c/a; no Jonah Hex	1.20	3.00	7.00
16, 17, 19-28, 30-38: Jonah Hex in all. 38-Last Jonah Hex			
	0.60	1.20	3.00
18-1st all Jonah Hex issue (7-8/73) & begins			
	1.10	2.20	5.50
39-70: 39-Origin/1st app. Scalphunter & begins			
	0.40	0.80	2.00

WEIRD WONDER TALES
Dec, 1973-No. 22, May, 1977
Marvel Comics Group

1-Wolverton-r/Mystic #6 (Eye of Doom)	0.50	1.00	2.50
2-22: 19-22-Dr. Druid (Droom)-r	0.40	0.80	2.00

WEIRD WORLDS
Aug-Sept, 1972-No. 9, Jan-Feb, 1974; No. 10, Oct-Nov, 1974

	Good	Fine	N-Mint
National Periodical Publications			
1-John Carter, Warlord of Mars & David Innes begin (1st DC app.);			
Kubert-c (#1-10 are 20¢ issues)	0.90	1.80	4.50
2-7: 7-Last John Carter	0.50	1.00	2.50
8-10: 8-Iron Wolf begins (1st app.) by Chaykin			
	0.40	0.70	1.75

WELCOME TO THE LITTLE SHOP OF HORRORS
May 1995_Present (2.50, color, limited series)
Roger Corman's Cosmic Comics

	Good	Fine	N-Mint
1	0.50	1.00	2.50

WEREWOLF (Also see Dracula & Frankenstein)
Dec, 1966-No. 3, Apr, 1967
Dell Publishing Co.

	Good	Fine	N-Mint
1-1st app. (Super hero)	1.10	2.20	5.50
2, 3	0.70	1.30	3.25

WEREWOLF BY NIGHT (Also see Giant-Size...)
Sept, 1972-No. 43, Mar, 1977
Marvel Comics Group

	Good	Fine	N-Mint
1-Ploog-a cont'd/Marvel Spotlight #4	5.70	17.00	40.00
2	2.90	8.60	20.00
3–5	1.90	6.00	13.00
6–10	1.70	4.20	10.00
11-20: 15-New origin; Dracula-c/sty	1.30	3.30	8.00
21-31	0.90	2.30	5.50
32-Origin/1st app. Moon Knight (8/75)	7.00	21.00	50.00
33-2nd app. Moon Knight	4.30	13.00	30.00
34-36, 38-43	0.70	1.40	3.50
37-Moon Knight cameo	1.30	3.00	7.50

WEST COAST AVENGERS
Sept, 1984-No. 4, Dec, 1984 (Mini-series)
Marvel Comics Group

	Good	Fine	N-Mint
1	0.60	1.20	3.00
2–4	0.30	0.60	1.50

WEST COAST AVENGERS (Avengers West Coast #48 on)
Oct, 1985-No. 102, Jan, 1994 (Regular series)
Marvel Comics Group

	Good	Fine	N-Mint
V2#1–20	0.30	0.60	1.50
21-41	0.20	0.40	1.00

42-John Byrne-a/scripts begin, end 57	0.40	0.80	2.00
43-49: 48-Becomes Avengers West Coast	0.20	0.40	1.10
50-Re-intro original Human Torch	0.30	0.60	1.50
51-74, 76-99: 87,88-Wolverine-c/sty	0.30	0.50	1.25
75-(1.50, 52 pgs.)-F. Four x-over	0.30	0.60	1.50
100-(3.95, 68 pgs.)-Red foil embossed-c; death of Mockingbird			
	0.80	1.60	4.00
101, 102: 101-X-Men x-over	0.30	0.50	1.25
Annual 1 ('86)	0.40	0.90	2.20
Annual 2 ('87, 1.25)	0.40	0.80	2.00
Annual 3 ('88)-Evolutionary War	0.60	1.10	2.75
Annual 4 ('89, 2.00)-Atlantis Attacks	0.40	0.90	2.20
Annual 5 ('90, 2.00). Annual 6 (91, 2.00)	0.40	0.80	2.00
Annual 7 ('92, 2.25)-Darkhawk app.	0.50	0.90	2.25
Annual 8 ('93, 2.95)-Polybagged w/card	0.60	1.20	3.00

WESTERN GUNFIGHTERS
Aug, 1970-No. 33, Nov, 1975 (1-6: 68 pgs.: 7: 52 pgs.)
Marvel Comics Group

1-Ghost Rider (western) begins, ends #7	1.00	2.00	5.00
2-33: 7-Origin Ghost Rider retold. 10-Origin Black Rider. 12-Origin			
Matt Slade	0.60	1.20	3.00

WESTERN KID, THE
Dec, 1971-No. 5, Aug, 1972 (All 20¢ issues)
Marvel Comics Group

1-Reprints; Romita-c/a(3)	0.70	1.30	3.25
2-5: 2-Romita-a; Severin-c	0.40	0.80	2.00
	0.50	0.90	2.25

WESTERN TEAM-UP
Nov, 1973 (20¢)
Marvel Comics Group

1-Origin & 1st app. The Dakota Kid	0.40	0.70	1.80

WETWORKS
June, 1994-Present (1.95, color)
Image Comics

1-"JULY" on-c; Gatefold wraparound-c; Portacio/Williams-c/a			
	1.00	2.00	5.00
1-Chicago Comicon Ed.	1.40	2.80	7.00
2-4	0.40	0.80	2.00
2-Alternate Portacio-c, see Deathblow #5	1.60	3.20	8.00

	Good	Fine	N-Mint
5-(2.50) 6-7	0.50	1.00	2.50
8-(1.95)-Newstand, WildStorm Rising pt. 7	0.40	0.80	2.00
8-(2.50)-Direct Market, WildStorm Rising pt. 7			
	0.50	1.00	2.50
Sourcebook 1 (10/94, 2.50)-Text & illos - no comics			
	0.50	1.00	2.50

WHAM-O GIANT COMICS
Apr, 1967 (Newspaper size, 98¢, one-shot, full color)
Wham-O Mfg. Co.

	Good	Fine	N-Mint
1-Radian & Goody Bumpkin by Wally Wood	5.00	15.00	35.00

WHAT IF?
Feb, 1977-No. 47, Oct, 1984
Marvel Comics Group (All are 52 pgs.)

	Good	Fine	N-Mint
1-Brief origin Spider-Man, F.F.	2.30	6.90	16.00
2-Origin Hulk retold	1.70	4.00	10.00
3-5	1.10	2.70	6.50
6-10: 8-D. Stevens p/i in backup "Man-Spider"			
	0.90	2.30	5.50
11, 12	0.90	1.80	4.50
13-Conan; Buscema-c/a	1.10	2.70	6.50
14-16	0.90	1.70	4.25
17-Ghost Rider & Son Of Satan app.	1.30	3.00	7.50
18-26, 29: 18-Begin 75¢-c. 19-Spider-Man. 22-Origin Dr. Doom retold			
	0.90	1.70	4.25
27-X-Men app.; Miller-c	1.60	4.70	11.00
28-Daredevil by Miller; Ghost Rider app.	1.60	4.70	11.00
30-"What If…Spider-Man's Clone Had Lived?"			
	2.00	5.00	12.00
31-Begin 1.00-c; X-Men app., Wolverine app.			
	2.10	6.40	15.00
32-47: 37-Old X-Men & Silver Surfer app.	0.50	1.00	2.50
Special (6/88, 1.50, color)	0.40	0.80	2.00

WHAT IF…? (2nd Series)
July, 1989-Present (1.25/1.50, color)
Marvel Comics

	Good	Fine	N-Mint
V2#1-Evolutionary War	1.00	1.90	4.75
2-5: 2-D.D., Punisher app.	0.60	1.10	2.75
6-X-Men	0.80	1.60	4.00
7-Wolverine app., Liefeld c/a(p)	0.90	2.30	5.50
8, 11: 11-McFarlane-c(i)	0.50	0.90	2.25

9, 12: X-Men	0.60	1.20	3.00
10-Punisher app.	0.60	1.20	3.00

13-15, 17-21, 23, 27-29: 13-Prof. X app.; Jim Lee-c. 15-Capullo-c/a.

23-X-Men	0.30	0.60	1.50
16-Conan battles Wolverine	0.90	1.80	4.50
22-Silver Surfer by Lim/Austin-c/a	0.60	1.20	3.00
24-Wolverine, Punisher app.	0.60	1.10	2.75
25-(1.50, 52 pgs.)-Wolverine app.	0.60	1.20	3.00
26-Punisher app.	0.40	0.80	2.00
30-(1.75, 52 pgs.)	0.40	0.70	1.75

31-40: 31-Cosmic Spidey & Venom app. 37-Wolverine

	0.30	0.60	1.50
41-(1.75, 52 pgs.)-Avengers vs. Galactus	0.40	0.70	1.75

42-49, 51-60: 43-Wolverine. 44-Venom/Punisher. 45-Ghost Rider.
46-Cable story. 47-Magneto. 49-Silver Surfer/Thanos. 52-Dr. Doom. 54-Death's Head. 58-Punisher. 59-Wolverine. 60-X-Men Wedding Album

	0.30	0.50	1.25

50-(2.95, 52 pgs.)-Foil embossed-c; "What If Hulk Had Killed Wolverine"

	0.60	1.20	3.00

61-76: 61-Begin 1.50-c; bound-in card sheet; Spider-Man; 74- X-Men.
76-Spider-Man; Last app. of Watcher in title.

	0.30	0.60	1.50

WHAT THE—?!
Aug, 1988-No. 24, Dec, 1992 (1.25/1.50, color, semi-annual)
Marvel Comics

1-Parodies in all	0.50	1.00	2.50
2, 4	0.30	0.60	1.50
3-X-Men parody; McFarlane-a	0.60	1.20	3.00
5-Punisher/Wolverine parody; Jim Lee-a	0.30	0.60	1.50

6-25: 6-Punisher/Wolverine. 9-Wolverine. 18-Star Trek parody
w/Wolverine & Thanos; Weapon X parody

	0.30	0.50	1.25

26-Fall Special (2.50, 68 pgs.)-Spider-Ham 2099-c/story; origin Silver
Surfer; Hulk & Doomsday parody

	0.50	1.00	2.50
Summer Special 1 ('93, 2.50)-X-Men parody	0.50	1.00	2.50

WHEELIE AND THE CHOPPER BUNCH (TV)
July, 1975-No. 7, July, 1976 (Hanna-Barbera)
Charlton Comics

1, 2-Byrne text illos (early-a)	1.30	3.00	8.00
3-7-Staton-a. 3-Byrne-c & text illos	0.90	1.70	4.25

	Good	Fine	N-Mint

WildC.A.T.S Trilogy #3 © Aegis Ent

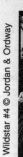

Wildstar #4 © Jordan & Ordway

WHERE CREATURES ROAM
July, 1970-No. 8, Sept, 1971 (Pre-hero reprints in all)
Marvel Comics Group

	Good	Fine	N-Mint
1-Kirby/Ayers-r. Ditko r-1,2,4,6,7	1.00	2.00	5.00
2-8-Kirby-r	0.60	1.20	3.00

WHERE MONSTERS DWELL
Jan, 1970-No. 38, Oct, 1975 (Pre-hero reprints in all)
Marvel Comics Group

1-Kirby/Ditko-r	1.00	2.00	5.00
2-10, 12: 4-Crandall-r. 12-Giant size	0.50	1.00	2.50
11, 13-37: 18, 20-Starlin-c	0.40	0.80	2.00
38-Williamson-r/World of Suspense #3	0.50	1.00	2.50

WHERE'S HUDDLES? (TV) (See Fun-In #9)
Jan, 1971-No. 3, Dec, 1971 (Hanna-Barbera)
Gold Key

1	1.40	3.50	8.50
2, 3: 3-Reprints most of #1	1.00	2.00	5.00

WHO'S WHO IN STAR TREK
Mar, 1987-No. 2, Apr, 1987 (1.50, color)
DC Comics

1, 2	1.00	1.90	4.75

WILDC.A.T.S ADVENTURES
Sept, 1994-Present (1.95, color)
Image Comics

1-5	0.40	0.80	2.00
6-(2.50) 7–10	0.50	1.00	2.50

Sourcebook 1 (1/95, 2.95)	0.60	1.20	3.00

WILDC.A.T.S: COVERT ACTION TEAMS (WildC.A.ts #7,12,13,16)
Aug, 1992-No. 4, Mar, 1993; No. 5, Nov, 1993-Present (1.95/2.50, color)
Image Comics

1-1st app.; Jim Lee-c/a in all, contains 2 trading cards (2 versions exist, each with a different card)	1.30	3.30	8.00
1-(All gold foil, signed)	6.00	19.00	45.00
1-(All gold foil unsigned)	2.10	6.00	15.00
1-Newsstand ed. w/o cards	0.40	0.80	2.00
2-(2.50)-Prism foil stamped-c; direct sales only ; contains coupon for Image Comics #0; 1st app. Wetworks by Portacio (4 pg. preview)	1.60	3.20	8.00
2-With coupon missing	0.40	0.80	2.00
2-Direct Sale misprint w/no prism on-c	0.40	0.80	2.00
2-Newsstand copy/no cards or prism-c	0.40	0.80	2.00
3-Lee/Liefeld-c	1.00	2.00	5.00
4-(2.50)-Polybagged w/Topps trading card; 1st app. Tribe by Stroman; Youngblood cameo	1.00	2.00	5.00
4-Variant w/Red Card	1.00	2.00	5.00
5-7-(1.95)	0.80	1.60	4.00
8-12-(2.50): 8-Cameo of X-Men's Jean Grey & Scott Summers	0.80	1.60	4.00
11-Alternate Portacio-c, see Deathblow #5	1.20	2.40	6.00
13-19-: 13-Jim Lee/Scott Willams-c; "HellC.A.T.s" story by C. Claremont, Jim Lee-p. 14-Larsen-a/story; "...: cover action teams" in indicia 16-T.Charest-p/c/pinup	0.50	1.00	2.50
20-(2.50)-Direct Market, WildStorm Rising Part 2, Bound-in card	0.50	1.00	2.50
20-(1.95)-Newstand, WildStorm Rising Part 2	0.40	0.80	2.00
...WildC.A.T.s Sourcebook 1 (9/93, 2.50)-Foil embossed-c	0.50	1.00	2.50
...WildC.A.T.s Sourcebook 2 (11/94, 2.50)-Wraparound-c	0.50	1.00	2.50
...: Compendium (6/93, 9.95) Polybagged r/#1-4 w/issue #0	1.20	2.90	7.00
...Special 1 (11/93, 3.50, 52 pgs.)-Travis Charest/Williams-c/a & pin-up	0.70	1.40	3.50

WILDC.A.T.S TRILOGY
June, 1993-No. 3, Dec, 1993 (1.95, color, mini-series)
Image Comics

	Good	Fine	N-Mint
1-(2.50)-Multi-color foil-c; Jae Lee-c/a	0.50	1.00	2.50
1-(1.95)-Newsstand ed. w/o foil-c	0.40	0.80	2.00
2, 3-Jae Lee-c/a	0.40	0.80	2.00

WILDSTAR: SKY ZERO
Mar, 1993-No. 4, Nov, 1993 (1.95, color, mini-series)
Image Comics

	Good	Fine	N-Mint
1-(2.50)-Embossed-c w/silver ink	0.50	1.00	2.50
1-Gold variant	2.90	9.00	20.00
1-Newsstand ed. w/silver ink-c, not embossed	0.40	0.80	2.00
2-4: Ordway-c/a in all	0.40	0.80	2.00

WILDSTORM
Dec 1994 (2.95/4.95, color)
Image Comics

	Good	Fine	N-Mint
...Rarities 1 (12/94, 4.95, 52 pgs)-Gen 13	1.40	2.80	7.00
...Swimsuit Special 1 (12/94, 2.95)	0.60	1.20	3.00
...Universe Sourcebook (5/95, 2.50)	0.50	1.00	2.50

WILDSTORM RISING
May 1995 (1.95/2.50, color)
Image Comics

	Good	Fine	N-Mint
1-(2.50)-Direst Market, WildStorm Rising Part 1, Bound-in card	0.50	1.00	2.50
1-(1.95)-Newsstand, WildStorm Rising Part 10.40		0.80	2.00
2-(2.50)-Direct Market, WildStorm Rising Part 10, Bound-in card	0.50	1.00	2.50
2-(1.95)-Newsstand, WildStorm Rising Part 10	0.40	0.80	2.00

WILD WILD WEST, THE (TV)
June, 1966-No. 7, Oct, 1969
Gold Key

	Good	Fine	N-Mint
1-McWilliams-a	14.00	41.00	95.00
2	9.00	28.00	65.00
3–7	7.10	21.00	50.00

WILL TO POWER
June, 1994-Present (1.00, color, 20 pgs., weekly)
Dark Horse Comics

	Good	Fine	N-Mint
1-12: 1-3-B.Sears-c	0.20	0.40	1.00

WITCHCRAFT
June, 1994-No. 3, Aug., 1994 (2.95, color, limited series)
DC Comics (Vertigo)

1-3-Kaluta-c Robinson-s	1.00	2.00	5.00
1-Platinum edition	4.30	13.00	30.00

WITCHING HOUR (Combined with The Unexpected with #189)
Feb-Mar, 1969-No. 85, Oct, 1978
National Periodical Publications/ DC Comics

1-Toth-a-Three Witches	2.90	8.60	20.00
2, 6: 6-Toth-a	1.70	4.20	10.00
3, 5-Wrightson-a. 3-Last 12¢ issue	1.30	3.00	7.50
4, 7, 9-12	1.00	2.50	6.00
8-Toth, Neal Adams-a	1.20	2.90	7.00
13-Neal Adams-c/a (2 pgs.)	0.90	1.70	4.25
14-Williamson/Garzon, Jones-a	0.90	1.70	4.25
15-20	0.50	0.90	2.25
21-85: 38-(100 pgs.)	0.20	0.40	1.10

WOLF & RED
Apr 1995– June 1995 (2.50, color, limited series)
Dark Horse Comics

1-3; Tex Avery characters	0.50	1.00	2.50

WOLFF & BYRD, COUNSELORS OF THE MACABRE
May, 1994-Present (2.50, B&W)
Exhibit A Press

1–4	0.50	1.00	2.50

WOLVERINE (Also see Incredible Hulk #180, 181 & Kitty Pryde &...)
Sept, 1982-No. 4, Dec, 1982 (Mini-series)
Marvel Comics Group

1-Miller-c/a in all	4.60	14.00	32.00
2, 3	3.10	9.40	22.00
4	3.60	10.70	25.00
TPB (7/87, 4.95)-r/1-4	1.30	3.30	8.00
TPB (9.95)-2nd printing	1.70	4.00	10.00

WOLVERINE (Also see Marvel Comics Presents)
Nov, 1988-Present (1.50/1.75/1.95, color)
Marvel Comics

1-Buscema-a begins, ends 16	4.30	13.00	30.00
2	1.90	5.60	13.00

	Good	Fine	N-Mint
3-5	1.50	4.00	9.00
6-9: 7, 8-Hulk app.	1.30	3.30	8.00
10-Before claws; 1st battle w/ Sabretooth	4.00	12.00	28.00
11-16: 11-New Costume	1.00	2.50	6.00
17-20: 17-Byrne-c/a begins, ends #23	0.80	1.60	4.00
21-30: 24, 25, 27-Jim Lee-c	0.60	1.20	3.00
31-40, 44, 47: 26-Begin 1.75-c	0.40	0.80	2.00
41-Sabretooth claims to be Wolverine's father; Cable cameo			
	1.30	3.00	7.50
41-Gold 2nd printing	0.30	0.60	1.60
42-Sabretooth & Cable app.; Sabretooth proven not to be Wolverine's			
father	1.00	2.00	5.00
42-Gold ink 2nd printing (1.75-c)	0.40	0.70	1.75
43-Sabretooth/Wolverine saga concludes	0.80	1.60	4.00
45, 46-Sabretooth-c/story	0.70	1.40	3.50
48, 49-Sabretooth app.; Weapon X sequel	0.50	1.00	2.50
50-(2.50, 64 pgs.)-Die-cut-c; Weapon X sequel concludes. Wolverine			
back to old yellow costume	1.00	2.00	5.00
51-74, 76-80: 51-Sabretooth-c/app. 55-57,73-Gambit app.			
60-64-Sabretooth storyline	0.40	0.70	1.75
75-(3.95, 68 pgs.)-Wolverine hologram on-c	1.00	2.50	6.00
81-84, 86: 81-Begin 1.95-c; bound-in card sheet			
	0.40	0.80	2.00
85-(2.50)-Newsstand edition	0.50	1.00	2.50
85-(3.50)-Collectors edition	0.70	1.40	3.50
87-90-(1.95)-Deluxe edition	0.40	0.80	2.00
87-90-(1.50)-Standard edition	0.30	0.60	1.50
91-Return from "Age of Apocalypse"	0.40	0.80	2.00
Annual nn (#1, 1989, 4.50)-The Jungle Adventure			
	0.90	1.80	4.50
Annual 2 (12/90, 4.95)-Bloodlust	1.00	2.00	5.00
Annual nn (#3, 8/91, 5.95)-Rahne Of Terra; Cable & New Mutants app.;			
2nd print exists	1.00	2.50	6.00
Battles the Incredible Hulk nn (1989, 4.95, 52 pgs.)-Reprints Incredible			
Hulk #180 & 181	0.80	2.00	5.00
Blood Hungry ('93, 6.95, 68 pgs.)-Keith-a; r/Wolverine stories from			
Marvel Comics Presents 85-92	1.20	3.00	7.00
Bloody Choices nn (1993, 7.95)	1.30	3.30	8.00
...Evilution nn (9/94, 5.95, graphic novel)	1.00	2.50	6.00
Global Jeopardy 1 (12/93, 2.95)-Embossed-c; Sub-Mariner, Zabu, Ka-Zar,			
Shanna & Wolverine; produced in cooperation w/World Wildlife Fund			
	0.60	1.20	3.00
Inner Fury nn (11/92, 5.95)-Metallic ink-c	1.00	2.50	6.00

Save The Tiger 1 (7/92 2.95)-Kieth-c; r/Wolverine stories from Marvel
 Comics Presents #1-10   0.60   1.20   3.00
...Typhoid's Kiss (6/94, 6.95)-r/Wolverine stories from Marvel Comics
 Presents #109-116   1.20   2.90   7.00

WOLVERINE AND THE PUNISHER: DAMAGING EVIDENCE
Oct, 1993-No. 3, 1993 (2.00, color, mini-series)
Marvel Comics
1-3: 2, 3-Indicia says Punisher & Wolverine…
                           0.40   0.80   2.00

WOLVERINE SAGA, THE
Sept, 1989-No. 4, Dec, 1989 (3.95, color, deluxe, mini-series)
Marvel Comics
1-Beginnings; Liefeld/Austin-c   1.00   2.00   5.00
2–4   0.80   1.60   4.00

WOLVERINE VS. SPIDERMAN
Mar 1995 (2.50, color, one shot)
Marvel Comics
1-r/Marvel Comics Presents # 48-50   0.50   1.00   2.50

WONDER WOMAN
No. 73, Apr, 1955-No. 329, Jan, 1986
National Periodical Publications/DC Comics
73-90: 73-1st code approved issue   12.00   36.00   95.00
91-94, 96, 97, 99   8.00   23.00   60.00
95-Atom Bomb cover   8.00   24.00   65.00
98-New origin & new art team (Andru & Esposito) begin (5/58)
                           9.00   26.00   70.00

Wolverine #86 © MEG

Wonder Woman #88 © DC

	Good	Fine	N-Mint
100 (8/58)	10.00	31.00	82.00
101-104, 106-110	7.00	20.00	52.00
105-Secret origin, scarce (4/59)	28.00	85.00	255.00
111-120	5.00	15.00	40.00
121-126: 126-Last 10¢ issue	3.00	9.00	25.00
127-130	2.00	5.00	12.00
131-150: 132-Flying saucer-c	1.30	3.00	8.00
151-158, 160-170: 170-(12/66)	1.20	2.90	7.00
159-Origin retold (1/66); 1st S.A. origin?	1.30	3.00	8.00
171-178	1.00	2.00	5.00
179-195: 195-Wood inks	0.80	1.60	4.00
196-198 (52 pgs.)-Reprints	0.80	1.60	4.00
199, 200: Jeff Jones-c. 200-(5-6/72)	1.00	2.00	5.00
201-210: 201, 202-Catwoman app.	0.30	0.60	1.50
211-230, 233-266, 269-280, 284-286	0.20	0.40	1.00
231, 232-JSA guest star	0.30	0.60	1.50
267, 268-Re-intro Animal Man (1980)	1.70	5.10	12.00
281-283: Joker-c/story	0.60	1.20	3.00
287-New Teen Titans app.	0.30	0.60	1.50
288-299, 301-328	0.20	0.40	1.00
300-(1.50, 76 pgs.)-JLA app.	0.30	0.60	1.50
329-Double size last issue	0.30	0.60	1.50

WONDER WOMAN
Feb, 1987-Present
DC Comics

	Good	Fine	N-Mint
0-(10/94)	1.00	2.00	5.00
1-Perez-c/a begins; covers only #25-60	0.60	1.20	3.00
2–20	0.30	0.50	1.25
21-49, 51-62: 24-Last Perez-a. 60-Vs. Lobo	0.20	0.40	1.00
50-(1.50, 52 pgs.)-New Titans, JLA app.	0.30	0.60	1.50
63-81: 63-New Direction & Bolland-c begin	0.30	0.50	1.25
82-84; 82-begin 1.50-c	0.40	0.80	2.00
85-1st Deodato-a	1.40	2.80	7.00
86,87	0.40	0.80	2.00
88-93; 88-Superman c & app.; 90-1st Artemis			
	0.80	1.60	4.00
94-98; 91-(11/94) 93-Hawkman app. 96-Joker-c			
	0.40	0.80	2.00
98-begin 1.75-c; 99–	0.40	0.70	1.75
100-(2.95)-Newsstand, Death of Artemis	0.60	1.20	3.00
100-(3.95)-Direct Market, Foil-c, Death of Artemis			
	0.80	1.60	4.00

Annual 1 ('88, 1.50)-Art Adams-a	0.40	0.80	2.00
Annual 2 ('89, 2.00)	0.40	0.80	2.00
Annual 3 ('92, 2.50)-Quesada-c(p)	0.50	1.00	2.50
Annual 4 ('95, 3.50)-Year One story	0.70	1.40	3.50
Special 1 ('92, 1.75)-Cont'd in W. W. #63	0.40	0.80	2.00

WORLDS COLLIDE
July, 1994 (2.50, color)
DC Comics

1-(2.50, 52 pgs.)	0.50	1.00	2.50
1-(3.95, 52 pgs.)-Polybagged w/vinyl clings	0.80	1.60	4.00

WORLD'S FINEST COMICS
No. 71, July-Aug, 1954-No. 323, Jan, 1986
National Periodical Publ./DC Comics

71-(Scarce)-Superman/Batman begin as team; Superman & Batman			
exchange identities	61.00	182.00	605.00
72-(Scarce)	47.00	142.00	425.00
73-(Scarce)	51.00	153.00	460.00
74	41.00	122.00	365.00
75	37.00	112.00	335.00
76-80: 75-1st code approved (3-4/55)	29.00	88.00	235.00
81-90: 88-1st Joker/Luthor team-up	23.00	69.00	185.00
91-93, 95-99	16.00	47.00	125.00
94-Origin Superman/Batman team retold	51.00	152.00	405.00
100-(3/59)	29.00	86.00	230.00
101-110	11.00	32.00	85.00
111-121: 121-Last 10¢ issue	8.00	24.00	65.00
122-128, 130-142: 125-Aquaman begins (5/62)			
	4.30	13.00	30.00
129-Joker/Luthor team-up-c/sty	6.00	17.00	40.00
143-150	2.90	8.60	20.00
151-155, 157-160	2.00	5.00	12.00
156-1st Bizarro Batman; Joker-c/sty	10.00	30.00	70.00
161,170-Giants G-28 & G-40	2.90	9.00	20.00
162-165, 167-169, 171-174: 169-(9/67)-3rd app. new Batgirl (cover and			
1 panel cameo)	1.70	4.20	10.00
166-Joker-c/story	2.00	6.00	14.00
175, 176-N. Adams-a; r/Det. 225, 226	1.70	5.10	12.00
177-Joker/Luthor team-up-c/story	1.70	5.10	12.00
178, 180-187	1.10	2.20	5.50
179, 188-Giants G-52 & G-64	1.70	4.20	10.00
189-196	0.90	1.70	4.25

	Good	Fine	N-Mint
197-Giant G-76	1.50	3.80	9.00

198, 199-3rd Superman/Flash race; see Flash 175 & Superman 199

	7.00	21.00	60.00

200-205: 204-Last 15¢ issue. 205-r/Shining Knight by Frazetta; Teen Titans
   x-over. 205, 207-212-(25¢, 52 pgs.)

	0.60	1.20	3.00
206-Giant G-88	0.90	1.70	4.25

207-248: 215-Intro Batman, Jr & Superman, Jr. 223-228-(100 pgs.).
   244-252-(84 pgs.). 253-265-(68 pgs.). 266-282-(52 pgs.)

	0.90	1.70	4.25
249- The Creeper by Ditko begins	1.10	2.20	5.50
250-270, 272-299, 301-323	0.50	0.90	2.25
271-Origin Superman/Batman team retold	0.50	1.00	2.50

300-(1.25, 52 pgs.)-New Teen Titans, JLA app.

	0.70	1.30	3.25

WRATH (See Prototype #4)
Jan, 1994-Present (1.95, color)
Malibu Comics

1-9: 2-Mantra x-over. 3-1st app. Slayer. 4,5-Freex app. 8-Mantra & Warstrike
   app. 9-Prime app.

	Good	Fine	N-Mint
1-9	0.40	0.80	2.00
1-Ultra 5000 Limited silver foil	2.10	6.40	15.00
Giant Size 1-(2.50, 44 pgs)	0.50	1.00	2.50

Wrath #1 © Mlibu

Xenya #1 © Sanctuary Press

X

X (See Comics' Greatest World & Dark Horse Comics #8)
Feb, 1994-Present (2.00, color)
Dark Horse Comics

1-7: 3-Pit Bulls x-over	0.40	0.80	2.00
8-15: 8-(2.50)-Ghost-c & app.	0.50	1.00	2.50
.../Hero Illustrated Special #2 (6/94, 1.00, 20 pgs.)			
	0.20	0.40	1.00
...: One Shot to the Head ('94, 2.50, 36 pgs)-F.Miller-c			
	0.50	1.00	2.50

X-CALIBRE
Mar 1995 - Present (1.95, color)
Marvel Comics

1-Age of Apocalypse	0.80	1.60	4.00
2-4	0.40	0.80	2.00

XENOBROOD
No. 0, Oct, 1994-Present (1.50, color, mini-series:7)
DC Comics

0-6: 0-"Xenobroods" in indicia	0.30	0.60	1.50

XENOTECH
Sept, 1993-Present (2.75, color)
Mirage Publishing

1-3-Bound w/2 trading cards: 2-(10/94)	0.60	1.10	2.75

XENYA
Apr, 1994-Present (2.95, color)
Sanctuary Press

1,2: 1-Hildebrandt-c; intro Xenya	0.60	1.20	3.00

X-FACTOR (Also see Spider-Man and X-Factor)
Feb, 1986-Present
Marvel Comics Group

1-(1.25, 52 pgs.)-Cont'd from FF 286; Baby Nathan apps. on 2 pgs.			
(2nd app. after X-Men 201)	1.70	5.00	12.00
2–5; 5-1st app. Apocalypse (2 pg. cameo)	1.00	2.00	5.00
6-1st full app. Apocalypse	2.00	4.00	10.00
7-10:10-Sabretooth app. (11/86, 3 pgs.) cont'd in X-Men #212; 1st app. in			
an X-Men comic	0.80	1.60	4.00
11-20: 13-Baby Nathan app. in flashback	0.60	1.20	3.00

	Good	Fine	N-Mint
21-23: 23-1st Archangel (cameo)	0.50	1.00	2.50
24-1st full app. Archangel	2.10	6.40	15.00
25, 26: Fall Of The Mutants in #24-26	0.80	1.60	4.00
27-30	0.40	0.80	2.00
31-37, 39, 41-49: 35-Origin Cyclops	0.30	0.60	1.50
38-(1.50, 52 pgs.)	0.40	0.80	2.00
40-Liefeld-c/a (4/88, 1st at Marvel?)	1.00	2.50	6.00
50-(1.50, 52 pgs.)-Liefeld/McFarlane-c	0.40	0.80	2.00
51-53-Sabretooth app. 52-Liefeld-c(p)	1.00	2.00	5.00
54-59: 54-Silvestri-c/a(p)	0.20	0.40	1.00
60-X-Tinction Agenda; New Mutants app.	1.30	3.30	8.00
60-Gold 2nd print	0.50	1.00	2.50
61, 62-X-Tinction Agenda; New Mutants app.			
	1.00	2.50	6.00
63-Portacio/Thibert-c/a begins	1.00	2.50	6.00
64-67, 69, 70: 65-68: Jim Lee co-plots. 66, 67-Baby Nathan app. cont'd			
in #68	0.40	0.80	2.00
68-Baby Nathan is sent into future	1.00	2.00	5.00
71-New team begins; Stroman-c/a begins	1.00	2.50	6.00
71-2nd printing (1.25-c)	0.30	0.50	1.25
72-74: 74-Last 1.00-c	0.30	0.60	1.50
75-(1.75, 52 pgs.)	0.40	0.70	1.75
76-83: 77-79: No Stroman-a	0.30	0.50	1.25
84-86: (1.50-c)-Polybagged w/trading card; Jae Lee-a; Jae Lee c-85, 86			
	0.40	0.80	2.00
87-91, 93-99,101: 87-92-Quesada-c/a. 88-1st app. Random			
	0.30	0.50	1.25
92-(3.50, 68 pgs.)-Wraparound-c w/Havok hologram on-c; begin X-Men			
30th anniversary issues; Quesada-c/a	0.70	1.40	3.50
92-2nd printing	0.70	1.40	3.50
100-(2.95, 52 pgs.)-Collectors Edition; embossed foil-c; death of Multiple			
Man	0.60	1.20	3.00
100-(1.75, 52 pgs.)-Newsstand Edition	0.40	0.70	1.75
102-105,107-111: 102-Begin 1.50-c; bound-in card sheet			
	0.30	0.60	1.50
106-(2.00)-Newsstand edition	0.40	0.80	2.00
106-(2.95)-Collectors edition	0.60	1.20	3.00
108-113-(1.95)-Deluxe edition 112-return from "Age of Apocalypse"			
	0.40	0.80	2.00
Annual 1 (10/86), 2 (10/87)	0.50	1.00	2.50
Annual 3 ('88)-Evolutionary War	0.50	1.00	2.50
Annual 4 ('89, 2.00)-Atlantis Attacks	0.50	1.00	2.50
Annual 5 ('90, 2.00)-New Mutants x-over	0.50	1.00	2.50

Annual 6 ('91, 2.00)-New Warriors, X-Force app.			
	0.50	1.00	2.50
Annual 7 ('92, 2.25)-1st Quesada-c/a on X-Factor			
	0.50	0.90	2.25
Annual 8 ('93, 2.95)-Bagged w/trading card	0.60	1.20	3.00
Annual 9 ('94, 2.95)-Austin-a(i)	0.60	1.20	3.00
...Prisoner Of Love ('90, 4.95)-Starlin scripts	1.00	2.00	5.00

X-FILES, THE
Jan 1995 - Present (2.50, color)
Topps Comics

1-Adaptation of T.V. Show	4.60	9.20	23.00
2	3.00	6.00	15.00
3-5	0.60	1.20	3.00
...ashcan-giveaway w/Star Wars Galaxy Mag. (B&W)			
	1.40	2.80	7.00

X-FORCE (See New Mutants #100)
Aug, 1991-Present (1.00/1.25/1.50, color)
Marvel Comics

1-(1.50, 52 pgs.)-Polybagged with 1 of 5 Marvel Universe trading cards inside; Liefeld a-1-7, 9p; c-1-9, 11p	0.80	1.60	4.00
1-With Cable card	1.00	2.50	6.00
1-2nd printing, metallic ink-c; no bag or card			
	0.30	0.60	1.50
2, 3: 2-Deadpool-c/story	0.40	0.80	2.00
4-Spider-Man x-over w/Spider-Man #16	0.60	1.20	3.00
5-10: 7, 9, 10-Weapon apps	0.30	0.60	1.50
11-15,19-24, 26-33 : 15-Cable leaves X-Force; Capullo-a begins, ends #25.			
26, 27-Capullo-c only	0.30	0.50	1.25
16-18-(1.50)-Polybagged w/trading card	0.40	0.80	2.00
25-(3.50, 52 pgs.)-Wraparound-c w/Cable hologram on-c; Cable returns			
	0.70	1.40	3.50
34-37,39-43: 34-Begin 1.50-c; bound-in card sheet			
	0.30	0.60	1.50
38-(2.00)-Newsstand edition	0.40	0.80	2.00
38-(2.95)-Collectors edition	0.60	1.20	3.00
40-43-(1.95)-Deluxe edition	0.40	0.80	2.00
44-Return from "Age of Apocalypse"	0.40	0.80	2.00
Annual 1 ('92, 2.25)-No Liefeld-c/a; 1st Capullo-a on X-Force			
	0.50	0.90	2.25
Annual 2 ('93, 2.95)-polybagged w/trading card; intro X-Treme			
	0.60	1.20	3.00

	Good	Fine	N-Mint
Annual 3 ('94, 2.95, 68 pgs.)	0.60	1.20	3.00
...And Spider-Man: Sabotage nn (11/92, 6.95)-r/X-Force #3,4 & S-M #16			
	1.20	2.90	7.00

XIMOS: VIOLENT PAST
Mar, 1994-No. 2, Mar, 1994 (2.50, color, limited series)
Triumphant Comics

1, 2	0.60	1.10	2.75

X-MAN
Mar 1995 - Present (1.95, color)
Marvel Comics

1-Age of Apocalypse	1.20	2.40	6.00
2–4	0.80	1.60	4.00
5	0.40	0.80	2.00

X-MEN (Uncanny X-Men, Nos. 142-present: see Giant-Size)
1-Origin & 1st app. The X-Men (Cyclops, Angel, Beast, Iceman & Marvel
   Girl begin); 1st app. Magneto & Prof. X

	390.00	1167.00	3500.00
2-1st app. The Vanisher	128.00	385.00	1155.00
3-1st app. The Blob	56.00	167.00	500.00
4-1st app. Quicksilver, Scarlet Witch; 2nd app. Magneto			
	48.00	145.00	435.00
5-Magneto & Evil Mutants-c/story	33.00	100.00	300.00
6-10: 6-Sub-Mariner app. 7-Magneto app. 9-Early Avengers x-over.			
10-1st S.A. app. Ka-Zar	24.00	72.00	215.00
11, 13-15: 15-Origin Beast	22.00	66.00	175.00
12-Origin Professor X; origin & 1st app. Juggernaut			
	29.00	88.00	235.00
16-20: 19-1st Mimic	10.00	29.00	78.00
21-27, 29, 30: 27-Spider-Man cameo	9.00	28.00	65.00
28-1st app. The Banshee	12.00	36.00	85.00
31-34, 36, 37: 34-Adkins-c/a	6.40	19.00	45.00
35-Spider-Man app. (8/67)	10.00	30.00	70.00
38-Origins of The X-Men feature in #38-57	9.00	28.00	65.00
39, 40: 39-New costumes	6.00	18.00	42.00
41-49: 44-1st app. G.A. Raven in S.A. 49-Steranko-c; 1st Polaris			
	5.70	17.00	40.00
50, 51-Steranko-c/a	6.40	19.00	45.00
52	4.00	12.00	28.00
53-Barry Smith-c/a; 1st comic book work	6.30	19.00	44.00
54, 55-Smith cover; 54-1st Alex Summers who later becomes Havok			
	6.40	19.00	45.00

56, 57, 59-63, 65: Adams-a	6.00	18.00	42.00
58-1st app. Havok (in costume)	9.00	27.00	62.00
64-1st Sunfire	6.60	20.00	46.00
66-Last new story with original X-Men (3/70); X-Men battle Hulk			
	5.00	15.00	35.00
67-70, 72: All 52 pgs. 67-Reprints begin (12/70); 9 month gap between			
#66 & 67), end #93	2.90	8.60	20.00
71, 73-93: 83-r/X-Men #35 (Spidey app.). 71-Last 15¢ issue			
	2.50	7.30	17.00
	2.10	6.00	15.00
94-New X-Men begin (8/75); see Giant-Size X-Men for 1st app.			
	31.00	93.00	310.00
94-Variant w/Mark Jewelers pull-out ad	30.00	90.00	300.00
95-Death of Thunderbird	8.00	25.00	58.00
96-99: 25¢ & 30¢ versions exist	6.60	20.00	46.00
100-Old X-Men vs. New X-Men	7.00	21.00	50.00
101-Phoenix origin concludes	5.70	17.00	40.00
102-107: 102-Origin Storm	2.90	8.60	20.00
108-Byrne art begins in X-Men; see Marvel Team-Up #53 for 1st Byrne			
X-Men	6.00	18.00	42.00
109-1st Vindicator	4.90	15.00	34.00
110, 111	2.90	8.60	20.00
112-119	2.40	7.00	17.00
120-1st app. Alpha Flight (cameo)	5.30	16.00	37.00
121-Alpha Flight (1st full story)	5.70	17.00	40.00
122-128: 123-Spider-Man x-over	2.30	6.90	16.00
129-1st app. Kitty Pryde; begin Dark Phoenix saga			
	2.70	8.00	19.00
130-1st app. Dazzler by Byrne (2/80)	2.40	7.30	17.00
131-135	2.00	6.00	14.00
136, 138	2.00	5.00	12.00
137-Phoenix dies; double size	2.10	6.00	15.00
139-Wolverine's new costume	3.70	11.10	26.00
140-Alpha Flight app. (also in #139)	3.00	10.30	24.00
141-Intro Future X-Men; Intro Rachel (Phoenix II)			
	3.90	11.60	27.00

X-MEN
Oct, 1991-Present (1.00/1.25, color)
Marvel Comics Group

1-(1.50, 52 pgs.)-Four different covers (a-d) by Lee; New team & Lee-c/a			
begins, ends #11	0.60	1.20	3.00
1-(3.95)-Prestige ed. (cover e); double gatefold-c; coated stock			

	Good	Fine	N-Mint
	0.90	2.30	5.50
2, 3, 5, 7	1.00	2.00	5.00
4-Wolverine back to old yellow costume (1/92); same dates as			
Wolverine #50	1.00	2.00	5.00
6-Sabretooth-c/sty; Thibert-i in 6-9	1.00	2.00	5.00
8-Gambit vs. Bishop-c/story	0.80	1.60	4.00
9-Wolverine vs. Ghost Rider	0.80	1.60	4.00
10-Return of Longshot	0.80	1.60	4.00
11-13: 11-Last Lee-c/a. 12, 13-Thibert-c/a	0.40	0.80	2.00
11-Silver ink 2nd print, came w/X-Men board game			
	3.00	8.60	20.00
14-16-(1.50-c)-Polybagged w/trading card	0.40	0.80	2.00
17-24, 26-29, 31: 28, 29-Sabretooth app.	0.30	0.50	1.25
25-(3.50, 52 pgs.)-Gambit hologram on-c; 30th anniversary issue			
	0.80	1.60	4.00
25-30th anniversary issue; B&W-c w/Magneto in color & Magneto			
Hologram; no price on cover	3.60	10.70	25.00
25-Gold	4.30	12.90	30.00
30-(1.95)-Wedding Issue; bound-in trading card sheet			
	0.80	1.60	4.00
32-41: 32-Begin 1.50-c; bound-in card sheet. 33-Gambit & Sabretooth-c			
& story	0.30	0.60	1.50
36,37-(2.95)-Collectors editions	0.60	1.20	3.00
38-43-(1.95)-Deluxe edition. 42-43-Smith a.0.40		0.80	2.00
Annual 1 ('92, 2.25)-Lee-c & layouts	0.50	0.90	2.25
Annual 2 ('93, 2.95)-Polybagged w/trading card; intro. Empyrean			
	0.60	1.20	3.00
Annual 3 ('94, 2.95, 68 pgs.)	0.60	1.20	3.00
…"Ashcan" #1	0.20	0.40	1.00
…:Fatal Attractions ('94, 17.95) r/X-Factor #92, X-Force #25, Uncanny			
X-Men #304 X-Men #25, Wolverine #75 and Excalibur#71			
	3.00	7.70	18.00
…: God Loves, Man Kills (8/94, 6.95)	1.20	2.90	7.00
…:The Coming of Bishop-('95, 12.95) r/Uncanny X-Men #282-285, #287-288			
	2.00	5.60	13.00

X-MEN ADVENTURES (TV)

Nov, 1992-No. 15, Jan, 1994; V2#1-Present (1.25, color)
Marvel Comics

1-Based on the TV cartoon series	0.90	2.00	5.50
2-5 : 3-Magneto-c/story	0.80	1.60	4.00
6-10: 6-Sabretooth-c/story. 7-Cable-c/story. 10-Archangel guest star			
	0.40	0.80	2.00

X-Men #36 © MEG

X-Men Adventures #8 © MEG

11-14: 11-Cable-c/story	0.30	0.50	1.25
15-(1.75, 52 pgs.)	0.40	0.70	1.75
V2#1-8: 4-Bound-in trading card sheet	0.30	0.50	1.25
9-13: 9-Begin 1.50-c	0.30	0.60	1.50
V3#1-6:1-(3/95)	0.30	0.60	1.50
...Captive Hearts/Slave Island-(TPB, 4.95)-r/X-Men Adventures #5-8			
	1.00	2.00	5.00
...Volume 3, The Irresistible Force, The Muir Island Saga (5.95, 10/94, TPB)-r/X-Men Adventures #9-12	1.00	3.00	6.00

X-MEN: ALPHA
1994 (3.95, color)
Marvel Comics

nn-Wraparound chromium cover	1.40	2.80	7.00
nn-(49.95) Gold logo	7.00	21.40	50.00

X-MEN/ALPHA FLIGHT
Dec, 1985-No. 2, Dec, 1985 (Mini-series)
Marvel Comics Group

1, 2-Paul Smith-a	0.80	1.60	4.00

X-MEN AND THE MICRONAUTS, THE
Jan, 1984-No. 4, April, 1984 (Mini-series)
Marvel Comics Group

1-4: Guuice-c/a(p) in all	0.30	0.60	1.50

X-MEN ARCHIVES
Jan, 1995-Present (2.25, color, limited series)
Marvel Comics
1-3-Featuring Legion; Claremont-s; Sienkiewicz-a

	Good	Fine	N-Mint
	0.50	0.90	2.25
4-Featuring Magneto-Claremont-s	0.50	0.90	2.25

X-MEN ARCHIVES FEATURING CAPTAIN BRITAIN
July, 1995-Present (2.95, color, limited series)
Marvel Comics

1	0.60	1.20	3.00

X-MEN CHRONICLES
Mar 1995 (3.95, color)
Marvel Comics

1-Wraparound-c, Age Of Apocalypse	1.40	2.80	7.00
2-Age of Apocalypse	1.00	2.00	5.00

X-MEN CLASSIC (Formerly Classic X-Men)
No. 46, Apr 1990-Present (1.25/1.50)
Marvel Comics

46-69, 71-78, 80-89,91-96,98,99	0.30	0.50	1.25
70, 79, 90,97-(1.75, 52 pgs.): 90-r/#166	0.40	0.70	1.75
100-109: 100-Begin 1.50-c 104- r/#X-Men #200			
	0.30	0.60	1.50

X-MEN CLASSICS
Dec, 1983-No. 3, Feb, 1984 (2.00, Baxter paper)
Marvel Comics Group

1-3: X-Men-r by N. Adams	0.60	1.20	3.00

X-MEN OMEGA
June 1995 (3.95, color, one-shot)
Marvel

nn-End of Age of Apocalypse	0.80	1.60	4.00
nn-(49.95)-Gold ed.	10.00	20.00	50.00

X-MEN PRIME
July 1995 (4.95, color, 56 pgs.)

nn-X-Men Reality Returns	1.00	2.00	5.00

X-MEN SPOTLIGHT ON... STARJAMMERS (See X-Men 104)
1990-No. 2, 1990 (4.50, 52 pgs.)
Marvel Comics

1, 2-Starjammers	0.90	1.80	4.50

X-MEN SURVIVAL GUIDE TO THE MANSION
Aug, 1993 (6.95, color)
Marvel Comics

1-Spiral bound	1.70	4.00	10.00

X-MEN: THE EARLY YEARS
May, 1994-Present (1.50, color)
Marvel Comics

1-16-r/X-Men #1-16 w/new-c	0.30	0.60	1.50

X-MEN: THE ULTRA COLLECTION
Dec 1994- Apr 1995 (2.95, color, limited edition)
Marvel Comics
1-5-All pin-ups, no story 3-Brereton gatefold-c of X-Force

5-Wraparound gatefold-c w/pull out poster	0.60	1.20	3.00

X-MEN: THE WEDDING ALBUM
1994 (2.95, color, magazine size)
Marvel Comics

1-Wedding of Scott Summers & Jean Grey	0.60	1.20	3.00

X-MEN 2099
Oct, 1993-Present (1.25/1.50, color)
Marvel Comics

1-(1.75)-Foil-c; Ron Lim/Adam Kubert-c/a	0.40	0.80	2.00
1-2nd printing (1.75)	0.40	0.70	1.75
1-Gold Edition (15,000 made); sold thru Diamond for $19.40	3.00	8.60	20.00
2-7: Lim-c/a(p) begin. 3-Death of Tina	0.30	0.50	1.25
8-19: 8-Begin 1.50-c; bound-in trading card sheet	0.30	0.60	1.50
20-23	0.40	0.80	2.00

X-MEN UNLIMITED
1993-Present (3.95, color, 68 pgs.)
Marvel Comics

1	1.20	2.40	6.00
2,4-7: 2-Magneto origin	0.80	1.60	4.00
3-Sabretooth c/Story	1.20	2.40	6.00

X-MEN VS. DRACULA
Dec, 1993 (1.75, color, 52 pgs.)
Marvel Comics

	Good	Fine	N-Mint
1-r/X-Men Annual #6: Austin-c(i)	0.40	0.70	1.75

X-MEN VS. THE AVENGERS, THE
Apr, 1987-No. 4, July, 1987 (1.50, color, mini-series)
Marvel Comics Group

	Good	Fine	N-Mint
1	0.70	1.40	3.50
2–4	0.50	1.00	2.50

X-O MANOWAR
Feb, 1992-Present (1.95/2.25, color)
Valiant

	Good	Fine	N-Mint
1-Partial origin; Barry Smith-a(p)	2.90	9.00	20.00
2-Barry Smith-c(p)	2.00	6.00	14.00
3-Layton-c(i)	1.00	4.30	10.00
4-1st app. Shadowman (cameo)	2.10	6.00	15.00
5, 6: 5-B. Smith-c; last 1.95-c. 6-Ditko-a(p)	0.90	2.30	5.50
7, 8: Unity x-over. 7-Miller-c	1.20	3.00	7.00
9-13: 12-1st app. Randy Calder	0.80	1.60	4.00
14, 15-Turok-c/stories	1.00	2.00	5.00
15- Variant: Hot Pink logo, available in Ultra Pro Rigid Comic Sleeves box; no price on cover	1.70	4.00	10.00
16-24, 26-43 : 20-Serial # contest insert. 27-29-Turok app. 28-w/bound-in trading card. 30-Solar app; 1st app. of "new good skin". 33-Chaos Effect Delta Pt. 3. 36-w/bound in "Sneak-Peek" card 42-w/20 pg Birthquake Prequel Bart- Sears/a	0.50	0.90	2.25
25-(3.50)-Contains bound-in Armorines #0	0.70	1.40	3.50
44-(2.50) Bart Sears-a; 45-49, 50-x, 50-o	0.50	1.00	2.50
0-(8/93, 3.50)-Wraparound embossed chromium-c by Joe Quesada; origin; Solar app.	0.70	1.40	3.50
0-Gold variant-c	2.90	9.00	20.00
Retribution trade paperback (1993, 9.95)-Polybagged with copy of X-O Database #1 inside	1.70	4.00	10.00
Yearbook 1 (4/95, 2.95)	0.60	1.20	3.00

XOMBI
Jun, 1994-Present (1.75, color)
DC Comics

	Good	Fine	N-Mint
0-(1/94, 1.95) Simonson-c; silver ink-c	0.40	0.80	2.00
1-13: 1-John Byrne-c	0.40	0.70	1.75
14,15-(2.50)	0.50	1.00	2.50

YAKKY DOODLE & CHOPPER (TV)
Dec, 1962 (Hanna-Barbera)
Gold Key

1	5.80	18.00	35.00

YELLOW CLAW (See Giant-Size Man-Thing 1-4)
Oct, 1956-No. 4, Apr, 1957 (All 10¢ issues)
Atlas Comics (Marvel)

1-Origin by Maneely	42.00	126.00	420.00
2-Kirby-a	31.00	93.00	310.00
3, 4-Kirby-a. 4-Kirby/Severin-c	29.00	86.00	285.00

YELLOW SUBMARINE
Feb, 1969 (Giant size, 68 pgs.)
Gold Key (Beatles movie tie-in)

35000-902: With pull-out poster	25.00	75.00	175.00
...Without poster	7.00	21.00	50.00

YOUNGBLOOD (See Brigade #4 & Megaton Explosion)
Apr, 1992-No. 4, Feb, 1993 (1.95/2.50, color)
No. 6, June, 1994 (No #5?)-Present (3.50, color, on-going series)
Image Comics

1-Contains 2 trading cards; Liefeld-c/a in all (1st Image comic); flip-book format	1.30	3.30	8.00
1-2nd printing	0.50	1.00	2.50
2-(JUN-c, July 1992 inside)-1st app. ShadowHawk, Prophet, Berzerkers, Kirby & Darkthorn; w/2 trading cards; flip bk	1.00	2.00	5.00
2-2nd printing (1.95)	0.40	0.80	2.00
3-(OCT-c, August 1992 inside)-1st app. Supreme in back-up; w/2 trading cards; flip-book format; 1st app. Showdown	0.50	1.00	2.50
0-(12/92, 1.95)-Contains 2 trading cards; two cover variations exist, green or beige logo; w/Image #0 coupon	0.40	0.80	2.00
4-(2/93)-2nd app. Keown's The Pitt; Bloodstrike app.	0.50	1.00	2.50
6-(3.50, 52pgs.)-Wraparound-c	0.70	1.40	3.50
7-10: 7,8-Liefeld-c(p)/a(p)/story. 8,9-(9/94). 9-J.Valentino-a(p)/story	0.50	1.00	2.50
...Battlezone 1 (MAY-c, 4/93 inside, 1.95)-Arsenal book; Liefeld-c(p)	0.40	0.80	2.00

	Good	Fine	N-Mint
...Battlezone 2 (7/94-2.95)-Wraparound-c	0.60	1.20	3.00

...Yearbook 1 (7/93, 2.50)-Fold-out panel; 1st app. Tyrax & Kanan

	0.50	1.00	2.50

YOUNGBLOOD: STRIKEFILE
April, 1993-Present (1.95/2.50/2.95, color, began as mini-series)
Image Comics
1-Flip book w/Jae Lee-c/a & Liefeld-c/a in all; 1st app. The Allies, Giger,
  & Glory

	0.40	0.80	2.00

2-4, 11-(2.50);11-Polybagged w/trading card

	0.50	1.00	2.50

5-10-(2.95): 5-Liefeld-c(p) 8 & 9-(11/94) 8-S.Platt-c

	0.60	1.20	3.00

YOUNG MEN
No. 24, Dec, 1953-No. 28, June, 1954
Atlas Comics
24-Origin Captain America, Human Torch, & Sub-Mariner which are
  revived; Red Skull app.

	Good	Fine	N-Mint
24-Origin Captain America...	68.00	203.00	675.00
25-28: 25-Romita-c/a	47.00	140.00	465.00

YOUNG ZEN: CITY OF DEATH
Late 1994 (3.25, B&W)
Entity Comics

	Good	Fine	N-Mint
1	0.70	1.30	3.25

YOUNG ZEN INTERGALACTIC NINJA
1993-No. 3, 1994 (2.95, B&W, limited series)
Entity Comics
1-(3.50)-Gold foil embossed logo; bagged w/chromium trading card by S.
Kieth

	Good	Fine	N-Mint
1-(3.50)...	0.70	1.40	3.50
2, 3-Gold foil embossed logo	0.60	1.20	3.00

ZATANNA
July, 1993-No. 4, Oct, 1993 (1.95, color, mini-series)
DC Comics

1–4	0.40	0.80	2.00

ZEN INTEGALACTIC NINJA
1987, (1.75, B&W)

1,2-Copyright-Stern and Cote	1.00	2.00	5.00

ZEN INTERGALACTIC NINJA
No. 0, June-July, 1993-No. 3, 1994 (2.95, B&W)
Entity Comics

0-Gold foil stamped-c; photo-c of Zen model	0.60	1.20	3.00
1-3-Foil stamped-c	0.60	1.20	3.00
0-(1993, 3.50)...All New Color Special; chromium-c by Jae Lee			
	0.70	1.40	3.50

ZEN INTERGALACTIC NINJA: APRIL FOOL'S SPECIAL
1994 (2.50,B&W)
Parody Press

1-w/flip story of Renn Intergalactic Chihuahua			
	0.50	1.00	2.50

ZEN INTERGALACTIC NINJA COLOR
1994-Present (2.25, color)
Entity Comics

1-(3.95)-Chromium die cut-c	0.80	1.60	4.00
1-(2.25-c)	0.50	0.90	2.25
0-(2.25)-Newsstand; Jae Lee-c; r/...All New Color Special #0			
	0.50	0.90	2.25
2-(2.50)-Flip-book format	0.50	1.00	2.50
2-(3.50)-Flip-book format; polybagged w/chromium trading card			
	0.70	1.40	3.50
3-5 -(2.50)	0.50	1.00	2.50
6-(2.95);7-	0.60	1.20	3.00
...Yearbook:Hazardous Duty 1 ('95)	0.60	1.20	3.00
...Ashcan - Tour of the Universe -(No price) Flip cover			

ZEN INTERGALACTIC NINJA MILESTONE
1994-No. 3, 1994 (2.95, color, limited series)
Entity Comics

	Good	Fine	N-Mint
1-3-Gold foil logo; r/Defend the Earth	0.60	1.20	3.00

ZEN INTERGALACTIC NINJA SPRING SPECTACULAR
1994 (2.95, B&W)
Entity Comics

	Good	Fine	N-Mint
1-Gold foil logo	0.60	1.20	3.00

ZEN INTERGALACTIC NINJA STARQUEST
1994-Present (2.95, B&W)
Entity Comics

	Good	Fine	N-Mint
1-7-Gold foil logo	0.60	1.20	3.00

ZEN INTERGALACTIC NINJA: THE HUNTED
1993-No. 3, 1994 (2.95, B&W)
Entity Comics

	Good	Fine	N-Mint
1-(2.95)-Newsstand edition; foil logo	0.60	1.20	3.00
1-(3.50)-Polybagged w/chromium card by Sam Kieth; foil logo			
	0.70	1.40	3.50
2, 3-(2.95)-Foil logo	0.60	1.20	3.00

ZERO HOUR: CRISIS IN TIME
No. 4(#1), Sept, 1994-No. 0(#5), Oct, 1994 (1.50, color, limited series)
DC Comics

	Good	Fine	N-Mint
4(#1)-0(#5)	0.30	0.60	1.50
"Ashcan"-(1994, free, B&W, 8 pgs.)	0.10	0.20	0.50

ZORRO
Jan 1966–Mar 1968 (All photo-c)
Gold Key

	Good	Fine	N-Mint
1-Toth-a	10.00	20.00	50.00
2,4,5,7–9-Toth-a	6.00	12.00	30.00
3,6-Tufts-a	5.00	10.00	25.00

ZORRO
Nov, 1993-Present (2.50, color)
Topps

	Good	Fine	N-Mint
0-(11/93, 1.00, 20 pgs.)	0.20	0.40	1.00
1,4,6–8,10,11: 1-Miller-c,10-Julie Bell-c, 11-Lady Rawhide-c			
	0.50	1.00	2.50
2-Lady Rawhide app (not in costume)	1.00	2.00	5.00
3-1st app. Lady Rawhide	2.00	4.00	10.00
5-Lady Rawhide-app.	1.00	2.00	5.00
9-(2.95)-Lady Rawhide-c & app.	0.80	1.60	4.00

Trading
Card
Listings

Introduction To Trading Cards

Welcome to the Overstreet Trading Card Price Guide. We will keep you current on all of the hottest comic and media related cards in the "Marketplace"...as well as those newly introduced! You can depend on the Overstreet Card Guide to provide accurate values for current non-sports cards. That's because the prices shown here are averages of genuine dealer retail prices, not estimates! The pricing information is compiled from data supplied by our **Board Of Advisors.** You will note that this compilation lists prices for card sets, singles, specialty cards, and even unopened boxes when warranted. We have not itemized every card single, per the opinions of our advisors. We concur with their view...namely that most cards are assigned an average price for all cards in that set. Where single cards prices do differ (e.g. specialty cards), card prices are listed separately. Prices often vary on certain individual cards within a set. As most collectors know, this is due to the popularity of a specific character, regionally specific market pressures, and/or the pressures of simple supply and demand. Collectors should take this into consideration when pricing cards.

Non-sport cards have been around for a long time , longer even than comic books or comic strips. In fact, cards were issued as far back as the Civil War era. For the most part, this Price Guide deals with non-sports cards from the mid 1960s to the present. This is what most collectors are primarily interested in. Gemstone Publications projects that if interest in new cards continues to increase at present rates, demand for older pre 1960s cards will escalate as well.

HOW DO I START COLLECTING CARDS?
(1) First, collect cards that you enjoy.
(2) Set a budget for yourself and keep within that budget. The wonderful thing about collecting trading cards is there are so many varieties to choose from. There have been so many different card sets published over the past thirty years that it is relatively easy to find some that you like and fit into your budget.

WHERE CAN I GET CARDS?
There are several different places to acquire non-sports cards:
(1) Comic book and Sports cards retailers. In most cases, they may carry many of the recently released non-sports cards.
(2) Local swap meets and flea markets.
(3) Many cities hold monthly sports cards and non-sports card shows and conventions.
(4) Mail order dealers.
Because the overhead costs associated with selling at a card show or swap meet are lower than at a regular retail store, a collector may find some material at lower prices. Another factor to consider is the element of competition. Dealers who set up at swap meets and card conventions often experience greater competition than shops, and therefore sometimes offer lower prices in order to more successfully compete.
The advantage of shopping at a retail store is that they usually have a better assortment of non-sports cards sets and chase cards. Many retail stores will also hold cards or put them on a lay-away plan for regular customers. These services are less likely to be offered by swap meet or card show dealers. Not only that, but shops have greater accessibility because of regular hours. Usually collectors take advantage of both sources.

HOW DO I BUY, SELL, AND TRADE CARDS?
Buying - Buying cards is not an exact science. Prices can vary from dealer to dealer. The best thing to do is to shop around until you find a dealer that you are comfortable with and can trust.
Never be afraid to bargain on the price of set of cards. The worst thing that can happen is that the dealer will say no. In many cases, a dealer may make a counter offer which is lower than his original asking price.
This principle applies to both retail stores as well as con-

vention dealers. It is important to remember though, that the retail stores have more bills to pay (higher overhead), so don't be disappointed if you are not always successful with your offer. If you don't feel comfortable with a price, just say "thanks" and try another location.

Trading - Trading non-sports cards with other collectors can be as fun as trading sports cards. When trading, it's seems to work well to trade "retail for retail". In other words, if you have a set of cards worth twenty dollars in the Overstreet Price Guide, trade for cards worth the same amount. Other factors can come into play that can change or otherwise affect this rule, but, for the most part, it's a good way to develop your trading skills.

Trading cards with a dealer can be a little more complicated. Usually, dealers will trade for about fifty to sixty percent of the value of the card or set of cards. For example, if a card set is retailing for ten dollars, the dealer may offer a trade value of five or six dollars for that set. Think about your deal ahead of time and remember your right to say no if you don't like the deal, just the way dealers have the right to say no when they don't like a trade that's being offered. And don't forget the option of making a counter offer . Often the price that is finally agreed to is somewhere in-between your ideal price and the dealer's ideal price!

Selling - The best way to sell cards is by attending card conventions as a dealer. If selling at a card convention is not your cup of tea then you can sell cards to a dealer. Selling cards to dealers will get you from twenty to fifty percent of the card or card sets value. That twenty dollar card set is worth ten to a dealer TOPS. It's always best to try and trade instead of out right sell a card. You will get more value out of the cards that way.

HOW DO I PROTECT AND STORE MY CARDS?

Like comic books, it is important to store cards in a protective environment. Cards can be damaged by the same things that can damage comic books. With this in mind, remember to store your cards in a cool, dry place.

Cards can fade and turn yellow or brown if exposed to sunlight and certain types of fluorescent lights. Store cards out of the light.

To keep cards from bending or getting rounded corners, place them into plastic, non-acid, "nine-card-sheets". 100, 200, 500, and 1000 count cardboard boxes or plastic cases are also a good way to store large quantities of cards and are less expensive than plastic sheets. These are available at any sports card shop.

THE "CHASE" IS ON!

Up until recently, the non-sports card industry has been fairly "low profile". In general, over the past thirty years, the subject matter for non-sports and entertainment cards has been primarily based upon the television and movie industry. These cards featured actual scenes from the TV show or movie. The card buyer had only one thing to collect, so card collecting wasn't very difficult.

In the 1970s, an added bonus was added to each pack of cards: a sticker. This marketing strategy was designed to motivate the unsuspecting card buyer to purchase more packs, because now there are two sets that need completing: a set of cards and a set of stickers. This wasn't difficult because every pack of cards had at least one sticker. Eventually the card buyer would get enough cards to complete the set.

This continued until Impel and Upper Deck did something to revolutionize the non-sports industry. They included, for the first time, a special card found only in a few of the packs. The card was a hologram and is now called the "chase" card. These "chase" cards were different, special, *and* harder to get. Their inclusion into selected packs of cards very successfully inspired card buyers to veritable purchasing frenzies.

Because these chase cards were available in such low numbers, the prices of the cards escalated to much higher values than ordinary cards...and much higher!

No longer did the average card buyer purchase a pack to put a set together. Instead they purchased packs to try and find the chase card. In fact, making sets of cards became a by-product of card acquisition while trying to get all the chase cards became a primarily collecting goal.

GRADING AND PRICING CARDS

Grading and pricing cards is much like grading and pricing comic books. Some elements of value are:

(1) Condition - The higher the better.

(2) Subject Matter - The more popular the more in demand and the more in demand the higher the value.

(3) Quantity Printed - Limited print runs mean less cards to go around.

(4) Age - Older cards are generally harder to find and therefore more valuable.

The condition of a card is among the most important factor in determining the price, but it is in no way absolute. For example, a card in a lower grade that is popular and hard to find can, and many times will, command a higher price than what is listed in a price guide, whereas, a mint set of an unpopular card could be worth less than the price listed. It is up to you, as the collector, to determine the price you are willing to pay for a given card or set.

Remember that grading is not an exact science and the grading scale below should be used as a starting point. Older cards prior to 1970 can be adjusted upwards 5% - 10% if they are in excellent condition or higher.

Grades
Mint (MT) - A card with no defects whatsoever. All corners are sharp, the color is vibrant with the original gloss. No printing defects such as off centering or color should be visible. Card should be sharp and in focus. 100%.

Near Mint (NM) - A card with any one of the following minor flaws: a corner with slight wear, slightly off centered. No color loss or yellowing should be visible. can have a very minor focus imperfection. 75%-95%.

Excellent (EX) - A card with any two of the following minor flaws: slight wear on a corner, slight off centering, the original gloss is diminished, very slight focus imperfection. 50%-75%.

Very Good (VG) - A card in this condition may have gloss loss, some yellowing of the borders may be visible, rounding at the corners, pictures can be slightly off focus. 20%-50%.

Good (GD) - A card in this condition can have scuffing at the corners and on the face, borders can be uneven and yellowing of the boarders is apparent, glossiness is no longer noticeable. 10%-20%.

Fair (FR), Poor (PR) - Cards in this condition are usually used for fillers until a better condition card can be found. These cards have brown and dirty borders, scuffing, well rounded off corners, water stains, writing and some may even have pieces missing. 2%-10%.

ADVENTURES OF BATMAN AND ROBIN, THE
Skybox 1995
Box	30.00
90 Card Set	20.00
Singles	.15
Pop-up Cards	1.00
Thermal Cards	5.00
Foil-Stamped Cards	7.00

AKIRA
Cornerstone 1994
Box	30.00
100 Card Set	20.00
Singles	.15
Insert-(3) chromium	8.00
(1) prism	30.00

BATMAN MOVIE SERIES I
Topps 1989
Box	12.50
132 Card Set (w/22 stickers)	10
Singles	.10
Stickers	.15
Factory Set (w/11 bonus cards)	
	18.00

BATMAN MOVIE SERIES II
Topps 1989
Box 10	32.00
Card Set (w/22 stickers)	9.00
Singles	.10
Stickers	.15
Factory Set (w/11 bonus cards)	
	20.00

BATMAN RETURNS
Topps 1992
Box	15.00
88 Card Set	10.00
Singles	.10
10 Stadium Club Card Set	4.00

BATMAN RETURNS STADIUM CLUB
Topps 1992
Box	15.00
100 Card Set (foil stamped)	
	15.00
Singles	.15

BATMAN: SAGA OF THE DARK KNIGHT
SkyBox 1994

Box	40.00
100 Card Set	15.00
Singles	.20
Spectra etched 1-5	10.00
Skydisk	75.00
Binder	12.00
Promo Skydisk	75.00
Promo Card Georgia Dome	10.00

BATMAN THE ANIMATED SERIES
Topps 1993

Box	25.00
100 Card Set	15.00
Singles	.15
6 Vinyl Cel Cards	10.00

BATMAN THE ANIMATED SERIES II
Topps 1994

Box	35.00
90 Card Set	15.00
Singles	.15
Cels 1-4	10.00
Danny Devito Autograph Card	75.00

BEAVIS AND BUTTHEAD
Fleer Ultra 1994

Box	35.00
150 Card Set	20.00
Singles	.15
Scratch and Sniff Cards 1-10	3.00

BOB MARLEY
Island Vibes

Box	65.00

50 Card Set	20.00
Singles	.15
Foil Etched	5.00
Gold Foil	7.00

BONE
Comic Images 1994

Box	40.00
90 Card Set	15.00
Singles	.15
Chromium Cards 1-6	9.00
Cartoon Covers Subset 1-3	15.00
Medallion card	25.00
Sketch card	75.00
Mini-press sheet	20.00

Chris Achilleos © FPG

CHRIS ACHILLEOS I
FPG 1992

Box	40.00
90 Card Set	15.00
Singles	.15
Silver Foil-stamped cards	5.00
Gold Foil-stamped cards	6.00

Autograph Card (250)	125.00

CHRIS ACHILLEOS II
FPG 1994

Box	35.00
90 Card Set	10.00
Metallic Storm Cards (5)	6.00
Autograph Card (1000)	45.00
Signed and Numbered 10-up	
Sheet	35.00
Binder	15.00

Darrell Sweet

CHROMIUM CONAN II
Comic Images 1994

90 Card Set	30.00
(variations exist of	
15,22,27,28,32,41, 45,52,55,73	
& 83)	
Prism Cards (6)	12.00
Foil Subset (3) one set/case)	
	15.00
Medallion Card	25.00
6-Card Uncut Sheet	20.00

Mini-Press Sheet	20.00
Uncut Sheet	100.00
Holochrome Cards	15.00

CONAN
Comic Images 1993

90 Card Set	40.00
Single Cards	.50
Six Prism Cards P1-P6	10.00
Holochrome Cards (2)	20.00
Promo Card (#89)	5.00

CROW
Kitchen Sink 1994

Box	45.00
100 Card Set	15.00
Chromium Cards (6)	15.00
Crow Vision Cards (10)	6.00

DARRELL SWEET
FPG 1994

Box	35.00
90 Card Set	15.00
Metallic Storm Cards (5)	9.00
Autograph Card (1000)	50.00
Signed and Numbered 10-up	
Sheet	35.00
Binder	15.00

DC BLOODLINES
SkyBox 1993

Box	22.00
81 Card Set	10.00
4 Foil Cards	14.00
Superman Redemption Card	
	15.00
Redeemed Card	20.00

DC COMIC CARDS SERIES 1
DC 1988

48 Card Set	20.00
Singles (1-48)	.50

DC COMIC CARDS SERIES 2
DC 1990

72 Card Set	30.00
Singles (49-120)	.50

DC COSMIC CARDS
Impel 1992

Box	10.00
180 Card Set	9.00
Singles	.10
Holograms DCH1-DCH10	4.00

DC COSMIC TEAMS CARDS
SkyBox 1993

Box	20.00
50 Card Set	12.50
Singles	.15
6 Holograms	5.00

DC MASTER SERIES
Skybox 1994

Box	35.00
90 Card Set	15.00
Singles	.15
Single Sided Foils (4)	10.00
Double-Sided Foils	15.00
Superman Skydisk SD2	75.00

DON MAITZ
FPG 1994

Box	35.00
90 Card Set	10.00
Metallic Storm Cards (5)	6.00
Autograph Card (1000)	45.00
Signed and numbered 10-up	
Sheet	35.00
Binder	15.00

DOOMSDAY: THE DEATH OF SUPERMAN
SkyBox 1992
(80,000 boxes produced: all have serial number)

Box	120.00
100 Card Set	45.00
Singles	.50
4 Specialty Cards, S1-S4	30.00
2 Superman Symbol Cards	
	25.00

DRACULA
Topps 1992

Box	39.00
100 Card Set	19.00
Singles	.15

EMPIRE STRIKES BACK
Topps 1980
Series I: 132 cards

(w/33 stickers)	40.00
Box	40.00

Series II: 132 cards

(w/33 stickers)	30.00
Box	40.00

Series III: 88 cards
(w/22 stickers)   30.00
Box   60.00
Singles   .50
Stickers   1.00

EVIL ERNIE
Krome Productions 1994
100 Card Set   18.00
Singles   .15
Krome Cards 1-5   7.00
Autographed Kromes 1-5
(black ink on back)   35.00
Autographed &
numbered cards   50.00
Evil Ernie Chrome Promo   8.00
Lady Death Chrome Promo
   15.00
Krome Productions chrome
Promo   5.00
Gold Convention Promo   15.00
Factory Chromium Set   50.00

GARGOYLES
Skybox 1995
Box   40.00
Full Set   20.00

Singles   .20
Pop-Up Cards   1.00
Foil Cards   5.00
Redemption Card   25.00

HILDEBRANDT
Comic Images 1992
Box   30.00
90 Card Set   14.00
Singles   .10
6 Prism Cards   10.00

HILDEBRANDT II
Comic Images 1993
Box   25.00
90 Card Set   13.50
Singles   .10
6 Chromium Cards   9.50
Autograph Card (250)   75.00

IMAGES OF SHADOWHAWK
Topps 1994
Box   20.00
100 Card Set   8.00
Singles   .15
Foil Cards 1-7   6.00
Mini-Promo Sheet   3.00

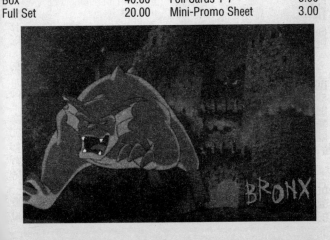

ShadowBart 50.00

IMAGE UNIVERSE
Topps 1995
Box 50.00
90 Card Set 20.00
Singles .25
HoloChrome 8.00
Clear Zone 8.00

JACK KIRBY
Comic Images 1994
Box 25.00
90 Card Set 10.00
Chromium Cards (6) 8.00
Subset (3) one set/case 15.00
Medallion Card 25.00
24KT Autograph Card (500)
45.00

JEFF JONES
FPG 1993
Each Box numbered, limited to
64,000 boxes

Box 32.00
90 Card Set 15.00
Singles .20
Ultra #D Holograms H1-3 7.00
Autograph Card 60.00

JOHN BERKEY:
SCIENCE FICTION ULTRA-
WORKS
FPG 1994
Box 30.00
90 Card Set 15.00
Singles .10
Metallic Storm 1-5 7.00
Signed 50.00
Gold Metallic Storm Set 1-5
55.00

JOHN BYRNE'S NEXT MEN
Dark Horse Comics 1993
Singles 1.00
Comic Coupon Redemption 1.00

JULIE BELL
Cardz 1994
Box 30.00
50 Card Set 10.00
Singles .15
Tekchrome Cards 1-10 2.00
Promos P1-P2 2.00
Autograph Card 45.00

KEITH PARKINSON
FPG 1994
Box 35.00
90 Card Set 9.00
Singles .15
Metallic Storm 1-5 7.00
Signed 50.00
Signed and Numbered 10 Card
Sheet 30.00

KEN KELLY
FPG Cards 1992

Box	29.00
90 Card Set	15.00
Silver Hologram Cards H1-H3	
	7.00
Autograph Card (1000)	150.00

KEN KELLY II
FPG 1994

Box	35.00
90 Card Set	10.00
Metallic Storm Cards (5)	6.00
Autograph Card (1000)	45.00
Sketch Card one/case	50.00
Binder	15.00
Capital City Conv. Signed Card	
	30.00

LADY DEATH CHROMIUM
Krome 1994

Box	65.00
100 Card Set	30.00
Singles	.20
Metallic Cel Cards (5)	15.00
Mystery Card	18.00
Autograph Card (1500)	45.00

LARRY ELMORE
FPG 1994

Box	35.00
90 Card Set	9.00
Singles	.15
Metallic Storm 1-5	7.00
Signed	50.00
Signed and numbered 10 card	
Sheet	25.00

LOIS & CLARK:
THE NEW ADVENTURES OF
SUPERMAN
Skybox 1995

Box	35.00
Full Set	20.00
Singles	.15
Tattoos	.25
Holochip Foil	8.00
Diffuser Foil	5.00
Photo Pin	4.00

MADMAN X 50

50 Card Set	20.00

MARS ATTACKS
Topps 1994

Box	55.00
100 Card Set	25.00
First Day Cards	3.00
Chrome Cards (4)	10.00
Gold Comic Redemption	
Cards	30.00
Zina Saunders Autograph Card	
	50.00

MARVEL FLAIR
Fleer 1994

Box	80.00
150 Card Set	45.00
Singles	.75
Power Blast	10.00

MARVEL FLAIR ANNUAL
Fleer 1995

Box	75.00
150 Card Set	40.00
Singles	.75
Power Blast	3.00
Holo Blast	4.00
Duo-Blast	6.00
Chromium	3.00

MARVEL MASTERPIECES
SkyBox 1992
(Each box numbered, limited to 350,000 boxes)

Box	100.00
Card Set	45.00
Singles	.75

Bonus Cards: 1-D-Thing vs. Hulk, 2-D-Surfer vs. Thanos, 3-D-Wolverine vs. Sabretooth, 5-D-Capt. America vs.

Red Skull	15.00
Bonus Card 4-D-Spiderman vs. Venom	18.00
Sealed Tin Box	50.00
Lost Masterpieces LM1-5	5.00

MARVEL MASTERPIECES-HILDEBRANDT
Fleer 1994

Box	50.00
140 Card set	25.00
Gold signature cards (140)	1.00
Holofoil (10)	3.00
PowerBlast (9)	4.00
Jumbo Pack Holofoils (10)	4.00

MARVEL MASTERPIECES 1993
SkyBox 1993
(Each box numbered, limited to 350,000 boxes)

Box	40.00
100 Card Set	20.00
Singles	0.15

Bonus Cards S1-S8	9.00

MARVEL METAL
Fleer 1995

Box	75.00
138 Card Set	45.00
Singles	.25
Flasher Singles	0.75
Gold Blasters	3.00
Metal Blasters	3.00

MARVEL UNIVERSE SERIES I
Impel 1990

Box	90.00
162 Card Set	40.00
Singles	.40
5 Holograms, MH1-MH5	10.00

MARVEL UNIVERSE SERIES II
Impel 1991

Box	55.00
162 Card Set	30.00
Singles	.25
5 Holograms, H-1-H-5	12.00

MARVEL UNIVERSE SERIES III
SkyBox (Impel) 1992

Box	25.00
200 Card Set	17.00
Singles	.20
5 Holograms, H-1-H-5	5.00

MARVEL UNIVERSE SERIES IV
SkyBox 1993

Box	24.00
180 Card Set	12.00
Singles	.10
Foil Cards	4.50
3-D Spider-Man Hologram #H-IV	30.00

MARVEL UNIVERSE
Fleer Flair 1994

Box	85.00
150 Card Set	50.00
Singles	.50
Power Blast Foil 1-18	5.00

MASK, THE
Cardz 1994

Box	35.00
100 Card Set	14.00
Tekchromes (10)	10.00

MAXX, THE
Topps 1994

Box	35.00
90 Card Set	12.00
Singles	.15

Foil cards 1-4, 6	7.00
Foil Card 5-Redemption	25.00
Autograph Card	35.00

MCFARLANE SERIES I
Comic Images 1989

45 Card Set	15.00

MCFARLANE SERIES II
Comic Images 1990

45 Card Set	15.00

MIGHTY MORPHIN POWER RANGERS
Collect-A-Card 1994

Box	40.00
72 Card Set	10.00
Singles	.20
Powercaps 1-10	.50
72 Card Power Foil Set	40.00
3-Card Prototype Set w/Cap	7.00

MIKE KALUTA
FPG 1994

Box	35.00
90 Card Set	10.00
Metallic Storm Cards (5)	6.00
Autograph Card (100)	45.00
Signed & Numbered	
10-up Sheet	30.00
Binder	15.00

MIKE PLOOG
FPG 1994

Box	35.00
90 Card Set	10.00
Singles	.15
Metallic Storm 1-5	6.00
Autograph Card	45.00
Signed 10-card sheet	25.00
Promo (two different)	1.00
Binder	15.00

OLIVIA SERIES I
Comic Images 1992

Box	23.00
90 Card Set	14.00
Singles	.10

6 Prism Cards	9.00

OLIVIA SERIES II
Comic Images 1992

Box	40.00
72 All Prism Card Set	20.00
Singles	.50
6 Chromium Cards	12.00

OLIVIA SERIES III
Comic Images 1994

Box	40.00
90 Card Set	15.00
Singles	.20
Holochrome Cards 1-6	9.00
Medallion Card	25.00
Special Set 1-3	50.00
Autograph	80.00

PEPSI-COLA TRADING CARDS
(2nd Ed.)
Dart Flipcards

Box	45.00
Set	15.00
Singles	.10
Chrome Cards	8.00
"Tall Boy" "Chase Card"	70.00

RETURN OF SUPERMAN
SkyBox 1993
(10,000 cases produced)

Box	35.00
100 Card Set	20.00
Foil Enhanced Cards	
SP1-SP4	12.00
1 Bonus Card	10.00

RETURN OF THE JEDI
Topps 1983

Series I:132 Cards (w/33 stickers	
	25.00
Box	20.00

Series II:88 cards
(w/22 stickers)   20.00
Singles   .10
Stickers   .15
Box   15.00

ROWENA
FPG 1993
Box   35.00
90 Card Set   15.00
Singles   .20
Holograms   8.00
Gold hologram set   45.00
Autograph card   50.00
Promo   1.00

ANDMAN PREMIUM CARDS
kybox 1994

Box   65.00
90 Card Set   20.00
Singles   .30
Gold Endless Cards 1-7   18.00
Morpheus Hologram   75.00
Silver Proto-Type
Endless Cards 1-7   30.00
Morpheus Prototype
Hologram   90.00
Autograph Cards   75.00
Binder   12.00

SKELETON WARRIORS
Fleer Ultra 1995
Box   35.00
100 Card Set   15.00
Singles   .15
Glow Cards   2.00
Power Blast   3.00
Cels   1.50

SPIDER-MAN
Fleer 1994
Box   35.00
150 Card Set   15.00
Singles   .15
Cels 1-12   4.00
Holograms 1-4   12.00
Gold Webs 1-6
(Jumbo Box)   9.00
Gold Webs 7-12
(Anco Box)   9.00

STAR TREK: DEEP SPACE NINE
Skybox 1994
100 Card Set   15.00
Singles   .20
Spectra Cards SP1-4   8.00
Gold Spectra Card SP5   15.00
Redemption Card   30.00
Promo and
Prototype Cards   2.00

STAR TREK MASTER SERIES
Skybox 1994

Box	25.00
90 Card Set	12.00
Spectra Etch (5)	8.00
Promos	1.00

STAR TREK MASTER SERIES II
Skybox 1994

Box	30.00
90 Card Set	15.00
Spectra Etch (5)	10.00
Promos	1.00

STAR TREK: THE NEXT GENERATION
Impel (SkyBox) 1992

Box	30.00
120 Card Set	20.00
Singles	.20
5 Bonus Cards	2.75
4 Hologram Cards	12.00
Mail Offer Hologram	25.00

Collector's Set in Tin (limited to 10,000)	75.00

STAR TREK: TNG EPISODE COLLECTION
Skybox 1994

Box	25.00
108 Card Set	10.00
Klingon Set (6)	10.00
Hologram Set (2)	30.00
Promos	1.00

SERIES 2

Box	35.00
96 Card Set	10.00
Singles	.10
Foils	9.00
Holograms	55.00

STAR WARS *(Also see Return of the Jedi)*
Topps 1977

•Series I: Blue,

66 Cards (w/11 stickers)	70.00
Singles	1.00
Stickers	2.00
Box	175.00

•Series II:Red,

66 Cards (w/11 stickers)	50.00
Singles	.75
Stickers	1.50
Box	120.00

•Series III: Yellow,

66 Cards (w/11 stickers)	50.00
Singles	.75
Stickers	1.50
Box	140.00

•Series IV: Green,

66 Cards (w/11 stickers)	50.00
Singles	.75
Stickers	1.50
Box	140.00

•*Series V:Brown,*
66 Cards
(w/11 stickers)   50.00
Singles   .75
Stickers   1.50
Box   100.00

STAR WARS GALAXY
Topps 1993
Box   50.00
140 Card Set   25.00
Singles   .25
6 Etched Foil Cards   15.00
Darth Vader Etched   20.00
Uncut Spectra Card Sheet
                               100.00

STAR WARS GALAXY II
Topps 1994
Box   35.00
135 Card Set   15.00
Singles   .15
Foil Inserts 1-6   7.00
Autograph redemption Card
                                75.00
Uncut Spectra Card Sheet
                               100.00

STAR WARS: A NEW HOPE
Metallic Images 1994
Box/Set   50.00

STAR WARS: THE EMPIRE STRIKES BACK
Metallic Images 1994
Box/Set   50.00

STAR WARS WIDEVISION
Topps 1995
Box   40.00
Full Set   25.00
Singles   .25
Topps Finest   15.00

TICK, THE
NEC 1992
36 Card Set   8.00
Singles   .20
Test Sheet #1 (10,000 made)
                                 5.00
Test Sheet #2 (5,000 made)
                                 5.00

ULTRA X-MEN
Fleer 1994
Box   75.00
150 Card Set   20.00
Singles   .15
Hildebrandt Portraits 1-9   4.00
Fatal Attractions 1-6   6.00
X-Men's Greatest Battles 1-6
(Jumbo Box)   8.00

STAR WARS

EXT. X-WING FIGHTERS — YAVIN — SPACE

Blue/Gold Team 1-6
(Anco 12-Card Pack Box) 12.00
Silver X-overs 1-6
(Anco 11 Card Pack Box) 12.00

VAMPIRELLA
Topps 1995

Box	35.00
90 Card Set	13.00
Singles	.20
Gallery Cards	8.00
Holo Glow Cards	10.00
Gold Cards	1.00

Grifter

VERTIGO
Skybox 1994

Box	60.00
Full set	30.00
Singles	.30

Foil Cards	15.00
Skydisc	85.00

WILDSTORM
Wildstorm 1994

Box	60.00
100 Card Chromium Set	40.00
Refractors (9)	6.00
Autograph Cards A1-A15 (each has 2 different fronts)	25.00
Chromium Poster one/case	40.00

X-MEN SERIES I
Impel (SkyBox) 1992

Box	85.00
100 Card Set by Jim Lee	30.00
Singles	.40
5 Holograms, XH-1 - XH-5	6.00

X-MEN SERIES II
SkyBox 1993

Box	60.00
100 Card Set	20.00
Singles	.20
9 Gold Foil Stamped Cards, G1- G9	5.00
3 Holograms, H1-H3	11.00
3-D Wolverine Hologram, H-X	40.00

"X-MEN, FLEER ULTRA"
Fleer 1994

Box	45.00
Full Set	25.00
Singles	.25
Fatal Attractions Cards	7.00
Team Portrait	5.00
Greatest battles	8.00
Team Triptych	9.00

X-MEN ULTRA '95
Fleer 1995

Box	45.00
Full Set	20.00
Singles	.25
Chromium Cards	10.00
Hunters and Stalkers	5.00
Suspended Animation	4.00

YOUNGBLOOD
Skybox 1995

Box	90.00
Full Set	30.00
Singles	1.00
Stickers	.50
Wiggle cards	8.00
Redemption cards	15.00
Skydisc	75.00

Premium Rings

At some point in their life, most people have been exposed to premiums. This exposure could come in the form of incredibly cool cereal "prizes" or in the form of some type of giveaway. The most popular manifestation of premiums was the premium ring. Rings like the **Lone Ranger Atom Bomb** or the **Radio Orphan Annie Triple Mystery Ring** held kids breathless with anticipation of the rings' arrival. Once merely a childhood passion, ring and premium collecting has become one of the hottest areas of collectibles in the last few years. This hobby has been receiving renewed attention with current ring releases such as **The X-Men**, **The Shadow**, and **The Phantom**. Reports of older rings selling for as much as $125,000 have also helped to strengthen the market. The following ring section is just a small sample of the types of rings you might come across while searching through that old box in the basement or that trunk in the attic. For your interest, we have compiled the following list to illustrate some of the different comic rings with the actual prices realized.

Arby's Bugs Bunny Flicker

Arby's Daffy Duck Flicker

Arby's Porky Pig Flicker

Arby's Yosemite Sam Flicker

Arby's Flickers
1987 (set of 4)
$20-$40 ea.

Archie
1993, Staber
Silver (50 made) - $150
Gold (5 made) - $750-

Batman (metal)
(3 diff.), 1966 (on card)
Complete on card (DC)
on card $60-$125 ea.
Ring only $15-$30

Batman Bat Signal
(metal), 1990 (DC)
$10-$20

Batman Bat Signal
(Diamond Comics Distr.)
14k gold w/diamond chips
(25 made), 1992 (DC)
$2000

Batman Bat Signal
(Party) (plastic), 1982(DC)
$1

Batman Bat Signal
(Diamond Comic Distr.)
silver (550 made) 1992 (DC)
$250

Batman Bat Signal
1990s c. 1964) (metal, w/sparkles)
(Rosecraft on card)(DC)
$10-$20

Batman Figure
(metal) (color, painted)
1990s, $5-$15

Batman Flicker(1)
"Member Batman Ring Club" to full figure "Batman/Robin" side by side.

Batman Flicker (2)
"Batman" face to "Robin" face.

Batman Flicker (3)
"Batman " chest view up to " Bruce Wayne" chest view up.

Batman Flicker(4)
"Robin" chest veiw up to "Dick Grayson" chest view up.

Batman Flicker(5)
"Batman" face to full figure swinging on rope.

Batman Flicker(6)
"Robin" face to full figure swinging on rope.

Batman Flickers
(Original silver base)
(set of 12), 1966
$10-$25 ea.

Batman Gold Face
(3D metal)(DC)
$25-$50

Batman Logo
1990s, (metal, blue/gold)(DC)
$5-$10

Batman Logo
(rectangle)(DC)
Nestle's (1980s)
$25-$50

Batman Prototype
1993, (metal)
$600

Captain America
(metal), 1980s (in color)
$50-$100

**Captain America
Mood**
1977 (metal)
$100-$250 ➡

Battlestar Galactica
(Alien)

Battlestar Galactica
(Commander Adama)

Battlestar Galactica
(Daggit)

Battlestar Galactica
(Cylon)
⬆

Battlestar Galactica
1978 (Universal Studios)
(metal)(photo) (4 in set)
$20-$40 each

Cat Woman
1991
(metal cloisonne)
Rosecraft
⬅ $20-$40

G.I. Joe Special Forces
1994
Blue Stone - $250, Black stone $400

G.I. Joe
1982 (came on card display with pinback)(metal)
on card - $100
ring only - $40-$75

G.I. Joe Coin
1964-1994 (30th salute)
1994 →
Gold - $400
Silver - $200
Bronze - $100

**Green Lantern
Glow-in-dark**
1992 DC Comics giveaway
$2

Note: Marty Nodell, creator of Green Lantern, has given away examples of this ring autographed $4 ea.

**Green Lantern
Water Jet**
(squirt), 1980s
(on card) $12-$24
(ring only), $8-$16

Incredible Hulk
1980s(metal)(Marvel Ent. Group)(in color)
$50-$100

**Marvel Flicker
Marvel Super Heros**

**Marvel Flicker
Captain America**

**Marvel Flicker
Dr. Strange**

**Marvel Flicker
Fantastic Four**

**Marvel Flicker
Incredible Hulk**

**Marvel Flicker
Human Torch**

**Marvel Flicker
Iron Man**

**Marvel Flicker
Spider-Man**

**Marvel Flicker
Sub-Mariner**

**Marvel Flicker
Thing**

**Marvel Flicker
Thor**

Marvel Flickers
(plastic silver base),
1970s
(Marvel Ent. Group)
$10-$20 ea.

Marvel Oval
1990s (set of 6)
(gumball)(metal)
$1. each

Set Includes:
Captain America,
Dr. Strange, Ghost
Rider, Hulk, Spider-
Man, Spider Woman

Mighty Morphin Power Rangers
1993 (5 rings on card)(plastic)
$3.00 complete

Robin Head (3D)
1980s(metal)(gold color)
$45-$90

Robin Logo Rec.
1980s(Nestles)
$25-$50

Robin (rubber) 1970s
$25-$50

Shadow
1994 (gold w/diamond inset)(25 produced)
(Diamond Comic Distr.)(numbered)
$750

Shadow
1994 (silver)(Diamond Comic Distr.)
(numbered)
$200

Spawn (Image Comics)
(1993) (silver & gold versions exist)
Silver - $250
Gold w/diamond - $1000

Spider (pulp character)
(pulp & theater giveaway)(scarce), 1930s
(silver base)(less than 20 known)
Good -$2500
Very Good- $3750
Fine - $5000
Very Fine - $7500
Near Mint - $10,000

Spider-Man
1993(Marvel Ent. Group)
(gold, silver, & bronze exsist)
Gold (limited to 12) $3000
Silver (limited to 50) $600
Bronze (limited to 50) $400
Prices given are Near-Mint Values

Sipder-Man
1994 (Marvel Ent. Group)(1200 minted)
Near-Mint $75

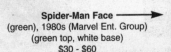

Spider-Man(vitamins)
1960s (metal)(Marvel Ent. Group)
$50 - $100

Spider-Man Face
(green), 1980s (Marvel Ent. Group)
(green top, white base)
$30 - $60

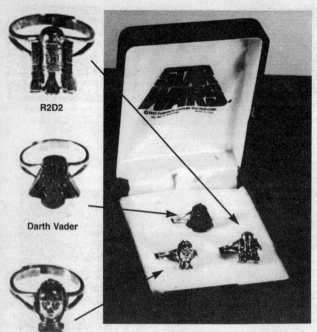

R2D2

Darth Vader

C3PO

Star Wars (set in box)1977 $40 - $80

Star Wars (8 diff.),
(C3PO, Fighter,
Force(lg.),Force(sm.), R2D2,
Vader, X-Wing, Yoda),1980s
$7 - $15 ea.

Superman Crusader
(silver metal) 1940s
$125 - $250

Superman Figure
1990s $2

Superman Emblem
1990s, $1

Superman Emblem
1993 (sold at Warner
Bros. stores)
$50 complete in box

Superman Emblem
(blue logo)(Nestle)
1980, $25 - $50

Superman Emblem
1970s (movie)(metal)
$25 - $50

Superman Emblem
1990s, $2 - $4

Superman Flicker
1960s (8 diff.)
(scarce)
$100 - $200 ea.

**Superman Magnetic
Kryptonite Ring**
ring only - $15 - $30

**Superman Magnetic
Kryptonite Ring**
(plastic, green top)(came in
box with Superman figure.
Magnetic ring will push
Superman down)
1990 (front of package)
$50 complete in package

Superman Prize Ring

1940s(membership), (rare)(gold plated center w/red color behind circled letters) (promoted in Superman & Action comics)(1600 issued in 1940)(examples have sold in Good for 22,500, Fine $50,000, VF for $80,000 & 125,000)(Only 10 known, one in near mint)(most are in good to fine condition)

Note: This ring is very rare with only 10 examples known, one in NM. It is currently the most valuable ring listed

Good-$16,000
Very Good-$28,000
Fine-$40,000
Very Fine-$80,000
Near Mint-$120,000

Superman Secret Compartment Ring (candy premium), 1940Note: Superman image printed on paper in red and blue and is affixed to inside of top. (rare)(12 known with 3 in VF to NM)

Good-$10,000
Very Good-$17,500
Fine-$25,000
Very Fine-$42,500
Near Mint-$60,000

Superman Secret Compartment Gum Ring (gum premium), 1940s, (rare)(only 10 known, none in near mint)

Good-$10,000
Very Good-$17,500
Fine-$25,000
Very Fine-$42,500
Near Mint-$60,000

Superman Tim Ring (silver color) (Given away at Superman Tim clothing stores)1940s (scarce)(only one known in NM, most examples exsist in low grades)

Good-$3,000
Very Good-$5,250
Fine-$7,500
Very Fine-$12,750
Near Mint-$18,000

**Teenage Mutant Ninja
Turtles (April O' Nell)**

**Teenage Mutant Ninja
Turtles (Donatello)**

**Teenage Mutant Ninja
Turtles (Leonardo)**

**Teenage Mutant Ninja
Turtles (Michaelangelo)**

**Teenage Mutant Ninja
Turtles(Raphael)**

**Teenage Mutant Ninja
Turtles(Rock Steady)**

**Teenage Mutant Ninja
Turtles**
1990s (8 diff.)(plastic,
in color)
Turtles - $30-$60 ea.
Others $25 - $50 ea.

**Teenage Mutant Ninja
Turtles (Shredder)**

**Teenage Mutant Ninja
Turtles (Splinter)**

Tekno Comix Logo
1994 (metal)(secret
compartment)
$5

Underdog
1970s (metal cloisonne)
$100 - $150

Wonder Woman
(rectangle)(DC)
Nestle's (1980)
$25-$50

X-Men Gold
1993 (Diamond Comic
Distr.)(w/diamond
chip,25 made)
$850

X-Men Silver
1993 (Diamond
Comic Distr.)
$150

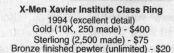

X-Men Xavier Institute Class Ring
1994 (excellent detail)
Gold (10K, 250 made) - $400
Sterliong (2,500 made) - $75
Bronze finished pewter (unlimited) - $20

X-O
(Valiant Comics)
1993
$60 - $80

Zorro Logo Ring
1960 (vending machine)
(silver & black base versions)
$40 - $80

Yellow Kid
Ring only available with
Yellow Kid Statue
only 100 produced
ring only :$800

Note: For a more detailed look at Premium Rings
check out the latest edition of the **Overstreet
Premium Ring Price Guide**. It is the most compre-
hensive guide on Premium Rings available today.

About the Cover Artist

Kelley Jones

As a means to finance his college studies, Kelley began drawing comics. He grew to prominence with his work in horror comics like **Sandman, Aliens, Batman & Dracula: Red Rain** and **Batman: Bloodstorm**. He fused superhero and horror with his work on the critically acclaimed **Deadman** specials. Kelley easily has one of the most recognizable and popular artistic styles in comics today. He is now the regular artist on the monthly **Batman** title, a job which he considers more an honor than a profession.

About the Author

Bob Overstreet, the leading authority on comic book values in the United States, can always be found rummaging through boxes of old comic books looking for data. He attends most of the major comic book conventions and has appeared on numerous radio and television shows across the country. He maintains an extensive collection of comic books and trading cards as well as radio premiums, Indian relics and antiques.

He began collecting comic books in 1952 and published his first book **The Comic Book Price Guide** in 1970. This book was one of the first price guides published outside of the top hobbies of coins, stamps, and antiques. The success of **The Comic Book Price Guide** and the fledgling field it represented inspired many other price guides to follow. Now know as **The Overstreet Comic Book Price Guide**, it has become the standard reference work in the field.